ANTIQUES
SOURCE | 2002
BOOK | 2003

THIS IS A CARLTON BOOK

Copyright © 2002 Martin Miller

This edition published by Carlton Books Limited 2002
20 Mortimer Street
London W1T 3JW

Edited and designed for Carlton Books by PAGEOne
Cairn House, Elgiva Lane, Chesham,
Buckinghamshire HP5 2JD

CREATIVE DIRECTOR Bob Gordon
DESIGNERS Mark Tattham, Louise Kerby and Gill Andrews

PRODUCTION Garry Lewis

A CIP catalogue for this book is available from the British Library.

ISBN 1 84222 532 4

ANTIQUES

SOURCE BOOK | 2002 2003

The Definitive Annual Guide to Retail Prices for Antiques and Collectables

MARTIN MILLER

Contents

Acknowledgements 6
How to Use This Book 7
Introduction 9

Antiquities 11
Architectural & Garden Furniture 19
Arms & Armour 33
Automobilia 43
Books, Maps & Atlases 51
Carpets & Rugs 68
Ceramics
    English 76
    European 105
    Islamic 115
    Oriental 123
Clocks, Watches & Scientific Instruments
    Clocks 131
    Watches 141
    Scientific Instruments 148
Coins & Medals 152
Collector's Items
    Advertising & Packaging 158
    Bottles 170
    Cameras 179
    Commemorative Ware 184
    Ephemera 191
    Gentleman's Accessories 204
    Handbags 206
    Kitchenalia 213
    Luggage 222
    Mechanical Music .226
    Paperweights 229
    Photographs 231
    Posters 239
    Radio 245
    Rock & Pop 247
    Scripophily & Paper Money 253
    Sewing Items 257
    Snuff Boxes & Smoking Equipment 261
    Telephones 264
    Walking Sticks 267
Decorative Arts
    Figures & Busts 273
    Lighting 277
    Metalware 286
Furniture
    Beds 291
    Bonheurs du Jour 295
    Bookcases 296
    Boxes 299
    Bureaux 308

Cabinets 310
Canterburies 319
Chairs 320
Chaises Longues & Day Beds 340
Chests of Drawers & Commodes 341
Davenports 352
Desks 353
Dining Tables 355
Doors 357
Dressers 361
Dumb Waiters & Whatnots 363
Mirrors 366
Miscellaneous 373
Screens 375
Settees & Sofas 377
Stools 380
Tables 384
Wardrobes 397
Glass 400
Jewellery 414
Marine Items 429
Musical Instruments .435
Silver & Pewter 440
Sporting Items
General 466
Fishing 473
Shooting 476
Taxidermy 479
Textiles & Fans 482
Toys, Games & Dolls .486
Treen 496
Tribal Art 498
Twentieth-Century Design
Ceramics 503
Furniture 518
Glass 532
Lighting 543
Metalware 547
Wine-Related Items 552
Works of Art & Sculpture
Asian/Oriental 560
European 563
Islamic 566
Russian 569
Writing Equipment 576

Period Reference 586
Glossary 590
Directory of Dealers .598
Directory of Antiques Markets 625
Index 631

ACKNOWLEDGEMENTS

GENERAL EDITOR
Martin Miller

EDITORS
Simon Blake
Marianne Blake
Abigail Zoe Martin

EDITORIAL ASSISTANT
Gemma Martin

EDITORIAL CO-ORDINATORS
Marianne Blake
Abigail Zoe Martin

PHOTOGRAPHIC/PRODUCTION
CO-ORDINATOR
Marianne Blake

PHOTOGRAPHERS
Abigail Zoe Martin
Anders Gramer

How to Use This Book

by Martin Miller

This is the third edition of the first full-colour antiques retail price guide published in the United Kingdom, a distinction which possibly deserves a little explanation. I started publishing antiques price guides in 1969 – and they have always been very successful – but one criticism that I have heard is from people saying, rather wistfully, 'I loved the book, but what a pity that everything in it was already sold.' And it was perfectly true, the books were designed more as compilations of information from auction sales which had already taken place than as immediate guides; as reference books rather than handbooks.

The difference with this book is that here we have used retailers, rather than auction houses, as our sources of information. Everything in this book is actually for sale at the time of going to press and many items, certainly some of the more arcane, will remain so for the lifespan of the book. As the introduction explains, a reputable and experienced dealer's assessment of the price of an antique is at least as reliable – and usually a great deal more reasoned – than a price achieved at auction, and so even when the item you wish to purchase from the book turns out to have been sold, you have a reliable guide to the price you should pay when you happen upon another.

The book is designed for maximum visual interest and appeal. In this issue there are more items in the silver and pewter, scientific instrument, coins and medals and twentieth-century ceramics sections, and a greater emphasis has been placed on furniture, books, jewellery and Russian works of art.

Should you happen upon something that you wish to purchase, simply note the dealer reference to the bottom right of the entry and look up the dealer's full name and details in the Directory of Dealers section towards the back of the book. You can telephone, fax and, in many cases, visit the dealer's website. All the dealers who have helped us with the book will be happy to assist you, and if the piece you wish to buy has already been sold, they will almost certainly be able to help you find another. The price shown against an entry is per individual item, unless the heading and description refer to more than one item, a set, or a pair. Should you wish to sell an item, the relevant section and dealer reference will again be of help, but do not expect to be offered the same price at which the dealer is selling.

Since the first *Antiques Source Book* was published, the way in which we look for antiques has remained almost the same, whether it is from the large fairs such as the D.M.G. Palm Beach International Art and Antique Fair run by David Lester, the Grosvenor House and Olympia antiques fairs in London, the N.E.C in Birmingham or the relaxed Coopers Antique Fair in Snape, Suffolk; they are all part of the same global antique market.

The internet has also considerably helped the international antiques market – we can now find with ease the prices of antiques sold at auction across the world, and view an antique dealer's website to search for that special piece.

We hope you find these instructions easy to follow. Good luck and enjoy your journey into the world of antiques.

Introduction

A contemporary and practical guide to antiques and collectables

The enjoyment of antique collecting is in finding that treasured item that you have been searching for. When embarking on your journey, it is impossible to know what you might find; you may start out by looking for a specific item and then end up falling in love with a Georgian table, a poster, or a photograph of a favourite film or film star. This is what makes antique buying and collecting so enjoyable.

There are, however, a few guide lines to remember - the quality, provenance and general condition has to be good, and the proportions should be pleasing to the eye. Whether you intend to buy a Regency chair, a George I chest on chest or an oak dresser, these factors all play a considerable part in the value of the item. Most collectors and dealers tend to specialise in one particular item or period, some for example may specialise in the Georgian period, whilst others will focus solely on Oriental works of art or English ceramics.

Antique fairs are great fun and vary from the large vetted fair, antique markets and smaller antique fairs that abound in cities and the countryside, to the European 'flea markets' in Paris, Belgium, Holland and Germany amongst others. The best days are Sundays and Saturdays - in that order. Sunday is the busiest day; dealers surround the squares, cafes and restaurants are open, and the atmosphere is one of excitement and anticipation! The finds are innumerable for the clever shopper; one may discover a Suzie Cooper dinner set, a painting at a reasonable price, a 1950s dinner set or even a beautiful Art Deco lamp.

The antiques business is fundamentally about knowledge. The value of an antique lies largely in the antique dealer's ability to know what to buy and sell, and a considerable amount of time is expended in learning and acquiring knowledge. The way that antiques are viewed and valued is constantly changing and it is therefore exciting to immerse yourself in this evolving and thriving industry.

There are now a huge range of items that are considered collectable, from advertising, photographs, kitchenalia, rock and pop records, automobilia and luggage, to musical instruments; all have their place in today's market.

The sudden boom in television gardening programmes along with magazine articles has made the idea of a designed garden almost commonplace, and this in turn has lead to an increase in demand for garden furniture, Italian stone figures, fountains and pagodas, which can enhance and add structure to the design of any garden. This change in attitude by the home owner has altered the way the garden is viewed. It is now seen as a space to be considered with as much thought and planning as any room in the house, with the garden designer playing an integral part in achieving the perfect garden to reflect the owner's personality and style. The interest in architectural detail is extensive, from Victorian roof tiles and corbels, to Georgian and Victorian doors, all are of great importance to the home owner, builder, interior decorator and antique dealer.

Throughout the book we place an emphasis on quality, rarity, age and condition. In our opinion the greatest of these are the first and last. If you buy a modern piece that has quality, at some point, in this age of mass production, it will probably gain rarity because so many things are thrown out.

June is the month when most of the dealers from around the world arrive in the UK, not only to attend the Grosvenor House and Olympia Fine Art and Antique Fairs, but also to go to Ascot and Wimbledon.

The fair at Grosvenor House was first held in 1934 and was to pave the way for the future of antique fairs worldwide. The concept for the fair came in a conversation between two antique dealers, Alex G. Lewis and Cecil F. Turner. They felt that a niche existed for a fair which would stimulate trade – an act of defiance against the prevailing economic gloom of the 1930s. Turner approached the chairman of Grosvenor House and the antique dealers fair that we know today was born. This has been followed with a number of other fairs being established, for example, the BADA and the LAPADA Fine Art and Antiques Fair.

Even the best introduction to antiques cannot replace leg work as a part of the learning process. Visit museums, stately homes and specialist dealers, attend auctions and courses and read books. Acquiring knowledge about antiques can be a very satisfying and rewarding experience.

Antiques give a sense of continuity. Living amongst the artefacts of past generations is a constant reminder that our possessions have survived the centuries. An antique, by its very nature, is an icon of security and longevity.

We hope you enjoy this book. Happy hunting!

Antiquities

Antiquities not only provide the collector with great investment opportunities, just as impressive are the stories they tell.

Most people don't even realise that an antiquity that seems to many to be something reserved for the shelves of the finest museum can also find a place in your home. Museums have far more material than can be displayed, for example, the Museum of Mexico has a million pieces of pre-Columbian artefacts in its basement, such as coins, jewellery and everyday utensils, which increasingly have become part of the collector's world. Rock star Mick Jagger has been collecting them for 30 years, while country legend Johnny Cash specialises in coins from biblical times. Not only are ancient coins items of incredible beauty, they have become quite an investment, with yearly returns often exceeding 25 percent. Of course, most coins will not reach the value of an Athenian decadrachm, which was sold at a 1974 auction.

Green Glass Balsamarium ▼

- *4th century AD*

A translucent green glass double Balsamarium cosmetic container with twin fused tubes and applied loop handles, with good iridescence.

- *height 17cm*
- £900   • Pars

Glass Flask ▼

- *6th century AD*

Pale green translucent glass flask. The globular body with six handles attached to the shoulder and collared rim.

- *height 7.5cm*
- £1,000   • Pars

Blue Ink Well ▶

- *1st century AD*

Royal blue and white marbled ink well; this container has been shaped into a cylinder and the top opening is quite small. The large flat base and small top hole would make this a practical inkwell.

- *height 7.5cm*
- £7,000   • Pars

Small Glass Pot ▲

- *6th century AD*

Pale green pot of baluster form, with eight handles connecting the flared rim to the shoulders of the body, raised on a splayed foot.

- *height 7.5cm*
- £6,500   • Pars

Harra Pan Vase ▲
- *1800–2200 BC*
Small terracotta vase of ovoid form with a deep truncated neck and geometric design applied to the body, from the Harra Pan civilisation.
- *height 9cm*
- **£250**   • Rasoul Gallery

Terracotta Vase ▲
- *1800–2200 BC*
Terracotta vase of ovoid form with a long inverted neck and a circular pattern on a black glaze.
- *height 18cm*
- **£500**   • Rasoul Gallery

Terracotta Wine Strainer ▲
- *1800–2200 BC*
Terracotta wine strainer of cylindrical form, with uniform perforations within the body.
- *height 15cm*
- **£600**   • Rasoul Gallery

Alabaster Cup ▼
- *3000BC*
Alabaster cup from Afghanistan, carved from one piece of stone, with a concave body, and an extended stem, raised on a splayed foot.
- *height 24cm*
- **£1,500**   • Sultani

Amlash Teapot ▼
- *6th–8th century*
Amlash teapot made from terracotta with two ear shaped side handles and a large domed cover.
- *height 12cm*
- **£3,500**   • Yacobs

Sumarian Mask ▲
- *2300–2000 BC*
Sumarian mask with an expressionless composure, with recesses for the eyes.
- *height 7cm*
- **£14,000**   • Yacobs

Roman Glass ▲
- *2nd century BC*
Roman glass flask of ovoid form with fluted neck and spiral decoration with good iridescence.
- *height 10cm*
- **£7,500**   • Yacobs

Perfume Bottle ▲

- *7th century AD*
Perfume bottle of globular form, with silver iridescence and pinched surface.
- *height 8.5cm*
- £1,000 • Pars

Cedonian Amphoriskos ▲

- *1st century AD*
Cedonian, mould-blown, amber glass Amphoriskos, the handles in cream glass, with a long cylindrical neck with inverted rim, the ovoid body incorporating a central frieze of geometric designs.
- *height 8.5cm*
- £2,500 • Pars

Green Glass Flask ▼

- *4th century AD*
Translucent green glass flask of bottle shaped form, with a cylindrical neck, splayed rim, strap handle and good iridescence.
- *height 11cm*
- £1,000 • Pars

Translucent Glass Flask ▼

- *4th century AD*
Small translucent blue glass flask with applied handle and thumb support, with a flattened globular body and dark blue spiral threads on the neck.
- *height 8cm*
- £800 • Pars

Expert Tips

Considering its age, beauty and fragility, Roman glass is a relatively affordable investment for the antiquities collector, and is a good place to start with.

Amphoriskos ▲

- *5th century AD*
Feather patterned long-necked amphoriskos with a turquoise ground, yellow and dark blue threads and amber colour glass handles.
- *height 14cm*
- £4,000 • Pars

Byzantine Flask ▲

- *Byzantine 7th century AD*
Byzantine translucent pale green hexagonal flask with strap handle. The surface of the glass has shallow indentations and is decorated with Christian symbols.
- *height 21.5cm*
- £6,000 • Pars

Roman Earrings ▼

- **2–3rd century AD**
Pair of Roman earrings with circular garnets set in gold roped banding, with suspended gold strands and beads.
- *length 3cm*
- £2,000   • Pars

Alabaster Drinking Vessel ▼

- **circa 2nd millennium BC**
Bactrian Afghanistan alabaster cylindrical drinking vessel, with engraved circular designs and turned lip.
- *height 10.5cm*
- £650   • Rasoul Gallery

Islamic Pendant ▲

- **circa 9–10th century AD**
Islamic gold pendant in the shape of a bird with beautiful intricate work.
- *height 0.5cm*
- £3,000   • Pars

Roman Gold Earrings ▲

- **circa 1st–3rd century AD**
Pair of late roman gold earrings of tear drop form with beaded circular design.
- *height 3cm*
- £2,000   • Pars

Roman Gold Pendant ▼

- **7–8th century AD**
Late Roman square gold pendant set with one amethyst lozenge shaped stone and flanked by two circular turquoise stones.
- *width 1.4cm*
- £450   • Pars

Gold Pendant ▲

- **circa 15th century AD**
Lozenge shaped green stone set within a circular gold pendant with a herringbone design.
- *width 1cm*
- £200   • Pars

Bactrian Vessel ▲

- **circa 2nd millennium BC**
Bactrian alabaster drinking vessel of cylindrical form from Afghanistan.
- *height 12cm*
- £550   • Rasoul Gallery

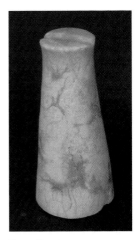

Proto-Bactrian Limestone Idol ▲

- *circa 2nd millennium*
Proto-Bactrian limestone fertility column idol.
- *height 14.5cm*
- £1,500   • Rasoul Gallery

Expert Tips

To test that Roman pottery is the genuine article, wet it with your fingers and if it smells very earthy it is probably the real thing. Make sure that you go to a reputable dealer.

Alabaster Vessel ▲

- *circa 2nd millennium BC*
Bactrian alabaster cylindrical drinking vessel with red marbling.
- *height 16cm*
- £1,300   • Rasoul Gallery

Stone Inkwell ▼

- *circa 2nd millennium BC*
Bactrian stone inkwell with two receptacles, carved with circular designs between triple banding.
- *9cm x 10cm*
- £1,200   • Rasoul Gallery

Bactrian Inkwell ▼

- *3rd millennium BC*
Bactrian stone inkwell with a geometric design around the neck, above a square base with an engraved circular pattern.
- *height 4cm*
- £250   • Rasoul Gallery

Bactrian Bronze Weight ▲

- *circa 3rd millennium BC*
Bactrian bronze weight with two handles in the form of leopard heads.
- *height 7.5cm*
- £1,000   • Rasoul Gallery

Bactrian Inkwell ▲

- *circa 3rd millennium BC*
Stone inkwell from the Bactrian period of conical form with an inverted conical base.
- *height 7.5cm*
- £450   • Rasoul Gallery

Bronze Lion ▼

- *4th century AD*
Bronze figure of a lion with a truncated body in a crouching position with his mouth open.
- *height 6cm*
- £2,300   • Rasoul Gallery

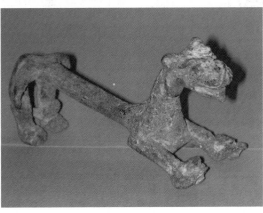

Amphoriskos ▼
- **5th century BC**

Feather patterned Amphoriskos with an ochre background with black and white feathering with clear glass handles.
- *height 12cm*
- **£2,500**
- Pars

Islamic Pendant ▲
- **7–8th century AD**

Early Islamic pendant with rubies and turquoise stones set in gold, with a further three lozenge shaped droplets.
- *length 3cm*
- **£4,000**
- Pars

Terracotta Vase ◄
- **1800–2200 BC**

Harra Pan civilisation terracotta vase of baluster form, from the Indus Valley with black banding and three geometric panels.
- *height 23cm*
- **£650**
- Rasoul Gallery

Amphoriskos ▼
- **5th century BC**

Feather patterned Amphoriskos with a black ground, yellow and white feathering and turquoise glass handles.
- *height 14cm*
- **£3,000**
- Pars

Bactrian Pot ▼
- *circa 2nd century BC*

Bactrian alabaster pot, with concave sides and splayed lip.
- *height 12cm*
- **£3,200**
- Yacobs

Green Glass Flask ▲
- **4th–6th century AD**

Green glass flask with bulbous body, indented sides and double handles.
- *height 13.5cm*
- **£1,000**
- Pars

Translucent Bowl ▼
- *1st century AD*
Roman, translucent, green pillar-moulded glass bowl of shallow form with vertical ribbing, the tondo with three wheel-cut concentric circles.
- *diameter 15cm*
- £2,000 • Pars

Roman Leopard ▲
- *1st century AD*
Roman bronze leopard with raised paw and head slightly turned, standing on a circular base.
- *height 4.5cm*
- £2,500 • Pars

Egyptian Mace Head ▲
- *late 4th millennium BC*
Egyptian black stone mace head.
- *height 10cm*
- £1,000 • Pars

Venetian Flask ▲
- *5th century BC*
Venetian flask with a pinched lip and strap handle, raised on a pedestal base, with a yellow and green diagonal design on a black ground.
- *height 10cm*
- £2,000 • Pars

Pottery Candleholder ▼
- *circa 8th century*
Byzantine pottery candle holder modelled as a church, with carved arches and openings with a geometric design.
- *height 29cm*
- £2,000 • Pars

Bronze Cat ▲
- *635–525BC*
Bronze cat from the Saite period dynasty or late bronze dynasty (625-525BC).
- *height 9.5cm*
- £6,000 • Pars

Aubergine Glass Flask ▲
- *7th century AD*
Aubergine glass flask with a single handle, a narrow neck and a bulbous body with applied circular raised design.
- *height 9cm*
- £700 • Pars

Roman Iridescent Flask ▼
- **4th century AD**
Iridescent green flask with silver and gold decoration.
- *height 12cm*
- £1,000   • Pars

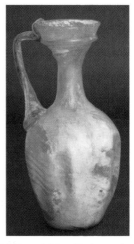

Green Glass Flask ▲
- **3rd–4th century AD**
Bottle shaped green glass flask, with globular body and cylindrical neck wound with clear spiral threads, four applied handles, flared foot and surface encrustation.
- *height 11cm*
- £6,500   • Pars

Indented Glass Flask ▲
- **4–6th century AD**
Green glass flask, with applied handle and six-sided body, with indented sides.
- *height 15cm*
- £1,000   • Pars

Aubergine Glass Jar ▼
- **7th century AD**
Small ovoid aubergine glass jar, with moulded rim and extensive iridescence.
- *height 7cm*
- £800   • Pars

Roman Cameo Ring ▶
- **circa 1st century AD**
Roman gold cameo ring decorated with an outstretched hand squeezing an ear inscribed 'Remember me and always be mine'.
- *width 2cm*
- £5,000   • Pars

Roman Flask ▲
- **1st century AD**
Roman blue glass flask, the body encircled with spiral threads.
- *height 9.4cm*
- £1,500   • Pars

Architectural & Garden Furniture

The boom in television gardening programmes has lead to an increase in demand for garden furniture and garden design.

The garden designers of the United Kingdom are currently leading the way with their innovative designs, as they once did in the past. Not since the time of Capability Brown, the greatest eighteenth-century landscape designer, and Edwin Lutyens, the house and garden architect, has there been so much excitement about the 'outdoor room'. The home owner increasingly sees his or her garden as a space to be considered with as much thought and care as any room in the house. Most garden furniture is made from wrought or cast iron and was produced in the Victorian era. Although age is important, it is not an essential, as decorative appeal and size also play an important part in the choosing of an item.

Louis Philippe Fireplace ▲
- *early 19th century*

French Louis Philippe black marble, monopodia chimneypiece. The breakfront frieze is carved with acanthus leaves and supported by scrolled legs terminating in lion's paws.
- *109cm x 88cm*
- **£11,500** • Crowther

Bronze Sundial ▶
- *1900*

Bronze circular sundial plate bearing the arms of the county of Cornwall engraved: 'Sol est Lux et Gloria Mundi, Newton Camborne 1900'.
- *diameter 34cm*
- **£2,500** • Crowther

English Sundial ▼
- *1716*

19th century English octagonal sundial wall plate inscribed 'Memento Mori'.
- *width 23cm*
- **£850** • Crowther

Stone Sundial ▲
- *circa 1870*

Stone sundial with a circular marble top supported on a hexagonal column, raised on a splayed foot.
- *height 129cm*
- **£2,100** • Drummonds

French Fire Screen ▼
- *mid 19th century*
French 18th century wrought
iron diaper work fire screen.
- *65cm x 60cm*
- £1,200 • Crowther

Stone Sundial ▼
- *mid 18th century*
Important English Portland stone
sundial, the triangular wasted
pedestal with moulded top and
canted corners, carved with rams
heads flanked by their lower legs
linked with drapery. The sides
with ribbon ties, and wreaths
around the central panel. The
base is carved with shells and
raised on C scrolled feet.
- *35cm x 24cm*
- £14,500 • Crowther

Lead Mask ▲
- *early 20th century*
Lead mask copied from an
original 18th century original,
depicting a cherub adorned with
full Bachannal regalia.
- *width 40cm*
- £300 • Crowther

Glazed Terracotta Urns ▲
- *late 19th century*
English glazed terracotta
conservatory urns, one of a pair,
stamped Doulton Lambeth and
incised with the numbers 8496
and 0088 and the letter M. The
ovoid bodies are decorated with
bold swags of fruit and flowers
hung from central wreaths with a
bronze glaze.
- *height 62cm*
- £11,750 • Crowther

Garden Bench ◄
- *20th century*
Iron lattice garden bench with
scrolled back and arms, above a
lattice seat, supported by shaped
legs on pad feet.
- *width 130cm*
- £395 • Drummonds

English Stoneware Urns ▼
- *19th century*
One of a pair of large English
Stoneware urns with loop handles
terminating in patriarch masks;
the campana form bodies with
everted lip over Greek key frieze
and gadrooning. Set on turned
socles over square bases.
Attributed to the workshops of
John Marriott Blashfield.
- *height 109cm*
- £23,500 the pair • Crowther

Cast Iron Vases ▼
- *mid 19th century*
Fine pair of French cast iron vases
stamped Val D'Osne formerly in
the collection of Lord Sainsbury.
The handles formed in the style
of cast ram's horns scrolls
springing from waterleaves set on
a Green Man masks. The out-
turned rim is supported on an
arcaded neck on a ribbon and
water-leaf moulding. The body is
decorated with floral lozenges and
gadrooning and set on a circular
socle.
- *height 73cm*
- £14,000 the pair • Crowther

Italian Water Fountain ▲
- *early 20th century*

Charming Italian Rosso Verona marble and bronze fountain by Rafffaello Romanelli. The marble bowl is supported on the shoulders of a bronze satyr crouching on a marble base. A laughing cherub stands with arms raised in the centre of the bowl, while being squirted by a frog crouching on the rim.
- *height 170cm*
- *diameter of bowl 92cm*
- £35,000   • Crowther

Stoneware Urns ▲
- *mid 19th century*

One of a pair of stoneware urns, each semi-lobed body with a frieze of stylised foliage beneath a rope twist and lobed rim, on a circular foot and square base stamped, 'Pulhams Terra Cotta Boxbourne'.
- *height 67cm*
- £9,500   • Crowther

Pair of Urns ▼
- *1910*

Pair of cast iron urns with egg and dart moulded rim above a lobed body, raised on a fluted, splayed foot on a square base.
- *58.5cm diameter*
- £460   • Drummonds

Stone Finials ▼
- *circa 1880*

One of a pair of English sandstone finials, finely carved with scrolled and leaf designs, surmounted with a stylised acorn finial.
- *height 200cm*
- £7,500   • Drummonds

Sir Walter Raleigh ▶
- *circa 1880*

Stone statue of Sir Walter Raleigh dressed in a tunic and breeches and holding his cloak.
- *height 120cm*
- £23,000   • Drummonds

Carved Stone Lions ▲
- *circa 1890*

One of a pair of late 19th-century stone lions in a crouching position, with tail swept onto one side and a finely carved expression.
- *44cm x 100cm*
- £14,000   • Drummonds

Cast Iron Fountain ▲
- *19th century*

Cast iron fountain from Ardennes, France, in the form of a young boy holding a staff in one hand and pointing with the other.
- *height 122cm*
- £3,400   • Drummonds

Cast Iron Urn ▼
- *circa 1890*
One of a pair of cast iron tulip urns of classical shape, with double handles, on a pedestal foot, raised on a plinth base.
- *64cm x 24cm*
- £750 • Drummonds

Classical Urn ▲
- *circa 1880*
Large classical urn with double handles from mask decoration, mounted on a plinth with wreath decoration.
- *height 150cm*
- £2,800 • Drummonds

Acorn Finials ▶
- *circa 1810*
One of a pair of late Georgian stone acorn finials with good patination.
- *55cm x 24cm*
- £600 • Drummonds

Terracotta Finial ▲
- *circa 1890s*
One of a pair of red terracotta finials with acanthus leaf designs above a splayed foot, raised on a plinth base.
- *height 170cm*
- £3,870 • Drummonds

Prague Lantern ▲
- *20th century*
A hexagonal lantern from Prague, with heraldic and floral swag decoration, surmounted by a finial with pierced designs.
- *height 100cm*
- £425 • Drummonds

French Well Head ◀
- *circa 1870*
Limestone well head with a wooden winch and handle within a steel housing, the limestone with good patination.
- *diameter 132cm*
- £3,400 • Drummonds

Stone Trough ▼

• *circa 1820*
A stone trough with attractive weathering of lichen and moss.
• *40cm x 78cm*
• £260   • Drummonds

Cast Iron Garden Roller ▼

• *circa 1870*
Cast iron garden roller with turned wooden handle and cast iron medallion with maker's logo.
• *height 120cm*
• £225   • Drummonds

Georgian Columns ▼

• *circa 1730s*
Three early Georgian stone columns with reeded capital, supported by square columns with chamfered corners, raised on stepped, plinth bases.
• *height 195cm*
• £785 each   • Drummonds

Roll Top Bench ▲

• *20th century*
A two seated roll top iron bench, with ladder back and seat, and scrolled arms and legs.
• *width 120cm*
• £425   • Drummonds

Neptune Fountain ▲

• *circa 1890*
Cast iron wall fountain showing Neptune sitting on his throne while wrestling with a carp.
• *height 155cm*
• £1,775   • Drummonds

Palladian Chimneypiece ▼

• *circa 1730*
An English Palladian statuary marble chimneypiece, after a design by William Kent. The projecting inverted breakfront shelf with moulded edge above a band of lotus moulding and a boldly carved egg and dart moulding, the frieze centred by a rectangular panel carved with a bacchante mask, the hair intertwined with berried vines, and a border of sienna marble.
• *166cm x 231cm*
• £315,000   • Anthony Outred

Stone Trough ▼

• *circa 1820*
A rectangular stone trough with good patination.
• *38cm x 89cm*
• £250   • Drummonds

French Copper Bath ▼

• *circa 1880*
French double skinned bath with copper lining, raised on cast iron claw feet.
• *length 167cm*
• £7,950   • Drummonds

Brass Lantern ▼

- **1880**

Brass lantern with glass front and sides with pagoda top and small round brass finials.
- *height 45cm*
- **£110**   • Myriad

Chinese Garden Seat ▶

- **1880**

Chinese ceramic garden seat with a cream glaze, pierced lattice panels, and lion mask decoration.
- *height 39cm*
- **£350**   • Ormonde

Galvanised Flower Bucket ▲

- **1960**

French flower vendors galvanised display bucket with carrying handles.
- *height 48cm*
- **£22**   • Myriad

Galvanised Tub ▲

- **1880**

One of a pair of galvanised water butts with an inverted linear design.
- *height 54cm*
- **£95**   • Myriad

Ceramic Garden Seat ▶

- **1880**

Chinese ceramic garden seat, in a green glaze, with black floral designs and a repeating pattern of spots.
- *height 39cm*
- **£350**   • Ormonde

Enamel Bucket ▼

- **1920**

French enamelled water bucket with a red rim, pale green body, hand painted strawberries and original handle.
- *height 29cm*
- **£78**   • Myriad

Expert Tips

Garden, unlike interior furniture, does not need to be perfect in order to create a beautiful garden, as some wear and distress can add mystery and delight to any design. All that is needed is a little imagination.

Green Stucco Pot ◀

- **1950**

Stoneware urn of ovoid form with green glazed lip and neck with rusticated finish to the body.
- *height 44cm*
- **£240**   • Myriad

Fire Grate ▲

- *circa 1727-1820*
Cast iron Georgian fire grate, with architectural and stylised leaf designs.
- *height 97cm*
- £4,200   • Drummonds

Fire Bellows ▶

- *circa 1900*
Large cast iron fire bellows with original leather membrane.
- *length 16cm*
- £980   • Drummonds

Shanks Cistern ▲

- *circa 1870*
A polished and lacquered cast iron shanks 3 gallon cistern with original brass fittings.
- *height 35cm*
- £875   • Drummonds

Iron Gong ▼

- *circa 1890*
Iron gong with a hand beaten finish supported by chains within a mahogany frame with turned decoration.
- *114cm x 75cm*
- £885   • Drummonds

Brass Fire Dogs ▲

- *circa 1800s*
A pair of decorative French brass fire dogs with shield motifs surmounted by flame finial designs, raised on acanthus scrolled feet.
- *height 54cm*
- £780   • Drummonds

Wash Basin ▲

- *circa 1900*
Edwardian ceramic wash basin with cast iron feet and original fittings.
- *height 80cm*
- £970   • Drummonds

Register Grate ▲

- *circa 1870*
Arched cast iron register grate with a polished metal finish and decorated with a peacock design.
- *height 97cm*
- £920   • Drummonds

Door Surround and Door ▲
• *Late 19th century*
Carved door surround and door,
consisting of two panel doors,
door surround and frieze, carved
with amorphic and foliate
designs.
• *224cm x 125cm*
• £1,250   • Drummonds

Oak Fireplace   ▼
• *circa 1890s*
Victorian mahogany fire place
with carved architectural pillars
surmounted by a carved frieze
with moulded cornice.
• *270cm x 90cm*
• £9,200   • Drummonds

Mahogany Door
Surround   ▶
• *Circa 1890*
Mahogany door frame with
moulded designs and beading,
surmounted by a carved frieze.
• *224cm x 125cm*
• £1,250   • Drummonds

Gothic Archway   ▼
• *circa 1800s*
Carved Gothic sandstone window
consisting of two arched windows
with Gothic tracery .
• *274cm x 137cm*
• £1,975   • Drummonds

Glazed Doors   ▲
• *circa 1890s*
Victorian glazed double doors
within a moulded frame
surmounted by an arched
moulded fanlight.
• *200cm x 125cm*
• £675   • Drummonds

Victorian Iron Gates ▲
- *circa 1880*

Pair of Victorian iron gates, heavily constructed with ball and spike finial designs.
- *200cm x 300cm*
- **£5,100**   • Drummonds

Oak Bar ▲
- *circa 1920s*

Circular oak bar with moulded panelled doors, consisting of a four door fridge unit, marble surround and surfaces.
- *length 635cm*
- **£5,900**   • Drummonds

Architectural Fireplace ▶
- *circa 1800–1900*

Carved wooden fireplace flanked by two architectural columns surmounted by a moulded mantle. With traces of white paint.
- *height 128cm*
- **£2,350**   • Drummonds

Gothic Window ▼
- *circa 1800s*

Carved gothic sandstone window.
- *89cm x 69cm*
- **£675**   • Drummonds

Fire Dogs and Grate ▶
- *circa 1900s*

Victorian serpentine–fronted cast-iron grate and fire back with a raised design of tulips, surmounted by two cherubs holding a wreath.
- *75cm x 80cm*
- **£3,600**   • Drummonds

English Rococo Chimneypiece ▲
- *circa 1840*

An English white marble chimneypiece signed D Af. The serpentine shaped shelf with moulded edge above an elaborately carved frieze decorated with scrolled acanthus leaves, with a central scallop carved shell above the hearth opening and a double moulded surround with relief flower heads above three small acanthus motifs terminating in scrolled leaves.
- *122cm x 193cm*
- **£38,000**   • Outrred

Musgraves Conservatory Radiator ▼
- *circa 1910*
One of a pair of cast iron Musgraves conservatory radiators consisting of twelve columns.
- *height 75cm*
- £850   • Drummonds

Regency Fireplace ▼
- *circa 1890*
White marble Regency fireplace, with reeded columns and black marble insert, surmounted by a carved frieze with urn decoration.
- *height 145cm*
- £18,950   • Drummonds

Victorian Radiator Cover ▲
- *circa 1900*
One of a pair of Victorian cast iron radiator covers with pierced panels and moulded column supports.
- *93cm x 49cm x 103cm*
- £1,400   • Drummonds

Stone Gargoyle ▲
- *circa 1880*
Carved stone gargoyle, formed as an eagle, with outstretched wings and head turned to one side, perched on a carved rock base.
- *101cm x 80cm*
- £825   • Drummonds

Art Deco Fireplace ▼
- *circa 1920*
Art Deco tiled fireplace with mottled effect and a reeded design running vertically either side of the hearth.
- *94cm x 138cm*
- £350   • Drummonds

Teak Pillars ▲
- *circa 18th century*
One of a pair of teak columns from the Kanatra province, with fluted stem on a pedestal base surmounted by a heavily carved capital, modelled on the banana flower.
- *height 214cm*
- £3,800   • Gordon Reece

Petite Palace Shutters ▶

- *circa early 19th century*
Pair of shutters from the Petite Palace, Hyderabad. Consisting of eight panels with pierced geometric designs and brass fittings.
- *182cm x 111cm*
- £1,600 • Gordon Reece

Bothwell Staircase ▲

- *circa 1800*
A carved mahogany Bothwell staircase with moulded panelling, heavily carved balustrade and moulded hand rails.
- *height 2,450cm*
- £3,600 • Drummonds

Mughal Panel ▲

- *18th century*
An 18th-century Indian sandstone Mughal panel, carved in relief with a flower at the centre and numerous sprays emanating from rocks. Set within a rope twist border.
- *66cm x 85cm*
- £9,200 • Gordon Reece

Cherub Fountain ▼

- *circa 1870*
Lead fountain, depicting a cherub wrestling a carp amongst the reeds.
- *height 84cm*
- £9,800 • Drummonds

Gujurat Columns ▼

- *circa 1900*
One of a pair of carved wooden pilasters from Gujarat, incorporating three different styles with Victorian influences. Standing on a stone base with traces of paint.
- *213cm x 31cm*
- £1,380 • Gordon Reece

Mughal Architectural Panel ▼

- *18th century*
An Indian Mughal panel divided into three sections, with carved floral designs in relief, set within an acanthus leaf border.
- *91cm x 102cm*
- £8,900 • Gordon Reece

Pottery Urn ▲
- *circa 1940*
One of a pair of pottery urns with lobed designs around the body and egg and dart motif to the splayed lip, standing on a pedestal base.
- *height 43cm*
- £480 • Myriad

French Chair ▲
- *circa 1950*
One of a set of four French wrought iron garden chairs with pierced geometric designs to back splat and seat.
- *height 87cm*
- £680 • Myriad

Mythical Yarli Lions ▼
- *18th century*
One of a pair of Mythical Yarli lions with elephant trunks, standing on top of human heads. Has traces of original paint remaining in excellent condition. Vellore Tamil Naou.
- *height 166cm*
- £7,800 • Gordon Reece

Indian Jarli Window ▼
- *17th century*
Indian Mughal Jarli window carved from red sandstone flanked by four cartouches in the form of Mirabs arches. The central Jarli of interlocking honeycomb is topped by a floral finial with a flower to left and right from Northern Rajastan.
- *83cm x 115cm*
- £5,800 • Gordon Reece

Wicker Chair ▶
- *circa 1920*
French provincial wicker conservatory chair painted pistachio green with a deep horseshoe back, apron front and splayed legs.
- *height 67cm*
- £240 • Myriad

Wrought Iron Chair ▲
- *circa 1950*
Set of four French wrought iron patio chairs with a heart shaped back scrolled arms and original white enamel paint.
- *height 87cm*
- £680 for set of four • Myriad

Carved Ceiling Panel ▲
- *circa 1850*
Carved rosewood ceiling panel with central flower within a stylised leaf motif, from Southern India.
- *length 56cm*
- £310 • Gordon Reece

Brass Urns ▼

- *circa 1910*
One of a pair of brass urns from
the modern movement, with
unusual angular double handles,
the whole on a pedestal foot
resting on a square base.
- *height 48cm*
- **£880**   • Myriad

Zinc Urns ▼

- *1920*
One of a pair of French urns
made from zinc with unusual
angular designs and a marbled
finish.
- *height 31cm*
- **£680**   • Myriad

Garden Folding Stool ▲

- *1950*
Folding picnic stool with a candy
striped linen seat supported by
four teak legs.
- *height 41cm*
- **£78**   • Myriad

Stone Flower Pot ▲

- *1970*
Stone flower pot with a fluted
body with carved designs in relief.
- *height 24cm*
- **£24**   • Myriad

Pink Pottery Bucket ▼

- *1910*
French ceramic pail with salmon
pink glaze and white interior with
a raffia covered handle.
- *height 24cm*
- **£18**   • Myriad

Expert Tips

*Unglazed period pottery of any
value should be covered up and
protected if left outside in the
winter, as ice can destroy it as it
expands in the cracks.*

Salt Glazed Urn ▼

- *1910*
French salt glazed pottery urn
with pinched lip and banding,
the body centred with a flower
motif in relief on a pedestal base.
- *height 41cm*
- **£120**   • Myriad

Watering Can ◄

- *1920*
Zinc watering can with an
elongated spout.
- *height 26cm*
- **£34**   • Myriad

Shanks Canopy Bath ▼
- *circa 1910*

Shanks, cast iron canopy bath, with original nickel fittings including numerous water-jets and large shower rose.
- *height 32cm*
- £9,800 • Drummonds

Copper Tub ▲
- *circa 1860s*

Large 19th century, circular copper tub, supported on a steel frame.
- *diameter 174cm*
- £16,500 • Drummonds

Italian Marble Bath ▼
- *circa 1890s*

Late 19th century Italian marble bath, with a carved frieze of stylised acanthus leaves.
- *length 188cm*
- £13,800 • Drummonds

London Ceramic Trap ▼
- *circa 1910*

London porcelain trap with bracket and seat, with rose and leaf decoration, to the inside and outside of the unit.
- *height 46cm*
- £1,125 • Drummonds

Lounge Bath ◄
- *circa 1910*

Lounge bath with ball and claw feet with original nickel plated fittings including built in waist and plunger units.
- *width 86cm*
- £1,950 • Drummonds

Arms & Armour

There are many avenues to choose from for the collector of militaria including weapons, pictures, prints, postcards, and medals.

Interest in arms and armour has never been greater and there is still a wealth of material to choose from at all price ranges. A fine weapon should be as beautiful as it is deadly, and therein lies its charm. Traditionally, at the top end of the market the price leaders such as pistols in their original cases and military headdresses continue to rise in value, although these must be in their original condition. Most swords available today date from the period after 1796 when British military patterns were standardised. Swords come in two types, those for action and those for dress wear. Court swords with decorative hilts and slender blades often have a good provenance and can also be highly decorative. Without the precise details of the weapons used, and by whom, history could be left severely wanting. It is the research shown by the collector which can unearth episodes in history.

Officer's Peaked Cap ▶
- **1940**
Officer's peaked cap of the Kriegsmarine Administration Service, with silver wire eagle cockage and braid, in excellent condition. Items of this branch of the Kriegsmarine are rarely seen!
- *size 8*
- **£795**   • Gordon's

Kriegsmarine Colani Jacket ▲
- **1940**
A rare Kriegsmarine Colani Jacket-Haupt Feldwebel, Coxwain rank, complete with breast eagle, shoulder boards and all original buttons.
- *medium*
- **£315**   • Gordon's

Prismatic Compass ▼
- **circa 1917**
British officers, First World War, military prismatic compass with original fitted leather case, dated.
- *diameter 5.5cm*
- **£200**   • Bentleys

Naval Officer's Sword ▼
- **1880**
Royal Naval Officer's sword retailed by Ashdown, 106 St. Georges Street, Portsmouth, with original gilding to guard and mounts and gilt brass lion's head on handle.
- *length 112cm*
- **£500**   • Seidler

Belgian Courtier's Sword ▼

- *circa 1860*

Belgian courtier's sword with
mother of pearl grip and brass gilt
guard, with foliate designs
together with a black leather
scabbard with gilt mounts.
Inscribed 'Docteur Lorthioir' and
the maker's mark 49 Rue des
Fabrique, Brussels.
- *length 85cm*
- **£200**   • Seidler

Royal Engineers Busby ▼

- *circa 1910*

Royal engineers officers bear fur
busby with the gilt flaming bomb
incorporating the Regiments
insignia, and patent leather
chinstrap.
- *height 14cm*
- **£375**   • Seidler

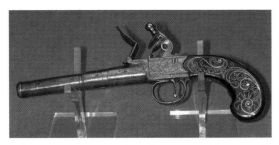

Fintlock Pistol ▲

- *circa 1790*

English flintlock three barrel tap
action pistol made by Clarke of
London. 62 Cheapside London.
- *length 21cm*
- **£1,900**   • Michael German

Captain's Jacket and Hat ▼

- *1855*

Scarlet tunic of a Captain in the
First Royal Tower Hamlets
Miliita (The King's Own Light
Infantry). Collar insignia of
Crown and Pip with tin case by
Flight Military Tailors,
Winchester, containing belts and
sashes. Plus an Officer's shako
(without plume) with K.O.L.I
plate.
- *large*
- **£1,650**   • Gordon's

General's Aiguilettes ▼

- *1940*

Third Reich General's aiguilettes,
in good condition with only
minor damage to parts of the gilt
wiring.
- *length 42cm*
- **£185**   • Gordon's

32 Calibre Percussion Revolver ◀

- *1860*

32 calibre double action Adams
revolver, with hexagonal barrel,
made under licence by Mass
Arms. Co. U.S.A. with modern
bullet mould.
- *length 21.5cm*
- **£550**   • Seidler

Turkish Holster Pistol ▼

- *circa 1800*

Fine Turkish flintlock holster pistol with silver mounts.
- *length 51cm*
- £1,700   • Michael German

Coconut Powder Flask ▼

- *circa 1810*

A coconut powder flask, carved and polished by a French POW in the West Indies. The carving depicts the Battle of Austerlitz, 1805.
- *length 14cm*
- £1,000   • Seidler

German Peaked Cap ▼

- *1940*

German W.W.II, peaked cap of the Luftwaffe Artillery. Blue with red piping, in good condition, badges and cockade. Makers mark 'Deutsche Wert Arbeit' inside.
- *size 8*
- £285   • Gordon's

Burmese Dagger ▲

- *circa 1830*

Burmese Dhar dagger with ornate silver handle and scabbard inlaid with nielio foliate design.
- *length 54cm*
- £620   • Michael German

Scottish Dirk ▼

- *circa 1860*

Scottish silver mounted highland dirk, complete with knife and fork, the handles carved from stag horn.
- *length 38cm*
- £1,600   • Michael German

Flintlock Blunderbuss ▼

- *circa 1700*

English flintlock blunderbuss of early type, maker Savage. Brass fittings and London proofmarks.
- *length 68cm*
- £3,200   • Michael German

Two-Cornered Hat ▼

- *circa 1800*

Metal trunk with 'Andrew Blair' inscribed on the lid, especially made to house a Naval Admiral's hat. The original hat is included, with original sash and lapels decorated with gold braiding.
- *width 42cm*
- £1,200   • Julian Smith

Midshipman's Hangar ▼

- *circa 1850*

Navy mid 19th century, Midshipman's Hangar, with brass guard, steel blade with original washer still present, without scabbard.
- *length 86cm*
- £275   • Seidler

Pith Helmet ▶

- *circa 1915*
Turn of the century linen pith
helmet for the overseas campaign
in India, in fine original
condition.
- *size 7*
- £120 • Bentleys

Luftwaffe Belt ▶

- *1940*
Luftwaffe other ranks late pattern
standard leather belt, with some
wear, but complete.
- *5cm x 3cm*
- £45 • Gordon's

SS Steel Helmet ▼

- *1940*
SS M-44 Steel helmet, a rare
early double decal version
complete with inner lining and
chin strap, stamped '54' on lining
and a maker's stamp on inside of
helmet, with most of original
finish still present.
- *Size 8*
- £1,195 • Gordon's

Japanese N.C.O. Sword ▶

- *circa 1939*
Japanese N.C.O. Katena sword
with polished folded steel blade
and original paintwork to handle.
No. 79275, with matching
scabbard number.
- *length 59cm*
- £290 • Seidler

Officers Belt Pistol ◀

- *circa 1840*
Officers 16 bore percussion pistol,
with double back action locks, by
Roper of Halifax.
- *length 30cm*
- £875 • Seidler

Khula–Khad Helmet ▶

- *circa 1800*
Fine Indo Persian Khula-Khad
helmet formed as a face with
horns, with chiselled steel
designs, gold inlays and chain
mail neck guard.
- *height 30cm*
- £3,200 • Michael German

Japanese Dagger ▼

- *circa 1870*
A Japanese Tanto dagger with
cloisonne hilt and scabbard, the
blade is unsigned.
- *length 35cm*
- £1,800 • Michael German

Pinfire Revolver ▼

- *circa 1870*
Continental pinfire carbine
revolver with 'Fabrique de Le
Page Freres a Liege, Maison a
Paris 12 Rue de Eugieue' etched
on barrel .
- *length 66cm*
- £1,200 • Michael German

Infantry Tunic ▼
- *1941*

Africa Corps infantry tunic with
four pockets complete with all
insignia and buttons. In excellent
condition.
- *large*
- £375   • Gordon's

Percussion Revolver ▲
- *circa 1854*

English Tranter patent,double
action, percussion revolver,
overlaid in gold, retailer B.
Cogswell 224 Strand, London, in
original fitted case,with
accessories.
- *length 32cm*
- £3,800   • Michael German

Belt Buckle ▼
- *1860*

Belt buckle for the St. Martin in
the Fields Rifle Volunteers
(Patent unit of Queens
Westminster).
- *width 7.5cm*
- £275   • Seidler

Danish Cavalry Sword ▼
- *1860*

Danish cavalry sword with
original polished steel scabbard
with maker's mark 17 S & K.
- *length 85cm*
- £220   • Seidler

SS Kepi Cap ▲
- *1940*

Early SS Kepi with Skull and
leather strap.
- *size 8*
- £975   • Gordon's

Percussion Carbine ▼
- *circa 1850*

Percussion carbine in working
order with original mould for the
making of ammunition and
walnut furniture, made by the
Westley & Richards & Co., with
a Whitworth patent, complete
with strap holders and ram rod.
- *length 103cm*
- £600   • Seidler

Trooper's Sabre ▼

- *circa 1908*

British trooper's sabre, pattern dated and inscribed W.W.I. Paint.
- *length 110cm*
- £275
- Seidler

Deane Harding Percussion Pistol ▼

- *circa 1840*

Deane Harding 54 calibre officer's percussion cap and ball pistol, with hexagonal barrel and original grip and varnish. London proof marks.
- *length 30cm*
- £750
- Seidler

Luftwaffe Paratrooper Helmet ▶

- *1940*

Luftwaffe paratrooper's helmet. Rare double decal version, with both Luftwaffe eagle and national shield. The chinstrap and liner are complete showing makers mark: Baumuster: Heisler Berlin C2 Hersteller F. W. Muller JR and sizes; Koptwelte GR 61 Stahlhaube Nr. 71, all clearly readable. Helmet stamped on the inside, 'ET71', paintwork and overall finish excellent.
- *size 8*
- £3,500
- Gordon's

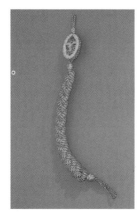

Schutzenschnur Silver Luftwaffe ▲

- *1940*

Pilot officer's silver braid of the Luftwaffe with an eagle and National Insignia.
- *length 14cm*
- £100
- Gordon's

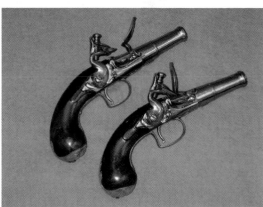

Russian Dagger ▼

- *circa 1880*

Russian Kinjal dagger with ornate silver hilt and scabbard, the blade with long grooves and foliate design in mechanical watering.
- *length 51cm*
- £1,400
- Michael German

Pocket Flintlock Pistols ▼

- *circa 1720*

Pair of English Queen Anne pocket flintlock pistols, with cannon barrels and silver lion mask butt caps, signed John Segelas. Hammers fitted with dog catches.
- *length 18cm*
- £3,400
- Michael German

French Belt Pistol ▼

- *1813*

French cavalryman's belt pistol with flintlock action, brass mounts and walnut furniture.
- *length 21.5cm*
- £1,000
- Seidler

Georgian Sword ▼
- *circa 1800*

Georgian officer's sabre with blue and gilt blade. Maker Johnston late Bland and Foster Sword Cutler and belt maker to his Majesty, 68 St. James' Street London.
- *length 92cm*
- £1,700 • Michael German

Fighting Axe ▼
- *circa 15th century*

Gothic fighting axe with iron blade and steel insert, with a later wooden shaft for display purposes.
- *length 158cm*
- £900 • Seidler

Jade Dagger ▲
- *circa 1800*

Indian dagger with mutton fat jade handle, inlaid with semi - precious stones, water steel blade and red cloth covered scabbard.
- *length 41cm*
- £3,800 • Michael German

Tibetan Helmet ▲
- *circa 1540*

15th century Tibetan helmet fashioned from iron plates, with plume holder.
- *height 32cm*
- £1,900 • Michael German

Luftwaffe Flying Helmet ▲
- *1940*

Luftwaffe flying helmet. Summer issue version, with canvas hood, straps, leads and sockets still present. Stamped inside earpiece. Ln 26602.
- *height 19cm*
- £245 • Gordon's

Pin Fire Revolver ▼
- *circa 1817*

Ten shot ll mil. pin fire revolver made in Belgium and proofed in Birmingham with matching numbers.
- *length 29cm*
- £800 • Seidler

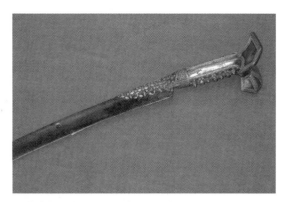

Turkish Sword ▲

- *circa 1840*
Turkish Yataghan sword with large ornate silver hilt with extending ears and blade with maker's stamp.
- *length 77cm*
- £1,400 • Michael German

Airforce Honour Dagger ▼

- *1937*
Airforce honour dagger lst pattern known as Bordoich, complete with hanging chains.
- *length 39cm*
- £295 • Gordon's

Helmet Plate ▼

- *1914*
Baden Reservists gilt metal helmet plate, modelled as a griffin centered with shield and cross swords.
- *width 14cm*
- £65 • Seidler

Artillery Parade Tunic ▼

- *1936*
Waffenrock Gebirgsjaeger artillery parade tunic, complete with ribbon bar of 5 and breast eagle shoulder boards.
- *medium*
- £325 • Gordon's

Regimental Sash Plate ▼

- *circa 1900*
South Lancashire colour sash plate commemorating all the battles that the regiment had served, with a blue enamelled and gilt foliate design below the fleur de lys.
- *diameter 10cm*
- £495 • Seidler

Light Infantry Buckle ▲

- *1881*
Duke of Somerset's Light Infantry officers belt buckle. With worn gilt, 1881 patent.
- *width 13cm*
- £120 • Seidler

Indian Axe ▲

- *circa 1830*
Ornate Indian battle axe with concealed dagger in handle, with ornate copper and brass chiselled overlay and steel blade with elephants and lion finials.
- *length 57cm*
- £1,100 • Michael German

Gerbirgsjaeger NCO's Peaked Cap ▼
- **1940**

Gerbirgsjaeger N C O's peaked cap. Maker's diamond on the inside. Uniform Krungshaus Karl Petrasch Klagenfurt. All outside emblems attached, complete and in good condition.
- *Size 8*
- **£495** • Gordon's

Luftwaffe Nachrichten Signals Tunic ▼
- **1940**

Luftwaffe Nachrichten (Signals) NCO tunic with four pockets, NCO shoulder boards with silver braid, one pip, tan piping and number 11, with piping and silver braid collar.
- *large*
- **£395** • Gordon's

Wheel-Lock Pistol ▶
- *circa 1620*

German wheel-lock holster pistol with fish tail but, sliding flash pan cover, and steel mounts.
- *length 62cm*
- **£5,800** • Michael German

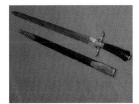

Hunting Sword ▲
- *circa 1850*

Continental hunting sword with grooved blade fluted ebony handle and plated mounts with dog head cross guard.
- *length 70cm*
- **£750** • Michael German

SA Dagger ▼
- *circa 1932*

SA honour dagger Rohm Widmung with partly erased inscription. The Ernst Rohm has been neatly erased from the blade but the rests remains. Some light wear on the scabbard, otherwise dagger in very good condition.
- *length 39cm*
- **£695** • Gordon's

Pocket Flintlock ▼
- *circa 1750*

French pocket pistol with flintlock action and steel barrels, signed Le Roy.
- *length 17cm*
- **£590** • Michael German

Luftschutz Dagger ▼
- **1939**

Luftschutz dagger, 1st pattern rankers issue, complete with single strap hanger, with the maker's mark 'Kroneck Ernst Erich Witte Solingen' on blade and 'RZM M5/71 OLC' on the hanger clip.
- *length 40cm*
- **£825** • Gordon's

Cheshire Regiment Belt Clasp ▼

- *1855*

Regimental belt clasp of the 22nd Cheshire Regiment shown with crown over regimental number and silver and gilt scrolled belt loops.
- *width 13cm*
- £135 • Seidler

Luftwaffe Dagger ▼

- *1937*

German Lufwaffe dagger, 2nd type, with yellow bakelite grip and original maker's mark 'Eickhorn Solingen', hanger straps and epee portepote.
- *length 37cm*
- £325 • Gordon's

Holster Pistol ▼

- *circa 1680*

English holster pistol by John Dafte, London, with strawberry leaf engraving and steel mounts. Fully stocked.
- *length 47cm*
- £4,600 • Michael German

Japanese Tanto ▲

- *circa 1860*

Japanese Tanto concealing a percussion pistol, with copper and brass fittings and burr-wood furniture.
- *length 48cm*
- £3,250 • Michael German

Scottish Full Dirk ▲

- *circa 1905*

Scottish military full dress dirk blade etched with battle honours for the Highland Light Infantry, coloured stones, regimental crest.
- *length 46cm*
- £1,800 • Michael German

Flintlock Pistol ▼

- *circa 1770*

Cannon barrelled flintlock pistol with riffled barrel. The stock with silver wired inlay designs, with maker's mark.
- *length 24cm*
- £1,250 • Michael German

Indo Persian Khula – Khad ▼

- *circa 1780*

Indo Persian Khula-Khad steel helmet, chiselled with foliate designs, sliding nose guard and top spike, with chain mail neck guard.
- *height 30cm*
- £1,400 • Michael German

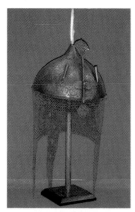

Automobilia

Motor racing and rallies are as popular today as they have ever been along with the collecting of automobile memorabilia.

The collection of automobilia is based predominantly around clubs, racetracks and personalities; for example any memorabilia relating to the Brooklands and Monte Carlo racetracks or the the Morgan, Aston Martin and MG car clubs is regarded as highly collectable. They provide items of interest to the collector, who is prepared to pay large sums of money for a certain badge or mascot to add to their collection. A huge industry has sprung up around the classic car and for the avid collector of automobilia the auto sales that take place across the country provide an opportunity to purchase anything from racing programmes, garage signs and car parts to archival photography. While a vintage car may be too expensive, memorabilia is affordable. To be auctioned shortly is the Bugatti Royal, which is estimated to fetch more than £7 million. What greater respect for its craftmanship can we bestow on the motor car?

R. A. C Badge ▼
- *circa 1930s*

Royal Automobile Club associate badge affiliated to the Junior Car Club (J.C.C.) Inter-war period. Chromed brass and vitreous enamel collars.
- *height 13cm*
- **£150**　　　　　• C.A.R.S

Bentley Drivers Club Badge ▶
- *1950s*

Bentley Drivers Club wheel spinner style club membership badge in chrome and painted enamel.
- *diameter 8cm*
- **£45**　　　　　• C.A.R.S

Brighton & Hove Badge ▲
- *1950s–70s*

Brighton & Hove Motor Club membership badge. Die struck brass, chrome plated with vitreous enamel colours.
- *diameter 6cm*
- **£40**　　　　　• C.A.R.S

Brighton & Hove Motor Club Badge ▲
- *circa 1920s*

Brighton and Hove Motor Club membership badge of the inter-war period. Die stuck brass, chrome plated with vitreous enamel.
- *diameter 6cm*
- **£200**　　　　　• C.A.R.S

Morgan Club Badge ▲

- *2001*
Morgan Sports Car Club present day membership badge, known as 'Sex Mog.' Cut brass with plastic based enamel colours.
- *diameter 7cm*
- £25   • C.A.R.S

Jaguar Mascot ▲

- *circa 1925–30*
Jaguar leaping cat car mascot by Desmo, after a design by Frederick Gordon Crosby, cast brass, chrome plated and mounted on a radiator cap. An after sales accessory mascot popular during the inter-war period.
- *length 20cm*
- £300   • C.A.R.S

Rolls-Royce Mascot ▶

- *circa 1920s*
Rolls-Royce flying lady known as 'The Spirit of Ecstasy' designed by Charles Sykes and patented in 1911. This very tall example is from the pre World War 1 period. In cast brass, nickel plated sometimes silver plated
- *height 17cm*
- £1,250   • C.A.R.S

R. A. C. Silver Jubilee Badge ▼

- *1977*
R.A.A Queen's Silver Jubilee 1977 specially produced limited edition commemorative badge sold with certificate. Die struck brass chrome plated with plastic based enamel colours.
- *diameter 10cm*
- £200   • C.A.R.S

British Motor Racing Badge ▲

- *circa 1940s*
British Motor Racing Marshall's badge produced in die struck brass, chrome plated with vitreous enamel colours.
- *12cm x 9cm*
- £150   • C.A.R.S

Bentley Mascot ▼
- *circa 1950s*
Bentley flying winged B radiator
mounted mascot, designed by
Charles Sykes. This example is
post World War II and is shown
to be leaning forward. Cast brass,
chronuim plated.
- *height 7cm*
- £250   • C.A.R.S

Bentley Mascot ▼
- *circa 1920s*
Bentley flying winged B radiator
mounted mascot designed by
Charles Sykes. This example is
from the 1920's roadster sports
model and is a large brass casting
used for a short period.
- *wing span 22cm*
- £400   • C.A.R.S

Bentley Winged B ▶
- *circa 1960–80*
Bentley winged B radiator shell
badge, pressed steel, chrome
plated with enamel central black
B label.
- *height 14.5cm*
- £100   • C.A.R.S

B. A. R. C . Badge ▲
- *circa 1930s*
Brooklands Automobile Racing
Club membership badge issued
during the inter-war period up
until the closure of the circuit in
1939. Die struck brass, chrome
plated and vitreous coloured
enamels. Produced by Spencer.
London. Usually with members
issue No. stamped on the reverse.
- *height 14cm*
- £400   • C.A.R.S

Brighton & Hove Motor Club Badge ▲
- *2001*
Brighton & Hove Motor Club
badge of the present day, cut
brass, chrome and plastic based
enamel colours.
- *diameter 6cm*
- £20   • C.A.R.S

Bentley B ▼
- *circa 1940s*
Bentley flying winged B radiator
mounted mascot, designed by
Charles Sykes. This example is
shown to be leaning backward.
Cast brass, chronuim plated.
- *wing span 17cm*
- £300   • C.A.R.S

Bentley Flying B ▼
- *circa 1920*
Bentley flying winged B radiator
mounted mascot designed by
Charles Sykes.
- *height 17cm*
- £300   • C.A.R.S

J. C. C. Badge ▼
- *1960–70*
The Junior Car Club existed to
cater for light cars and
motorcycles including Morgan
type three wheelers. Membership
badge in die struck brass, nickel
or chrome plated with vitreous
enamel colours.
- *height 14cm*
- £200   • C.A.R.S

Dolphin Brighton & Hove Mascot ▼

- *circa 1920–30*
Brighton and Hove Car Club mascot for radiator mounting in the form of a dolphin like sea monster. Cast brass nickel plated. This car club is the oldest club in the UK.
- *height 14cm*
- £200 • C.A.R.S

Mercedes Radiator Grill ▼

- *circa 1950*
Mercedes Benz radiator shell with grill and star mascot, pressed steel chromium plated.
- *width 65cm*
- £100 • C.A.R.S

Brooklands Club Award ▶

- *circa 1930s*
Brookland Automobile Racing Club. Special speed award for attaining a timed lap speed of 130mph or more on the outer circuit. The red vitreous enamel label riveted beneath the wings. Only about a dozen or so of the 130mph badges were awarded and they are recorded in the W B Boddy book History of Brookland Motor Course' showing the date of issue and the speed attained and in which car.
- *height 14cm*
- £5,500 • C.A.R.S

Brooklands Society Badge ▲

- *circa 1990s*
B.S (Brooklands Society) membership badge in cut brass, chromium plated with plastic based coloured enamels.
- *height 14.5cm*
- £25 • C.A.R.S

Brooklands Society Badge ▼

- *circa 1960s–1980s*
B.S (Brooklands Society) membership badge in die struck brass, chrome plated with vitreous coloured enamels.
- *height 14.5cm*
- £100 • C.A.R.S

B. A. R. C. Badge ▲

- *1920–30s*

Brookland Automobile Racing Club. Special speed award for attaining a timed lap speed of 120 mph or more on the outer circuit. The red vitreous enamel label riveted beneath the wings.
- *height 14cm*
- **£5,500**   • C.A.R.S

B. A. R. C. Badge ▲

- *circa 1930s*

Brookland Automobile Racing Club committee members' badge (a standard issue badge with the legend 'Committee' on a yellow label beneath the wings, only a very few were issued) 1,500.
- *height 14cm*
- **£2,000**   • C.A.R.S

Expert Tips

The most famous car mascot is the Spirit of Ectasy, which was created for Rolls Royce by Charles Sykes in 1910. The earliest and most prized mascot is that for the Vulcan Motor Company from 1903.

B. A. R. C. Badge ▼

- *From 1907*

Brookland Automobile Racing Club member's and guests brooches. Every year on joining a member would be issued with a pin brooch tag in gilt brass with vitreous coloured enamel centre with two smaller versions on coloured string for the guests. These were sent to the member in an official box with the matching year date shown. The dates issued were from the opening of the circuit in 1910.
- *height 14cm*
- **boxed sets £200**   • C.A.R.S

Brooklands Aero Club Badge ▼

- *circa 1930s*

Brooklands Aero Club membership badge issued during the inter-war period up until the closure of the circuit in 1939. Die cast brass, chrome plated and vitreous coloured enamels. Produced by Spencer of London.
- *height 14cm*
- **£550**   • C.A.R.S

M. S. C. C. Badge ▲

- *circa 1970–80*

M.S.C.C. Morgan Sports Car Club shield shape membership badge of the 4/4 owner's (special anniversary issue dates thereon) Die struck with vitreous coloured enamels.
- *height 14cm*
- **£75**   • C.A.R.S

Steering Wheel Ashtray ▲

- *circa 1950s*

Ashtray in the form of a steering wheel in moulded porcelain produced by Beswick, England for Les Leston (Motoring Suppliers).
- *diameter 19cm*
- **£55**   • C.A.R.S

J.C.C. Ashtray ▲

- *circa 1920s*

Ashtray of the J.C.C. Junior Car Club produced in epns, with the club badge positioned in the centre.
- *diameter 14cm*
- **£75**   • C.A.R.S

Morgan Badge ▼

- *circa 1970*

The Morgan three wheeler club.
A die struck aluminium badge
with the design on the front of a
Morgan Aero Super Sports three
wheeler trike.
- *9cm x 8cm*
- £30   • C.A.R.S

Brooklands Society Badge ▼

- *1960s–70s*

Brooklands Society membership
badge in pressed steel with plastic
covered circuit emblem within a
shield.
- *8cm square*
- £65   • C.A.R.S

Expert Tips

*Collecting brochures of new
motor cars could be a wise
investment, as this kind of
memorabilia increases in value.*

Bentley Flying 'B' ▶

- *circa 1950*

Bentley flying winged B radiator
mascot in die cast brass chrome
plated for S type Bentley.
- *height 6cm*
- £150   • C.A.R.S

Morgan Badge ▲

- *circa 1945–1995*

50th Anniversary Morgan three
wheeler club badge die struck
brass chrome plated with
coloured plastic based enamels.
- *height 9cm*
- £45   • C.A.R.S

Morgan Three Wheeler Badge ▼

- *circa 1970s*

The Morgan Three Wheeler
Club badge, die struck brass
chrome plated and coloured
plastic based enamel club
members badge in the form of a
triangle shape, with a Morgan
Aero Super Sports three wheeler
trike.
- *9cm x 8cm*
- £45   • C.A.R.S

Morgans Commemorative Badge ◀

- *1962*

Morgans finest hour 23-24 June
1962 commemorative badge in
die struck brass chrome plate with
plastic based coloured enamels.
- *height 8cm*
- £40   • C.A.R.S

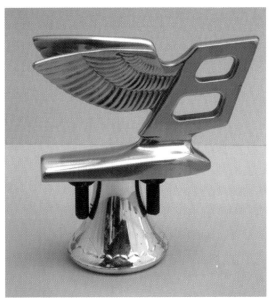

Club Badge ▲
- *1950s–70s*
British racing and Sports Car
Club badge in die struck brass,
chrome plated with coloured
vitreous enamels.
- *height 10cm*
- **£75**   • C.A.R.S

J. R. D. C. Badge ▲
- *circa 1920s*
Junior Racing Driver Club, die
struck thin brass shield shape
badge.
- *height 10cm*
- **£200**   • C.A.R.S

B. R. D. C . Badge ▼
- *circa 1920s*
British Racing Drivers Club
badge. Die struck gilded brass
with coloured vitreous enamels,
produced with holes on either
side of the wings for radiator rill
fixing.
- *height 11cm*
- **£400**   • C.A.R.S

B.A. R. C. Badge ◀
- *1950s–70s*
British Automobile Racing Club
member's badge in die struck
brass chrome plated with
coloured vitreous enamels.
- *height 10cm*
- **£75**   • C.A.R.S

B. R. D. C. Badge ▼
- *circa 1950*
British Racing Drivers Club die
struck brass and nickel plated
with coloured vitreous enamels.
- *height 11cm*
- **£350**   • C.A.R.S

Jaguar Badge ▲
- *circa 1950*
Jaguar Drivers Club members
badge in the form of a steering
wheel. In die struck brass chrome
plated with central cats head in
brass and red vitreous enamel
legend on scroll beneath. Made
by Pinches, London with
members name engraved on
reverse.
- *diameter 8cm*
- **£75**   • C.A.R.S

R. A. C. Award Plaque ▲
- *1939*
Award plaque for 'Eighth Annual
Rally of the R.A.C. London to
Brighton' 1939, in pressed hollow
cast brass. Mounted on a wood
plinth.
- *17cm x 11cm*
- **£100**   • C.A.R.S

Bentley B

- *circa 1931*

Bentley flying winged B of the single wing early experimental type design of 1931 die cast, nickel plated brass.
- *height 6cm*
- £400 • C.A.R.S

Jaguar Mascot

- *1950s*

Small Jaguar leaping cat bonnet mascot, in die cast brass chrome plated for MK.10. Jaguar still used today on modern Jaguars.
- *length 11cm*
- £20 • C.A.R.S

Jaguar Mascot ▲

- *circa 1950s*

Jaguar large leaping cat bonnet mascot in die cast brass chrome plated.
- *length 13cm*
- £55 • C.A.R.S

Jaguar Bonnet Mascot ▼

- *circa 1920s*

Jaguar leaping at bonnet mascot in die cast brass chrome plated with lozenge shaped base, designed by Frederick Gordon Crosby.
- *length 19cm*
- £200 • C.A.R.S

Brooklands Badge ◄

- *1930s*

Brookland School of Flying Ltd, membership badge in die struck, nickel plated brass, with coloured vitreous enamels. The centre having a banked bi-plane coming into land with the club house and grass in view.
- *height 5.5cm.*
- £1,500 • C.A.R.S

Brooklands Badge ▲

- *circa 1920s*

Brooklands Flying Club membership badge in die struck gilded brass, the shield with a frontal view of a mono-plane in black vitreous enamel on a red enamel background. Screw and nut base mounting.
- *height 11.5cm*
- £950 • C.A.R.S

Expert Tips

One growing area of interest is period automobile and motorcycle apparel, which can include goggles, boots, and heavy leather jackets and trousers.

Books, Maps & Atlases

The binding of a book can considerably add to its appeal and in some cases can be more fascinating than the words contained within.

The current collector's market is saturated with books so it is important to know how to determine a book's value before you start to invest. Look out for first editions as these can add considerable value to your purchase, along with whether the book is from a collectable author or illustrator. A book can be collectable in later editions if the first tends to have a high price that places it out of reach for most collectors. The fascination in collecting old maps lies not only in their historical value, but also in their decorative appeal. It is thought that the first printed atlas dates back to around 1477, using maps drawn by the Greek geographer, Claudius Ptolemy. It is now rare to find a complete atlas as the majority have been broken up over the years. The value of an atlas not only depends on colour and condition but also the area depicted.

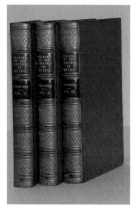

Vile Bodies ▼
- **1930**

Vile Bodies by Evelyn Waugh. First edition of Waugh's scarce second novel, with his own striking title-page design in red and black. Crown 8vo. Bound in a smart recent full morocco, banded and gilt.
- **£450** • **Ash Books**

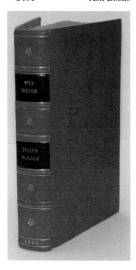

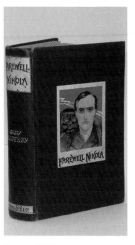

Farewell Nikola ▲
- **1901**

Farewell Nikola by Guy Boothby. First edition. The final adventures of one of the world's first fictional super-villains. Plates by Harold Piffard. Crown 8vo. Original bevelled cloth with pictorial onlay; white enamel on spine. Publishers: Ward, Lock & Co, London.
- **£75** • **Ash Books**

Conquest of Mexico ▼
- **1843**

History of the Conquest of Mexico with a preliminary view of the ancient Mexican civilisation, and the life of the Conqueror, Fernando Cortes, by William Hickling Prescott. London. Richard Bentley. First edition. Engraved frontispiece portraits, facsimile, and two folding maps. Bound in polished calf with gilt and marbled edges by Clarke and Bedford.
- **£500** • **Ash Books**

David Robert's Spain ▲
- 1837

First edition of David Robert's first set of published views of Spain. Finely bound in half dark green morocco with gilt tooled green moire cloth, hand coloured tinted lithograph title and 25 hand coloured tinted lithograph plates by Thomas Allom, W. Gauchi, Thomas Shotter boys, Louis Hage and T. S. Cooper after David Robert.
- *height 56cm*
- **£6,000**   • Peter Harrington

Expert Tips

Damage to a book is cumulative. The repeated incorrect handling and storage of a book can ruin it.

The Fairy Tales of the Brothers Grimm ▲
- 1909

A beautiful copy of *The Fairy Tales of the Brothers Grimm*, limited edition: number 41 of 750, signed on the limitation page by Arthur Rackham. Originally bound by Bayntun Riviere of Bath and more recently in full burgundy morocco, with gilt titles.
- *height 29.5cm*
- **£4,950**   • Peter Harrington

Alhambra ▼
- 1835

John F. Lewis's sketches and drawings of the *Alhambra*, made during a residence in Granada, in the years 1833-4. Published in London by Hogson, Boys & Graves. Bound in recent half dark brown morocco with gilt title, ruling to the spine and 25 tinted lithograph plates by Lewis, Harding, Lane & Gauchi.
- *height 55cm*
- **£2,750**   • Peter Harrington

Bill the Minder ▼
- 1912

Bill the Minder by W. Heath Robinson. Limited edition of 380 copies, of which this is no.167. Signed on the limitation page by Arthur Rackham. Bound by the Chelsea Bindery, others untrimmed. With sixteen colour plates and many monochrome illustrations by W. Heath Robinson.
- *height 29.5cm*
- **£2,750**   • Peter Harrington

The Old Regime Court, Salons, and Theatres ▶
- 1880

The Old Regime Court, Salons, and Theatres by Lady Catherine Charlotte. Published by Richard Bentley & Son, London - Vol.II, with Madam Geoffrin. From the library of W. A. Foyle with ex-libris.
- *height 20cm*
- **£9,750**   • Peter Harrington

The Wind in the Willows ▲
- 1908

First edition of *The Wind in the Willows*, by Kenneth Grahame. With a frontispiece by Graham Robertson. Methuen & Co. Ltd. London. Publisher's blue cloth with gilt titles and illustrations.
- *height 20cm*
- **£4,500**   • Peter Harrington

Ulysses ▲
- 1922

First edition of *Ulysses* by James Joyce. Limited to 1000 copies on Dutch handmade paper. This is one of 750 printed on handmade paper and numbered 501 (of 251 - 1000). Published by Shakespeare and Company, 12, Rue de L'Odeon, Paris.
- *height 26cm*
- **£23,500**   • Peter Harrington

Clarendon ▼

● **1712**
The History of the Rebellion and Civil Wars in England, begun in the year 1641. Oxford: printed at the Theatre. A very good early edition of Clarendon. Clarendon was Chancellor to both Charles I and Charles II. Panelled calf, banded and ruled in gilt.

● **£495** ● **Ash Books**

Dream Days ▼

● **1899**
Dream Days by Kenneth Graham, New York & London.

● **£100** ● **Ash Books**

The Noh Plays of Japan ▼

● **1922**
The Noh Plays of Japan by Arthur Waley. New York: Alfred A. Knopf. First American edition. Translations of the most celebrated Noh plays. Eight plates of masks. Original linen-backed boards.

● **£125** ● **Ash Books**

Complete English Traveller ▲

● **1771-3**
The Complete English Traveller by Robert Sanders and Nathaniel Spencer. London: J. Cooke. First edition. A handsome and well illustrated folio containing sixty plates that offer a general survey of the whole of Great Britain.

● **£950** ● **Ash Books**

A Treatise on Money ▲

● **1930**
A Treatise on Money by John Maynard. New York: Harcourt, Brace & Co. First edition: the American issue of the London sheets. Two volumes. Demy 8vo.

● **£350** ● **Ash Books**

The Fortune of War ▼

● **1979**
The Fortune of War, Patrick O'Brian. London: William Collins Sons & Co. First edition. The sixth of the Jack Aubrey and Stephen Maturin novels.

● **£400** ● **Ash Books**

Maitland's History of London ▼

● **1756**
Maitland's History of London, Vol I & II. London: for T. Osborn & J. Shipton and J. Hodges. Second edition. Originally published in one volume in 1739. Five general maps (two folding), nineteen maps of wards and parishes (five folding); views of over sixty principal buildings on forty-two plates (three folding), and over eighty churches.

● **£2,950** ● **Ash Books**

Memoirs of the Life of Grammont ▲

• **18th century**

Memoirs of the Life of Count de Grammont, containing, in particular, the amorous intrigues of the court of England in the reign of King Charles II. Printed: London and sold by J. Round.W. Taylor. J. Brown. 1714.

• £350　　　　• Ash Books

Malay Sketches ▲

• **1896**

Malay Sketches by Sir Frank Athelstane Swettenham, the distinguished colonial administrator and linguist. London: John Lane. Second edition (i.e. impression) of the original 1895 publication.

• £50　　　　• Ash Books

Orange Fairy Book ▶

• **1906**

First edition of the *Orange Fairy Book* by Andrew Lang. Published in 1906.

• £300　　　　• Ash Books

Prehistoric Man ▼

• **1862**

Prehistoric Man by Sir Daniel Wilston. Cambridge: Macmillan & Co. First edition. Extensive researches into the origin of civilisation in the old and the new world. Colour frontispiece. Map bound without half-titles, in a handsome half roan.

• £250　　　　• Ash Books

Antiquities of Surrey ▼

• **1736**

Antiquities of Surrey by Nathanael Salmon. London: for the Author. First edition; mottled calf expertly re-backed and refurnished, banded and gilt.

• £300　　　　• Ash Books

Grimm's Household Tales ▲

• **1946**

Grimm's Household Tales by Brothers Grimm (Jacob Ludwig & Wilhelm Carl). London: Eyre & Spottiswode. Foolscap 4to. Bound in a later full morocco, banded and gilt; all edges gilt.

• £250　　　　• Ash Books

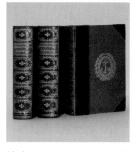

Shakespeare ▲

• **1925–32**

The Tragedies, Comedies and Histories of Shakespeare. London. Oxford University Press. A prettily bound set of the three separately published volumes of the Oxford India-paper edition. Edited by W. J. Craig with a full glossary.

• £250　　　　• Ash Books

Harry Potter ▼

- **1997–2000**

An extremely scarce set of first editions of the *Harry Potter* series by J.K. Rowling, which includes: *'The Philosopher's Stone'*, *'The Chamber of Secrets'*, *'The Prisoner of Azkaban'* and *'The Goblet of Fire'*. Published by Bloomsbury, London. All signed.
- *20cm x 13cm*
- **£27,500** • **Peter Harrington**

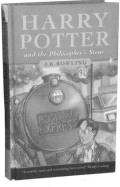

The Cat in the Hat ▼

- **1957**

First edition of *The Cat in the Hat* by Dr. Seuss. Original pictorial paper covered boards complete with dust wrapper. Illustrated throughout by the author.
- *29cm x 21cm*
- **£8,500** • **Peter Harrington**

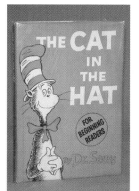

Peter Rabbit ▶

- **1902**

The Tale of Peter Rabbit by Beatrix Potter. First edition, and first issue of the flat spine.
- *14cm x 10cm*
- **£50,000** • **Peter Harrington**

Three Guineas ▲

- **1938**

First edition of *Three Guineas* by Virginia Woolf. Published by The Hogarth Press, London. Pale yellow cloth, gilt titles to spine, complete with dust wrapper. Illustrated with photographic plates.
- *18cm x 12cm*
- **£500** • **Peter Harrington**

Lady Chatterley's Lover ▲

- **1932**

First authorised UK edition of *Lady Chatterley's Lover* by D.H Lawrence. Publisher's brown cloth with gilt title to spine. Complete with dust wrapper. Published by Martin Secker, London.
- *19cm x 12.4cm*
- **£450** • **Peter Harrington**

Little Lord Fauntleroy ▼

- **1886**

First UK edition of *Little Lord Fauntleroy* by Francis Hodgson Burnett. London: Frederick, Warne and Co. With 26 illustrations after Reginald B. Birch.
- *22cm x 14.5cm*
- **£210** • **Peter Harrington**

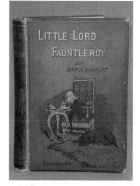

The Hound of Death and Other Stories ▼

- **1933**

The Hound of Death and Other Stories by Agatha Christie. First edition. Published by Odhams Press Limited, London.
- *18.5cm x 13cm*
- **£350** • **Peter Harrington**

Expert Tips

Most paper items are susceptible to damage from ultaviolet (UV) and visible light. If UV is present it should be eliminated using filters over windows and bulbs.

Sense and Sensibility ▼

• **1811**
First edition of Jane Austen's masterpiece, *Sense and Sensibility*. Published in London by T. Egerton, 1811. Three volumes, finely bound in contemporary mottled calf.
• *18.5cm x 11.4cm*
• **£60,000**   • **Peter Harrington**

How the Grinch Stole Christmas ▼

• **1957**
First edition of *How the Grinch Stole Christmas* by Dr. Seuss. Published by Random House, New York. Original pictorial paper covered boards. Housed in a red cloth solander box with a green gilt lettered label. Illustrated by the author. Inscribed in the first blank page, 'for Pamela Benepe! Dr. Seuss'.
• *29cm x 20cm*
• **£6,500**   • **Peter Harrington**

Doctor Zhivago ▶

• **1958**
First edition of *Doctor Zhivago* by Boris Pasternak translated from the Russian by Max Hayward and Manya Harari. Collins and Harvill Press, London. Original publisher's red cloth, felt lettered spine, complete with dust wrapper.
• *21cm x 14cm*
• **£150**   • **Peter Harrington**

Arabian Nights ▲

• **1937**
The Arabian Nights by Parish Maxfield. Edited by Kate Douglas Wiggin and Nora A. Smith published in New York by Charles Scribner and Sons. Illustrated by Maxfield Parish with 9 colour illustrations.
• *24cm x 17cm*
• **£75**   • **Peter Harrington**

Omar Khayyam ▲

• **1884**
Rubiyat of Omar Khayyam rendered into English verse by Edward Fitzgerald with drawings by Elihu Vedder. Published by Houghton Mifflin and Company, Boston.
• *40cm x 33cm*
• **£475**   • **Peter Harrington**

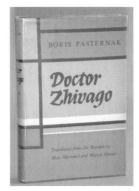

Poems by Christina Rossetti ▼

• *circa 1920*
Poems by Christina Rossetti with illustrations by Florence Harrison published by Blackie and Son.
• *26cm x 21cm*
• **£475**   • **Peter Harrington**

Winnie the Pooh ▼

• **1924-8**
Set of books by A.A. Milne including: 'When We Were Very Young', 'Winnie the Pooh', 'Now We Are Six', and 'The House at Pooh Corner'.
• *22cm x 15cm*
• **£12,000**   • **Peter Harrington**

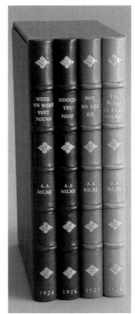

Map of Essex ▲

- *1636*

The rare first issue of the Janssonius map showing Essex, entitled, "Essexi Descriptio. The Description Of Essex". First published in Amsterdam, Holland, by the Dutch master Janssonius (1588-1664) in the 'Atlas Appendix' of 1636. With copper line engravings on paper. In full contemporary hand colour.

- *38cm x 49cm*
- **£550**　　● **Ash Books**

Map of Norfolk ▼

- *circa 1646*

A fine seventeenth century map of the county of Norfolk, England, from the Dutch master Joannes Janssonius (1588-1664). The map is highly decorated with a pastoral cartouche, shields, putti, sailing ships and a sea monster. This was originally produced for the 'inovus atlas ...' (Amsterdam 1646).

- *38cm x 49cm*
- **£395**　　● **Ash Books**

Expert Tips

Providing a good environment, safe handling and storage conditions are critical to preserving book collections.

Map of Scotland ▼

- *circa 1630s*

A decorative map of Scotland by the Dutch cartographer Janssonius entitled, "Scotia Regnvm, Amsterdam" and dated1636. This map was originally produced for the 'Janssonius Atlas Appendix' of 1636. It is decorated with the royal arms, sailing ships, and a cartouche featuring unicorns, sheep and thistles.

- *38cm x 49.5cm*
- **£495**　　● **Ash Books**

Seutter British Isles ◀

- *18th century*

Original hand coloured map of the British Isles by Matthaeus Seutter. A scarce antique map of the British Isles, with an elegant military lion and unicorn cartouche. In another corner an angel with a trumpet bears aloft the arms of the four nations, and sailing ships off the coast. Originally engraved by Tobias Conrad Lotter (1717-1777) for Seutter's Atlas Minor in the 1740s.

- **£250**　　● **Ash Books**

Map of Somerset ▲

- *circa 1630s*

An amorial map of the county of Somerset, in England by Janssonius entitled "Somerset-Tensis Comitatvs Somerset Shire". Amsterdam: G.Valk & P. Schenk, 1636. This was first published by Janssonius (1588-1664).The map appears here in its final form, with the addition of grid lines to the original Janssonius image.

- *37.5cm x 49cm*
- **£395**　　● **Ash Books**

Merian Map of the British Isles ▼

- *mid 17th century*

Map of the British Isles from Mathaus Merian the Elder (1593-1650). With a baroque title piece draped in cornucopia, the Royal Arms, sailing ships etc. Originally produced for the 'Neuwe Archontolgia Cosmica' (Frankfurt 1638) and here in a later issue, with Merian's name removed.

- **£400**　　● **Ash Books**

Map of Huntingdonshire ▲

- *1645*

Map of Huntingdonshire by J.
Willem Blaeu with the
inscription, "Hvntingdo-Nensis
Comitatvs, Huntington- shire".
Published in Amsterdam.
Decorated with a ribanded
display of coats or arms, the
Stuart Royal Arms, and a hunters
and hounds title-piece, with
stags, falcon, boar, hare and
rabbit. Originally produced by
Blaeu in1645.

- **£350**   • **Ash Books**

City of London, Westminster and Southwark ▼

- *1720*

*A New Plan Of The City Of
London, Westminster And
Southwark.* Published in London:
in 1720. Originally produced to
accompany John Strype's revised
edition of John Stow's 'Survey of
London'. The map is dedicated to
Sir George Thorold, Lord Mayor
in 1719-1720.

- *48.5cm x 66cm*
- **£950**   • **Ash Books**

Map of Northumberland ▼

- *1645*

Map Of Northumberland by J.
Willem Blaeu, entitled,
"Comitatvs Northvmbria;
Vernacule Northumberland" and
produced in Amsterdam in1645.
Decorated with shields, the Royal
Arms, a draped title-piece, ships,
cherubs, and a scale-bar showing
a 17th-century surveyor at work.
Copper line engraving on paper.
Full contemporary hand colour.

- *41cm x 49cm*
- **£350**   • **Ash Books**

Map of Lothian ◀

- *circa 1500s*

A map depicting the area of
Lothian in Scotland, by the
Dutch cartographer Joannes
Janssonius, 1646, Amsterdam. A
fine example of this well-known
map of the Edinburgh region.

- *36.5 cm 54cm*
- **£400**   • **Ash Books**

Binding Fit for a King ▼

- *1620-1630*

Extremely rare Renaissance
gold binding, jewelled and
enamelled. Possibly made for
King Christian IV of Denmark.
Enamelled with a design of
different flowers, and a central
plaque with the nativity, and
decorated with 52 diamonds.

- *9.1cm x 6.4cm*
- **£85,000**   • **Bernard Shapero**

Map of the Orkney & Shetland Isles ▲

- *1654*

*Map of the Orkney and Shetland
Isles* by Willem Janszoon Blaeu,
Amsterdam, 1645. With the
inscription, "Oradvm Et
SchetandiE Insvlarvm
Accuatissima Descriptio". The
maps are finely decorated.

- *40.5cm x 53cm*
- **£350**   • **Ash Books**

London ▲

- *1673*

An early map of London by
Wenceslas Hollar, with the coat
of arms of the City of London,
fifteen of the great Livery and
Merchant Companies and those
of Sir Robert Vyner of Viner.

- **£400**   • **Ash Books**

Expert Tips

*Hands should be clean and dry
before handling paper items, as
the oils from fingers can cause
staining on the paper.*

Early Binding for Pillone ▼

• *15 April 1507*
Extremely rare early 16th century North Italian binding of half blind-stamped morocco over bevelled wooden boards, leather clasps at top and bottom and two at fore-edge. The title and Pillone arms are painted on the upper board, and the leaf of a large format legal work is used as front endpaper. The binding is preserved in a modern cloth covered box and comes from the library of Odorico Pillone.
• *45cm x 29cm*
• **£20,000**   • **Bernard Shapero**

Miniature Renaissance Binding ▼

• *1621*
French Missal binding in gold, glass, enamel and one emerald. Missel. Troyes, C. de Villiers. Contains calendar for the years 1621-37, bound in a preserved contemporary binding of green glass cut in imitation of rose emeralds, each attached by 4 gold clasps to a gold enamelled white background. This binding contains one emerald, but where it is in the binding, no-one has recorded.
• *5cm x 3.5cm*
• **£65,000**   • **Bernard Shapero**

Scribbling Pad ▲

• *circa 1580*
German scribbling pad, (possibly Dresden). This fine 16th century binding has been attributed to Jakob Krause, who was active in Dresden during the last quarter of the 16th century, working predominantly for elector Augustus of Saxony (one of the foremost patrons for book bindings of the Renaissance). In spite of the provenance of the binding, the surviving entries in the book are in Italian. Some of Krause's works are known to have been presented to foreign rulers. German renaissance bindings are of the greatest rarity.
• *14.5cm x 10cm*
• **£6,750**   • **Bernard Shapero**

Book of Common Prayer ▲

• *1638*
The book of Common Prayer and Administration of the Sacraments: and other Rites and Ceremonies of the Church of England [and] the New Testament . Published in London by Robert Barker and in Edinburgh by Robert Young, 1638. This is a presentation of prayers by Queen Anne. Preserved in the J.R. Abbey collection, with large morocco gilt label describing its royal provenance.
• *17cm x 11.5cm*
• **£22,500**   • **Bernard Shapero**

The Old Regime Court, Salons, and Theatres ▼

• *1880*
The Old Regime Court, Salons, and Theatres by Lady Catherine Charlotte. Published by Richard Bentley & Son, London. Full tan morocco with full gilt decorated spine and covers. Enhanced with hand painted oval portraits, Vol 1. With La Duchess de Berri. The portrait is surrounded with seed-pearls.
• *height 20cm*
• **£9,750**   • **Peter Harrington**

The Beautiful and the Damned ▼

• *1922*
Presentation copy of *The Beautiful and the Damned* inscribed twice by F. Scott Fitzgerald. The first inscription reads:- 'Sincerely F Scott Fitzgerald' and the later reads: 'Believe it or not this was in this book when it came to me from the Tyron bookshop. I must have autographed it for some book-seller and it fell into a stock of remainders. Such is fame.' Charles Scribner and Sons.
• *height 19cm*
• **£22,500**   • **Peter Harrington**

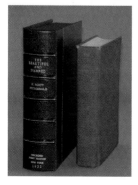

Mobile Etude ▲

- *1962*
Mobile Etude pour une
Representation des Etats Unis. by
Michel Butor. Published in Paris
by Gallimard. One of 25
numbered copies with
contemporary black leather
backed dark grey boards and an
intricate mosaic onlay of coloured
paper cubes. Preserved in original
grey board cover with perspex
back, t.e.g., matching grey board
slipcase. This work is dedicated to
Jackson Pollock.
- *23.6cm x 18.7cm*
- **£5,000** • **Bernard Shapero**

Bronze Book Box ▲

- *mid-19th century*
A set of three household books
including cash accounts, journal,
and visitor and address book.
London, 3 vols. Uniformly bound
in red morocco, red morocco
labels on spine. Preserved in the
original red morocco brass box,
each side decorated with 3 large
banded chalcedony in cabochon
setting, the clasps with one large
cabochon, the whole can be
locked, with original key in side.
- *18cm x 11cm*
- **£2,500** • **Bernard Shapero**

Tacitus ▼

- *1809*
Folding engraved frontispiece
map, with contemporary vellum,
in the style of Edwards of Halifax.
The covers are decoratively
bordered in gilt, the front cover
with a watercolour of
Buckingham Palace and the back
cover with a watercolour of
Garrick's Villa At Hampton.
With the inscription,"De Moribus
Germanorum, et de Vita
Agricolae. Ex editione Gabrielis
Brotier. Locis annalium et
historiarum ab eo citatis, selectis
et additis, cura Richardi Relhan
Cambridge".
- *24.4cm x 15cm*
- **£6,000** • **Bernard Shapero**

Rosalind and Helen ▼

- *1820*
Rosalind and Helen by Shelley,
Percy Bysshe. London, Ollie. First
edition. Magnificently bound by
Sangorski & Sutcliffe in dark blue
morocco, richly gilt, adorned
with 92 jewels, the upper cover
with gilt border decorated with
foliage and dot-work, with red
fruit onlays, around panel of
white morocco within which is
an elaborate design of interleaved
hearts in different colours around
a large gilt fleur-de-lys,
interspersed with floral designs.
The back cover with gilt border
surrounding a panel inlaid with a
mother-of-pearl lyre. The back
liner with a flat panel containing
a mother-of-pearl heart, both
these panels surrounded by an
inlaid design of vines and grapes.
- *22.5cm x 13.5cm*
- **£30,000** • **Bernard Shapero**

Bible ▲

- *1690–1700*
Biblia Das Is De Gantsche H.
Schrifture. Published in
Amsterdam by N. Burgers, 1681.
Title within architectural border,
tortoiseshell binding, (1690-
1700), with engraved silver book
furniture, corner pieces, two small
hinges to each joint, clasps, one
clasp with initials of the owner
engraved on the inside.
- *14cm x 8cm*
- **£5,000** • **Bernard Shapero**

The Tempest ▲

- *1926*
The Tempest by William
Shakespeare, illustrated by
Arthur Rackham. London,
William Heinemann. In
contemporary full deep-blue
morocco du cap, the lower board
and decorated doublure are
decorated in an elaborate
grolieresque retrospective design
consisting of onlaid, interlaced
strapwork in three colours, red,
saffron and tan, all edged in gilt.
The book itself is one of 520
copies, reserved for America and
signed in ink by Arthur
Rackham.
- *29.5cm x 23cm*
- **£2,500** • **Bernard Shapero**

Hans Andersen's Fairy Tales ▼

- 1913

Signed limited edition of *Hans Andersen's Fairy Tales*. Constable and Company Ltd, London. Limited to 100 copies, this one being numbered 59 and signed on the limitation page by W. Heath Robinson. White illustrations.
- *height 29.5cm*
- £3,950   • Peter Harrington

The Natural History of Barbados ▼

- 1750

First edition and subscribers large paper copy of *The Natural History of Barbados*. In ten books by Griffith Hughes. Printed in London for the author. Bound in half brown calf and gilt lettered with burgundy.
- *height 43cm*
- £6,500   • Peter Harrington

Wind in the Willows ▶

- 1940

Wind in the Willows by Kenneth Grahame, with an introduction by A.A Milne and 16 colour illustrations by Rackham. Limited edition of 2020 copies of which this is number 420. New York: The Limited Editions Club.
- *height 28cm*
- £2,000   • Peter Harrington

Diversions of a Diplomat in Turkey ▲

- 1893

By Samuel S. Cox, published by Webster, New York. Contains observations by U.S. Ambassador to Turkey from 1885-1887. Portrait frontispiece, 2 coloured lithographs, wood-engraved illustrations throughout.
- £220   • Bernard Shapero

The Spirit of the East ▼

- 1839

By David Urquhart. Colburn, London. Second edition. Lithographed folding map and one plan. In 1830 Urquhart was sent on a tour of the northern territory and the frontier and this work is a study of the Greeks and the Turks, and highlights his admiration for the Turks.
- £575   • Bernard Shapero

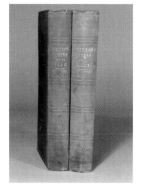

Arms of King Charles II ◀

- 1660

"An appeal to Caesar: wherein gold and silver is proved to be the Kings Majesties Royal Commodity. Which by the Lawes of the Kingdom, no person of what degree soever, but the Kings Majestie, and his Privy Counsel, can give license to transport gold and silver..." By Violet, London.
- *22.6cm x 16.5cm*
- £7,500   • Bernard Shapero

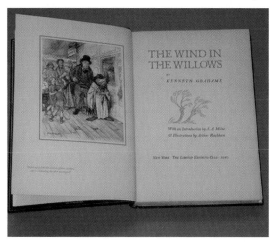

The Lion, the Witch and the Wardrobe ▲

- **1950**

The Lion, the Witch and the Wardrobe by C.S. Lewis. First edition. Illustrations and colour frontispiece by Pauline Baynes. The first and best known of the Narnia chronicles. Post 8vo. Bound in an elegant recent green quarter-morocco, banded and gilt. Published by Geoffrey Bles.

- **£850**   • **Ash Books**

Cooke's View of the Thames ▲

- **circa 1811**

Views of the Thames, from the Source to the Sea by Samuel Owen and William Bernard Cooke. London: by W. B. Cooke. Eighty-four tissue guarded etched plates. Contemporary full morocco, all edges gilt.

- **£750**   • **Ash Books**

Expert Tips

When purchasing an illustrated book, make sure that you check that it still contains all the original plates, as just one missing could seriously devalue the item.

The Greater London ▼

- **circa 1884**

The Greater London: A Narrative of its History, its People, and its Places by Edward Walford. London: Cassell & Co. Heavily illustrated with 400 wood engravings. Two volumes Crown 4to. Original decorative cloth gilt.

- **£195**   • **Ash Books**

History of Lace ▼

- **1900**

A History of Hand-Made Lace by Emily Jackson. Dealing with the origin of lace, the growth of the great lace centres. Published by Upcott Gill. First edition. Plates and numerous illustrations. Original decorative cloth gilt in an eye-catching lace and cobweb design

- **£185**   • **Ash Books**

Sea-Kings of Crete ▶

- **1910**

The Sea-Kings of Crete by James Baikie. Publishers: Adam & Charles Black, London. First edition. Plates. Maps. Original decorative cloth, top edge gilt.

- **£75**   • **Ash Books**

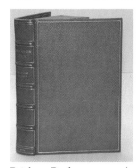

Alone ▲

- **1938**

Alone by Richard E. Byrd. Published by Putnam, London. First British edition. Admiral Byrd's harrowing account of his Antarctic sojourn. Decorations by Richard E. Harrison. Demy 8vo.

- **£60**   • **Ash Books**

Brighton Rock ▲

- **1938**

Brighton Rock by Graham Greene. First edition. Crown 8vo. Bound in a striking full crimson morocco, banded and extra gilt by Bayntun-Riviere. All edges in gilt. Published by William Heinemann.

- **£850**   • **Ash Books**

Uncle Tom's Cabin ▼

- *1852*
Uncle Tom's Cabin; or, Life Among the Lowly by Harriet Beecher Stowe. Boston, John P. Jewett & Company. First edition. Two volumes finely bound by Bayntun-Riviere.
- *height 18cm*
- **£3,500** • **Peter Harrington**

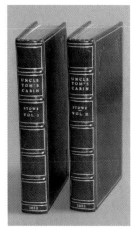

Letters by Mary Wollstonecraft ▼

- *1796*
The first account of a business trip made by a woman, Mary Wollstonecraft, written during her short residence in Sweden, Norway and Denmark. Published by J.J. Johnston, St. Paul's Churchyard, London. First edition bound in full tan calf, with gilt lettered and a burgundy label.
- *height 21.5cm*
- **£1,250** • **Peter Harrington**

Gerard Mercator Atlas ▼

- *1632*
Gerardi Mercatoris Atlas sive Cosmographicae Meditatones. Amsterdam, Johann Cloppenburg, with fine hand-coloured copperplate 'architectural' title and 179 fine recent hand coloured copperplate maps.
- *22cm x 28cm*
- **£27,500** • **Peter Harrington**

Decline and Fall of the Roman Empire ▲

- *1777*
Six volumes of *The History of the Decline and Fall of the Roman Empire*, by Edward Gibbon published London, printed for W. Strahan and T. Cadell. 6 volumes 4, 5 and 6 are first editions. With author's frontis portrait in vol.1, and 2 folding maps.
- *height 29cm*
- **£3,500** • **Peter Harrington**

Blackstone Commentaries ▼

- *1765–1769*
Blackstone Commentaries by Sir William Blackstone. A rare first edition. With the engraved 'Table of Consanguinity' and the 'Table of Descents' in Vol 11. The date is stamped in black at the base of each spine.
- *28cm x 22cm*
- **£9,750** • **Peter Harrington**

Gone with the Wind ▼

- *1936*
Gone with the Wind by Margaret Mitchell. First edition. Macmillan Company, New York. Original publisher's grey cloth, complete with dust wrapper.
- *height 22cm*
- **£3,950** • **Peter Harrington**

Winnie the Pooh ◄

- *1926*
Limited to 1/350 *Winnie the Pooh* by A.A. Milne, with wonderful onlaid binding, and decorations by Ernest H. Shephard. Methuen & Co. London, numbered copies, signed by Milne and Shephard.
- *23cm x 17cm*
- **£8,500** • **Peter Harrington**

Jeeves and the Feudal Spirit ▼

- *1954*

First edition of *Jeeves and the Feudal Spirit* by P. G. Wodehouse. Herbert Jenkins Limited, London. Fine publisher's red cloth with black titles on spine. Complete with a dust wrapper.
- *19cm x 13cm*
- £250 • **Peter Harrington**

The Long Good-Bye ▼

- *1953*

The Long Good-Bye by Raymond Chandler. First edition. Hamish Hamilton, London, 1953. Original publisher's brown cloth, complete with dust wrapper.
- *18.5cm x 12cm*
- £950 • **Peter Harrington**

The Hound of the Baskervilles ▶

- *1902*

First edition of *The Hound of the Baskervilles* by Arthur Conan Doyle. Published by George Newnes Limited, London. Bound in recent full burgundy morocco, gilt lettering and decoration to spine.
- *19cm x 12cm*
- £1,200 • **Peter Harrington**

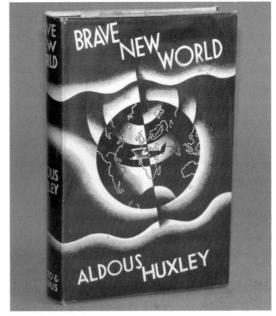

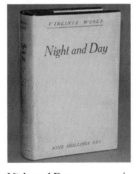

Night and Day ▲

- *1919*

First edition of *Night and Day* by Virginia Woolf, published by Duckworth & Co., Covent Garden London.
- *19.6cm x 12cm*
- £23,500 • **Peter Harrington**

Brave New World ▲

- *1932*

First edition of *Brave New World*, signed by the author Aldous Huxley.
- *20cm x 13cm*
- £15,000 • **Peter Harrington**

Matilda ▼

- *1988*

First edition of *Matilda* by Roald Dahl. Jonathan Cape, London. Illustrated by Quentin Blake. Publisher's red cloth, with gilt title on spine.
- *23.5cm x 15cm*
- £85 • **Peter Harrington**

Wodwo ▼
- **1967**

Wodwo by Ted Hughes. London, Faber & Faber. First edition: in the first issue binding, lettered in gilt rather than silver. Poems, stories and a radio play. Demy 8vo. In the Berthold Wolpe dust-jacket.
- £125   ● Ash Books

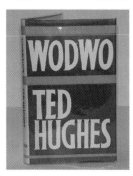

Bible ▶
- **1607**

The Book of Common Prayer translated according to Hebrew and Greek, and conferred with the best translations in Diuers languages. London: Robert Barker Crown 4to. Contemporary panelled calf, with bossed brass corners and centre-pieces.
- £500   ● Ash Books

Early Adventures ▲
- **1887**

Early Adventures in Persia, Susiana and Babylonia including A Residence among the Bakhtiyari and other wild tribes before the discovery of Nineveh, by the archeologist John Murray, London. First Edition. 2 Volumes. Contains 2 plates, 3 folding maps and advertisements.
- £575   ● Bernard Shapero

Vicar of Wakefield ▲
- **1890**

The Vicar of Wakefield by Oliver Goldsmith. London: Macmillan & Co. A fine large-paper copy of the first Hugh Thomson illustrated edition bound in half crushed morocco, banded and gilt, by Otto Schulze & Co. of Edinburgh.
- £250   ● Ash Books

Virgil ▼
- **1680**

Virgil (Publius Virgilius Maro): Leiden: Jacob Hack / Amsterdam: Abraham Wolfgang. Three volumes of The Ecologues, the Georgics and the Aeneid in a fine scholarly variorum edition, with notes, edited by Jacobus Emmenessius, with plates by Leiden.
- £450   ● Ash Books

The Happy Prince ▼
- **1888**

The Happy Prince and Other Tales by Oscar Wilde. Publishers: David Nutt, London. First edition, only 1,000 copies were printed. Illustrations by Walter Crane and Jacob Hood. Plates and illustrations. Bound in an elegant later half morocco by Riviere & Son.
- £1,000   ● Ash Books

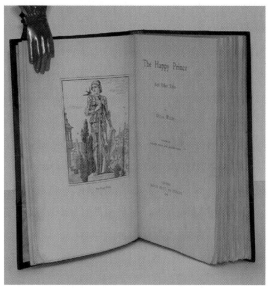

Bambi ▼

• *1928*
Bambi: A Life in the Wood by Felix
Salten. Published in London by
Jonathan Cape. First edition in
English. Translated from the
original German by Whittaker
Chamber, with an introduction
by John Galsworthy. Crown 8vo.
Bound in a smart recent half
green morocco, banded and gilt
retaining the original pictorial
endpapers.

• **£350**   • **Ash Books**

Frederick de Wit ▼

• *17th century*
Fine seventeenth-century map of
the British Isles from the engraver
and mapseller Frederick de Wit
(1630-1706). Decorated with the
arms of England, Ireland and
Scotland and an attractive title-
piece of frolicking nymphs.
Original hand colour.

• **£600**   • **Ash Books**

Crimson Fairy Book ▼

• *circa 1890*
First edition of the *Crimson Fairy
Book* by Andrew Lang.

• **£350**   • **Ash Books**

Chichester ▲

• *1676*
Sussex described and divided into
rapes with the situation of
Chichester by John Speed.
Copper line engraving on paper
by Jodocus Hondius.

• **£750**   • **Ash Books**

Map of London ▲

• *1658*
Map of London by Abraham Saur.
Frankfurt: Johan Bayern, Johann
Willhelm Ammon & Wilhelm
Serlin 1658. A scarce and
previously unrecorded miniature
woodcut plan of London, deriving
from known sixteenth-century
precursor, originally produced to
illustrate *Saur's Parvum, Thetrum
Urbuim*.

• **£500**   • **Ash Books**

Map of the Americas ▲

• *1782*
Map of the Americas, published
in Amsterdam: Arend Fokke
1782. Pleasant and scarce antique
map of the Americas, drawn and
engraved by H. Klockhoff bearing
the Amsterdam imprint of Arend
Fokke. Copper line engraving on
paper, original hand colour.

• **£125**   • **Ash Books**

British Isles ▼

• *circa 1706*
A map of the British Isles
produced for Oorlogs Tabetten,
published by Daniel de la Feuille.
Copper line engraving on paper,
with full original hand colour.

• **£200**   • **Ash Books**

The World ▼

• *1777*
The World. A scarce map of the
world in hemispheres, drawn and
engraved by H. Knockhoff. 1777-
1784, bearing the Amsterdam
imprint of Arend Fokke.
Published in Amsterdam 1777.
Copper line engraving on paper.

• **£195**   • **Ash Books**

Monde ▼

• *1706*
A very attractive antique map of
the world in hemispheres by
Daniel de la Feuille. This was
originally produced for Oorlogs
Tabetten and published in
Amsterdam in 1706.

• **£500**   • **Ash Books**

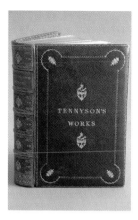

Tennyson's Works ▲

- *1882*

Tennyson's Works published in London by Kegan Paul. Finely bound by Sangorski & Sutcliffe in full green morocco, spine faded to antique brown, gilt title and decoration to spine. With a fore-edge painting showing 'The Lady of Shalott' after William Holman Hunt, and a portrait of Tennyson.
- *18cm x 13cm*
- **£350**　　• **Peter Harrington**

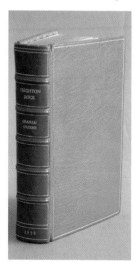

Brighton Rock ▲

- *1938*

First edition of *Brighton Rock* by Graham Greene, published by William Heinemann Ltd London, bound by the Chelsea Bindery.
- *18.5cm x 13cm*
- **£950**　　• **Peter Harrington**

The Poetical Works of Percy Bysshe Shelley ▼

- *1908*

The Poetical Works of Percy Bysshe Shelley. Macmillan and Co., Limited London. Bound by Riviere in full tree calf, and gilt lettered green morocco label and gilt decoration to spine with marbled end papers, all edges gilded.
- *18cm x 12cm*
- **£475**　　• **Peter Harrington**

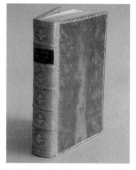

La Reine des Neiges ▼

- *1911*

Hans Christian Andersen, *La Reine des Neiges et Quelques Autres Contes.* Illustration by Edmund Dulac. Publishers decorated vellum, with 29 full colour illustrations by Edmund Dulac. Published by H.Piazza Paris.
- *20.5cm x 24cm*
- **£850**　　• **Peter Harrington**

Kew Gardens ▶

- *1919*

Kew Gardens by Virginia Woolf with woodcuts by Vanessa Bell. There were only 150 copies made and Virginia Woolf set the type.
- *23cm x 14cm*
- **£18,000**　　• **Peter Harrington**

The Tempest ▲

- *1926*

Deluxe edition of Shakespeare's *The Tempest,* illustrated by Arthur Rackham. Published by William Heinemann Ltd. London. Limited to 520 copies of which this is No. 128. Signed by Rackham.
- *32cm x 26cm*
- **£3,250**　　• **Peter Harrington**

The Kingdom of the Pearl ▲

- *1920*

The Kingdom of the Pearl by Leonard Rosenthal, illustrated by Edmund Dulac. Limited edition of 675 copies of which this is No. 67. Published by Nisbet & Co. London. With ten captioned tissue pasted colour illustrations.
- *30cm x 24cm*
- **£600**　　• **Peter Harrington**

Carpets & Rugs

European needlework carpets of the nineteenth century have become anan interesting area for the collector.

Carpets and rugs were initially made by nomadic tribes, with the Persians being amongst the first carpet weavers of the ancient civilisations. Through centuries of creativity they achieved a unique degree of excellence in their craft. The element of luxury with which the Persian carpet is associated today provides a marked contrast with its humble beginnings as an article of need to protect the nomadic tribes from the cold, as well as a form of writing for the illiterate. Their bright colours and magical designs brought relief to these people's hardy lives. Out of necessity was born art and their beauty found them new homes throughout the ancient and modern world.

Persian Jozan Rug ▼
- *circa 1890*
A rare Persian Jozan rug in perfect condition decorated with deer and an angular floral design in ochre, red, blue, green and black.
- *137cm x 204cm*
- **£4,500**   • **Oriental**

Bakhtiari Rug ▼
- *circa 1940*
Bakhtiari rugs woven by nomads and villagers of Luri, Kurdish and other ethnic origins from the Chahar Mahal region of Iran. With a medallion design.
- *140cm x 228cm*
- **£2,300**   • **Oriental**

Baluchi Carpet ▲
- *1860*
Section of a Baluchi carpet from Baluchistan
- *length 280cm*
- **£2,800**   • **David Black**

Expert Tips

Carpets are a great way to fill large expanses of wall space. Remember, moths love a good carpet so keep them well sprayed with anti-moth repellant.

French Panel ◄
- *circa 1760–1780*
French needlepoint panel with central figured cartouche in petit point.
- *51cm square*
- **£1,950**   • **Classic Fabrics**

Indian Durrie ▲
- *circa 1880*
Indian cotton durrie made by prisoners in the North Indian gaols. Dyed with indigo and turmeric.
- *length 203cm*
- **£740**   • **Gordon Reece**

Tekke Rug ▲
- *circa 1920*
Acha-Tekke are woven by the famous tribesmen from the Tekke tribe who are noted for their fine work. In geometric design in reds, cream and black.
- *20cm x 200cm*
- **£1,400**   • **Oriental**

Melas Rug ▶
- *1880*
Melas prayer mat from Turkey, with a central design of a red mosque bordered with rosettes and stars.
- *length 125cm*
- **£1,250**   • **David Black**

Kashan Rug ◀
- *circa 1920*
Kashan pictorial rug with peacocks in red, blue and green design surrounding a central vase.
- *137cm x 207cm*
- **£4,500**   • **Oriental**

Kashan Medallion Rug ▲
- *circa 1920*
Kashan rug with classical elongated medallion designs in coral and dark blue and corner decorations. Extremely good example of a curvilinear Persian floral rug.
- *137cm x 207cm*
- **£4,500**   • **Oriental**

Anotonian Kilim ▲

- 1920

Western Anotonian kilim covering a beechwood chest.
- 50cm x 90cm
- £750   • Oriental

North Persian Runner ▶

- circa 1890

Runner from northern Persia.
- 2.5cm x 91cm
- £2,500   • David Black

Western Anotonian Kilim Cushion ▲

- 1920

Western Anotonian kilim converted into a cushion cover.
- 35cm square
- £45   • Oriental

Expert Tips

The vast region between the Caspian Sea and the western borders of China is central to the history of Oriental carpets. It was home to the Scythian nomads in whose tombs the earliest known knotted carpet, made some 400 years before Christ, was discovered.

Luri Gabbeh Rug ▲

- circa 1880

Exceptional Luri Gabbeh banded design rug from south west Persia with incredible use of natural dyes contrasted by woven bands of cotton pile.
- length 148cm
- £3,250   • Gordon Reece

Sharshavan Cushion ▶

- 1920

Cushion made from a Sharshavan rug, which was originally part of a cradle.
- 35cm square
- £65   • Oriental

Bibibaff Quajquoli ▲

- circa 1940

An unusual and fine example of a Bibibaff Quajquoli.
- 80cm x 118cm
- £1,100   • Oriental

Karabagh Cushion

- *1920*

Karabagh kilim converted into a cushion cover.
- *35cm square*
- £50
- Oriental

Luri Gabbeth Rug

- *mid 20th century*

A Luri Gabbeth rug from the Zagros mountains of southern Persia. With bold design of red, blue, brown and cream, the borders with red squares and cream centres.
- *length 180cm*
- £1,450
- Gordon Reece

Turkaman Cushion

- *1860*

Fragment of a Turkaman used as a cushion cover.
- *47cm square*
- £150
- David Black

Kilim Stool

- *1930*

Anotonian kilim upholstered stool.
- *30cm x 40cm*
- £125
- Oriental

Turkish Yurik Runner

- *1870*

A section of a Turkish Yurik runner with four hexagonal designs of blue, red, green, and gold in the centre panel, surrounded by a pink border with blue flowers.
- *length 300cm*
- £1,800
- David Black

Bakhtiari Rug

- *circa 1940*

Bakhtiari rug with a glorious central medallion design in blue, green, coral and cream. The reverse of the carpet shows a very open weaving technique with wefts which may have a bluish hue.
- *127cm x 207cm*
- £490
- Oriental

Bownat Marriage Rug

- *circa 1920*

Bownat marriage rug, produced by a small tribe in Southern Iran. The rug shows courting birds and the name and date in Arabic of the couple to be married. These rugs are some of the most beautiful tribal weaving produced today.
- *210cm x 293cm*
- £1,650
- Oriental

Turkaman Utensils Bag ▲
- 1880

Unusual bag for kitchen utensils from the Turkaman tribe in brown and cream with a geometric design, with green and pink tassels.
- *65cm x 36cm*
- £200   • Oriental

Chinese Carpet ▲
- 1850

Section of a Chinese carpet from the Ning Xia Province.
- *68cm square*
- £800   • David Black

Tibetan Rug ▲
- *circa 1880*

Tibetan rug with three central medallions and a key border in indigo dye.
- *length 168cm*
- £1,200   • Gordon Reece

Belouch Rug ▲
- *circa 1920*

Belouch rug from western Afghanistan and eastern Iran, where lions from the nomadic and semi-nomadic Belouch Tribes represent courage. All Belouch rugs are made with woollen warps and wefts with lustrous wool pile, and the Belouch are noted for their "prayer rug" designs. Typical Botay design.
- *92cm x 184cm*
- £420   • Oriental

Needlepoint Panel ▲
- *circa 19th century*

Needlepoint panel of floral design made into a footstool.
- *diameter 30.5cm*
- £258   • Classic Fabrics

Shahsavan Kilim ▲
- 1890

Shahsavan kilim with broad geometric designs in blue, red, cream and gold.
- *width 350cm*
- £3,250   • David Black

Baluchi Rug

- *1880*

Baluchi prayer rug from Baluchistan with a central cream panel depicting navy blue stars, with red and white squares bordered by a navy, cream, red and white geometric design.
- *length 240cm*
- £850   • David Black

Karabagh Cushion ▲
- *circa 1920*

Karabagh kilim converted into a cushion cover.
- *width 48cm*
- £60   • Oriental

Kilim Stool ▲
- *1920*

Western Anotonian kilim covering a stool.
- *60cm square*
- £395   • Oriental

Ning Xia Province Carpet ▶
- *1850*

Section of a Chinese carpet with dragon designs from Ning Xia Province.
- *68cm square*
- £800   • David Black

Persian Kilim ◀
- *circa 1880*

Kilim made by the nomads of Persia and dyed with rose madder from the Luti Tribe.
- *length 225cm*
- £1,200   • Gordon Reece

Western Anotonian Kilim Cushion ▲
- *1920*

Western Anotonian kilim converted to a cushion cover.
- *35cm square*
- £45   • Oriental

Expert Tips

Bakhtiari rugs and carpets are woven by a mixed group of nomads of Luri, Kirdish and other ethnic origins, who now occupy the Chahar Mahal region of Iran. The most famous Bakhtiari composition is the panelled garden design.

Shuli Gabbeth Rug ◀

- *circa early 20th century*
Shuli Gabbeh wool rug.
- *length 163cm*
- £620 • Gordon Reece

Anotonian Kilim Stool ▲

- *1930*
Western Anotonian kilim
covering a stool.
- *width 65cm*
- £240 • Oriental

Thracean Rug ▲

- *circa 1870*
Thracean kilim from Turkey with
geometric pattern.
- *119cm x 107cm*
- £1,500 • David Black

Malayer Runner ▲

- *circa 1880*
Malayer runner made by the
Malayers who live sixty miles
south of Hamadan in West
Central Persia. The rug is
decorated with blue, red, ochre
and burnt orange vegetable dyes.
- *100cm x 490cm*
- £2,950 • Oriental

Luri Jijim Rug ▲

- *20th century*
Luri Jijim rug with brown, navy,
blue and cream, woven striped
design, and navy, blue and red
binding on the edge.
- *length 283cm*
- £990 • Gordon Reece

Kilim Cushion ▶

- *1870*
Fragment of a kilim from Turkey
used as a cushion cover.
- *47cm x 38cm*
- £150 • David Black

Tent Trappings ▲

- *1920*
Tent trappings in red, purple,
orange and cream with red,
yellow and brown tassels.
- *height 50cm*
- £65 • Oriental

Tent Trappings ▲
- *1940*

Tent trappings in red, purple, orange and cream with beaded tassels.
- *55cm x 13cm*
- £65 • Oriental

Tibetan Wool Rug ▲
- *circa 1890*

Tibetan rug of natural dyes with a red background with three circles in the centre. Wool on warp and weft.
- *length 145cm*
- £950 • Gordon Reece

Indian Dhurrie ▲
- *circa 1860*

Indian cotton dhurrie with a blue background with pink and yellow geometric designs and a pink key pattern design, on a yellow background with a yellow border.
- *269cm x 251cm*
- £2,800 • David Black

Sarouk Rug ▲
- *circa 1940*

Typical Harati design with a large medallion in the centre, the ground colour is coral with blue, pink and cream. Sarouk is a small village of approximately 1000 houses, west of Iran.
- *89cm x 118cm*
- £1,100 • Oriental

Hammadan Runner ▲
- *1870*

Section of a Hammadan runner.
- *length 300cm*
- £1,500 • David Black

Western Anotonian Kilim ◄
- *circa 1900*

Western Anotonian kilim converted into a cushion cover.
- *width 65cm*
- £125 • Oriental

Indian Dhurrie ▲
- *1850*

Indian dhurrie, a blue foliate design and gold torchieries, on a pink background.
- *156cm x 230cm*
- £950 • David Black

Ceramics

Condition is a major factor when estimating the value of a ceramic as it is very easy for a piece to become damaged.

The golden age of European porcelain is the eighteenth century, the era of Meissen in Germany, Sèvres in France, Capodimonte in Italy and Bow, Chelsea and Worcester in England. The everyday domestic pottery of this century has steadily risen in value and is now very collectable. The nineteenth century also offers immense scope to the collector; at one end there are the superb Empire style cabinet wares, such as vases and urns with fine painting and gilding, made by Worcester, and at the other end are Staffordshire figures, which present a fascinating tableau of the social and political history of the Victorian era. Chinese porcelain continues to exert a magnetic pull over the west, which began in the seventeenth century, when the European nobility began to compete for the finest pieces.

English Ceramics

Quatralobe Tea Set ▼
- *circa 1890*
English quatralobe cup, saucer and plate, gilded with a delicate floral design. Part of a set of four.
- *height of cup 6cm*
- £65   • A. Piotrowski

Crown Derby Cup and Saucer ▲
- *circa 1880*
Royal Crown Derby cup and saucer decorated with pink roses, and wild flowers, with raised gilding.
- *height 7cm*
- £65   • A. Piotrowski

Staffordshire Piper ▼
- *1800*
Staffordshire pottery figure of a piper crisply moulded and decorated with pastel and matt black enamel colours.
- *height 22cm*
- £620   • Dando

Coalport Cup and Saucer ◄
- *circa 1864*
Coalport cup and saucer of lobed design, with stylised floral designs and profuse gilding, with ear shaped handle.
- *height 8cm*
- £125   • A. Piotrowski

Coalport Cup and Saucer ◄

- *circa 1850*

Coalport cup and saucer profusely gilded with floral and swag designs between six roundels.
- *height 7cm*
- £79 • A. Piotrowski

English Dessert Plate ▼

- *circa 1880*

Painted plate with red admiral butterfly and wild flowers on a white ground, within a salmon pink border with scalloped rim and gilding.
- *diameter 22cm*
- £115 • A. Piotrowski

Painted Plate ◄

- *circa 1860*

Hand painted plate with an oriental harbour scene with a ribboned border and gilding.
- *diameter 23.5cm*
- £115 • A. Piotrowski

Sweet Dish ▼

- *circa 1870*

Hand painted English sweet dish with corn, ferns, insects, a ladybird and a butterfly on a cornflower blue ground, raised on a splayed foot.
- *diameter 21cm*
- £98 • A. Piotrowski

English Painted Plate ▼

- *circa 1860*

English plate with a hand painted scene of boats at harbour, within a raised ribbon border with gilt jewelling and banding.
- *diameter 23.5cm*
- £115 • A. Piotrowski

English Painted Plate ▲

- *circa 1860*

English hand painted plate centred with a romantic landscape within a ribbon border, with raised gilding and banding.
- *diameter 23.5cm*
- £115 • A. Piotrowski

Expert Tips

English and European porcelain is rising in value and commands much the same price in New York, London, or Munich.

Derby Cup and Saucer ◄

- *circa 1820*

Derby cup and saucer, the inside of the cup and the plate boldly decorated with orange blossom and leaf designs.
- *height 5cm*
- £95 • A. Piotrowski

Worcester Mug ▲

- *1780*
Cylindrical Worcester porcelain
tankard decorated with a painted
urn in purple enamel, with
garlands and sprays of
polychrome flowers between
underglaze blue and gilt bands.
Crescent mark.
- *height 13.5cm*
- £1,050   • Dando

Painted Cup ▲

- *circa 1850*
English cup and saucer centred
with a landscape showing a
classical ruin, within a gilded
floral border.
- *height 6cm*
- £98   • A. Piotrowski

Wileman & Co. Cup
and Saucer ▲

- *circa 1895*
Wileman & Co. The Foley china,
English white cup, saucer and
plate with gilt borders, hand
painted with swallows and
flowers.
- *height 6cm*
- trio £85   • A. Piotrowski

Wedgwood Figure ▼

- *circa 1810*
Unusual English Wedgwood
figure of a young boy feeding a
biscuit to a spaniel on a plinth
base.
- *height 18.5cm*
- £750   • Dando

Worcester Sauce Boat ▼

- *1756*
Worcester cos lettuce moulded
sauceboat, painted with scattered
floral sprays, and a twig moulded
handle. Unmarked.
- *length 8.75cm*
- £1,250   • Dando

Coalport Cream Jug ▲

- *circa 1835*
Coalport cream jug with gilded
floral designs on a blue ground
with small hand painted panels of
birds.
- *height 12.5cm*
- £165   • Dando

Caughley Plates ▲

- *circa 1785–90*
One of a pair of Caughley plates
with scalloped edges and
underglaze blue border, probably
painted and gilded at Worcester.
'S' mark in underglaze blue.
- *diameter 23cm*
- £650   • Dando

Worcester Bowl ▲

- *1765–70*
Worcester 'Queen Charlotte' pattern waste bowl with dark blue and white panels with floral designs and gilding.
- *diameter 12cm*
- **£275**   • Dando

Derby Dish ▼

- *circa 1815–20*
Derby lozenge shape dessert dish of Trotter pattern, with cartouches of hand painted flowers.
- *length 28cm*
- **£580**   • Dando

Worcester Cup and Saucer ▲

- *circa 1770*
Faceted Worcester coffee cup and saucer decorated with panels of polychrome flowers and gilding between underglaze blue bands.
- *diameter of saucer 5.25cm*
- **£795**   • Dando

Worcester Heart Shaped Dish ▲

- *1780*
Worcester attractive heart shaped dish decorated with sprays of flowers within an underglaze blue border with gilt foliate pattern. Crescent mark in underglaze blue.
- *length 27cm*
- **£875**   • Dando

English Ceramics Jug ▲

- *circa 1840*
Large English ceramics milk jug with painted floral decoration and gilding.
- *height 16cm*
- **£420**   • Dando

Spode Miniature Basket ▼

- *circa 1825*
Miniature spode porcelain basket decorated with an exotic bird and foliage in raised gilding against a mazarin blue ground.
- *length 10cm*
- **£475**   • Dando

Bow Candlestick ▲

- *1765*
A large Bow porcelain double figure group of Columbine and a young boy, seated with a dog in front of an elaborate floral bocage. Fitted with two candle sconces with metal supports.
- *height 23cm*
- **£1,850**   • Dando

Miniature Ewer and Stand ▼
- *circa 1835*
English ceramics miniature ewer and stand with original porcelain stopper, with a painted floral panel set within gilded borders.
- *height 11cm*
- £420   • Dando

Staffordshire Violinist ▼
- *circa 1840–45*
Staffordshire figure of a violinist in theatrical costume wearing a pink plumed hat.
- *height 21cm*
- £260   • Dando

Staffordshire Boy Piper ▶
- *1820*
Staffordshire spill holder showing a group with a seated piper playing to a pig and a duck.
- *height 17.2cm*
- £655   • Dando

Chimney Sweep ▲
- *circa 1810*
Early Staffordshire pottery figure of a chimney sweep decorated in overglaze colours.
- *height 18cm*
- £445   • Dando

Staffordshire Cats ▲
- *circa 1870*
Pair of Staffordshire cats, painted black and white, with yellow collars.
- *height 8cm*
- £475   • Dando

Staffordshire Spill Vase ▼
- *1815*
Staffordshire pottery 'Game Spill' vase of unusual and fine quality in the form of a hollow tree, hung with various game and a hunters satchel. Pearlware with overglaze enamel colours.
- *height 22cm*
- £400   • Dando

Staffordshire Country Gentleman ▼
- *1870*
Staffordshire figure of a country gentleman, presenting a basket of trout, whilst standing on a naturalistically styled base.
- *height 25.5cm*
- £295   • Dando

Staffordshire Figure ▼
- **1890**
Staffordshire model of a lady seated on a wall, with a swan at her feet.
- *height 18cm*
- **£150**   • Bellum

Staffordshire Pheasants ▼
- **1860**
Pair of Staffordshire pheasants with unusual orange and blue markings on the wings standing on a rusticated base.
- *26cm x 12cm*
- **£1,500**   • J.Oosthuizen

Leopard Spill Vases ▶
- **1845**
Pair of Staffordshire spill vases showing two leopards with bocage, standing on a naturalistically formed base.
- *16cm x 11cm*
- **£3,600**   • J.Oosthuizen

Sailor with Parrot ▲
- **1880**
Staffordshire figure of a man in theatrical dress with a plumed hat, holding a parrot.
- *height 20cm*
- **£175**   • Bellum

Elephant Spill Vases ▲
- **1830**
Pair of grey elephant spill vases with pink saddles.
- *15cm x 10cm*
- **£2,700**   • J.Oosthuizen

Dinner Plate ▼
- *circa 1880*
Blue and white dinner plate decorated with classical ruins with a scrolled floral border.
- *diameter 25cm*
- **£145**   • Barrett & Towning

Staffordshire Gardeners ▲

- *circa 1860–70*

Staffordshire spill vase group of two figures, probably gardeners, the man is holding a basket of flowers and there is a potted plant behind the seated girl.

- *height 21cm*
- £185
- Dando

Staffordshire Soldier ▲

- 1880

Staffordshire figure of an officer in a blue uniform with gilt buttons and a floral sash, within a bocage.

- *height 15cm*
- £175
- Bellum

Theatrical Dancers ▼

- 1850

Staffordshire group of theatrical dancers depicting Miss Glover and Mrs Vining as Yourawkee and Peter Wilkins.

- *height 20cm*
- £295
- Dando

Staffordshire Group ▼

- 1880

Staffordshire group showing a gentleman with a dog under his arm and a lady wearing tartan.

- *height 17cm*
- £225
- Bellum

Staffordshire Inkwell ▶

- 1880

Staffordshire inkwell showing a boy and his sister seated on an orange base.

- *height 11.5cm*
- £175
- Bellum

Staffordshire Figure ▲

- 1880

Staffordshire figure of a girl wearing a blue dress seated on a large, horned goat.

- *height 12cm*
- £240
- Bellum

Staffordshire Children ▲

- 1880

Staffordshire spill vase with two children seated by the trunk of a tree with a bird resting on a garland of orange flowers.

- *height 14cm*
- £225
- Bellum

Staffordshire Castle ▲
• *1855*
Very rare Staffordshire model
commemorating Malakoff Castle
from the Crimean War.
• *22cm x 24cm*
• **£750**   • **J.Oosthuizen**

Staffordshire Group ▲
• *1850*
Staffordshire group depicting
Uncle Tom and Little Eva.
• *height 21cm*
• **£360**   • **J.Oosthuizen**

Staffordshire Spill Vases ▲
• *1880*
Pair of Staffordshire spill vases
modelled as two white stallions,
standing on an oval moulded
base.
• *height 30cm*
• **£1,500**   • **J.Oosthuizen**

Baden Powell   ▼
• *1899*
Staffordshire figure of Baden
Powell, founder of the Scout
Movement and the leader of the
British Troops of the Siege of
Mafeking.
• *height 42cm*
• **£450**   • **J.Oosthuizen**

Staffordshire Cavalry Officer   ▼
• *1880*
Staffordshire model of a mounted
cavalry officer on a very fine
horse.
• *height 30cm*
• **£450**   • **J.Oosthuizen**

Duke of Wellington   ▲
• *1845*
Staffordshire figure of the Duke of
Wellington wearing full uniform
of blue and gold.
• *height 23cm*
• **£380**   • **J.Oosthuizen**

Shepherd and Shepherdess   ▲
• *1790*
Early salt glaze group depicting a
shepard and shepherdess with a
goat, sheep and dog at their feet.
He is playing on the flute for his
female companion.
• *height 28cm*
• **£2,400**   • **J.Oosthuizen**

Staffordshire Group   ◄
• *1855*
Staffordshire group depicting two
lovers under a green bower.
• *height 24cm*
• **£300**   • **J.Oosthuizen**

Staffordshire Greyhounds ▼

- **1860**

Pair of terracotta greyhounds recumbent on a cobalt blue base.
- *height 9cm*
- **£300** • J.Oosthuizen

Terracotta Greyhounds ▼

- **1890**

Pair of Staffordshire terracotta greyhounds sitting attentively on a circular moulded base.
- *height 10cm*
- **£300** • J.Oosthuizen

Staffordshire Group ▼

- **1830**

Unusual Staffordshire group depicting a dog with puppies and a cat with kittens.
- *height 11cm*
- **£2,500** • J.Oosthuizen

Staffordshire Giraffes ▼

- **1900**

Pair of Staffordshire giraffes reclining by a palm tree, on an oval moulded base.
- *height 14cm*
- **£2,700** • J.Oosthuizen

Staffordshire Lions ▲

- **1860**

Pair of Staffordshire lions with a lamb resting at their side, reclining on an oval moulded base, with gilding.
- *27cm x 17cm*
- **£6,500** • J.Oosthuizen

Spill Vases ▲

- **1845**

Staffordshire spill vases modelled as a pair of lions with bocage, standing on an oval base with gilding.
- *height 14cm*
- **£2,400** • J.Oosthuizen

Expert Tips

Functional redwares made from alluvial clay, were first made in America from around 1625, and continued well into the 19th century. New England pieces tend to be plain, though often with richly coloured glazes.

Staffordshire Group ▼
- *circa 1850*

Early Staffordshire brown and white spaniel with puppy, resting on an oval white base with gilding.
- *height 8.5cm*
- £460
- Dando

Copper Lustre Jug ▼
- *circa 1840*

Large copper lustre jug with moulded band of shamrocks and thistles in pale blue relief.
- *height 19cm*
- £210
- Dando

Ralph Wood Group ▲
- *1785*

Fine quality Ralph Wood group of the 'Vicar and Moses' showing two seated figures, painted in brown and grey hues.
- *height 23.5cm*
- £1,650
- Dando

Samuel Alcock Spaniel ▲
- *circa 1835*

Samuel Alcock model of a brown and white spaniel sitting attentively on a yellow base.
- *height 14cm*
- £440
- Dando

Staffordshire Stag ▼
- *1810*

Fine quality Staffordshire pottery stag shown recumbent on a naturally formed oval base.
- *height 19cm*
- £740
- Dando

Staffordshire Figure ▲
- *circa 1810*

Staffordshire pottery figure of Iphegenia shown gathering her skirts with her head to one side.
- *height 18.5cm*
- £850
- Dando

Musician ▲
- *circa 1840*

Small figure of a boy musician, playing a penny whistle with a poodle at his side.
- *height 16cm*
- £215
- Dando

St Mark ▲
- 1850

Staffordshire figure of St Mark with a lion recumbent at his side, on a rock moulded base.
- *height 24cm*
- £450 • J.Oosthuizen

Queen Victoria's Children ▲
- 1880

Staffordshire group depicting Queen Victoria's children.
- *height 41cm*
- £275 • J.Oosthuizen

Spill Vases ▼
- 1860

Pair of Staffordshire spill vases modelled as foxes with chickens in there mouths, standing on a foliate base.
- *height 25cm*
- £1,600 • J.Oosthuizen

Little Red Riding Hood ▼
- 1860

Staffordshire figure of Little Red Riding Hood seated with a fox.
- *height 26cm*
- £185 • J.Oosthuizen

Staffordshire Zebras ▲
- 1865

Pair of prancing Staffordshire zebras on a foliate oval base with gilding.
- *height 16cm*
- £725 • J.Oosthuizen

Staffordshire Actor ▲
- 1855

Man in theatrical dress sitting on a branch, with a parrot on his shoulder and a spaniel at his side, with gilding on a green foliate base.
- *height 37cm*
- £450 • J.Oosthuizen

Staffordshire Children ▲
- 1850

Pair of Staffordshire figures modelled as children playing with rats, raised on oval moulded bases with gilding.
- *height 15cm*
- £800 • J.Oosthuizen

Staffordshire Group ▲
- 1880

Ivory Staffordshire group modelled as a cow with her calf, standing on an oval moulded base with gilding.
- *16cm x 21cm*
- £350 • J.Oosthuizen

Bacchus ▼
• 1870
Staffordshire figure of Bacchus astride a pink wine barrel holding a bunch of grapes.
• height 34cm
• £245   • J.Oosthuizen

Lord Byron ▼
• 1870
Staffordshire figure of Lord Byron standing with one arm resting on his hip wearing a white tunic holding an emerald green bag and pale pink cape over his shoulder.
• height 42cm
• £250   • J.Oosthuizen

Staffordshire Jug ▲
• circa 1800
Staffordshire jug showing four horses and a coach with a driver and two other figures. On the side of the carriage are the words the "Liverpool Fly" the initials J.R. under the lip, and a cartouche of flowers with the following poem: 'The Ale is good, Then pray pour out, The Glafs is full, Come Drink a bout'.
• height 18cm
• £1,650   • Jonathan Horne

Brickmaker's Staffordshire Jug ▲
• circa 1815
Staffordshire jug with the words ;Succefs to all Jolly Brickmakers 1815', under the lip and a cartouche on each side depicting artisans at work.
• height 19cm
• £1,750   • Jonathan Horne

Staffordshire Castle ▶
• circa 1830
A cream Staffordshire castle with four turrets standing on a bushy mound.
• 15cm x 18cm
• £880   • Jonathan Horne

The Marriage Act ▼
• circa 1820
Staffordshire group entitled, 'The Marriage Act'.
• 17cm x 17cm
• £4,450   • Jonathan Horne

Duke Of York Jug ▼
• circa 1795
A large Staffordshire jug with a green handle and band to rim with a blue cartouche surrounded by a green band depicting the Duke of York in cream relief, surrounded by cannons, flags and bayonets.
• height 13cm
• £1,250   • Jonathan Horne

Bough Pot ▶

- *circa 1800*
Staffordshire tulip holder with a
central panel depicting a pastoral
scene, flanked by putti, with
mask and leaf decoration to the
scalloped rim, raised on three
glazed bun feet.
- *height 13cm*
- £1,850   • Jonathan Horne

Staffordshire Dandies ▲

- *circa 1820*
A Staffordshire couple, the lady
wearing a large yellow hat with
blue feathers, a pink jacket and
yellow skirt, the gentleman
wearing black morning coat with
top hat and yellow trousers.
- *height 221cm*
- £1,780   • Jonathan Horne

The Marriage Act ▲

- *circa 1820*
Staffordshire group inscribed with
the words, 'The New Marriage
Act, John Frilland, Anne Bore
aged 21, that is right says the
parson amen says the clerk'.
- *17cm x 17cm*
- £4,450   • Jonathan Horne

Clock with Figures ▼

- *1815*
Staffordshire group depicting a
long case clock flanked by two
figures leaning against a pillar.
The man holding a scroll, and a
lady leaning against a pillar with
her hand raised.
- *height 27cm*
- £1,250   • Jonathan Horne

Bear Teapot ▶

- *1815*
Staffordshire teapot modelled as a
bear wearing a muzzle and collar.
- *height 17cm*
- £2,850   • Jonathan Horne

Mounted Staffordshire Figure ◀

- *circa 1820*
Staffordshire figure of a mounted
cavalry officer wearing a blue
uniform with gold braiding, at full
charge brandishing his sabre.
- *height 28cm*
- £2,950   • Jonathan Horne

Liverpool Cream Jug ▲

- *1790*
Liverpool cream jug depicting
pastoral scenes representing
summer, and winter the reverse.
- *height 19cm*
- £550   • Jonathan Horne

Davenport Calceony Teapot ▲
- *circa 1805*

Davenport silver-form teapot in the Grecian style with a leaf pattern and black banding.
- *height 14cm*
- £595 • Libra

Davenport Sauce Tureen ▲
- *circa 1810*

Davenport sauce tureen and cover on a fixed stand in the form of overlapping oak leaves, with black handles and finial.
- *height 18cm*
- £560 • Libra

Ridgway Puzzle Jug ▲
- *circa 1820*

Ridgway blue and white puzzle jug, with pierced decoration to the neck and rim, painted with a rural landscape.
- *height 22cm*
- £750 • Libra

Creamware Jug ▲
- *circa 1790*

Creamware milk jug decorated with a compass with the inscription 'Come box the compass' with a man with a rope in hand and the words 'Invented by Murphy a Dutchman'.
- *height 15cm*
- £340 • Libra

English Delft Jug ▼
- *1730*

Small English delft jug with original cover, painted with flowers and a stylised leaf design.
- *height 18cm*
- £295 • Libra

Blue and White Cup ▼
- *circa 1820*

Blue and white cup and saucer decorated with apples, blossom and leaves.
- *height 6cm*
- £190 • Libra

Spode Basket ▼
- *circa 1810*

Spode lattice work basket with shaped rim, painted with a delicate green and red foliate design, raised on four ochre feet.
- *width 27cm*
- £175 • Libra

Agate Teapot ▼
• *1755*
Staffordshire blue and brown
agate teapot on pecton shell
design with a recumbent dog
finial.
• *height 14cm*
• **£4,950**   • Jonathan Horne

Delftware Fuddling Cup ▼
• *1650*
Delftware fuddling cup consisting
of three small interlaced
containers. Each container is
filled with a different alcoholic
beverage, before being passed
amongst friends.
• *height 7.5cm*
• **£6,600**   • Jonathan Horne

Staffordshire Turkeys ▼
• *circa 1820*
A rare and unusual pair of
Staffordshire turkeys. The male
with his plumes displayed, both
on a naturalistically formed green
glazed base.
• *height to head 9cm*
• **£4,450**   • Jonathan Horne

Delftware Pessett Pot ▲
• *1885*
Pessett pot with painted oriental
figures and a pagoda in the
background, with blue striped
design on the handles and spout.
• *12cm x 12.5cm*
• **£1,750**   • Jonathan Horne

Flower Brick ▼
• *circa 1760*
A rare blue and white flower
brick, with twenty-one
receptacles and painted panels of
water lilies, chrysanthemums and
a bird within a dark blue border.
• *10cm x 15cm*
• **£1,450**   • Jonathan Horne

Delftware Jar ▼
• *1690*
Delftware jar inscribed with, 'O
HIRVNDINV', below a winged
angel.
• *height 18cm*
• **£3,950**   • Jonathan Horne

Flower Brick ▼
• *1730–40*
One of a pair of very rare flower
bricks, with twenty-one
receptacles and a sepia and yellow
fern design, with houses in the
background.
• *10cm x 15cm*
• **£7,500**   • Jonathan Horne

Chestnut Horse ▼

- *circa 1800*

Chestnut horse with tail raised and head bowed, with a white saddle and yellow girth, a fine example of Prattware.
- *height 16cm*
- £4,400　　• Jonathan Horne

Prattware Skewbald Horse ▼

- *circa 1800*

Prattware skewbald horse with a blue glazed saddle, on a plinth base.
- *height 16cm*
- £4,400　　• Jonathan Horne

Staffordshire Tea Pot ▼

- *1813*

Rare black Staffordshire teapot and cover, inscribed, 'India Portugal, Spain, Victoria 21st June 1813', with a laurel wreath.
- *height 24cm*
- £990　　• Jonathan Horne

Expert Tips

Staffordshire figures often took their inspiration from popular paintings or prints and were based upon actual events such as the theatre.

Prattware Horse ▲

- *circa 1800*

Prattware dapple grey horse, with head erect, a long black tail and blue saddle, standing on a plinth base.
- *height 16cm*
- £4,550　　• Jonathan Horne

Staffordshire Gentleman ▲

- *circa 19th century*

Staffordshire country gentleman with a yellow hat, brown jacket and boots and cream trousers.
- *height 16cm*
- £780　　• Jonathan Horne

Prattware Tea Caddy ▼

- *late 18th century*

Prattware tea caddy with a brass cover, depicting a comical scene in relief of two ladies.
- *height 13cm*
- £550　　• Jonathan Horne

Staffordshire Platter ▼

- *1800*

Small Staffordshire plate with dark blue, scalloped border, with a raised design of a lobster in the centre.
- *length 11.5cm*
- £750　　• Jonathan Horne

Earthenware Jug ▲

- *13th century*
English earthenware jug of
bulbous form with incised
banding and a burnt orange glaze.
- *height 20cm*
- £2,950   • Jonathan Horne

English Earthenware Jug ▲

- *13th century*
English earthenware jug of
bulbous form with handle, in
good condition.
- *height 28cm*
- £2,200   • Jonathan Horne

Earthenware Vessel ▼

- *1270–1350*
Earthenware elongated vessel
with a light green glaze and
thumb prints around the base and
top of handle, from Mill Green,
Essex.
- *height 30cm*
- £4,400   • Jonathan Horne

Red-Ware Tea Kettle ▲

- *circa 1770*
Red-ware tea kettle with double
rope twist handle, and mask
decoration to the base of the
spout.
- *height 23cm*
- £3,950   • Jonathan Horne

Earthenware Vessel ▲

- *circa 14th century*
Earthenware vessel with a green
glaze, found in the foundations of
a house in Grace Church Street,
London in 1873.
- *height 21.5cm*
- £1,950   • Jonathan Horne

Earthenware Jug ▲

- *16th century*
Small earthenware jug of bulbous
proportions, with moulded
handle, splayed lip and a green
glaze.
- *height 14cm*
- £780   • Jonathan Horne

Blackware Teapot ▼
- *circa 1765*
Small blackware teapot, with ear shaped handle and a raised floral design, on pad feet, with a bird finial lid.
- *height 8cm*
- £475 • Jonathan Horne

Blackware Bowl ▲
- *circa 1765*
Blackware bowl decorated with a raised design of gilt fruit and trailing foliage.
- *diameter 14cm*
- £660 • Jonathan Horne

Saltglazed Jug ▼
- *13th century*
Saltglazed jug of bulbous form, with strap handle and turned decoration to the neck.
- *height 22cm*
- £1,300 • Jonathan Horne

Blackware Coffee Pot ▲
- *circa 1765*
Blackware coffee pot, raised on three feet with a pinched lip, moulded handle and a bird finial cover.
- *height 15cm*
- £550 • Jonathan Horne

English Sauce Tureen ◀
- *circa 1820*
English blue and white sauce tureen and cover on fitted base with a landscape depicting grazing rabbits within a country setting.
- *height 17cm*
- £375 • Libra

Earthenware Jug ▼
- *12th century*
English earthenware vessel with a dark green glaze and circular design around the neck found at Sible Headingham, Essex.
- *height 29cm*
- £5,500 • Horne

Sauce Tureen ▼
- *circa 1820*
India flowers sauce tureen and cover, with floral sprays on a red ground with gilding and acanthus leaf decoration (known as clobbered).
- *height 17.5cm*
- £520 • Libra

Creamware Teapot ▼
- *circa 1795*
Creamware teapot with a foliate pattern in green and a central cartouche painted with a basket of wild flowers.
- *height 17cm*
- £470 • Libra

Creamware Teapot ▶

- *circa 1775*
Small creamware teapot with red and black mottled design, twig spout and handle and a red finial cover.
- *14cm*
- £750
- Libra

Davenport Tureen and Cover ▲

- *circa 1820*
Davenport polychrome sauce tureen and cover, on fixed stand with chinoiserie designs within a key pattern border, with gilt banding and a leaf shaped finial.
- *height 17cm*
- £228
- Libra

Wedgwood Teapot ▲

- *circa 1790*
Small Wedgwood teapot decorated with a tulip pattern in magenta, with designs on spout and handle with a flower finial cover.
- *height 12.5cm*
- £420
- Libra

Swansea Pinwheel Pepperpot ▲

- *1870*
Swansea blue and white 'Pinwheel' pepperpot of bulbous form raised on a splayed foot.
- *height 11cm*
- £270
- Libra

Stone China Vase ◀

- *circa 1825*
One of a set of four stone china vases decorated with an apple blossom design with gilt banded decoration.
- *height 11cm*
- £360
- Libra

Swansea Moulded Jug ▼

- *circa 1825*
Swansea daisy pattern moulded jug, with C scroll handle and shaped lip with red, blue, green and white stripes and a black diagonal stripe across the body.
- *height 22cm*
- £150
- Libra

Pearlware Jug ▼

- *circa 1815*
Pearlware moulded jug decorated with pink roses, cornflowers and leaves, with black banded decoration.
- *height 12cm*
- £125
- Libra

Derby Squab Tureen ▶

- *circa 1760*

Finely painted Derby Squab
tureen, naturalistically styled as a
bird, with floral encrustation.
- *height 10cm*
- £3,400   • Stockspring

Charles Bourne Vase ▲

- *circa 1820*

Charles Bourne vase with a band
of finely painted flowers, between
gilded floral borders on a blue
ground.
- *height 15cm*
- £480   • Stockspring

Yates Egg Cups ▼

- *circa 1820*

An early and rare set of six egg
cups with stand by Yates, with
finely painted flowers between
scrolled cartouches, centred with
birds.
- *height 5cm*
- £750   • Stockspring

Chelsea Dish ▲

- *circa 1750*

Chelsea lozenge shaped dish
decorated with floral sprays of
pink roses, with a scalloped edge
with gilt trim and scrolling.
- *diameter 25cm*
- £1,450   • Stockspring

Worcester Dish ▼

- *circa 1750*

Worcester dish in the form of a
leaf, centred with a floral spray of
roses and wild flowers, with a soft
green border.
- *diameter 18cm*
- £1,980   • Stockspring

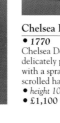

Chelsea Derby Mug ◀

- *1770*

Chelsea Derby white mug
delicately painted in a soft palette
with a spray of pink roses, with
scrolled handle and gilt rim.
- *height 10cm*
- £1,100   • Stockspring

Derby Figures ▼
• **1765**
Pair of Derby figures of a young
girl holding a basket and her
companion holding a lamb under
his arm, standing on a scrolled
base scattered with flowers.
• *height 24cm*
• **£3,600 the pair** • Stockspring

Worcester Creamer ▼
• *circa 1765*
Worcester cream jug with a
central cartouche of two Chinese
men in a landscape carrying a
lantern, and a blue floral design
on the inside of the moulded rim.
• *height 7cm*
• **£760** • Stockspring

Derby Figure ▲
• *circa 1770*
Derby figure of a young maiden
wearing a white dress and bonnet
holding a basket of green and red
grapes under her arm, on a
circular base with gilt banding.
• *height 14cm*
• **£1,180** • Stockspring

Bow Candleholder ◀
• *circa 1760*
Bow candleholder encrusted
with yellow and pink flowers
around the trunk of a tree with
two pheasants perched on the
top and a central flower
candleholder.
• *height 23cm*
• **£1,850** • Stockspring

Bow Plates ▼
• *circa 1760*
One of a pair of octagonal Bow
plates decorated with the Quail
pattern, showing a chinoiserie
tree with terracotta and gold
flowers and a terracotta trim
linked with gold.
• *diameter 22cm*
• **£1,680** • Stockspring

Bow Grape Sellers ▲
• *circa 1760*
Pair of Bow figures, of a young
girl wearing a pink hat with finely
painted dress of pink flowers and
boy seated with matching
breeches, and outstretched arm
holding grapes.
• *height 16.5cm*
• **£3,800 pair** • Stockspring

English Chinoiserie Mug ▲

- *circa 1790*

English blue and white mug decorated with a chinoiserie design, with turned decoration and ear shaped handle.
- *height 8.5cm*
- £180 • Libra

Goldfinch Sugar Bowl ▲

- *1820*

Blue and white sugar bowl with twin handles, moulded rim and finial lid, decorated with floral designs and centred with a goldfinch.
- *height 10cm*
- £280 • Libra

Spittoon ▲

- *1820*

Rare spittoon with moulded decoration and spout, decorated with floral designs and a rural scene.
- *height 10cm*
- £325 • Libra

Pepperpot ▼

- *1795*

Underglazed blue and white pepperpot painted freely with groups of flowers, raised on a splayed foot.
- *height 3cm*
- £115 • Libra

Salopian Tea Bowl ▼

- *1810*

Salopian polychrome tea bowl and saucer pictured with a woodcutter and his wife seated holding a baby, with a gate and church in the background.
- *diameter 8cm*
- £170 • Libra

Sugar Shaker ▲

- *1820*

Unusually shaped blue and white sugar shaker with floral designs to the neck and a chinoiserie style landscape on the body, raised on a splayed foot.
- *height 11cm*
- £50 • Libra

Hall Cup Plate ▲

- *1820*

Cup-plate manufactured by 'Hall' centred with a hyena within a floral border with urn decoration.
- *diameter 11cm*
- £185 • Libra

Soup Tureen ▶

- **1827**
Soup tureen manufactured by
Jones to celebrate the Coronation
of George IV.
- *height 31cm*
- **£1,273**   • Libra

Leeds Egg Cup ▲

- **1820**
Leeds blue and white egg cup
decorated with two boys fishing
beside a river within a parkland
setting.
- *height 7cm*
- **£195**   • Libra

Dresden Sauceboat ▲

- **1225**
Dresden sauceboat with scrolled
handle, shaped lip, vase and floral
decoration, raised on a moulded,
splayed foot.
- *height 8cm*
- **£120**   • Libra

Platter ▶

- **1820**
Blue and white platter with a
moonlit naval battle scene
surrounded by tropical shells and
fauna.
- *width 53cm*
- **£1,350**   • Libra

Tea Bowl and Saucer ▲

- *1790*
Pearlware tea bowl and saucer,
with finely fluted decoration,
painted with a dark blue trailing
band with stylised flowers.
- *diameter 8.5cm*
- **£195**   • Libra

Ewer and Bowl ▼

- **1820**
Blue and white ewer and bowl
decorated with a view of
Worcester, and the word
'Worcester' inscribed on the base.
- *height of jug 20cm*
- **£490**   • Libra

Royal Doulton Pepper Pot ▲

- *1884*

Royal Doulton pepper pot with blue glazed neck decorated with a raised, repetitive design, above a turned body, raised on a moulded foot.

- *height 8cm*
- £65 • Lynda Brine

Doulton Jug ▲

- *1876*

Royal Doulton Lambeth jug designed by Frank Butler with a silver lid and thumb piece, the body decorated with a stylised leaf pattern, with jewelling.

- *height 17cm*
- £235 • Lynda Brine

Fruit Bowl ▲

- *1920*

Blue and white fruit bowl with a rural scene with cows in the fore ground, within a bold floral border.

- *diameter 19cm*
- £140 • Libra

Staffordshire Figure of Neptune ▼

- *1830*

Figure of Neptune with trident, standing on a rock encrusted with seashells with a sea monster at his feet.

- *height 18cm*
- £495 • Pieter Oosthuizen

Davenport Stilton Dish and Cover ▼

- *1860*

Davenport blue and white stilton dish and cover decorated with a Chinoiserie harbour scene.

- *height 35cm*
- £2,600 • Libra

Staffordshire Group ▶

- *1850*

Staffordshire figure of a lady wearing a pink top with a floral skirt holding a baby, with a child at her side.

- *height 23cm*
- £395 • Pieter Oosthuizen

Staffordshire Group ▲

- *1850*

Staffordshire group seated on a mossy bank with a tree in the back ground

- *height 25cm*
- £595 • Pieter Oosthuizen

Staffordshire Musician ▲

- *1840*

Staffordshire figure of a musician wearing a yellow hat with blue plumes, holding a mandolin with a lamb and flowers at his feet.

- *height 24cm*
- £425 • Pieter Oosthuizen

Newhalls Walberton Teapot ▲

- *1810*

Newhalls Walberton patent teapot and cover, with a gilt finial lid and foliate designs. The body is profusely gilded and decorated with a painted landscape, with a blue enamelled band at the base of the spout.
- *height 16cm*
- £1,290   • Stockspring

Staffordshire Archer ▲

- *1840*

Staffordshire figure of a lady archer wearing a plumed hat and green coat, holding a bow and arrow, standing on a plinth base.
- *height 17cm*
- £295   • Pieter Oosthuizen

Pepper Pot ▼

- *1884*

Royal Doulton pepper caster of bulbous form, with pewter cover and finial top, the neck and body decorated with a stylised leaf design, with jewelling.
- *height 10cm*
- £95   • Lynda Brine

Derbyshire Bowl ▼

- *1810*

Derbyshire double handled sugar bowl, decorated with a pink heart shaped pattern and gilt foliate designs and banding.
- *height 9cm*
- £360   • Stockspring

Newhall Jug ▲

- *1814*

Newhall cream jug with pinched lip, decorated with a floral ribbon design and raised on a moulded foot.
- *height 9.5cm*
- £280   • Stockspring

Mason's Jug ▲

- *1812*

Small Mason's jug with scrolled handle and pink Imari design around the body, with gilt trailing foliage and banding.
- *height 7cm*
- £170   • Stockspring

Worcester Sauce Tureen ▲

- *1820*

Worcester double handled sauce tureen, finely painted with a floral design on a yellow, white and grey enamel, with gilt acorn finial.
- *height 14cm*
- £480   • Stockspring

King of Prussia Teapot
- *1765*

Staffordshire salt glaze teapot with black arrow pattern, and a cartouche of the King of Prussia with stylised twig handle, spout and finial top.
- *height 9cm*
- £3,850 • Jonathan Horne

Creamware Teapot ▲
- *1765*

English creamware teapot with farm hands resting in a pastoral setting, and a cottage on the reverse, with leaf designs to the handle and spout.
- *height 10cm*
- £1,100 • Jonathan Horne

Saltglaze Teapot ▲
- *circa 1765*

Staffordshire salt glaze teapot decorated with pink wild flowers on a crimson ground, with twig handle and spout.
- *height 10cm*
- £2,100 • Jonathan Horne

Staffordshire Teapot ▲
- *circa 1765*

Staffordshire salt glazed teapot with a musician wearing a pink jacket and a black hat, in chinoiserie style, playing a flute, whilst seated on a riverbank.
- *height 9.4cm*
- £3,650 • Jonathan Horne

Staffordshire Creamer ▼
- *circa 1765*

Early Staffordshire creamer with the inscription 'William Dixson' within a cartouche of flowers. The side of the jug is a painted figure of a musician wearing a red jacket and black tri-cornered hat.
- *height 18.4cm*
- £6,850 • Jonathan Horne

Staffordshire Sauceboat ▼
- *circa 1745*

Staffordshire sauce boat with a scrolled handle, decorated with a pink house and clouds, with shaped rim and foot.
- *height 8cm*
- £1,850 • Jonathan Horne

Saltglazed Stand with Teapot ▼
- *circa 1755*

Staffordshire teapot decorated with green and yellow vases and foliate design around the handle and spout, and standing on three raised feet.
- *height 8cm*
- £3,950 • Jonathan Horne

Pink Lustre Jug ▼
- *1825*
Pink Lustre jug which is part of a set of ten cups and saucers with cream jug and two small bowls.
- *height 7cm*
- £280　　　　　　• Libra

Swansea Mug ▼
- *1870*
Blue and white Swansea mug with chinoiserie decoration and a bamboo moulded handle.
- *height 18cm*
- £340　　　　　　• Libra

Blue and White Jug ▲
- *1817*
Large blue and white jug decorated with an Indian hunting scene with elephants and hounds giving chase to a tiger.
- *height 28cm*
- £1,700　　　　　• Libra

Winchester Measure Jug ▼
- *1815*
Winchester measure jug with scrolled handle and pinched lip, with moulded leaf design around the neck and blue banded decoration.
- *height 14cm*
- £290　　　　　　• Libra

Wine Jug ▲
- *circa 1820*
Large blue and white wine jug, with a scene depicting wine makers at the press, with vine and fruit decoration.
- *height 24cm*
- £1,150　　　　　• Libra

Lustre Ware Jug ◄
- *1826*
Pink Lustre ware jug inscribed 'John Evendon aged 17, 1826', with a view of the River Wear in Sunderland.
- *height 12.5cm*
- £140　　　　　　• Libra

Sugar Bowl ▼
- *1825*
Dawson Squire and Lackey blue and white sugar bowl, with cover and finial lid, decorated with a scene depicting a castle in a parkland setting.
- *height 10cm*
- £245　　　　　　• Libra

Worcester Dish ▶

- *circa 1768*
Worcester oval Imari pattern dish with a central cartouche of a pagoda and a orange blossom tree with clouds to the side, and twig orange handles.
- *length 28cm*
- £11,500   • Stockspring

Worcester Tea Bowl ▼

- *1760*
Small Worcester tea bowl decorated with a courting couple in a classical setting, a small dog and garden roller in the foreground.
- *height of bowl 5cm*
- £560   • Stockspring

Worcester Jug ▼

- *circa 1765*
Small Worcester jug decorated with a spray of pink flowers, with an orange line and scalloping on the inside of the rim.
- *height 8.5cm*
- £980   • Stockspring

Chelsea Dish ▼

- *circa 1760*
Chelsea dish in the shape of a peony encircled by a green leaf, with a turquoise handle in the shape of a branch with a bud.
- *diameter 19cm*
- £2,700   • Stockspring

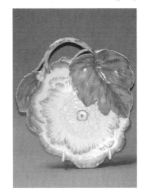

Longton Hall Plate ▼

- *circa 1755*
Longhton Hall plate decorated with a raised design of strawberries and flowers, with a central panel of birds and a parrot in a tree.
- *diameter 24cm*
- £1,890   • Stockspring

Worcester Jug ▲

- *1805*
Worcester jug with terracotta, dark blue and white floral and scroll design, with gold trim on rim and handle.
- *height 18cm*
- £1,280   • Stockspring

Worcester Cornocuperies ◄

- *circa 1756-8*
Pair of blue and white moulded Worcester cornocuperies decorated with small blue flowers. Workman's mark.
- *height 22cm*
- £4,500   • Stockspring

Large Worcester Mug ▲

- *circa 1805*
Large Worcester mug, with two yellow enamel bands between gilt banding and a central repetitive design of stylised feathers.
- *height 12cm*
- £680   • Stockspring

Minton Cup ▼

- *circa 1805*
Minton cup decorated with three cartouches and a foliate design in terracotta, set amongst profuse gilding. With mark on base: M.205.
- *height 6.5cm*
- £139   • Stockspring

Lowestoft Tea Bowl ▲

- *circa 1760*
Lowestoft tea bowl decorated with a blue and white chinsoserie scene depicting a house behind a wall with a tree and birds.
- *height of bowl 5cm*
- £690   • Stockspring

Worcester Tea Bowl ▲

- *circa 1740*
Worcester octagonal tea bowl with finely painted sprays of flowers and insects with gilding, from the studio of James Giles.
- *height 5cm*
- £420   • Stockspring

Pinxton Jug ▶

- *circa 1805*
Small Pinxton cream jug with a scrolled handle and shaped rim with blue banding, the body delicately painted with three fuchsia sprigs.
- *height 10cm*
- £690   • Stockspring

European Ceramics

Coffee Pot and Teapot

- *circa 1800*

Meissen coffee and teapot, part of a set including milk jug, sugar bowl, cups and saucers, cake plates and one large plate.
- *height 27cm*
- £2,550 • London Antique

Dresden Europa and The Bull

- *circa 1860*

Dresden group of Europa and the Bull, the lady wearing a lilac tunic, and the bull with a garland of flowers around its neck.
- *height 22cm*
- £350 • Gloria Sinclair

Neptune

- *1760*

Meissen figure of Neptune astride a sea-horse with trident.
- *height 15cm*
- £980 • Stockspring Antiques

Dresden Cup and Saucer

- *circa 1880*

Dresden cup standing on three paw feet and saucer decorated with orange borders and a central cartouche of boats in a harbour.
- *height 10cm*
- £285 • London Antique

Meissen Figurative Group

- *circa 1880*

Meissen figurative group of Diana the Huntress seated on a lion holding a cornucopia of flowers, with cherubs holding a key and garlands.
- *26cm x 24cm*
- £1,580 • London Antique

Westerwald Storage Jar

- *17th Century*

Rhineland blue salt glazed stainwear jar, with pewter cover and handle, with a cartouche on each side depicting William III, within a raised floral design.
- *height 27cm*
- £4,850 • Jonathan Horne

Expert Tips

Originating in the Kangxi period famille vert is a palette of enamels in which a strong green predominates. It influenced the decoration of English soft paste porcelain in the 18th century, before being overtaken by famille rose colours.

Meissen Salts

- *circa 1736-40*

Meissen salts modelled by J.F. Eberlein, basket shaped bowl with rope twist handles painted with a bird, supported by three male caryatid figures terminating in gilt-edged double scroll feet. Completed by Eberlein for the Sulkowsky service. Listed in the factory records of June 1736.

- *height 10cm*
- £1,950   • London Antique

Saltglazed Stainwear Tankard

- *1690*

Westerwald saltglazed stainwear tankard with a pewter cover and cartouches decorating the body showing portraits of royalty.

- *height 17cm*
- £1,650   • Jonathan Horne

Dresden Goblet

- *circa 1880*

Dresden goblet with saucer decorated with cherubs and children playing, with a blue iridescent interior and gilt leaves circling the base and saucer marked with a Crown and Dresden.

- *height 9cm*
- £465   • London Antique

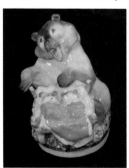

Russian Bear

- *circa 1890*

Russian mother bear with two baby bears in a cradle covered with an orange cover with white spots, set on a circular floral and green base.

- *height 20cm*
- £250   • Gloria Sinclair

Parisian Porcelain Plates

- *1830*

Part of a set of six Parisian porcelain plates with a green border and gilt foliate designs with dragon flies and a central cartouche of painted rose and tulips, cornflowers and pansies.

- *diameter 16cm*
- £980 • Stockspring Antiques

Dresden Group

- *circa 1870*

Dresden group of young girl and two men around a pillar with a cherub holding a rose, on the base is a basket overflowing with pink roses and garlands.

- *height 30cm*
- £675   • Gloria Sinclair

French Bisque Figures ▲

- *circa 1860*
French Bisque courting couple in 18th-century costume in a romantic pose.
- *height 38cm*
- £375   • Gloria Sinclair

Meissen Teabowl and Saucer ▼

- *circa 1745*
Meissen tea bowl and saucer, each decorated with landscape scenes within gilt quatralobe cartouches with dark brown edges, painted with flowers and insects in the manner of J.G. Klinger.
- *height 5cm*
- £2,800   • London Antique

Volkstand Romantic Group ▼

- *circa 1860*
Volkstand romantic couple, the young girl with blonde hair and outstretched arm wearing a pale green dress with pink flowers while a youth wearing a floral tunic has his arm around her waist.
- *height 24cm*
- £475   • Gloria Sinclair

Meissen Lattice-Work Plate ▲

- *circa 1750-75*
Meissen plate with sprays of flowers, and insects and a butterfly, within a lattice-work border marked with blue cross swords.
- *diameter 23cm*
- £245   • London Antique

Rhineland Jug ▲

- *17th century*
Rhineland Westerwald saltglazed stainwear vessel of bulbous form with strap handle, turned neck and a floral pattern on a blue glazed ground.
- *height 26cm*
- £850   • Jonathan Horne

Miniature Cup and Saucer ▶

- *circa 1880*
Miniature cup, saucer and cover with painted panels of figures and flowers on a yellow ground, by Helena Wolfsohn.
- *height 4cm*
- £148   • London Antique

Expert Tips

Pâte-sur-pâte was a method of decoration developed at Minton in the late 1860s. Layers of slip were built up on the unfired ground colour, then tooled to the required design and then fired.

Miniature Flower Pot ▼

- *circa 1900*
Miniature flower pot decorated with flowers, a bird, insects and a butterfly. Made in Paris, France.
- *height 11cm*
- £48   • London Antique

Continental Figurative Group ▼

- *circa 1880*
Continental romantic figurative group modelled as a gentleman seated beside a small round table, wearing a finely painted floral brocade jacket, accompanied by a lady and her mother, on a serpentine base with a central Royal Crest and a gold 'D'.
- 22cm x 25cm
- £255   • London Antique

Expert Tips

Imari refers to a type of Japanese porcelain made from the beginning of the 17th century, which featured decoration based on native textiles and brocade.

Westerwald Ewer ▲

- *1630*
Westerwald blue and white ewer with pewter cover, a central cartouche of Jesus on the cross with two figures either side, ten angels each side of the handle and lion mask decoration on lip.
- *height 23cm*
- £3,300   • Jonathan Horne

Meissen Figurative Group ◄

- *circa 1880*
Meissen figurative group with two children seated around a central column encrusted with flowers, a central cartouche of gilt scrolling, and blue and pink flowers on a circular moulded base with a conversion for an electric light.
- *height 26cm*
- £485   • London Antique

Meissen Teapot ▶

- *circa 1735*
Meissen billet shaped teapot and cover with a painted cartouche on each side, within a purple lustre and gilt scrollwork, encircling a Kauffahoftei scene of merchants and their wares.
- *height 10cm*
- **£6,500**   • **London Antique**

Royal Vienna Huntsman ▲

- *circa 1890*
Royal Vienna prancing white horse with a huntsman and hounds on a white base.
- *height 20cm*
- **£320**   • **Gloria Sinclair**

Dresden Coffee Pot ▲

- *circa 1800*
Dresden white coffee pot decorated with yellow and lilac floral swags and gilt scrolling around the base, handle and spout. With Crown and Dresden on the base.
- *height 19cm*
- **£180**   • **London Antique**

Saltglazed Jug and Cover ▲

- *17th century*
Westerwald blue and cream saltglazed stainwear jug of bulbous form with a pewter handle with cartouches of cherubs with wings and a gentleman with a wig, wearing a hat.
- *height 23cm*
- **£2,800**   • **Jonathan Horne**

Royal Vienna Plate ▲

- *circa 1870*
Royal Vienna plate hand painted with a scene of lovers in a boat, with one cherub holding a basket and the other has his arm around the lady, to the side is a man pulling up the anchor.
- *diameter 24cm*
- **£375**   • **Gloria Sinclair**

Dresden Cup and Saucer ▼

- *circa 1880*
Dresden tall moulded cup and saucer decorated with lilac and orange flowers, with gilt scrolling to the rim and handle, and saucer.
- *height 9cm*
- **£1,125**   • **London Antique**

Meissen Tea Bowl and Saucer ▲

- *circa 1735*
Meissen tea bowl and saucer painted with a continuous scene of a merchant's encampment beside an estuary and the interior with a quayside scene.
- *height 5cm*
- **£2,450** • London Antique

Gilded Plate ▲

- *circa 1814-60*
Meissen plate with heavily gilded water serpents with shells, and a central flower, within a gilt rope border. Blue cross swords.
- *diameter 22cm*
- **£165** • London Antique

Dresden Teapot ▲

- *circa 1843*
Dresden blue miniature square teapot of bulbous form, with a central cartouche of a courting couple in a pastoral setting on a white background, marked A.R. Helena Wolfsohn Dresden.
- *height 9cm*
- **£145** • London Antique

Westerwald Tankard ▶

- *circa 1600*
Blue and cream saltglazed stainware tankard with three cartouches depicting scenes of Frankfurt, with turned decoration, pewter lid and thumb piece.
- *height 17cm*
- **£2,500** • Jonathan Horne

Dresden Trembleuse ▲

- *circa 1880*
Dresden 'trembleuse' cup and saucer decorated with pink, yellow and orange flowers. The saucer has a lattice container to hold the cup in place for trembling hands. Blue crown and 'D' on the base, by Helena Wolfsohn.
- *height 11.5cm*
- **£2,325** • London Antique

Expert Tips

Sèvres porcelain has been extensively faked. Many minor French factories used the interlaced Ls mark on their wares. They are identifiable through their inferior quality.

Meissen Salts ▶

- *circa 1750*
Pair of Meissen salts of a lady and gentleman with tri-cornered hats seated on a pair of baskets.
- *height 15.5cm*
- **£780** • London Antique

Meissen Moulded Dish ◀

- *circa 1835-40*

Meissen dish relief-moulded with gothic leaves and scrolls emanating from a central flower head within a foliate under glaze in gold on a green ground.

- *diameter 32.5cm*
- £275 • London Antique

Sèvres Tray ▼

- *1767*

A scalloped edged Sèvres tray with blue banding and gilding, the centre of the tray decorated with flowers, by Francois le Vavassaur.

- *length 28cm*
- £780 • Stockspring Antiques

Kauffman Self Portrait ▲

- *circa 1985*

Ceramic self portrait by Angelica Kauffman from Germany, set in a carved oval giltwood frame with deep moulding and central ribbon.

- *17.5cm x 12cm*
- £985 • London Antique

Berlin Luisentasse ◀

- *circa 1890s*

Berlin cabinet cup and saucer (Luisentasse), the cup applied with a biscuit profile bust of Queen Louise of Prussia to sinister, on a vermiculated gilt oval medallion, the rims with a gilt formal foliate border.

- *height 10cm*
- £995 • London Antique

Berlin Cup and Saucer ▲

- *circa 1850*

Berlin cup and saucer, with gilt foliate medallions on a pale salmon pink ground.

- *height 6cm*
- £235 • London Antique

Hochst Group ▶

- *1780*

A group depicting figures of children playing set on a naturalistically formed base.

- *height 14cm*
- £1,700 • Stockspring Antiques

Meissen Coffee Pot ◀

- *circa 1745*
Meissen pear shaped coffee pot with a scrolled handle and satyr mask to the base of the spout, finely painted with floral sprays, with crossed swords. Mark 'Z' incised on the rim of the foot.
- *height 20cm*
- £3,350 • London Antique

Chantilly Mug ▲

- *1735*
Chantilly white porcelain mug decorated with a hand painted chinoiserie design of bamboo and flowers.
- *height 9cm*
- £1,680 • Stockspring Antiques

Westerwald Mug ◀

- *17th century*
Westerwald blue and cream saltglazed stainwear tankard with ear shaped handle and a central frieze of figures in relief, between turned banding.
- *height 12cm*
- £660 • Jonathan Horne

Expert Tips

Samson copied Chinese and Japanese wares, sometimes very convincingly, and used a smooth, well controlled, slightly blue glaze.

Miniature Cup and Saucer ▲

- *circa 1899*
Miniature Dresden coffee cup and saucer encrusted with pale lilac flowers, raised on six straight circular legs.
- *height 4cm*
- £185 • London Antique

Bear Inkwell ▲

- *circa 1890*
Russian group with two bears eating strawberry jam from bowls, and a log in the centre, and on the lid is a large ladle covering an ink well, set on a moulded white base.
- *height 15cm*
- £280 • Gloria Sinclair

Meissen Shell Salt ▲

- *circa 1755*
Meissen shell salt in the form of
an upturned shell the interior
painted with a spray of puce, iron-
red and yellow flowers with
scattered sprigs, on scroll moulded
feet, blue crossed swords mark.
- *diameter 10.2cm*
- **£1,200** • **London Antique**

French Cup and Saucer ▲

- *circa 1860*
French cup, saucer and plate,
centred with a cartouche of a
chateau with gilt banding.
- *plate diameter 18.5cm*
- **£140**   • **A. Piotrowski**

Nudenmiller Sauce Boat ▲

- **1780**
Nudenmiller sauce boat with
scrolled handle and shaped rim,
with floral sprays and gilding.
- *width 15cm*
- **£400** • **Stockspring Antiques**

Dutch Delft Kylins ▼

- **1860**
One of a pair of Dutch Delft Kylins
decorated with a blue and white
floral design, seated with their
mouths open.
- *height 32cm*
- **£795**   • **Gloria Sinclair**

Limoges plate ▲

- **1895**
Limoges plate enamelled with a
floral spray of crimson and pink
flowers with green and gold
leaves, within a heavily gilded
border.
- *diameter 23cm*
- **£115**   • **A.Piotrowski**

Irish Belleek Basket ▲

- *circa 1880*
Irish Belleek moulded cream
latticework basket with three
bunches of roses and daisies.
- *height 5cm*
- **£155** • **London Antique**

Sèvres Dinner Plate ▲

- *circa 1814*
Sèvres dinner plate decorated
with cherubs holding roses, on
the side is the royal crest of M
Imple de Sèvres, lst Empire.
- *diameter 24cm*
- **£225** • **London Antique**

Meissen Tea Bowl and Saucer ◀

- *circa 1750*
Meissen tea bowl and saucer
painted with a central cartouche
of merchants' boats, with a yellow
background and purple flowers.
- *height 5cm*
- **£1,950** • London Antique

Saltglazed Vessel ▼

- **1670**
Westerwald saltglazed stainwear
vessel of bulbous form, with
turned decoration and floral
designs between courtly figures.
- *height 20cm*
- **£650** • Jonathan Horne

Limoges Plate ▲

- **1895**
Limoges plate enamelled with a
floral spray of chrysanthemums
on a cream ground within a
heavily gilded border.
- *diameter 23cm*
- **£115** • A. Piotrowski

Lion and The Hare ▲

- *circa 1890*
Russian lion seated and
holding a white hare
by his neck.
- *height 15cm*
- **£240** • Gloria Sinclair

Dresden Cup and Saucer ◀

- *circa 1900*
Dresden cup and saucer standing
on three paw feet decorated with
pink panels of courting couples
and flowers divided by gilt
scrolling design.
- *height 4cm*
- **£235** • London Antique

Dresden Groups ▶

- *circa 1870*
A pair of Dresden groups showing
amorous courting couples.
- *height 22cm*
- **£500** • Gloria Sinclair

Expert Tips

*English slipwares and German
stonewares have been honestly
copied as well as faked. Copies
of Raeren Brown stoneware are
often very close to the style of
the originals, but are marked by
the maker, for example, H.S.
for the pottery maker Hubert
Schiffer.*

Islamic Ceramics

Persian Bowl ▼

- *circa 12th century*
Persian bowl with a black and
blue circular design.
- *diameter 20cm*
- £1,200   • Sultani Antique

Bamiyan Bowl ▲

- *11–13th century AD*
Pottery Bamiyan bowl from
Afghanistan with a deep
turquoise glaze.
- *diameter 17cm*
- £600   • Pars

Turquoise Bamiyan Ewer ▼

- *11–13th century AD*
Turquoise Bamyan earthenware
ewer, with strap handle, the spout
in the form of a cows' head, with
an unusual rim and a turquoise
glaze.
- *height 22.5cm*
- £4,000   • Pars

Persian Water Vessel ◄

- *circa 800 BC*
Persian water vessel in the form
of a duck with an elongated beak
with a turquoise glaze.
- *height 15cm*
- £8,000   • Sultani Antique

Timori Bowl ▼

- *circa 15–16th century*
Timori bowl decorated with a
blue hexagonal design around the
inside of the rim, and a central
blue and white flower design,
with a central turquoise circle
with a black cross.
- *diameter 19cm*
- £900   • Rasoul Gallery

Rose Water Bottle ▲

- *circa 14th century*
Rose water bottle from Heart, the
West of Afghanistan. Tiamurid
Dynasty, in a style imitating
Chinese porcelain in the City of
Heraz and decorated with an
Islamic pattern, with a floral leaf
design on the base.
- *height 10cm*
- £800   • Rasoul Gallery

Pre-Ottoman Vase ▲

- *circa 10th century*
Green monochrome vessel of
baluster form with two moulded
handles with extensive open
work to the body.
- *height 35.5cm*
- £800   • Pars

Nishapur Bowl ▶
- *11–13th century AD*
Nishapur slip ware earthenware
bowl of shallow design with a
green, cream and brown glaze
with an incised petal design.
- *diameter 26cm*
- £350 • Pars

Persian Vessel ▲
- *13th century AD*
Persian olive green glazed pottery
vessel with four small moulded
handles with an incised design on
the body with stops to the base.
- *19.5cm x 11cm*
- £700 • Pars

Nishapur Bowl ◀
- *circa 9–10th century*
Nishapur, Persian buffware
pottery bowl, of deep rounded
form with slightly inverted rim
decorated in manganese brown
and yellow, with a bold seated
female figure wearing a shirt with
floral designs and spotted
trousers, holding a flower and
looking into a mirror surrounded
by Kufic inscriptions and small
arabesque motifs.
- *diameter 21.6cm*
- £1,500 • Rasoul Gallery

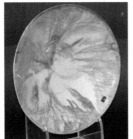

Gorgon Ewer ▲
- *circa 12th century*
A 12th century Gorgon ewer
with strap handle, fine
iridescence on a blue ground and
stops to the base.
- *height 16cm*
- £4,000 • Yacobs Gallery

Monochrome Pottery Jug ◀
- *circa 12th century*
Monochrome pottery jug with
strap handle and thumb piece
with a pierced transparent floral
design, raised on a pedestal base.
- *height 18cm*
- £1,500 • Sultani Antique

Polychrome Islamic Bowl ▲
- *circa 10th century*
A polychrome Islamic bowl
Manaie with four figures on
horseback within cartouches on a
cream ground.
- *diameter 22cm*
- £3,500 • Solaimani Gallery

Gold Lustre Bowl ▶

- *circa 12th century*
Gold lustre bowl with ten panels decorated with a floral design, and a lady seated in the centre.
- *diameter 17cm*
- £4,500 • Sultani Antique

Kashan Vase ▲

- *circa 12th century*
An Islamic vase of bulbous proportions with thumb piece. The body with circular bands of writing and floral designs, raised on a pedestal foot, with stops to the base.
- *height 13cm*
- £1,200 • Solaimani Gallery

Lead-Glazed Bowl ▲

- *11–13th century AD*
Nishapur earthenware glazed bowl decorated with a stylised leaf design, in a ochre, green and brown glaze.
- *diameter 19cm*
- £300 • Pars

Six-Sided Star Bowl ▲

- *circa 12th century*
Small brown glazed bowl with a six-sided star in a cream glaze inside, with scrolling around the inside of the rim.
- *diameter 14cm*
- £800 • Sultani Antique

Bamiyan Bowl ▼

- *12th century*
Bamiyan pottery bowl decorated with a green and brown star, and stylized leaf designs, over a cream underglaze.
- *diameter 17.5cm*
- £600 • Rasoul Gallery

Terracotta Ewer ▲

- *circa 12th century*
Terracotta small ewer of baluster form, with a long upturned spout and strap handle, with a chevron design running around the middle of the body, raised on a circular foot.
- *height 19.5cm*
- £400 • Rasoul Gallery

Persian Pottery Dish ▲

- *10–11th century AD*
Large pottery dish decorated with a green and brown glaze with an inscribed circular design with beading.
- *diameter 34cm*
- £1,500 • Pars

Persian Model ◄

- *11–13th century AD*
Persian model of a stable with a turquoise glaze and fine iridescence, with numerous models of animals applied to the surface.
- *8cm x 14cm*
- £10,000   • Pars

Bamiyan Water Vessel ►

- *circa 10th century*
Afghanistan water vessel of globular form with a strap handle, short neck with a pinched lip, and a dark green glaze with stops to the base.
- *height 16.6cm*
- £500   • Sultani Antique

Kashan Vase ▲

- *circa 12th century*
12th century Kashan vase of baluster form, with a blue linear design on a white ground.
- *height 10cm*
- £3,500   • Yacobs Gallery

Islamic Bowl ▲

- *circa 12th century*
An Islamic bowl with a broad rim with Kufic writing set within the border, with yellow designs.
- *diameter 30cm*
- £2,800   • Solaimani Gallery

Islamic Fluted Vase ▲

- *17th century AD*
Vase with stylised pheasant amongst cherry blossoms, within an arched border, with an unusual off centre fluted neck.
- *33cm x 16cm*
- £1,500   • Pars

Bamiyan Storage Jar ►

- *circa 12th century*
Small heavily glazed turquoise Bamiyan storage jar, with stops to the base.
- *height 11.5cm*
- £400   • Rasoul Gallery

Bamiyan Pottery Bowl ▲

- *12th century*
Bamiyan pottery bowl decorated
with a green and brown star
pattern with a cream underglaze.
- *diameter 19cm*
- £1,000　　• Rasoul Gallery

Persian Dish ▲

- *circa 10th century*
Persian bowl with three panels
with Kufic inscriptions in blue
and yellow ochre.
- *diameter 29cm*
- £3,000　　• Sultani Antique

Guazin Water Jug ◀

- *circa 12th century*
Pottery water jug from Guazin
with unusual brown, black and
sandstone glaze.
- *height 21cm*
- £1,200　　• Sultani Antique

Bamiyan Turquoise Bowl ▼

- *circa 12th century*
Small Bamiyan turquoise bowl,
centered with a small bird, with a
ribbed design radiating from the
centre.
- *height 6cm*
- £500　　• Rasoul Gallery

Nishapur Vessel ▲

- *11–13th century AD*
Nishapur pottery dish known as
silhouette ware, decorated with a
green glaze and a cream lotus
design in the centre, raised on a
splayed foot.
- *diameter 22cm*
- £550　　　　　• Pars

Kashan Jar ▲

- *12–13th century*
A small Kasham jar of bulbous
form with strap handle and acorn
thumb piece in a cobalt-blue
glaze.
- *height 13cm*
- £800　　　　　• Pars

Expert Tips

*The French art nouveau glass,
by makers such as Gallé, was
heavily influenced by the
technique and style of early
Islamic potters, in particular
their use of translucent and
iridescent decoration and
enamelling.*

Kufic Bowl ▶

- *11–13 century AD*
Turquoise pottery bowl of deep proportions with Kufic script running around the body, with turned decoration and a wide splayed lip.
- *diameter 22cm*
- £1,200 • Pars

Persian Bowl ▲

- *10–11th century AD*
Persian pottery bowl with a cream glaze and two concentric bands bearing inscriptions in a cobalt blue glaze.
- *diameter 20cm*
- £1,000 • Pars

Expert Tips

If you are intending to buy a piece that is quite common you must make sure that it is in optimum condition, with no cracks. On the other hand a rare piece with a crack can still be quite valuable.

Water Jug ◀

- *circa 12th century*
Persian small water vessel, of conical form with strap handle, brown circular designs, and raised on a circular foot.
- *height 14.4cm*
- £250 • Rasoul Gallery

Samakan Bowl ▼

- *circa 11th century*
Central Asian bowl, probably Samakan, with a floral pattern and Kufic inscriptions, translated as, "Prosperity and Health to the owner of the bowl".
- *diameter 19cm*
- £1,200 • Rasoul Gallery

Persian Bowl ◀

- *12th century*
Persian bowl decorated with a central figure of a lady and inscribed with Kufic and Persian writing.
- *diameter 21cm*
- £2,20 • Sultani Antique

Persian Water Vessel ▲

- *circa 12th–13th century*
Persian water vessel of baluster form with strap handle and thumb piece, decorated with birds and circular designs, with Kufic and Arabic inscriptions with a pink lustre glaze.
- *height 21cm*
- £6,500 • Sultani Antique

Timori Bowl ▲

- *circa 15–16th century*
Timori bowl decorated with a blue glazed hexagonal design around the inside, with a central blue, white and black flower in the center.
- *diameter 19cm*
- £1,000 • Rasoul Gallery

Minoae Bowl ▲

- *12th century*
Minoae bowl with black and blue banding and a central design.
- *diameter 21.5cm*
- £1,500   • Sultani Antique

Turqouise Bamiyan Bowl ▲

- *12th century*
Turquoise Bamiyan bowl, decorated with a stylized fish, with the head of a lion.
- *diameter 12cm*
- £1,000   • Rasoul Gallery

Iranian Bowl ▲

- *12–13th century AD*
Iranian lead glazed earthenware bowl with an outer geometric design, within circular bands of blue and red, with a stylised floral design to the centre.
- *diameter 18cm*
- £400   • Pars

Harat Bowl ▼

- *circa 12th century*
Turquoise Harat bowl with a raised lip with black banding and Arabic writing running around the body, raised on a pedestal foot.
- *height 12cm*
- £1,200   • Sultani Antique

Early Saljuq Vessel ▶

- *9–10th century AD*
Early Saljuq Islamic pottery vessel of bulbous form with strap handle and panels of pierced designs, raised on a pedestal foot.
- *height 15cm*
- £450   • Pars

Ghaznavi Herat Water Jug ▲

- *circa 12th century*
Ghaznavi Herat water jug of bulbous form with a turquoise glaze with horizontal black stripes, raised on a splayed foot.
- *height 15cm*
- £700   • Sultani Antique

Pre-Ottoman Terracotta Vessel ▲

- *circa 10th century*
Terracotta vessel of bulbous form with wide lip and double handles, decorated with openwork, raised on a circular foot ring.
- *height 35.5cm.*
- £500   • Pars

Persian Bowl ▼

- *circa 10th century*
10th century Persian bowl with Kufic inscriptions within a deep border on a cream glazed base.
- *diameter 8cm*
- £6,000   • Yacobs Gallery

Gold Lustre Bowl ▲

- *circa 12th century*
Small Persian gold lustre bowl
with a scrolled design running
around the rim with a band of
Kufic writing below.
- *diameter 7.5cm*
- **£4,000** • **Sultani Antique**

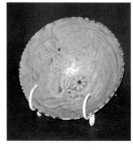

Persian Lustre Bowl ▲

- *circa 12th century*
Turquoise bowl decorated with a
raised design of two intertwined
lions.
- *diameter 15cm*
- **£600** • **Sultani Antique**

Expert Tips

*When buying pieces in the
country of origin ensure that
you are fully acquainted with
the law and up to date on the
paperwork required. Also make
sure that you have all the
documentation required to
authenticate the item.*

Central Asian Bowl ▲

- *11th century*
Leaf pattern bowl from central
Asia with brown Arabesque
design inside.
- *diameter 18.5cm*
- **£550** • **Rasoul Gallery**

Safaviv Box ▲

- *circa 14th century*
Safaviv cosmetic box decorated
with a deer in a cobalt blue glaze
in a romantic setting.
- *11cm x 15cm*
- **£900** • **Rasoul Gallery**

Small Bamiyan Bowl ▼

- *circa 12th century*
Bamiyan turquoise bowl with a
band of Kufic writing on the
inside of the splayed lip, centred
with a star design.
- *height 7cm*
- **£550** • **Rasoul Gallery**

Persian Vessel ▼

- *circa 12th century*
Small Persian vessel of bulbous
form, with four molded handles,
raised on a pedestal foot with
stops to the base.
- *height 7.5cm*
- **£350** • **Rasoul Gallery**

Persian Ceramic Bowl ▼

- *circa 12th century*
Medium sized Persian bowl with
Arabic inscriptions on the inside
of the rim and a peacock and
three Persian ladies, with a gold
lustre finish.
- *height 10cm*
- **£2,700** • **Sultani Antique**

Oriental Ceramics

Mandarin Vases ▲

- *circa 1780*

Pair of Mandarin vases and covers
with figurative scenes reserved on
a gilt ground with rouge de vert
wirh diaper covers showing small
landscape scenes and dogs. With
Fo. Qianlong period finials.
- *height 37cm*
- £20,000   • Cohen & Cohen

Satsuma Vases ▲

- *circa 1870*

A pair of gold Satsuma vases of
baluster form, painted with holy
men and a dragon who keeps
away the evil spirits and brings
prosperity to the family.
- *height 23cm*
- £450   • Barrett/Towning

Swato Dish ▼

- *15th century*

A slip decorated Swato dish,
raised from a shipwreck off the
coast of East Timor, from the late
Ming Dynasty. The centre is
decorated with a spray of
chrysanthemums, in a stippled
and feather technique, the simple
scroll border with stippled
blooms, all on an even cobalt -
blue ground. The underside is
plain, with a grit base.
- *diameter 38cm*
- £650   • Ormonde Gallery

Ming Dish ▲

- *16-17th century*

Ming dish with scalloped rim and
a raised floral design under a
green glaze.
- *diameter 15cm*
- £3,800   • Ormonde Gallery

Transitional Food Jar ▼

- *1640*

Blue and white transitional food
jar of ovoid form, with a floral
design running around the
shoulders, and figures in a
pastoral setting running around
the body.
- *height 16cm*
- £550   • Ormonde Gallery

Chinese Bowl ◀

- *circa 1736-1795*

Rare salesman's bowl showing
different patterns available to
customers ordering from China.
Qianlong Period.
- *diameter 11cm*
- £3,000   • Cohen & Cohen

Cylindrical Hat Stand ▲

- *circa 19th century*
Cylindrical shape porcelain hat
stand painted with a pink cherry
blossom tree with a song bird,
sitting above a pond, with a poem
dedicated to the owner with leaf
shape openings for airing. Seal of
manufacturer on the base. Ex
Guonxi period.
- *height 29cm*
- **£385**   • **Iren Rakosa**

Chinese Sauce Tureen ▶

- *circa 1760*
Very rare Chinese export sauce
tureen and cover, modelled as a
sitting quail on its nest and
painted in iron red, black and
green. Qianlong period.
- *height 9cm*
- **£6,700**   • **Cohen & Cohen**

Expert Tips

*To authenticate a piece of Ming
blue and white ware, it is
necessary to study the following
aspects of the piece: painting
techniques, wash methods,
lines, brush strokes, form and
shape, clay and glazes used and
the evolution of motifs.*

Chinese Vase ▼

- *circa 1770*
A fine quality Chinese export
porcelain, two handled vase,
decorated with a turquoise
chicken skin ground and bright
'Mandarin' panels. Quianlong
Period.
- *height 24cm*
- **£420**   • **Andrew Dando**

Famille Rose Teapot ◀

- *circa 1790*
Famille rose teapot with a scene
after Watteau of Europe, in a
garden watched by Pierot.
Qianlong Period.
- *height 12cm*
- **£1,000**   • **Cohen & Cohen**

Chinese Spoon Dish ▲

- *circa 1760*
Miniature Chinese export spoon
dish with shaped rim and a
central panel of fruit and flowers
in a bowl.
- *length 13cm*
- **£240**   • **Andrew Dando**

Annamese Dish ▲

- *12th century*
Annamese dish with scalloped
edge with a bold chrysanthemum
in the centre, under a olive-green
glaze.
- *diameter 15cm*
- **£250**   • **Ormonde Gallery**

Meiping Vase ▶

- *circa 1745*
Famille rose Meiping vase of globular form, boldly painted with a phoenix among branches of prunus blossom. From the Qianlong period.
- *height 34cm*
- £9,100 • Cohen & Cohen

Lemonade Jug ▲

- *circa 1780-1820*
Very rare (so far only one known) Canton enamel lemonade jug decorated with a pastoral scene and figures. The yellow background is decorated with foliate designs and pink blossom, with a lip incorporating a blue foliate design, with a chrysanthemum to the centre.
- *height 18cm*
- £1,200 • Ormonde Gallery

Octagonal Meat Dish ▼

- *circa 1760*
Famille rose octagonal meat dish, brightly enamelled with butterflies feeding from fruit and flowers within a mottled border of pale green and brown. From the Qianlong period.
- *length 33cm*
- £1,300 • Cohen & Cohen

Famille Rose Plate ◀

- *circa 1760*
Chinese export porcelain famille rose pattern plate.
- *diameter 32cm*
- £340 • Andrew Dando

Chinese Coffee Cup ▲

- *circa 1760*
Chinese export coffee cup of unusual size with ear shaped handle and a famille rose pattern.
- *height 8cm*
- £95 • Andrew Dando

Glazed Jug ▲

- *11th century*
Globular shaped jug with strap handle, wide splayed neck, lobbed body and spout, raised on a circular foot with stops to the base.
- *height 24cm*
- £950 • Ormonde Gallery

Chinese Export Vases ▲
- *circa 1780*
A pair of Chinese export vases and stands in Mandarin palette on turquoise ground, each with a tapering square section and butterfly handles. Qianlong period.
- *height 24cm*
- £24,000 • Cohen & Cohen

Sawankalok Bowl ▲
- *15th century Tia*
Sawankalok green bowl with a wide lip with a moulded rim, above a stylised lotus flower design, centred with a chrysanthemum.
- *diameter 26cm*
- £280 • Ormonde Gallery

Expert Tips

Early Ming potters used calligraphic strokes to draw the motifs. The pieces are thicker and more translucent than late Ming pieces which have a thinner, transparent glaze.

Chinese Teapoy ▲
- *circa 1790*
Chinese export polychrome teapoy and cover with a scene after Watteau of Europeans in a garden, watched by a Pierrot. Qianlong period.
- *height 16cm*
- £1,750 • Cohen & Cohen

Incense Burner ▼
- *5th century*
Green circular incense burner of two tiers with a dog on the upper section, the whole resting on three feet.
- *height 7cm*
- £150 • Ormonde Gallery

Chinese Bowl ▼
- *circa 18th century*
Elegant blue bulbous bowl supported on three button feet.
- *diameter 24cm*
- £480 • Iren Rakosa

Quianlong Plates ▼
- *1760*
One of a pair of Chinese export porcelain plates, painted with elaborate scenes within border in famille rose enamels.
- *diameter 21.5cm*
- £750 • Andrew Dando

Sung Dynasty Bowl ◄
- *11-12th century*
Sung Dynasty bowl with an incised repetitive design of stylised flowers, under a green glaze.
- *diameter 20.4cm*
- £400 • Ormonde Gallery

Chinese Tankard ▼

- *circa 1770*
Export Chinese porcelain tankard with 'Mandrin' style panel depicting a courtly scene.
- *height 24cm*
- **£235** • Andrew Dando

Desk Set ▲

- *circa 1760*
Rare and unusual famille rose desk set from the Qianlong period. Comprising five quill holders, two inkwells with pewter liners and a covered box.
- *height 6cm*
- **£4,800** • Cohen & Cohen

Oriental Cup ▼

- *16th century*
Blue and white cup with a wide splayed rim, with a blue lattice design running around the exterior, above a song bird with prunus blossom.
- *height 5cm*
- **£450** • Ormonde Gallery

Tea Bowl and Saucer ▲

- *circa 1735*
Chinese export porcelain tea bowl and saucer, profusely gilded with floral sprays and cartouches of prunus with a central panel of a Chinese gentleman.
- *diameter of cup 6cm*
- **£225** • Andrew Dando

Chinese Marriage Plate ▲

- *circa 1750*
Exceptionally rare Chinese export marriage plate made for the Dutch market, with a polychrome depiction of the ship Slooten, from the Qianlong period.
- *diameter 36cm*
- **£12,500** • Cohen & Cohen

Nanking Bowl and Saucer ▲

- *1790*
Nanking blue and white bowl and saucer with pagoda scenes and later English gilding.
- *diameter of saucer 13cm*
- **£125** • Andrew Dando

Sauce Tureen and Cover ▶

- *circa 1765*
Rare Chinese export sauce tureen, cover and stand of English creamware form. Painted with the arms of Parker imp. Nesbitt, within a diaper border. Qianlong period. Made for the widow of the second Earl of Macclesfield (Parker), she was a Nesbitt.
- *height of tureen 13cm*
- **£16,000** • Cohen & Cohen

Chinese Dinner Plate ◀

- *circa 1740*
Fine Chinese export famille rose dinner plate from the Qianlong period, painted with the 'Arbour Pattern' after Cornelis Pronk.
- *diameter 23cm*
- £5,200 • Cohen & Cohen

Chinese Candlesticks ▼

- *circa 1770*
Pair of famille rose candlesticks of European silver form, on octagonal bases, painted with Chinese domestic scenes on a gilt ground. Qianlong period.
- *height 18cm*
- £10,700 • Cohen & Cohen

Storage Jar ▼

- 1640
Blue and white storage jar of bulbous proportions decorated with a repetitive pattern of blue flowers on a white ground.
- *height 35cm*
- £550 • Ormonde Gallery

Stoneware Jar ▲

- *Tang 618-906 AD*
Stoneware jar of globular form, with a flared neck and an uneven straw coloured glaze around the middle from the Tang Dynasty, raised on a circular foot.
- *height 12cm*
- £352 • Ormonde Gallery

Famille Rose Ewer ▼

- *circa 1760*
Famille rose ewer and cover with C shape handle and matching basin all painted with flowering chrysanthemum growing from rockwork. Qianlong period.
- *height of ewer 22cm*
- £5,000 • Cohen & Cohen

Expert Tips

The early Ming period is marked by a strict control of political and cultural development, for example, a decree was issued in 1371 during the reign of Hong Wu forbidding certain subjects such as previous emperors, queens, lions or saints on porcelains.

Famille Rose Plate ▲
- *circa 1760*
One of a pair of Chinese export plates, painted with elaborate scenes within borders in famille rose enamel.
- *diameter 22cm*
- £750 pair ● Andrew Dando

Chinese Soup Plate ▲
- *1775*
Octagonal Chinese export soft paste porcelain soup plate.
- *diameter 23cm*
- £150 ● Andrew Dando

Oriental Jar ▲
- *circa 16th century*
Small blue and white jar with an inverted rim and tapered body, decorated with a repeated design of fir trees.
- *height 5cm*
- £240 ● Ormonde Gallery

Inkwell ▲
- *Sung Dynasty 11-12th century*
Ink well from the Sung Dynasty of compressed globular form with a stylised flower pattern in relief, under a green glaze.
- *height 10cm*
- £350 ● Ormonde Gallery

Chinese Export Basin ▲
- *circa 1725*
Yongzheng period Chinese export basin, richly decorated in rouge de fer and gilt, with the arms of Mertins imp. Peck. The border is decorated with famille rose flower heads.
- *diameter 39.5cm*
- £8,500 ● Cohen & Cohen

Grisaille Chinese Plate ▶
- *circa 1750*
Important Chinese export plate decorated en grisaille with a portrait of Martin Luther above a panel of Christ and his disciples all within a gilt scroll border. Qianlong Period.
- *diameter 24cm*
- £2,250 ● Cohen & Cohen

Chinese Chocolate Pot ◄

- *circa 1775*
Unusual Chinese export bulbous chocolate pot.
- *height 19.5cm*
- £9,000   • Cohen & Cohen

Tea Bowl and Saucer ▲

- *circa 1770*
Famille rose tea bowl and saucer, decorated with a group of European figures in a garden within a gilt, pink and grisaille border. Qianlong period.
- *height of cup 4.5cm
diameter of saucer 13cm*
- £950   • Cohen & Cohen

Famille Rose Plate ▼

- *circa 1740*
One of a pair of fine and rare famille rose botanical plates, each vividly painted with a cornucopia of European flowers, made in the Qianlong period.
- *diameter 23cm*
- £10,700   • Cohen & Cohen

Chinese Export Plate ▲

- *circa 1760*
Chinese export famille rose porcelain plate with floral sprays and gilding.
- *diameter 15cm*
- £375   • Andrew Dando

Expert Tips

During the early Ming period the majority of the wares produced tended to be of a functional nature such as bowls, plates, covered jars and incense burners, with only a narrow range of motifs.

Chinese Hat Stand ▶

- *circa 19th century*
Porcelain hat stand of cylindrical form with a polychrome glaze of scholarly objects, flora and Buddhist symbols. The stand has a six leaf shape opening for airing. Seal at the base. Ex-Guonxi period.
- *height 29cm*
- £350   • Iren Rakosa

Clocks, Watches & Scientific Instruments

The world of the scientific instrument is fascinating and the subject is still in its infancy as far as collectors are involved.

Einstein once said, "Space and time are modes by which we think, not conditions under which we live." The time that we know through clocks and calendars was invented. The measurement of time is an ancient science, though many of its discoveries are relatively recent. The Cro-Magnons recorded the phases of the moon some 30,000 years ago, but the first minutes were counted accurately only 400 years ago. From the mysteries of our past come the wonders of Newgrange in Ireland and Stonehenge in England. These Neolithic peoples' industry and minds laid out the foundation of understanding time. Timekeeping is a mirror reflecting the progress of science and civilisation. Today a clock is one of the most personal of antiques. For many years it was one of the few items, besides the home and the bed, to be mentioned in a will.

Clocks

English Longcase Clock ◀
- *circa 1800*
Flame mahogany English 8-day longcase clock with brass square dial and subsidiary silvered second ring, the florally engraved centre dial inscribed, 'John Smith, Chester'.
- *220cm x 56cm*
- £5,900 • Gütlin Clocks

Chagrin Mantle Clock ▲
- *1920*
English made chagrin leather cased clock, with a white face and white ivory stringing, the whole resting on ivory feet.
- *height 14cm*
- £2,750 • Bentleys

Scottish Longcase Clock ▲
- *circa 1830*
Flame mahogany belly door longcase clock by Christie and Barrie of Abroath, with Scottish 8- day, break arch, painted dial. 'The Cotters Saturday Night' painted in the break arch with four seasons to the corner spandrels. 8- day movement with subsidiary seconds and date.
- *220cm x 38cm*
- £6,500 • Gütlin Clocks

Mahogany Longcase Clock ▼

- *circa 1770*

A George III mahogany five pillar brass dial longcase clock with 8-day brass dial movement with silver chapter ring. Subsidiary seconds and date with separate engraved makers name plaque. Chimes the hours on a bell.

- *224cm x 56cm*
- £9,500   • Gütlin Clocks

English Bracket Clock ▼

- *circa 1840*

Mahogany English bracket clock by 'Taylor' of Bristol. The twin gut fusee movement with shoulder plates and hour strike on a bell. White painted convex dial signed Taylor of Bristol with black spade hands.

- *53.5cm x 30cm x 18cm*
- £3,500   • Gütlin Clocks

Victorian Bracket Clock ▲

- *circa 1870*

An English triple fusee black ebonised quarter chiming Victorian bracket clock. The 3 train movement striking the quarters on 8 bells with hour strike on a gong. The brass dial with silvered and engraved chapter ring, silvered strike/silent ring and finely chiselled brass spandrels.

- *38cm x 30.5cm*
- £5,500   • Gütlin Clocks

Bracket Clock ▲

- *circa 1850*

Burr walnut double fusee English bracket clock by 'Payne & Co', 163 New Bond Street, London. Numbered clock No.3234. The double chain fusee 8-day numbered and signed English movement.

- *43.5cm x 30.5cm*
- £6,500   • Gütlin Clocks

Grand Sonnerie Bracket Clock ▼

- *circa 1750*

Oak cased original verge escapement Austrian Grand Sonnerie bracket clock. The triple fusee Austrian movement of short duration (30-hour) with original verge escapement. Makers name plague signed 'Augustin Heckel'.

- *53.5cm x 25.5cm*
- £3,90   • Gütlin Clocks

Timepiece Clock ▼

- *circa 1830-35*

Victorian flame mahogany unnamed single fusee timepiece clock, the single gut fusee 8-day English movement with original pendulum holdfast.

- *29cm x 17.5cm*
- £1,800   • Gütlin Clocks

Victorian Bracket Clock ▲

- *circa 1890-1900*
Small Victorian mahogany balloon style, English bracket clock, with a boxwood inlay. The 8- day numbered and stamped French movement chiming the hours and half hours on a gong,
- *28cm x 17.5cm*
- £1,200   • Gütlin Clocks

English Bracket Clock ▲

- *circa 1880-90*
English ebonised and gilt bronze mounted substantial 3-train 10-bell or 4-gongs (Westminster chime) bracket clock. Retailed in Scotland by 'Hamilton, Crighton & Co, 41 George Street, Edinburgh.
- *68.5cm x 33cm*
- £6,500   • Gütlin Clocks

Oak Bracket Clock ▼

- *circa 1870*
English oak quarter striking 8-bell bracket clock retailed by 'Christie', Cannon Street, London. The 8-day 6-pillar chain fusee signed Victorian movement of large size chiming the quarters every 15-minutes on 8-bells with hour strike on a large gong.
- *71cm x 43cm*
- £4,500   • Gütlin Clocks

Cathedral Clock ▼

- *circa 1880-90*
Victorian yellow oak, Gothic English substantial 3-train, 8-bell (Westminster chime) bracket clock, modelled as a cathedral with English three train, 6-pillar, chain fusee movement.
- *81.5cm x 25cm*
- £6,500   • Gütlin Clocks

Ting-Tang Bracket Clock ▲

- *circa 1890*
Oak German quarter striking ting-tang bracket clock by W. & H. with 8-day quarter striking German movement. The silvered dial with separate chapter ring subsidiaries and retailers plaque engraved 'Bonner', Brighton.
- *35.5cm x 28cm*
- £1,600   • Gütlin Clocks

Mahogany Bracket Clock ▲

- *circa 1900*
Mahogany and gilt mounted English quarter (Westminster chime) bracket clock, the substantial triple chain fusee movement chiming on 8-bells or 4-gongs.
- *84cm x 43.5cm.*
- £13,300   • Gütlin Clocks

133

French Lyre Clock ▲

- *1880*
French Ormolu mounted birds
eye maple, lyre clock with foliate
ormolu mounts.
- *height 44cm*
- £2,000 • Vincent Freeman

Skeleton Clock ▲

- *circa 1860*
English cathedral two train
skeleton clock modelled as a
cathedral encased in dome
shaped glass case on a moulded
marble base.
- *height 65cm*
- £4,000 • Vincent Freeman

French Zodiac Clock ▼

- *1885*
French clock made for the
Spanish market with barometer,
thermometers and revolving signs
of the zodiac. The clock is
encased within a globe of the
world with a silver cloud
formation running through the
centre of the piece.
- *height 43cm*
- £3,000 • Vincent Freeman

German Porcelain Clock ▼

- *circa 1880*
German porcelain clock modelled
as a cherub sitting in a chariot
drawn by two lions, raised on a
painted rectangular base with a
painted panel of a landscape.
- *51cm x 46cm*
- £3,500 • Vincent Freeman

French Clock Set ▲

- *1800*
French slate mantle clock set,
with eight day movement and
inlaid with brass. With two side
urns, the base of each urn
decorated in brass with a scene of
children playing within a forest
setting with animals.
- *height 46cm*
- £375 • Julian Smith Antiques

Viennese Clock ▲

- *1880*
Vienna clock with porcelain
cartouches of celestial scenes
with blue enamelled architectural
pillars and gilding, raised on gilt
ball feet.
- *height 40cm*
- £4,000 • Vincent Freeman

First Empire Mantle Clock ▼

• *circa 1830*
Gilt ormolu and bronze first empire French mantle clock by 'Douillon'. The case with two cherubs holding the face with gilt swag mounts in the centre. 8-day silk suspension movement, silvered watersilk dial signed by retailer. Chimes hours & half hours on a bell.
• *46cm x 47cm*
• £2,400 • Gütlin Clocks

French Clock ▼

• *circa 1880*
French gilt brass glass clock with signed ivory miniature pendulum surrounded by diamonte stones. The pendulum with a hand painted miniature ivory portrait of a maiden. 8-day movement by 'Mougin'.
• *30.5cm x 18.5cm*
• £1,500 • Gütlin Clocks

Gilt Ormulu Mantle Clock ▲

• *circa 1860*
Gilt ormolu French mantle clock with 8-day movement chiming hours and half hours on a bell. The case in the form of a wine barrel with cherubs sitting on the barrel, supported by male figures. 12 piece white enamel cartouche dial with fleur de leys hands and black Roman numerals.
• *51cm x 36cm*
• £2,800 • Gütlin Clocks

'Le Paute' Fils Clock ▲

• *circa 1812*
Birds-eye maple and ebony strung French wooden mantle clock. The fine quality silk suspension movement by 'Le Paute' & Fils. Hrs du Roi (Horologer to the King). Signed silvered dial.
• *35.5cm x 15cm*
• £2,500 • Gütlin Clocks

First Empire Clock ▼

• *circa 1870*
French gilt ormolu and bronze mantle clock in the form of an oil lamp with an angel being warmed by the lamp. 8-day movement with hour and half hour strike on a bell. White enamel dial with black roman numerals and finely chiselled gilt brass hands.
• *35.5cm x 20cm*
• £2,800 • Gütlin Clocks

Propeller Blade Clock ▲

• *circa 1900*
An industrial timepiece propeller blade clock with ships capstan containing a compass, gilded lifebelt, apothec and anchor. An 8-day cylinder escapement timepiece French movement, gilded dial with black roman numerals and fleurs de lys hands.
• *33.5cm x 34.5cm*
• £1,600 • Gütlin Clocks

Expert Tips

The springs from which pendulums are suspended are fragile and easily broken in transit. Secure or remove pendulums on long journeys.

French Lyre Clock ▼

- *circa 1900*

A satinwood and gilt ormolu mounted French timepiece lyre clock retailed by 'Howell and James', Paris. 8-day French movement with original English lever escapement, convex cream enamel dial with hand painted swags of roses boarding black arabic numerals.

- *25.5cm x 12.5cm*
- **£1,600**   • Gütlin Clocks

Three Piece Clock Garniture ▼

- *circa 1870*

French gilt bronze and cloisonne enamelled three piece clock garniture. 8-day movement chiming hours and half hours on a bell. The gilt bronze and blue porcelain case with fine cloisonne enamelling and urn shaped side pieces.

- *40.5cm x 22.5cm*
- **£3,700**   • Gütlin Clocks

3 Piece Clock Garniture ▲

- *circa 1860*

A gilt bronze and jewelled pink porcelain French 3 piece clock garniture, gilt bronze case with porcelain panels surmounted by an urn with gilt bronze mounts, 8-day French movement chiming hours and half hours on the bell.

- *43cm x 30.5cm*
- **£5,500**   • Gütlin Clocks

Mantle Clock ▲

- *circa 1890*

A white Paris Bisque French timepiece mantle clock with small French 8-day timepiece movement, white convex enamel dial with roman numerals and counter poised moon hands.

- *25.5cm x 15.5cm*
- **£750**   • Gütlin Clocks

Black Marble Clock ▼

- *circa 1860*

French black marble mantle clock with a gilt bronze figure of a maiden reading a book resting on a column with a lyre beside her, 8-day French movement. Hour and half hour strike on a bell.

- *61cm x 56cm*
- **£3,500**   • Gütlin Clocks

French Four Glass Clock ▼

- *circa 1870*

A polished brass French four day glass clock with diamonte bezel, 8-day movement with hour and half hour strike on a gong and mercury pendulum, the white enamelled dial painted with pink music sheets.

- *25.5cm x 5cm*
- **£1,600**   • Gütlin Clocks

Mantle Clock ◄

- *circa 1880*

French gilt metal and porcelain mantle clock, the gilt ormolu case swags to the sides, acanthus cast gallery to the base raised on toupie feet. The pink porcelain panels with gilt- bordered white reserves painted with flowers.

- *51cm x 25.5cm*
- **£2,300**   • Gütlin Clocks

Marble Clock Set ▲

- *circa 1860*

Gilt bronze and rouge marble French figural three piece drummer boy timepiece clock set. 8-day movement with original cylinder escapement, gilt ormolu hands and two branch gilt ormolu and rouge marble matching candlesticks.

- *33cm x 12.5cm*
- £3,500
- Gütlin Clocks

Red Boulle Clock ▲

- *circa 1880*

French red tortoiseshell and ormolu mounted scarlet red boulle clock. The French 8- day twin barrel movement by 'Mougin'. Original numbered pendulum and one-piece enamel dial signed by the retailer 'Hamilton & incher', Paris.

- *35.5cm x 17.5cm*
- £1,800
- Gütlin Clocks

Porcelain Mantle Clock ▼

- *circa 1860*

Gilt bronze and blue jewelled porcelain French mantle clock, the finely chiselled case with original mercury gilding with three blue porcelain urns. 8-day French movement striking hours and half hours on a bell.

- *41cm x 30.5cm*
- £2,700
- Gütlin Clocks

Four Glass Mantle Clock ▼

- *circa 1890*

A gilt- brass mounted green onyx striking four glass mantle clock and garnature, the oval case with moulded top and base on bun feet. The lanceolate leaf bezel containing a white enamel dial with Arabic numerals decorated with painted floral swags and pierced gilt-metal hands.

- *30.5cm x 20cm*
- £2,900
- Gütlin Clocks

Miniature Carriage Clock ◄

- *circa 1890-1900*

French miniature satin gilded, gorged case 8-day carriage clock timepiece with original leather travelling box. The small sized 8-day movement with silvered cylinder platform escapement.

- *7.5cm x 5cm*
- £1,200
- Gütlin Clocks

Mahogany Portico Clock ▲

- *circa 1840*

Flame mahogany French first empire and gilt ormolu mounted portico clock, with 14-day French movement with hour and half hour strike on a bell supporting a finely chased ormolu regulator type gridiron pendulum.

- *50.5cm x 25.5cm*
- £3,000
- Gütlin Clocks

Brass Carriage Clock ▲

- *circa 1880-90*

French polished brass corniche cased carriage clock timepiece. The 8-day French timepiece movement with original silvered English lever platform escapement, with brass corniche style case with solid cast scroll shaped carrying handle.

- *11cm x 7.5cm*
- £550
- Gütlin Clocks

137

Carriage Clock ▲
- *circa 1880-90*
French polished brass corniche cased carriage clock timepiece with alarm, the 8-day movement with alarm sounding on a bell.
- *11cm x 7.5cm*
- £550 • Gütlin Clocks

French Carriage Clock ▲
- *circa 1890-1900*
French miniature polished brass Corniche cased 8-day carriage clock timepiece with 8-day movement and silvered English lever platform escapement.
- *7.5cm x 5cm*
- £950 • Gütlin Clocks

French Carriage Clock ▼
- *circa 1880-90*
French carriage clock with 8-day French timepiece movement and original silvered cylinder platform escapement, the polished brass corniche style case with solid cast scroll shaped carrying handle.
- *10.4cm x 10cm*
- £550 • Gütlin Clocks

Brass Carriage Clock ▼
- *circa 1880-90*
French polished brass Anglaise Riche case chiming carriage clock. The 8-day French chiming movement striking the hours and half hours on a gong with original silvered English lever platform escapement.
- *12.5cm x 8.2cm*
- £1,800 • Gütlin Clocks

English Bracket Clock ▲
- *circa 1860*
A solid mahogany and brass inlaid English bracket clock with quarter striking triple fusee. Retailed by 'Dixon'of Norwich chiming every quarter on 4 bells. With 8- day triple fusee movement.
- *68.5cm x 41cm*
- £5,500 • Gütlin Clocks

Gothic Bracket Clock ▲
- *circa 1839*
An early English flame mahogany silvered dial gothic bracket clock. The 8- day 2- train gut fusee movement with hour and half hour strike on a large nickered bell signed and dated 'D.Shaw', Leicester 1839.
- *71cm x 46cm*
- £3,900 • Gütlin Clocks

3-Piece Garniture ▶

• *circa 1860*

Cappi de monte porcelain 3 piece garniture, the finely painted pale blue case with figure of maiden and two cherubs. With 8-day French movement and hour and a half hour strike on a bell.

• *43cm x 22.5cm*
• £5,500 • Gütlin Clocks

Library Four Glass Clock ▼

• *circa 1840*

A black ebonised Scottish library four-glass clock by 'J. & W. Mitchell', 119 New Cannon Street, Glasgow. The 8-day double chain fusee movement with hour and half hour strike on a large original nickeled bell and pendulum holdfast.

• *23cm x 15cm*
• £4,800 • Gütlin Clocks

English Bracket Clock

• *circa 1870*

Black ebonsied and gilt ormolu mounted 3 train quarter striking triple fusee English bracket clock, chiming on 8 bells with hour strike on a gong.

• *81cm x 42cm*
• £3,900 • Gütlin Clocks

Bracket Clock ▲

• *circa 1850*

An English three train quarter striking ebonised and gilt ormolu mounted bracket clock standing on its original bracket. The movement chiming on 9 bells with hour strike on a large nickeled bell.

• *56cm x 22cm*
• £4,500 • Gütlin Clocks

English Bracket Clock ▲

• *circa 1880*

English mahogany cased pad-top bracket clock with 8- day French numbered and signed movement, chiming the hours and half hours on a gong.

• *33cm x 22.5cm*
• £5,500 • Gütlin Clocks

Mahogany Bracket Clock ▼

• *circa 1880*

English mahogany and heavily inlayed bracket clock with columns. The numbered and signed French 8-day movement chiming the hours and half hours on a gong by 'Mougin'.

• *259cm x 20cm*
• £1,800 • Gütlin Clocks

Palais Royale Clock ▼

• *circa 1830*

Fine and rare Palais Royale mother of pearl and gilt brass table clock, with a musical box playing: two airs, records, the time, the day and the date.

• *height 21cm*
• £16,500 • Trevor Philips

Mantle Clock ▲
- *1904*

A small red leather and silver fronted timepiece mantle clock. Silver hallmarked Birmingham 1904. 8-day movement on platform escapement in very original condition, white enamel dial with Roman black numerals and black spade hands.
- *20cm x 10cm*
- **£850** • Gütlin Clocks

French Mantle Clock ▲
- *circa 1830*

First empire French ormolu and bronze mantle clock by 'Gaullin', Paris. With 8-day silk suspension movement. The arched case depicting pomegranates, torches and an oil lamp, flanked by figures of Cupid & Psyche in a romantic pose, the rectangular plinth with stylised leaf mouldings, applied with a butterfly mount.
- *78cm x 48cm*
- **£5,900** • Gütlin Clocks

Ormulu Mantle Clock ▼
- *circa 1880*

A Gilt bronze ormolu French mantle clock with blue porcelain panels. The Fine ormolu case depicting a woman rested on a rock with her dog with original mercury gilding. The porcelain panels of fine quality with pictures of flowers, 8-day movement with hour and half hour strike on a bell. White enamel dial with black Roman numerals. Dial signed by the retailers 'Maitrot a Dijon'. The movement is by Vincenti and Cie.
- *46cm x 51cm*
- **£2,900** • Gütlin Clocks

Gilt Bronze Clock ▼
- *circa 1870*

Gilt bronze French clock. The finely chiselled case with maidens to sides surmounted by an urn with draping ormolu swags. With 8-day French movement with hour and half hour strike on a bell. The back door of this clock is engraved, 'Antony Bailly & LYON'.
- *63.5cm x 38cm*
- **£4,500** • Gütlin Clocks

Tortoiseshell Boulle Clock ▲
- *circa 1880*

An ormolu mounted French tortoiseshell boulle clock in a Renaissance style. 8-day French square plate movement chiming hours and half hours on the bell with gilt ormolu 12 piece dial and enamel cartouches showing black Roman numerals.
- *58.5cm x 33cm*
- **£1,900** • Gütlin Clocks

French Mantle Clock ▲
- *circa 1830*

Gilt ormolu first empire French mantle clock by Lugrunge & Paris. The finely chiselled gilt bronze case with a maiden and cupid and a laurel wreath to bottom of case. Convex enamel dial with black Roman numerals. 8-day silk-suspension movement chiming hours and half hours on a bell.
- *40.5cm x 30.5cm*
- **£2,300** • Gütlin Clocks

Watches

Jaeger Le Coultre Watch ▲

- *circa 1960*
Jaeger Le Coultre Memovox
(alarm) Stainless steel wrist
watch with silver digits on a
silver face and automatic
movement.
- *diameter 4cm*
- £1,500　　　• AM-PM

Rolex Cushion Watch ▲

- *1920s*
Gentleman's Rolex cushion
wristwatch set in 9ct gold. With
white enamel dial, auxiliary
sweep seconds and a red number
12. Rolex signature underneath
the dial.
- *diameter 2.5cm*
- £950　　　• AM-PM

Ladies Rolex Wristwatch ▼

- *1940*
Ladies 18ct rose gold Rolex
wristwatch with original
expanding strap with the Rolex
symbol on the buckle square face
with scalloped lugs. Gold digits
on a white face.
- *diameter 2cm*
- £1,800　　　• AM-PM

Ladies Oyster Watch ▼

- *1920s*
Ladies Rolex Oyster wristwatch
set in 14ct gold With mechanical
movement, a sunburst dial,
auxiliary sweep seconds and a
white face with gold numbers.
- *diameter 2cm*
- £1,500　　　• AM-PM

Ladies Swiss Watch ▶

- *1920s*
Ladies Swiss made wristwatch in
18ct rose gold with enamel dial
with old cut diamonds on the
bezel, on an expandable 18ct rose
gold bracelet.
- *diameter 1.7cm.*
- £500　　　• AM-PM

Rolex Wristwatch ▲

- *1960s*
Gentleman's Rolex Oyster
perpetual Air King Model
wristwatch in steel and gold.
Automatic movement, white dial
with gold digits, with a sunburst
bezel.
- *diameter 3cm*
- £1,400　　　• AM-PM

Oyster Speedking Watch ▲

- *1950s*
Boys size Rolex Oyster
Speedking. Stainless steel
mechanical movement with silver
digits and expandable Rolex
Oyster bracelet.
- *diameter 2.8cm*
- £950　　　• AM-PM

Ladies Swiss Watch ▼

- *1920s*
Ladies Swiss made 18ct gold with a white enamelled dial with Roman numerals.
- *diameter 2.7cm*
- £400
- AM-PM

Gentleman's Rolex Watch ▼

- *1960*
Gentleman's Rolex Oyster perpetual explorer wristwatch on a Rolex Oyster expandable bracelet.
- *diameter 3cm*
- £2,400
- AM-PM

Hexagonal Watch ▲

- *1920s*
Ladies silver hexagonal wristwatch with white enamel dial, auxiliary sweep seconds and a red number twelve.
- *diameter 2cm*
- £250
- AM-PM

Tiffany & Co. Watch ▲

- *1920s*
Ladies Tiffany & Co. Set in 9ct rose gold white enamelled dial with Arabic numerals with a red number 12.
- *diameter 2cm*
- £500
- AM-PM

Rolex Oyster Watch ◄

- *1920s*
Rolex Oyster precision auxiliary sweep seconds white dial. 2, 4, 8, 10, and 12 in Arabic numerals, set in stainless steel.
- *diameter 1.6cm*
- £650
- AM-PM

Omega Watch ▼

- *1950s*
Swiss made men's Omega 18ct gold mechanical movement watch with auxiliary sweep seconds and a gold dial with gold hands and gold digits.
- *diameter 3.1cm*
- £650
- AM-PM

Expert Tips

Pocket watches date back to 1675. Engraved or hand painted pictures of rural or hunting scenes add value, as do those of classical mythology, so keep a look out for these.

Ladies Movado Watch ▼

- *1940s*
Ladies Movado Swiss made 8ct rose gold wristwatch with a square face and two-tone dial with Arabic numerals.
- *diameter 1.9cm*
- £450
- AM-PM

Omega Watch ▽

- *circa 1915*

A First World War officers large size wristwatch with original mesh 'Trench Guard'. The white enamel dial with subsidiary seconds, signed Omega. The case struck Omega Depose No. 9846 case # 5425073. The movement with Swan Neck Micro Reg. Signed Omega # 211504.
- *diameter 4.2cm*
- **£2,250**   • Anthony Green

Rolex Watch ▽

- *1924*

Gentleman's silver cushion shaped wristwatch. The movement signed 'Rolex 15 Jewels Swiss Made' Cal 507 Rebberg Depose. The case back signed RWC Ltd. (Rolex Watch Company). The case frame #655. The dial signed 'Rolex Swiss Made' Lug size 22.5mm.
- *width 2.3cm*
- **£2,850**   • Anthony Green

Rolex Watch ▲

- *1935*

A 9ct gold gentleman's Rolex wristwatch. The dial signed Rolex Swiss Made, with subsidiary seconds. The case signed Rolex 25 World Records Geneva Suisse R.W.C. Ltd. #19736 ref#2356 Movement Sig Rolex Precision 17 Rubis Patented Superbalance Swiss Made.
- **£4,500**   • Anthony Green

Rolex Watch ▲

- *circa 1947*

An Oyster 'Royal' waterproof Rolex wristwatch, with centre seconds. The case signed 'Rolex Geneve Suisse' with screw down Oyster button and case # 506021 Ref# 4444.
- **£1,550**   • Anthony Green

Pocket Watch ▶

- *circa 1920*

A high grade fully jewelled minute repeating open face pocket watch, with dial with subsidiary seconds. The case with Swiss control marks for 18ct gold and case # 62837. Repeating activated by a slide on the band.
- **£4,800**   • Anthony Green

Peerless Wristwatch ▽

- *1934*

A gentleman's wristwatch, the movement jewelled to the centre signed 'Peerless' Swiss Made # 332257 with S & Co Logo. The case # 331618-2 & FB fo Francis Baumgartner Borgelle case designer Enamel dial subsidiary seconds.
- *diameter 3.3cm*
- **£2,750**   • Anthony Green

Rolex Officer's Wristwatch ▽

- *circa 1916*

An early First World War 'Officer's' wristwatch. The silvered dial signed Rolex & Swiss Made. The movement #4636 and signed Rolex Swiss 15 Jls. Case signed with 'W & D' for Wilsdorf & Davis, the original founders of the Rolex empire. Case # 769936.
- **£2,500**   • Anthony Green

Romer Wristwatch ▲

- *1950s*

Ladies Swiss made Romer wristwatch set in 9ct gold on a 9ct gold bracelet with safety chain. White dial with 3,6,9,12 Arabic numerals.
- *diameter 1.2cm*
- £250 • AM-PM

Bulova Wristwatch ▲

- *1920s*

Ladies Bulova wristwatch set in 18ct gold with white dial. 3,6,9,12 Arabic numerals with serrated lugs, on a black leather cocktail strap.
- *diameter 1.1cm*
- £200 • AM-PM

Omega Watch ▼

- *1950s*

Gentleman's Omega watch set in 9ct gold on a white dial with gold Arabic numerals and auxiliary sweep seconds.
- *diameter 2.9cm*
- £350 • AM-PM

Vacheron Constantin Watch ▼

- *1960s*

Gentleman's Vacheron Constantin 18ct white gold wristwatch with oblong design black dial with white gold digits.
- *diameter 1.9cm*
- £1.300 • AM-PM

Universal Geneve ▶

- *circa 1939*

An early 18ct gold 'Compax' two button chronograph with subsidiary seconds, minute and hour recording dials.
- £3,900 • Anthony Green

Lemania ▲

- *1953*

An Air Ministry RAF issue, pilots high grade one button chronograph with a steel case. The dial signed Lemania & with MOD Arrow, with minute recording dial and sweep second dial. The case with fixed bar lugs and back with ordinance marks: Arrow AM/6B/551 333/53.
- £1,800 • Anthony Green

Omega Seamaster Watch ▲

- *1950s*

Gentleman's Omega seamaster wristwatch set in stainless steel with a black dial with white Roman numerals. Mechanical movement and a screw back case. Red second hand.
- *Diameter 2.9cm*
- £300 • AM-PM

Lady's Oyster Watch ▲

- **1930s**
Rolex Oyster precision ladies
stainless steel wristwatch with a
white dial and trianglular digits.
- *diameter 1.8cm*
- **£650**   • AM-PM

Benson Watch ▲

- **1940s**
J.W. Benson ladies wristwatch set
in 9ct gold with fancy lugs amd
white dial with Arabic numerals.
- *diameter 1.7cm*
- **£250**   • AM-PM

Oyster Wrist Watch ▼

- **1950s**
Gentleman's Rolex Oyster Royal
watch set in stainless steel with a
white mottled dial with 3,6,9
Arabic numerals, Mercedes hands
and mechanical movement.
- *diameter 2.6cm*
- **£800**   • AM-PM

Rolex Wristwatch ▼

- **1918**
Ladies Rolex wristwatch with
white enamelled dial set in 9ct
gold. Black Arabic numerals.
- *diameter 2cm*
- **£580**   • AM-PM

Gentleman's Longines Watch ▶

- **1930s**
Gentleman's Longines oblong
design set in 14ct. rose gold, with
white dial set with gold Arabic
numerals and auxiliary sweep
seconds.
- *diameter 1.8cm*
- **£950**   • AM-PM

Longines Watch ▲

- **1940**
Ladies Longines wristwatch set in
stainless steel with 3, 6, 9 Arabic
numerals. Screw back, for
original waterproofing.
- *diameter 1.9cm*
- **£340**   • AM-PM

Omega Seamaster Wristwatch ▲

- **1940s**
Gentleman's Omega Seamaster
wristwatch set in stainless steel
automatic movement, two tone
dial with gold digits.
- *diameter 2.9cm*
- **£300**   • AM-PM

Rolex Watch ▼

- *circa 1920s*

Silver Tonneau shaped
gentleman's wristwatch. The
white enamel dial signed Rolex,
with luminous numerals and
hands and subsidiary seconds.
The 3pc case signed Rolex 7
Worlds Records Gold Medal
Geneva Suisse (RWC Ltd)
#64948. The lever movement
signed Rolex Swiss made. 15
Rubies.

- £2,550   • Anthony Green

Omega Watch ▼

- *circa 1938*

An 18ct gold wrist chronograph
with subsidiary seconds and 30
minute register dial. The main
dial with outer tachymeter scal.
Inner pulsations scale and base
1000 scale. The case signed
Omega & with Swiss control
marks. CS #9174757. The
movement signed Omega Watch
Company. 17 Jls #9388131.C333.

- £6,500   • Anthony Green

Aviator's Chronograph ▲

- *circa 1968*

An aviator's 'Navitimer'
chronograph by Breitling, with
subsidiary dials for sweep seconds,
minute and hour recording. Outer
rotating bezel allowing various
aviation calculations. Case #
1307320 Ref # 806.

- £1,800   • Anthony Green

Hunting Chronograph ▲

- *1907*

Swiss made Hunting Split
Secondsi Chronograph with
subsidiary minute recording and
sweep second dials. Case ~
130519. The white enamel dial
signed S. Smith & Son 9. The
Strand London Maker to the
Admiralty.
142B 68 Non Magnetizable
Swiss Made.

- £2,950   • Anthony Green

Flightmaster
Chronograph ▼

- *circa 1978*

A steel aviator's 'Flightmaster'
chronograph by Omega, with
multifunction dial and internal
rotating bezel. This watch comes
with the original box and papers.

- £1,800   • Anthony Green

Propelling Pencil ▼

- *circa 1920*

French propelling pencil with
timepiece in engine turned body.
With Swiss lever 15 jewelled
movement. French control marks
and struck. 925 monogram to
case 'MA'.

- £1,950   • Anthony Green

Gentleman's Pocket
Watch ▶

- *circa 1890*

Gold gentleman's pocket by
Balbi, Buenos Aires. With black
Roman numerals on a white face
with a subsidiary second dial. The
front of the case is engraved with
a house with mountains in the
background, surrounded by a
floral design, with diamonds.

- *2.5cm*
- £950   • Bellum Antiques

Fob Watch ▲

- **1910**
Large gold fob watch by Vetex Revue, with black Roman numerals on a white face with a subsidiary seconds dial.
- *diameter 5cm*
- **£223** • Bellum Antiques

Gold Fob Watch ▲

- **1900**
9ct rose gold plated fob watch with Roman numerals and a subsidiary semi-concealed dial.
- *diameter 4.5cm*
- **£595** • Bellum Antiques

Expert Tips

Check that the case of a pocket watch labelled gold really is gold, particularly when purchasing an American watch. Also make sure the mechanism is in good wworking order.

Gold Pocket Watch ▼

- *circa 1880*
Gold gentleman's pocket watch. Black Roman numerals, gold seconds on a white enamel face, with a foliate engraved design on the back of the case.
- *diameter 3cm*
- **£400** • Bellum Antiques

Half Hunter ▼

- *circa 18th century*
Half Hunter gold fob watch with blue Roman numerals on the outer casing of the watch surrounding an inset white dial.
- *diameter 4cm*
- **£975** • Bellum Antiques

Fly-Back Chronograph ▶

- *circa 1970*
A rare German air force issue aviator's 'Fly-Back' chronograph by Heuer in steel. The black dial with subsidiary seconds and minute recording dial 1 and red '3H' in circle, case #6445-12-146-3774 and stamped 'BUNDWEHR'.
- **£2,200** • Anthony Green

Gentleman's Pocket Watch ▲

- *circa 1870*
Austrian gentleman's pocket watch with a cover engraved with a cartouche depicting a parrot on a swing surrounded by a foliate design.
- *diameter 1.5cm*
- **£400** • Bellum Antiques

Omega Fob Watch ▲

- *circa 1900*
Gold Omega pocket watch with Arabic numerals on a white face, with gold hands and a subsidiary seconds dial. Swiss made.
- *diameter 1.5cm*
- **£345** • Bellum Antiques

Scientific Instruments

Miniature Microscope ▲
- *mid 19th century*
An exceptionally fine mid-19th century miniature microscope by Ross. Incorporating a highly unusual device form mechanical stage and further unusual procedures for focusing the instrument and has a hand-held simple microscope and other accessories.
- *height 20cm*
- £4,750 • Trevor Phillips

Microscope Oil Lamp ▲
- *circa 19th century*
Microscope illuminating oil lamp incorporating an adjustable bullseye condenser. by R & J Beck of London and retailed by Walmsley of Philadepphia, sole American agents.
- *height 32cm*
- £1,500 • Trevor Phillips

Portable Microscope ▼
- **1830**
Portable microscope by Carpenter. 24, Regent Street London, housed in its original mahogany box.
- *height 32cm*
- £1,500 • Trevor Phillips

Cuff-Type Microscope ▲
- *circa 19th century*
Fine and very rare Cuff-type miniature microscope by Cuff. In its original mahogany box which doubles as a stand for the microscope. The accessories include fish plate, ivory slides, a series of objectives, live stage and nose cone.
- *height 22cm*
- £6,000 • Trevor Phillips

Mariner Compass ▼
- **1860**
Drum, gimble mounted, mariners compass with wind, rose and degree scale.
- *diameter 7.5cm*
- £1,500 • Trevor Phillips

Portable Microscope ▼

- *circa 19th century*

Portable microscope illuminating lamp. Housed in its original black japanned tin travelling box.

- *height 33cm*
- £1.400   • Trevor Phillips

Binocular Microscope ▲

- *1880*

A binocular microscope by Henry Crouch of London. Housed in its original box with many accessories, and has a fully mechanical stage sub-stage mechanism and is finished in gilt bronze.

- *height 43.5cm*
- £3,900   • Trevor Phillips

Monocular Microscope ▼

- *1850*

Fine binocular and monocular microscope by Ross of London. No 336 in its original brassbound box with numerous accessories.

- *height 50cm*
- £6,500   • Trevor Phillips

Library Globe ▶

- *1821*

12-inch library globe by Cary, supported on a mahogany stand with a rope twist carving to the central column. The tripod ledge is joined by a cross-stretcher supporting a compass, with a facsimile compass rose. The cartouche reads as follows: Cary's new terrestrial globe, Delineated from the best Authorities extant; Exhibiting the late Discoveries towards the North Pole, and every improvement in Geography to the present time London: Made & Sold by G & J Cary, 86 St. James's Street March15th 1821.

- *height 66cm*
- £14,750   • Trevor Phillips

Terrestrial Globe ▼

- *1824*

Eight-inch terrestrial globe by Delamarche and is supported on an ebonised beech stand which has four quadrants giving the names and latitudes of various different cities.

- *height 20cm*
- £7,500　　● Trevor Phillip

Travelling Thermometer ▼

- *circa 1810*

Fisherman's or travelling thermometer in original wooden morocco case. Signed: Richardson, 1 Drury Lane, Holborn, London.

- *height 12cm*
- £875　　● Trevor Phillips

Boxwood Nocturnal ▲

- *mid 18th century*

Fine boxwood nocturnal. The central volvelle marked for the Great Bear G and Little Bear L constellations, the centre scale marked with a calendar and hour scale. The reverse of the instrument is marked with the polar distance correction for the Pole star for both the Great and Little Bear constellations when finding the latitude marked Sam Bosswell Fecit on the fiducial arm and David Boswell on the handle.

- *height 25cm*
- £10,750　　● Trevor Phillips

Pocket Globe ▼

- *mid 19th century*

Unsigned but probably German. Composed of 12 engraved, hand coloured gores with the continents outlined in primary colours. Housed in a blue card box, the lid marked: 'The Earth and its inhabitants'. The box contains a folded engraved and hand coloured illustration of 16 males from various parts of the world in their national costumes, labelled in English, French and German.

- *diameter 5cm*
- £3.500　　● Trevor Phillips

Noon-Day Cannon Dial ▼

- *early 19th century*

Fine noon-day cannon dial by Boucar, 35 Q de L'Horloge, Paris. The marble base supports a brass cannon, adjustable magnifier and calendar scale. The sun dial graduated from 5 to 12 to 7, with brass gnomon correct for latitude 48.5 and 13 minutes.

- *height 26cm*
- £5,750　　● Trevor Phillip

Map Measure ▼

- *early 19th century*

Map measure by W. & S.Jones, 30 Holborn, London. The gilt brass case incorporates an enamel dial graduated in Arabic numerals, housed in its original leather case.

- *height 8cm*
- £3,750　　● Trevor Phillips

Expert Tips

The original finish is what gives a scientific item its value, so be careful, as many instruments have been ruined by the lavish use of metal polishes combined with the buffing wheel.

Six Drawer Telescope ▲

• **1854**
Miniature travelling 6 drawer
telescope signed: Baker, 244 High
Holborn, London. Housed in its
original leather case with extra
eye-piece and folding stand.
• *height 9cm*
• **£1,550**   • **Trevor Phillips**

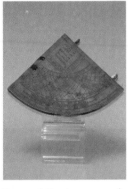

Boxwood Quadrant ▲

• *circa 18th century*
English boxwood quadrant
incorporating 5 star positions.
• *height 12.5cm*
• **£6,500**   • **Trevor Phillips**

Pocket Globe ▶

• *circa 1834*
Fine 3 inch pocket globe by
Newton Son & Berry, 66
Chancery Lane, London. Housed
in its original simulated fish-skin
case. The interior with celestial
gores for the northern and
southern celestial poles.
• *height 7.5cm*
• **£6,500**   • **Trevor Phillips**

Sand Glasses ▼

• *mid 17th century -early 19th
century*
Group of 3 sand glasses.
Manufactured from glass, brass
and wood, each glass has a
different time duration and would
have been used for a number of
timing uses including marine,
business, legal and ecclesiastical
use.
• *height 27cm*
• **£3,000**   • **Trevor Phillips**

French Armillary Sphere ▲

• *late 19th century*
French armillary sphere signed on
the enamel charter ring Grivolat
Horloger, Paris. The dial is
constructed of steel and brass.
• *height 61cm*
• **£5,750**   • **Trevor Phillips**

Coins & Medals

Coins and medals are an accurate and interesting way to trace the ascent of civilisation.

Since the dawn of time man has been involved with war and a collector's market has sprung up from the paraphernalia associated with conflict and order. Medals are probably the most popular collecting area of all militaria, and the more documentation available to denote provenance, for example, title, rank, and regiment, the more valuable the medal becomes. The two main types of medals are Campaign and those awarded for Bravery in Action, such as the Distinguished Conduct Medal, first issued after the Crimean War. Most cherished of all is the Victoria Cross, always highly priced, although the value depends on the action and the deed.

The Napoleonic wars are a popular period for collectors, along with medals from the Crimean War, Indian Mutiny and other Victorian wars. Medals from the Boer War are plentiful and popular. Coins, from their earliest beginnings, around 1000 BC, and up to the present day, bestow history on us in a way that is both fascinating and accurate.

Good Conduct Medal ▼
- **1909**
Volunteer Long Service Good Conduct medal with Edward VII bust, awarded to: 1538 Sgt I. Harrison. 2nd V.B. Notts & Derby R. With Daily Mail Empire Day rifle competition. Silver award medal, named to recipient and dated 1909.
- *diameter 4cm*
- **£65**   • C. F. Seidler

Anna-Luisen Order ▲
- **1918**
Medal commemorating the Anna-Luisen (Schwarzbury-Rudelstadt).
- *diameter 3cm*
- **£395**   • C. F. Seidler

Luftwaffe Retired Pilot's Badge ◄
- **1935–45**
Luftwaffe retired pilot's badge with maker's mark: C.E. Junker Berlin SW66.
- *diameter 4cm*
- **£925**   • Gordons Medals Ltd

War Service Cross ▲
- **1912**
War Service Cross of Imperial Austria made from gold with enameling and official mint maker's mark. Hallmarked 1912.
- *diameter 3cm*
- **£280**   • C. F. Seidler

Third Reich Army Long Service Cross ▼

- *1935–45*

Gold Third Reich Army Long Service Cross awarded for 40 years service, with gilt eagle standard and oak leaves on ribbon. A very fine specimen.
- *diameter 4cm*
- **£225** • **Gordons Medals Ltd**

Luftwaffe Combined Pilot/Observer's Badge ▼

- *1935–45*

Luftwaffe combined pilot / observer's badge. Two part gilt and silver, mid-war version, in super crisp condition. Makers marked: CEJ for Junckers.
- *diameter 4cm*
- **£650** • **Gordons Medals Ltd**

British War Medal ▼

- *1914–19*

1914-15 Star, British War medal, Victory medal, and Royal Naval Volunteer Reserve Long Service Good Conduct medal, as awarded to: 1/945. R. Ryandell. Sig. R.N.V.R. Bristol DIV.
- *diameter 4cm*
- **£135** • **C. F. Seidler**

Third Reich Medal ▲

- *1935–45*

1939 Iron Cross 2nd Cl., Danzig Cross, 2nd Cl., the latter, one of only 254 awarded, maker's mark on reverse: B.V.A. Hulse-Berlin.
- *diameter 4cm*
- **£365** • **Gordons Medals Ltd**

Crimean War Medal ▲

- *1854–5*

Crimean War medal with 3 Clasps; Alma, Inkerman, Sebastopol, regimentally impressed naming: Serjt J McBlain Scots Fusilier Guards.
- *diameter 4cm*
- **£425** • **Gordons Medals Ltd**

Army of India Medal ▼

- *1799–1826*

Army of India medal, 1799-1826, with three clasps; Allighur, Battle of Delhi, Laswaree, as awarded to: Lieut Alexr Duncan, Brigade Major. Officially impressed naming Alexander Duncan who served during the Second Mahratta War of 1803-4 and later became a General. He retired in 1854 and died in 1859. This is a very rare medal, one of only 150 three clasp medals awarded, of which not many have survived, 28 were issued with clasp combination.
- *diameter 4cm*
- **£6,950** • **Gordons MedalsLtd**

German Imperial Group ▼

- *1900–18*

Iron Cross 2nd Cl., 1914; Prussia, German Service Cross 1900-1918; Officer's Long Service Cross for 25 yrs; Friedrich Wilhelm 3rd Civil Service medal, 2nd Cl., 1847-1918, in silver; Army Lower Ranks Long Service medal for 15 yrs; Wilhelm 1st Centenary medal 1897; Braunschweig: Military Service Cross 2nd Cl., 1914-1918 and Service Cross 1st Cl., in gold. All mounted court style for wear.
- *diameter 18.5cm*
- **£475** • **Gordons Medals Ltd**

Naval Service Medal ▲
• *1914–19*
Naval Distinguished Service medal with GVR bust, as awarded to: A8654. J. Crorkran. Sea. R.N.R. Mediterranean Service, 23 March, 1918. This award was mentioned in the London Gazette on 7.8.1918, and was approved for services in action with enemy submarines.
• *diameter 4cm*
• £395 • Gordons Medals Ltd

DSO Miniature Medal Group ▲
• *1895–1902*
An unattributable contemporary group of three miniatures comprising: Distinguished Service Order, VR Gold Type, Delhi Durbar medal 1902, and India General Service medal with 3 clasps; Punjab Frontier 1897-98, Samana 1897, Tirah 1897-98. Medals mounted for wear with attachment pin by Spink & Son - London.
• *diameter 6cm*
• £145 • Gordons Medals Ltd

Khedive's Star ▼
• *circa 1890*
Khedive's star dated 1882. Unnamed as issued.
• *diameter 4cm*
• £55 • Gordons Medals Ltd

Purple Heart Award ▼
• *1932–present*
Purple heart medal of the Vietnam period. This is awarded for gallantry, the wounded or those killed in action in the service of the military forces of the United States of America.
• *diameter 4cm*
• £24 • Gordons Medals Ltd

British Victory Medal ▲
• *1914–19*
British Victory medal, as awarded to Lieutenant J.C Holmes RAF, and Ceylon Planters Rifle Corps medal. Inscribed on rim with: 'Marathon Race, L.C.P.L.J.C. Holmes Kandy 1913'. This man was killed in action on Sunday the 1st September 1918 in Egypt, aged 29. Having served in the Ceylon Planter's Rifle Corps, transferred on 17/11/1915 to the Yorkshire Regiment, was later commissioned as a 2nd Lieutenant and joined the Royal Flying Corps and latterly the Royal Air Force.
• *diameter 12cm*
• £325 • Gordons Medals Ltd

Military Cross ▲
• *1914–19*
Military Cross, GVR, unofficially named on reverse: A. Melville Kennedy. 8th BN. Royal Scots Fusiliers June 1917.
• *diameter 4cm*
• £395 • Gordons Medals Ltd

Inter-Allied Victory Medal ◄
• *1914–19*
Inter-allied Victory medal for the Great War, this is the Italian version, with maker's mark: 'Sacchimi - Milano'.
• *diameter 4cm*
• £14 • Gordons Medals Ltd

Boer War Medal ▼

- **1899–1900**

Queen's South Africa medal, 1899-1900 with six clasps; Relief of Kimberley, Paardeberg, Driefontein, Johannesburg, Diamond Hill, Wittebergen, as awarded to: 82180 Bomb: WHLR: H. BlissEett. 'P' BTY: R.H.A. This man was wounded during a Victoria Cross action at Nooitedacht on the 13th of December 1900.

- *diameter 4cm*
- **£375** • Gordons Medals Ltd

Campaign Service Medal ▼

- **1970–82**

Campaign Service medal with one clasp; Northern Ireland, South Atlantic medal 1982, with rosette, UN Cyprus medal (UNFICYP), as awarded to: 24501637 Gunner J.C Howe Royal Artillery. Group mounted court style for wear.

- *diameter 12cm*
- **£345** • Gordons Medals Ltd

Victorian Crown ▼

- **1887**

Mounted example of a Victorian crown with fine enamels.

- **£95** • James Vanstone

Air Force Cross ▲

- **1960–present**

US Airforce, Air Force cross.

- *diameter 5cm*
- **£43** • Gordons Medals Ltd

Distinguished Service Medal ▲

- **1970–present**

US Defence Distinguished Service medal.

- *diameter 5cm*
- **£43** • Gordons Medals Ltd

Victoria Half Crown ▲

- **1876**

Enamel half crown commemorating the reign of Queen Victoria with fine enamels.

- **£250** • James Vanstone

Five Mark ▼

- **1875**

Unusual five mark coin. Well-defined example centred with the Habsburg Eagle.

- **£350** • James Vanstone

George II Crown ▼

- **1743**

Rare example of George II crown with fine enamels representing England, Scotland and Ireland.

- **£400** • James Vanstone

British Medal ▼

- **1890–97**

British South Africa Company medal without clasp. Inscribed on the reverse: Rhodesia 1896. As awarded to: 93593 Shoeg.Smith W.Didoe. 10.B.Y.R.A. Died in South Africa on 26th May 1900.

- *diameter 4cm*
- **£295** • Gordons Medals Ltd

Royal Air Force Brooches ▼
- *circa 1918*
Pair of Royal Air Force
sweetheart brooches made from
15 carat gold, with original box.
- £200   • James Vanstone

Masonic Collar Jewel ▼
- *1920*
30th degree Masonic collar jewel
with hinged crown above a
double-headed phoenix clutching
a double-edged sword.
- £60   • James Vanstone

Edward VII Florin ▼
- *1802*
Edward VII florin. A scarce
example in enamel, centred with
Britannia.
- £150   • James Vanstone

George IV Shilling ▲
- *1826*
A George IV shilling. Unusual
because both sides are enamelled.
- £250   • James Vanstone

Masonic Jewel ▲
- *1930*
St John's Lodge whole Masonic
jewel. This hallmarked jewel
bears a good quality enamel of St
John the Martyr.
- £70   • James Vanstone

Victoria Crown ▲
- *1845*
1845 crown with the head of the
young Queen Victoria, centred
with enamel bearing the Royal
Standard.
- £100   • James Vanstone

Grand Master Jewel ▼
- *1850*
A jewel of the grand master's
Masonic Lodge, with a face with
rays of light radiating behind,
within an enamel blue circle.
- £50   • James Vanstone

Half Crown ▼
- *1854*
Enamel Victorian half crown
with the Royal Standard within a
laurel border.
- £35   • James Vanstone

Rose Cross ▼
- *1900*
15ct gold exceptionally rare Rose
Cross with coloured jewel and a
swan within degrees and dividers
surmounted by a hinged crown
with seven stars.
- £350   • James Vanstone

Knight Templar Collar ▲
- *1850*
Unusual Knight Templar's collar jewel with enamelled double cross in silver, gold, red, black and white .
- £100   • James Vanstone

Founder Jewel ▲
- *1940*
Hall marked silver Founder jewel with Masonic symbols painted on the enamel, set between two pillars
- £40   • James Vanstone

George IV Shilling ▲
- *1820*
Attractive example of the George IV shilling with enamel centre, with the Crown and Lion.
- £40   • James Vanstone

Victorian Shilling ▼
- *1897*
Victorian shilling with enamel standard and the date 1897.
- £25   • James Vanstone

Diamond Jubilee Medal ▼
- *1897*
Commemorative medal for the Diamond Jubilee of Queen Victoria decorated in silver, gilt and paste settings. The central cartouche of Queen Victoria is set within twenty-four paste diamonds within the angle and the divider.
- £60   • James Vanstone

Canada General Service Medal ▼
- *1866–70*
Canada General Service medal 1866-70, with one clasp; Fenian Raid 1866, as awarded to: 311 Pte. A. Carroll, 7th Bn. Royal Fusiliers.
- *diameter 4cm*
- £295   • Gordons Medals Ltd

Gold Post Master Jewel ▲
- *1930*
9ct gold Post Master jewel representing the guild of Freeman Lodge, decorated with the City of London's coat of arms.
- £140   • James Vanstone

Burmese Rupee ▲
- *1920*
Burmese rupee centred with a peacock. Whilst of exceptionally high quality this example is one of the more common seen on the market.
- £120   • James Vanstone

Victorian Crown ▲
- *1897*
A Victorian crown with a strong depiction of George and the dragon highlighted in enamel. Reasonably common example.
- £60   • James Vanstone

Collector's Items

From car boot to old boot, collectables continue to mesmorise and captivate the serious and amateur rummager alike.

Elvis and Hendrix may be dead and the Beatles disbanded, but they're all still making record sales; whether its instruments, records, concert posters or autographs - even a rocker's underwear - memorabilia of these and other pop musicians is shooting up in value. Internet sites have sprung up to trade on signed photographs of celebrities, but watch out, as not all of these are genuine. Cinema posters are also steadily rising in value, from 'Breakfast at Tiffany's' to 'Goldfinger', all have a

place in the collector's market. The pioneer of French poster advertising was Jules Cheret, and, like Henri de Toulouse-Lautrec, he transformed the Parisian boulevards into an enormous art gallery. Poster enthusiasts would emarge at night to sponge off new creations from the hoardings! Keep a space in your collection for photographs, as some are proving to be a highly lucrative investment, no longer being seen as a mass produced image, but as art.

Advertising and Packaging

Castle Polish ▲
- 1930

Red tin of Castle Ballroom floor polish with a picture of a castle.
- *height 11cm*
- £13   • Huxtable's

Bisto Tin ▼
- 1960

Tin of Bisto with a girl with a green hat and a boy with a red hat, both sniffing the aroma from a gravy boat.
- *height 19cm*
- £14   • Huxtable's

Pearce Duff's Custard Powder ◀
- 1950

Tin of Pearce Duff's custard powder with a picture of a bowl of custard and pineapple, plums and pears on each side.
- *height 11.5cm*
- £13   • Huxtable's

My Fair Lady Talc ▲
- 1960

Cusson's My Fair Lady talc showing a photograph of a blonde haired lady.
- *height 14cm*
- £14   • Huxtable's

Everyman's Hair Cream ▲
- *1950*

Everyman's brilliantine hair cream in a glass bottle with a pink rose beneath the words, 'Kenrosa made in England'.
- *height 13cm*
- £12   • Huxtable's

Ty-phoo Tea ▲
- *circa 1950–60*

Ty-Phoo tea in a grey box surrounded by a foliate wreath with the words 'Delicious, Economical, Refreshing'.
- *height 12.5cm*
- £7   • Huxtable's

Brasso ▼
- 1960

Tin of Brasso with 'Brasso' written in white letters on a red ground with a blue and white striped sun design in the background.
- *height 13cm*
- £7   • Huxtable's

Evening in Paris Hair Cream ▼
- 1940

Evening in Paris hair cream by Bourjois, in a dark blue glass bottle with dark blue writing on a pale blue background.
- *height 15cm*
- £13   • Huxtable's

Lyons Pure Ground Coffee ◄
- 1930

Green tin of Lyons pure ground coffee.
- *height 10.5cm*
- £17   • Huxtable's

Dried Eggs U S. A. ►
- *circa 1940*

Gold tin inscribed with the words 'Pure dried whole Eggs U S A 5 Ounces net weight equal to-12 eggs' in black writing.
- *height 11cm*
- £16   • Huxtable's

Cue Hair Dressing ▲
- *1955*

Glass bottle of Cue Hair dressing, a Colgate Product.
- *height 14cm*
- £10   • Huxtable's

Saturday Night Lotion ▲
- *1930*

Saturday Night Lotion in a clear glass bottle decorated with a man in a top hat and a lady in evening dress.
- *height 14cm*
- £15   • Huxtable's

Ty-Phoo Tea ▼

- *circa 1950–60*

Ty-Phoo Tea in a red box with white writing and the words 'Ty-Phoo Tea' in white, surrounded with a foliate wreath and 'Authorised 1/9 price'.
- *height 12.5cm*
- £7
- Huxtable's

BP Anti-Frost ▼

- *1962*

Green oil can with BP in yellow writing on a green shield with the words 'Anti–Frost' in red on a white background.
- *height 14cm*
- £20
- Huxtable's

Chillexine for the Udder ▲

- *circa 1930*

Bell & Sons in white writing with 'Limited Chillexine' in yellow writing on a brown background and 'For the Udder' in white writing with a picture of a cows udder.
- *height 20.5cm*
- £26
- Huxtable's

Tide Washing Powder ▲

- *1950*

Yellow packet of Tide with orange circles and the words 'Tide' and 'Gives clothes a whiteness bonus' in dark blue.
- *height 17cm*
- £19
- Huxtable's

Persil Soap Powder ▼

- *1950*

Persil in a green box with a red circle the words 'Persil washes whiter Yes it does!' in white.
- *height 18cm*
- £15
- Huxtable's

Kay-Tee ▼

- *1958*

Plastic bottle of Kay-Tee golden washing up liquid by Kearley and Tong Ltd, London.
- *height 20cm*
- £9
- Huxtable's

My Guinness Tray ▼

- **1955**

Metal tray with a pelican balancing a mug of Guinness inscribed with the slogan, 'My Goodness My Guinness'.
- *diameter 27cm*
- £55 • Huxtable's

Colman's Mustard ▼

- **1935**

Small red, yellow and black tin of Colman's mustard, with a red bull's head in the centre.
- *height 5cm*
- £8 • Huxtable's

Lyons Tea ▲

- **1925**

Set of four Lyon's tea tins, each one inscribed with a different slogan, -'Degrees Better', 'Lyons has stood the test of time', 'Mirror for reflection, Lyon's tea for perfection', 'All the year round drink Lyon's tea'.
- *height 14cm*
- £200 • Huxtable's

Gramophone Needle Tins ▲

- **1910-1940**

Six gramophone needle tins. The National Band, Pathe, Salon-Tanz Nadeln. Sem Aeor-needles.
- *4cm square*
- £30-100 each • Huxtable's

Player's Glass Ash Tray ▼

- **1950**

Glass ashtray depicting a man in naval uniform surrounded by a white life ring and inscribed with 'Player's Navy cut' in black writing.
- *width 15cm*
- £20 • Huxtable's

Oxo Cube ▲

- **1950**

Dark blue painted red metal box with 'Oxo cube' in yellow writing and the slogan 'Invaluable for cooking'.
- *35cm square*
- £40 • Huxtable's

A1 Salt ▲

- **1940**

Metal sign with two ladies, one cutting salt and the other opening a packet of 'A1 crushed lump salt.'
- *height 25cm*
- £20 • Huxtable's

Orlox Beef Suet ▼
- *circa 1930*
Cardboard box of Orlox Beef Suet with the picture of a red bull. In excellent condition.
- *height 9cm*
- £5 • Michael Laws Antiques

Chipso Soap Flakes ▼
- *circa 1930*
White cardboard box for Chipso soap flakes with a blue and yellow design and inscribed with the words, 'Fine for fine things'.
- *height 15cm*
- £10 • Michael Laws Antiques

Collecting Box ▲
- *1914*
Alexandra Day collecting box.
- *height 13cm*
- £16 • Michael Laws Antiques

Glass Jug ▲
- *1950*
Glass water jug inscribed in blue with the words 'Senior Service Satisfy'.
- *height 21cm*
- £15 • Michael Laws Antiques

Oxo Cubes ▲
- *circa 1930*
Metal tin with red and black geometric design with the inscription 'Oxo Cubes' in cream writing on the top of the lid.
- *width 10cm*
- £12 • Michael Laws Antiques

Ipso Washing Powder ▲
- *circa 1930*
Red cardboard box with the inscription 'The Wonder Worker IPSO washes by itself' displayed on a sheet and basket.
- *height 13cm*
- £10 • Michael Laws Antiques

Reeves Colour Box ▶
- *circa 1940*
Light and dark blue cardboard box with the inscription 'Reeves Students Colour Box', decorated with a seated dalmatian.
- *width 20cm*
- £20 • Michael Laws Antiques

Ashtray ▼
- **1955**
Ashtray with 'Don't forget your Anadin tablets' written in white writing on a red background and decorated with a two-tone green Anadin packet.
- *15cm square*
- **£12**   • **Huxtable's**

Thorne's Creme toffee ▲
- **1924**
Royal blue tin with gold scrolling and the words, 'Thorne's Extra Super Creme Toffee and British Empire Exhibition Souvenir'.
- *height 5.5.cm*
- **£30**   • **Huxtable's**

Huntley and Palmers Biscuits ▼
- **1927**
A British toy tank containing Huntley & Palmers biscuits.
- *height 9.5cm*
- **£800**   • **Huxtable's**

Sandwich Tin ▲
- **1930**
French yellow sandwich tin with a red handle and trim, and Mickey Mouse offering Pluto some sweets on the lid.
- *8cm x 18cm*
- **£150**   • **Huxtable's**

Aero Chocolate ▲
- *circa 1930*
Unused bar of Aero chocolate in a brown wrapper with cream writing by Rowntrees.
- *width 11cm*
- **£20**   • **Huxtable's**

Gray Dunn's Biscuits ▶
- **1915**
Yellow ochre bus with red roof and wheels with figures looking out of the window and a bus conductor. With the letters 'Gray Dunn's Biscuits' in red and 'Lands End to John O' Groats'.
- *height 9.5cm*
- **£1500**   • **Huxtable's**

Black & White Scotch Whisky ▼

- **1960**

Burleigh Ware white pottery jug, made in Great Britain, with two small terrier dogs, one black and one white, and the words 'Black & White Scotch Whisky Buchanan's', decorated on the side with the Royal Crest.
- *height 12cm*
- **£30** • Huxtable's

Ideal Home Cleanser ▼

- **1930**

Unopened cardboard packet of soap with a metal lid and a picture of a house and garden. Inscribed in dark blue and bordered in white with the words 'Ideal Home Cleanser' and below in yellow 'contains Pure Palm & Olive Oil Soap.'
- *height 25cm*
- **£44** • Huxtable's

Johnnie Walker ▲

- **1940**

Striding jovial figure of a gentleman in a gold top hat with a brown bow, red jacket with tails, cream breeches, black boots with gold trim and tassels, carrying a black cane and standing on a dark green base with 'Johnnie Walker' in gold writing.
- *height 37cm*
- **£120** • Huxtable's

Slazenger Advert ▲

- **1960**

Cardboard advertisement for cricket bats by Slazenger with photographs of cricketers in action including Garfield Sobers, Colin Cowdrey and Mike Smith.
- *height 35cm*
- **£30** • Huxtable's

William Lawson's Figure ▼

- **1930**

Figure of a boxer in fighting pose, with brown hair and moustache, blue eyes, red breeches and a gold sash, and black boots, standing on a yellow ochre and black base with the inscription 'William Lawson's Rare Scotch Whisky'.
- *height 36cm*
- **£160** • Huxtable's

Guinness Mug ▼

- **1955**

Large plastic mug of Guinness inscribed on black with white writing 'Guinness is good for you'.
- *height 32cm*
- **£120** • Huxtable's

Rinso Box ▲
- 1950

Green box of Rinso showing a clothing line with two dresses and sheets blowing in the wind.
- *height 14.5cm*
- £12   • Huxtable's

Volga Caviar ▲
- 1930

Turquoise tin of Caviar Volga Malossol from Russia.
- *diameter 10.5cm*
- £28   • Huxtable's

Expert Tips

Keep a look out for the interesting packaging of today, as those items could become the collectables of tomorrow. Store them properly to keep them in their original condition.

Lifebuoy Soap ▶
- 1938

Lifebuoy soap in a red box showing a lifeguard throwing a life-ring with a cartoon bubble above with the words 'More than a good soap - a good habit!' written on it.
- *height 15.5cm*
- £18   • Huxtable's

Oxydol ▼
- 1950

Yellow box of Oxydol with dark blue circles and the words 'Oxydol' in white with a white star.
- *height 13.5cm*
- £11   • Huxtable's

Cure-C-Cure ▼
- 1960

Yellow tin of tube repair outfit with a red car and the words 'Cure-C-Cure by Romac', made in England.
- *length 13cm*
- £12   • Huxtable's

Robin Starch ▲
- 1930

Box of Robin Starch, which can also be used as a dry shampoo. Decorated with green and white stripes and a robin on a branch with a yellow sunburst background. Inscribed 'Robin The new starch', on the lid and 'Nursery & Dusting powder'.
- *height 9cm*
- £14   • Huxtable's

Jester Towel Soap ▲
- 1930

Orange and red box of Jester towel soap with a picture of a jester and the words 'for economy and cleanliness' printed on the side.
- *length 15.5.cm*
- £15   • Huxtable's

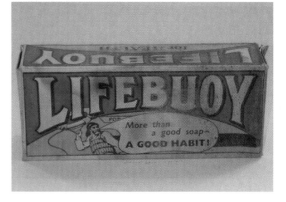

Coffee Packet ▲

- *circa 1920s*

A packet of 'delicious coffee', 'fresh roasted' by George Bowman of 84 Main Street, Cockermouth. 4oz nett weight.

- *24cm x 19cm*
  - £5 • **Keith Old Advertising**

Probyn's Sign ▲

- *circa 1930*

An enamel sign for Probyn's Guinness's Stout – the Harp label. From the Argus Brand showing a picture of two stout bottles.

- *65cm x 40cm*
  - £400 • **Keith Old Advertising**

Cherry Blossom Shoe Stand ▶

- *circa 1930*

A tin and wood shoe stand advertising Cherry Blossom shoe polish in dark tan, with printed transfer on its sides.

- *height 30cm*
  - £150 • **Keith Old Advertising**

McVities & Prices Digestive Biscuits ▼

- *1930*

Small red tin with a cream lid and a boy seated on a red tin of McVitie & Price's Digestive Biscuits.

- *diameter 8cm*
  - £12   • **Huxtable's**

Redbreast Tobacco Tin ▼

- *1930*

Ogden's Redbreast Flake tobacco tin, made in Liverpool, decorated with a robin shown perched on a branch.

- *width 14cm*
  - £12 • **Keith Old Advertising**

Pot Lid ▲

- *circa 1890s*

Areca Nut toothpaste for 'Beautiful White Teeth' with black and white underglazing, made in London.

- *diameter 6cm*
  - £85 • **Keith Old Advertising**

Show Card ▲

- *circa 1890*

Greensmith's Derby dog biscuits showcard (chrono lithograph) showing a clown holding a hoop for a dalmatian to jump through.

- *45cm x 34cm*
  - £200 • **Keith Old Advertising**

Book mark ▼
- *circa 1910*

A book mark advertising give-a-ways. The one is for Wright's Coal Tar Soap. The Nursery Soap, inscribed with the words, 'The Seal of Health and Purity.'
- *length 15.4cm*
- **£12** • **Keith Old Advertising**

Player's Ash Tray ▼
- *1930*

Pottery Player's ashtray showing an interior scene with a man seated smoking a pipe, a lady in a green dress, a hound, and the words 'Player's Tobacco Country Life and cigarettes'.
- *width 11.5cm*
- **£25** • **Huxtable's**

Golden Leaf Tobacco Tin ▲
- *circa 1912*

Golden leaf navy cut tobacco tin, manufactured by Louis Dobbelmann, Rotterdam. Showing an angel blowing a horn and flying on wings in the center of the tin, surrounded by flowers and the Dutch flag.
- *width 8cm*
- **£60** • **Keith Old Advertising**

Grimbles Brandy ◄
- *circa 1900*

Grimbles royal cognac brandy of Albany St, London. 3s per bottle. Set in a red shield with gold foliate design.
- *height 45cm*
- **£30** • **Michael Laws Antiques**

Senior Service Tobacco ▲
- *1940*

Red plaque with the written inscription 'Senior Service Satisfy - Tobacco at its best'.
- *height 28cm*
- **£15** • **Michael Laws Antiques**

Ceramic Coaster ▼
- *circa 1890s*

A white beer coaster advertising The Cannon Pale Ale, from the Cannon Brewery Co Ltd and bottled by Plowman & Co Ltd, London.
- *diameter 16cm*
- **£175** • **Keith Old Advertising**

Rennies Indigestion Tablets ▼

• **1960**
Yellow box of Rennies Indigestion tablets containing 24 boxes, inscribed with the words, 'Just the right size for pocket or handbag'.
• *width 9cm*
• **£16**   • Huxtable's

Macleans Toothpaste ▲

• **1960**
Macleans toothpaste in a white box with a dark blue line, by Beecham of Ireland Limited, Dublin.
• *width 19cm*
• **£8**   • Huxtable's

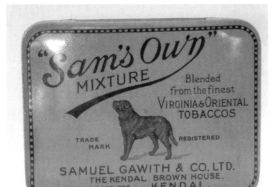

Palmolive Soap ▲

• **1930**
Unused Palmolive soap in green paper wrapping with a black bank and the word 'Palmolive' in yellow.
• *length 8cm*
• **£5**   • Huxtable's

Camay Soap ▼

• **1950**
Unused Camay soap with a turquoise and yellow wrapper showing a cartouche of a lady and inscribed in black 'Camay the soap of beautiful women'.
• *length 8cm*
• **£6**   • Huxtable's

Peter's Ideal Chocolate ▼

• **1950**
Peter's ideal milk chocolate shop dummy in a brown wrapper with gold writing.
• *width 11cm*
• **£15**   • Huxtable's

Nestlé's Chocolate Bar ▼

• **1930**
Unopened Nestlé's honey and almond milk chocolate bar.
• *width 10cm*
• **£20**   • Huxtable's

Sam's Own Tobacco ◄

• **1930**
Yellow ochre tin with a brown Labrador and black writing stating 'Sam's Own mixture blended from the finest Virginia and Oriental Tobaccos' by Samuel Gawith and Co. Ltd. The Kendal, 1792.
• *width 11cm*
• **£19**   • Huxtable's

Huntley & Palmers ▼
- *1930*
Yellow tin for Huntley & Palmers
biscuits showing a young lady
smiling with dark hair and eyes,
wearing a blue scarf.
- *width 13.5cm*
- **£24**   • **The Manic Antique**

Gin Fizz Stocking Box ▼
- *circa 1956*
Cardboard box for stockings with
a picture of a lady sitting cross
legged on a stool at a bar holding
a glass, and inscribed with, 'Gin
Fizz Crestmont created in Italy' in
red lettering on a white
background.
- *18cm square*
- **£18**   • **The Manic Antique**

Art Deco Tin ▶
- *1920*
Art Deco tin showing a smiling
lady in a white dress, holding a
letter and seated on a large
cushion. Beside her is a Pekinese
wearing a pink bow,, a vase and a
large pink lampshade on a red
circular table.
- *width 23cm*
- **£20**   • **The Manic Antique**

India and China Tea ▲
- *1920*
White enamel sign for Indian and
China tea in red writing, with
heads of an Indian and a Chinese
man.
- *width 71cm*
- **£55** • **Michael Laws Antiques**

Duncan Chocolates ▲
- *1930*
Cardboard box for Duncan
Edinburgh chocolates, showing a
young girl wearing a yellow ruff
holding a bunch of flowers,
wearing a blue hat with yellow
pom-poms.
- *height 5cm*
- **£15**   • **The Manic Antique**

Walter Palm Toffee Tin ▼
- *1950*
'Walter's Palm Toffee' tin with a
lady in a red and white striped
bikini with matching sunshade,
towel and holding a bottle of
orange juice on the beach.
- *24cm square*
- **£25**   • **The Manic Antique**

Huntley and Palmers ▼
- *circa 1950*
Circular biscuit tin with a pink
and white striped sunshade above
a garden chair and table with
cocktail shaker and glasses and a
tin of cocktail biscuits.
- *diameter 18cm*
- **£15** • **Michael Laws Antiques**

Bottles

Porcelain Snuff Bottle ▼
- *circa 1900*

Chinese porcelain snuff bottle with topaz stopper and silver rim.
- *height 7.5cm*
- £65 • Bellum Antiques

Opaque Bottle ▲
- *circa 1900*

Chinese opaque glass snuff bottle decorated with emerald green flowers and an oriental bird. With a cornelian stopper set within a silver rim.
- *height 7.5cm*
- £175 • Bellum Antiques

Snuff Bottle ▼
- *circa 1900*

Opaque glass Chinese snuff bottle with a stylised sepia leopard chasing its tail.
- *height 6cm*
- £145 • Bellum Antiques

Pagoda Snuff Bottle ▲
- *circa 1900*

Chinese white snuff bottle decorated with crimson fish underneath a pagoda roof. Green stone stopper set in silver.
- *height 7cm*
- £175 • Bellum Antiques

Blue Glass Bottle ▲
- *circa 1900*

Blue glass Chinese snuff bottle with green stone stopper set in silver.
- *height 6cm*
- £95 • Bellum Antiques

Chinese Bottle ▲
- *circa 1900*

Chinese snuff bottle decorated with a panda and palm trees with a semi precious stone stopper set in silver.
- *height 8cm*
- £95 • Bellum Antiques

Turquoise Bottle ▼

- *circa 19th century*
Turquoise porcelain snuff bottle.
- *7cm x 5cm*
- £220   • Ormonde Gallery

Chinese Bottle ▼

- *circa 19th century*
Fossiliferous stone snuff bottle
known as pudding stone with
tiger eye stone stopper.
- *7.5cm x 5.5cm*
- £185   • Ormonde Gallery

Smokey Quartz Snuff Bottle ▼

- *circa 19th century*
Smokey quartz shield shaped
snuff bottle with lion's heads
carved on the sides.
- *7cm x 5cm*
- £250   • Ormonde Gallery

Quartz Snuff Bottle ▲

- *circa 19th century*
Black quartz snuff bottle with
greyish white skin; carved in
relief with lion beneath a banana
tree, with a rose quartz stopper.
- *7cm x 4.5cm*
- £650   • Ormonde Gallery

Expert Tips

*As a rule the number of glass
layers and design of the carving
on a bottle is the most important
consideration to make when
choosing an item. Also check
that the stoppers are intact.*

Glass Perfume Bottle ◀

- 1870
Cranberry glass with gilt overlay
perfume bottle.
- *height 10cm*
- £420   • Lynda Brine

Green Porcelain Bottle ▲

- *circa 19th century*
Chinese moulded green porcelain
snuff bottle with moulded lattice
design.
- *6cm x 5cm*
- £300   • Ormonde Gallery

Porcelain Bottle ▼

- *circa 19th century*
Porcelain bulbous moulded relief
snuff bottle with a cartouche on
each side showing the immortals.
- *6.5cm x 5.2cm*
- £350   • Ormonde Gallery

Snuff Bottle ◄

- *circa 19th century*
Smokey quartz snuff bottle.
- *height 2.5cm*
- £250   • Ormonde Gallery

Glass Snuff Bottle ▼

- *circa 19th century*
Glass snuff bottle with red
overlay carved relief of a water
dragon chasing the flaming pearl
with green jade stopper.
- *height 6.5cm*
- £220   • Ormonde Gallery

Chinese Bottle ▲

- *circa 19th century*
Chinese bulbous shaped porcelain
snuff bottle with a design showing
dragons circling each other.
- *height 9cm*
- £220   • Ormonde Gallery

Crystal Snuff Bottle ▲

- *circa 19th century*
Quartz rock crystal snuff bottle
with engraved foliate design with
chrysanthemum.
- *height 2.5cm*
- £220   • Ormonde Gallery

Japanese Perfume Bottle ▲
- *1890*

Japanese cylindrical perfume bottle made from bone decorated with a foliate design.
- *length 13cm*
- **£795** • Bellum Antiques

Double Ended Bottle ▲
- *1890*

Double ended perfume bottle with silver stoppers engraved with a foliate design.
- *height 10cm*
- **£195** • Bellum Antiques

Pump Action Perfume Bottle ▲
- *circa 1920*

Red glass perfume bottle with silver screw top lid with a pump action spray and a hand painted butterfly on one side.
- *height 13cm*
- **£250** • Bellum Antiques

Victorian Perfume Bottle ▼
- *1899*

Small cut glass perfume bottle with a silver stopper.
- *height 5cm*
- **£95** • Bellum Antiques

Glass Perfume Bottle ▲
- *1880*

Circular glass bottle with silver top.
- *height 8cm*
- **£225** • Bellum Antiques

English Perfume Bottle ▲
- *1896*

Porcelain white perfume bottle with floral design and a silver top.
- *length 8cm*
- **£1,850** • Bellum Antiques

Twisted Glass Bottle ▲
- *1890*

Twisted glass perfume bottle with an opal and diamond stopper.
- *length 6.5cm*
- £550   • **Bellum Antiques**

Blood Stone Bottle ▲
- *circa 19th century*

Blood stone snuff bottle and stopper from China.
- *7.5cm x 3.2cm*
- £220   • **Ormonde Gallery**

Cameo Bottle ▼
- *1860*

Thomas Webb Cameo bottle in original box.
- *height 11cm*
- £2,750   • **Lynda Brine**

Perfume Bottle ▼
- *1870*

Glass perfume bottle with a silver gilt stopper with amethyst stones inscribed M.S.V.
- *height 9cm*
- £425   • **Lynda Brine**

Heart Shaped Bottle ▶
- *1870*

Silver heart-shaped bottle with scrolled design.
- *height 9cm*
- £520   • **Lynda Brine**

Silver Scent Bottle ▲
- *1760*

Silver lozenge shaped perfume bottle with a foliate design.
- *height 11.5cm*
- £650   • **Lynda Brine**

Cranberry Perfume Bottle ▲
- *1870*

Cranberry glass perfume bottle with moulded bubbles with a silver lid.
- *height 10cm*
- £400   • **Lynda Brine**

Blue Glass Bottle ▼
- *circa 1900*

A blue glass Chinese snuff bottle with an orange flame effect, silver stone.
- *height 7cm*
- £70   • Bellum Antiques

Ceramic Bottle ▼
- *circa 1900*

Ceramic Chinese snuff bottle in the shape of a cabbage leaf, with a stopper encrusted with semi-precious stones.
- *height 9cm*
- £165   • Bellum Antiques

Circular Wooden Bottle ▼
- *circa 1900*

Unusual circular wooden Chinese snuff bottle, with a semi-precious stone stopper and the body decorated with a dragon and lotus flower.
- *diameter 10cm*
- £225   • Bellum Antiques

Chinese Opaque Glass Bottle ▲
- *circa 1900*

An opaque glass Chinese snuff bottle decorated with a rocky landscape and a semi precious stone stopper set in silver.
- *height 8cm*
- £125   • Bellum Antiques

Glass Perfume Bottle ▼
- *circa 1920*

Cut glass perfume bottle with a generous silver stopper encrusted with flowers and decorated with a foliate design.
- *height 14.5cm*
- £445   • Bellum Antiques

Chinese Bottle ▼
- *circa 1900*

Opaque glass Chinese snuff bottle decorated with butterflies, a bat and cherry blossom, with a silver stopper.
- *height 7cm*
- £145   • Bellum Antiques

Cut Glass Perfume Bottle ▼

- *circa 1910*
A glass perfume bottle with lattice design around the middle and a silver stopper.
- *height 11.5cm*
- £150 • Bellum Antiques

Glass Perfume Bottle ▼

- *circa 1903*
Cut glass perfume bottle with a silver rim and glass lozenge shaped stopper.
- *height 8cm*
- £85 • Bellum Antiques

Hour Glass Bottle ▲

- *circa 1920*
Hour glass shape perfume bottle with a silver stopper.
- *height 6.5cm*
- £150 • Bellum Antiques

Cylindrical Bottle ▲

- *circa 1920*
Cylindrical shape perfume bottle with a silver stopper with inset with green stone.
- *height 8cm*
- £110 • Bellum Antiques

Clear Glass Bottle ▼

- *circa 1900*
Clear glass perfume bottle with a mother of pearl stopper set in silver.
- *height 6.5cm*
- £150 • Bellum Antiques

Cut Glass Bottle ▼

- *1893*
Cut glass cylindrical perfume bottle with ornate foliate designed stopper.
- *height 8cm*
- £140 • Bellum Antiques

Art Deco Perfume Bottle ▼

- *circa 1920*

Art Deco perfume bottle with stopper set in a silver plated base with blue stone set in the centre.

- *14cm x 12cm*
- £155   • Teresa Clayton Trio

Faceted Bottle ▼

- *1930*

Glass perfume bottle faceted design with a silver-plated rim and a pink silk action pump spray with tassel.

- *height 15.5cm*
- £158   • Teresa Clayton Trio

Victorian Perfume Bottle ▶

- *1880*

Victorian bulbous shaped faceted glass perfume bottle with silver stopper decorated with foliate design.

- *height 6.5cm*
- £128   • Teresa Clayton Trio

Glass Bottle ▲

- *circa 1930s*

Glass perfume bottle with moulded base, and a lozenge shaped stopper.

- *height 20cm*
- £145   • Teresa Clayton Trio

Art Deco Bottle ▼

- *circa 1920*

Art Deco glass perfume bottle with geometric design and a circular faceted lozenge shaped stopper.

- *height 14.5cm*
- £135   • Teresa Clayton Trio

Wedgwood Bottle ▼

- *circa 1930*
Wedgwood blue bottle with silver plate stopper.
- *height 4cm*
- £85   • Teresa Clayton Trio

Silver Bottle ▼

- *1893*
Small silver bottle ornately engraved with a floral design.
- *height 5cm*
- £158   • Teresa Clayton Trio

Ruby Red Bottle ▶

- *1880*
Ruby red double ended perfume bottle with silver stoppers.
- *height 12.5cm*
- £188   • Teresa Clayton Trio

Candy Stripe Bottle ▲

- *circa 1850*
Candy stripe pink glass perfume bottle with a rose gold stopper.
- *height 6cm*
- £288   • Teresa Clayton Trio

Ruby Bottle ▶

- *1911*
Ruby red perfume bottle with a foliate design engraved in the silver stopper.
- *height 7cm*
- £98   • Teresa Clayton Trio

Green Double Bottle ▲

- *1880*
Green perfume bottle with pinch back stoppers.
- *length 13cm*
- £168   • Teresa Clayton Trio

Cameras

Bolex Projector ▲
- *circa 1960*
An M.A. Bolex projector.
- *height 50cm*
- £150   • Mac's Cameras

Kodak Eastman ▲
- *circa 1920*
No.2 Hawkette brown
tortoiseshell effect bakelite
folding camera by Kodak.
- *height 18cm*
- £69   • Jessops

Contax G1 Camera ▲
- *circa 1990*
Contax G1, 35mm camera with
an F2 Planar lens by Carl Zeiss.
- *height 8cm*
- £50   • Mac's Cameras

Ensign Auto-speed Camer ▼
- *1932*
Ensign auto-speed camera
inscribed on the side, 100 mm
F4.5 lens, with focal plane shutter
speed of 15-500 sec.
- *height 20cm*

Newman & Guardia ▼
- *1913*
The new ideal Sybil camera by
Newman & Guardia with an
unusual Ross Express 136mm F4.5
Lens. The camera takes 3 and
quarter by 4 and a quarter inch
film.
- *height 23.5cm*
- £249   • Jessops

Zenit B Camera ▲
- *circa 1960*
Zenit B camera with 300mm lens.
- *height 8cm*
- £69   • Mac's Cameras

Bolex Camera ▼
- *circa 1960*
A Bolex P1 zoom cine camera.
- *height 38cm*
- £149   • Mac's Cameras

Mick A Matic ▲
- *1971*
Mick A Matic American camera in the shape of Mickey Mouse made by Child Guidance Product Inc.
- *height 20cm*
- £49   • Jessops

Bolex Super 8 ▲
- *circa 1970*
Bolex Super 8 480 Macrozoom.
- *height 19cm*
- £170   • Mac's Cameras

Miniature Mec 16 ▶
- *1950*
German miniature Mec 16 camera with an unusual pressed gold tin casing. With original leather case.
- *width 10cm*
- £99   • Jessops

Sputnik Camera ▼
- *1950*
Russian Sputnik camera and case with 75mm F4.5 Lomo lens.
- *height 8cm*
- £149   • Jessops

Balda Camera ▲
- *circa 1960*
Balda proximeter 2 and a quarter square camera with a range finder. 35mm lens including poxymetre.
- *height 9.5cm*
- £90   • Mac's Cameras

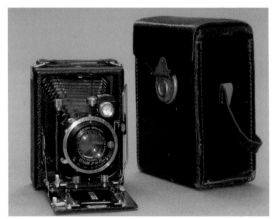

Rolleicord Camera ▲
- *circa 1955–65*
Rolleicord Triotar Camera 1.3.5 F 75cm.
- *height 19cm*
- £70   • Mac's Cameras

Wallace Heaton ▶
- *1925–35*
Wallace Heaton Zodel model folding camera with a 105mm F3.8. Zodellar lens and original leather case with handle.
- *height 14cm*
- £149   • Jessops

Rajar Bakelite Camera ▼

- *1929*

Rajar black bakelite No.6.
Folding camera. With 120 roll
film, with 6 x 9cm negative size.
- *height 17cm*
- £49   • Jessops

Ensign Cupid Camera ▼

- *1922*

Ensign Cupid simple metal-
bodied camera. 4 x 6cm exposures
on 120 film. The design is based a
1921 prototype for a stereo
camera which was never
produced. Mensicus achromatic
F11 lens. Available in black, blue,
grey and some other colours.
- *height 8cm*
- £89   • Jessops

Rolleiflex Camera ▼

- *circa 1955–65*

Rolleiflex camera with a Tessar
1.3.8. F7.5mm lens.
- *height 19cm*
- £70   • Mac's Cameras

Revere Stereo 33 ▲

- *1950*

Revere Stereo 33 made in the
U.S.A. 35mm F3.5 Amaton.
Complete with its original leather
case.
- *width 19cm*
- £249   • Jessops

Tennents Lager Can Camera ▲

- *1980*

Promotional Tennents lager can
camera.
- *length 12cm*
- £39   • Jessops

The New Special Sybil ▶

- *1914–35*

The new special Sybil. Ross
Xpress F4.5 112mm. N & G
special shutter.
- *height 16cm*
- £149   • Jessops

Kodak Camera ▲

- *circa 1960*

Kodak 35 camera with an F4.5
51mm lens.
- *height 6cm*
- £50   • Mac's Cameras

Retina Kodak Camera ▲
- *circa 1960*

Retina -Xenar F2.8 45mm lens by Kodak.
- *height 8cm*
- £70 • Mac's Cameras

Franke & Heidecke Rolly Camera ▲
- *1921–40*

Frank & Heidecke Braunschweig, Germany, Rolley Heidoscop three lens stereo camera including its own case. 7.5cm F4.5 Tessar Lens.
- *height 17cm*
- £699 • Jessops

Soligor Camera ▲
- *circa 1960*

Soligor 50mm lens Japanese made auto lens.
- *height 7cm*
- £74 • Mac's Cameras

Robin Hood Camera ▼
- *1930*

Black marbelised bakelite Robin Hood camera with a picture of Robin Hood by Standard Cameras of Birmingham. Takes darkroom loaded single sheets of 45 x 107mm film. Originally came with film, paper and darkroom safelight. Sometimes seen in England, but rarely seen elsewhere.
- *height 5cm*
- £69 • essops

Miniature Tessina ▼
- *1960*

Swiss made miniature Tessina camera in the style of a watch, with meter and strap. It took exposure on 35mm film, which was divided up in special cartridges.
- *width 6.8cm*
- £899 • Jessops

Mamiya ▲
- *1959*

Japanese Mamiya 16 camera.
- *width 11.5cm*
- £49 • Jessops

Contina Zeiss Camer ▲
- *circa 1960*

Zeiss Contina camera with an F2.8 45mm Novica lens.
- *height 7cm*
- £30 • Mac's Cameras

Eastman Kodak Camera ▼

- *circa 1950*

Eastman Kodak camera. The shutter is made in Rochester, N.Y. with an F7.3 10mm lens.
- *height 16.5cm*
- £70 • Mac's Cameras

Coronet 3 D Camera ▼

- 1953

Coronet 3 D marbelised bakelite stereo camera. Takes 127 film. Single speed shutter. Twin F11 meniscus fixed focus lenses.
- *height 8cm*
- £79 • Jessops

Kodak Stereo Camera ▼

- *1954–59*

Kodak stereo 35mm camera with Kodak Anaston F3.5 35mm lens, Kodak flash 200, shutter 25-200 with stereo viewer. With original box.
- *width 17cm*
- £249 • Jessops

Balda Jubilette Camera ▼

- 1938

German Balda Jubilette camera commemorating the 30th anniversary of Balda Werk. Folding 35mm similar to the Baldina. F2.9 50mm lens. Baltar, Trioplan, or Corygon. Compur shutter.
- *height 13cm*
- £69 • Jessops

Weston Lightometer ▲

- 1940

Weston lightometer 703 Weston Electrical Instrument Corp Neward. N.J. U.S.A.
- *width 12cm*
- £50 • Jessops

Plate Camera ▶

- *circa 1950*

Plate camera by Aldiss -Butcher with an F4.5 lens with 6 inch focus.
- *height 18cm*
- £70 • Mac's Cameras

Wrayflex ▲

- 1950

English Wrayflex 1 with outfit lens. Only approximately 1600 ever made. With original leather camera and lens case. Lens 50mm F2. Unilite.
- *height 9cm*
- £799 • Jessop

No. 4 Ensign Camera ▲

- *circa 1950*

No.4 Ensign carbine camera made in England with a Trichro shutter F77 lens anaston.
- *height 15cm*
- £40 • Mac's Cameras

Bust of General ▼
- *circa 1900*
A terracotta pottery bust of a general wearing a hat.
- *height 18cm*
- £120   • P. Oosthuizen

Pottery Jug ▼
- *circa 1890*
Pottery jug modelled as a man with a top hat and a crown on the back of his head.
- *height 15cm*
- £195   • P. Oosthuizen

Doulton Jug ▶
- *circa 1900*
Doulton commemorative jug depicting a soldier with a rifle and the words 'The Handy Man' in the centre and Capt H. Lambton on one side and Capt. P. M. Scott.
- *height 21cm*
- £625   • P. Oosthuizen

Doulton Jug ▲
- *circa 1900*
Doulton jug with a cartouche of the Prime Minister of South Africa flanked by a kangaroo, beaver and ostrich.
- *height 20cm*
- £590   • P. Oosthuizen

Copeland Commemorative Cup ▲
- *circa 1899*
A Copeland commemorative three handled cup, with a cartouche depicting Queen Victoria with the words 'Victoria Queen and Empress comforter of the afflicted' with flags from the Transvaal War 1899. Imperial Federation around the rim, and 'Unity is strength' around the base.
- *height 13cm*
- £1250   • P. Oosthuizen

Soldier Figurine ▲
- *circa 1900*
A model of a soldier standing with a rifle on a circular base with the inscription 'A gentleman in khaki'.
- *height 15cm*
- £68   • P. Oosthuizen

Masks Jug ▼
- *1935*

Masons ironstone jug commemorating King George and Queen Mary, a limited edition of 1000. With King George and Queen Mary in profile within a wreath border.
- *height 19cm*
- **£275** • Hope & Glory

Memorial Plaque ▶
- *1972*

An oval basalt plaque of the Duke of Windsor in memoriam.
- *8.3cm x 10.8cm*
- **£48** • Hope & Glory

Commemorative Plaque ▼
- *1914/15*

Bone china plaque commemorating the alliance between Germany and Austria, Kaiser Wilhelm II and Franz Joseph.
- *diameter 23.5cm*
- **£170** • Hope & Glory

Royal Albert Commemorative Mug ▲
- *1935*

Bone china Royal Albert commemorative mug of the Silver Jubilee of King George V and Queen Mary.
- *height 7cm*
- **£58** • Hope & Glory

Loving Cup ▼
- *1936/37*

Loving cup to commemorate the proposed Coronation of Edward VIII.
- *height 25.3cm*
- **£135** • Hope & Glory

Copeland Mug ▼
- *1936/7*

Earthenware mug for the proposed Coronation of Edward VIII, made by Copeland for Thomas Goode of London.
- *height 9.8cm*
- **£95** • Hope & Glory

Wedgwood Mug ▼
- *1939*

Wedgwood mug to commemorate the visit of King George and Queen Elizabeth to America with the inscription 'Friendship makes Peace'.
- *height 10cm*
- **£165** • Hope & Glory

Jubilee Jug ▼
- 1897
Doulton commemorative jug of
Queen Victoria's Diamond
Jubilee with a silver rim and olive
green cartouches showing Queen
Victoria.
- *height 16cm*
- £240   • Hope & Glory

Doulton Mug ▼
- 1901
Doulton bone china mug
depicting Queen Victoria in
memoriam with purple
decoration around the rim, and
decorated with a prayer book,
inscribed below with the words,
"She wrought her people lasting
good".
- *height 7.6cm*
- £475   • Hope & Glory

Diamond Jubilee Beaker ▲
- 1897
Goss white bone china beaker
celebrating Queen Victoria's
Diamond Jubilee.
- *height 9.7cm*
- £110   • Hope & Glory

Royal Wintonia Mug ▲
- 1911
Royal Wintonia earthenware mug
for the Investiture of Edward
Prince of Wales made for the City
of Cardiff.
- *height 8cm*
- £90   • Hope & Glory

Royal Doulton Beaker ▼
- 1902
Royal Doulton earthenware Kings
coronation beaker celebrating the
coronation of Edward VII in rare
purple.
- *height 9.8cm*
- £95   • Hope & Glory

Princess Mary Mug ▼
- 1929
Earthenware mug to
commemorate the visit of
Princess Mary Viscountess
Laschelles to Castleford.
- *height 8.6cm*
- £175   • Hope & Glory

Coronation Mug ▼
- 1911
Green and white coronation mug
of George V. Manufactured by
Booths.
- *height 7.5cm*
- £70   • Hope & Glory

Commemorative Cup ▲
- *circa 1900*

A commemorative cup with three handles. With W.H. Goss on the base, depicting The Dominion of Canada, South Africa 1900 with a soldier and a flag and H.M. Queen Victoria beneath the coat of commemorative ware.
- *height 8.5cm*
- **£125** ● P. Oosthuizen

Kitchener Figure ▲
- *circa 1915*

Staffordshire figure of Kitchener standing with his hand on his belt and a sword by his side on an oval base with the word 'Kitchener' on it.
- *height 35cm*
- **£220** ● P. Oosthuizen

Queen Victoria Plate ▶
- *1887*

Bone china plate depicting Queen Victoria's Golden Jubilee with Queen Victoria in the centre with a crown above her head, flanked by flags with a wreath border.
- *diameter 21.3cm*
- **£95** ● Hope & Glory

Winston Churchill Figure ▼
- *circa 1943*

Ceramic figure of Winston Churchill, with the inscriptions "Our Gang Copyright The Boss" on the base of his right foot and "The Bovey Pottery England" on the base of his left foot.
- *height 12cm*
- **£150** ● P. Oosthuizen

Glass Soldier ▼
- *19th century*

Glass figure of a soldier standing holding a rifle.
- *height 20cm*
- **£78** ● P. Oosthuizen

Queen Victoria Mug ▲
- *1838*

Staffordshire Queen Victoria coronation mug with a most unusual black and white depiction of the young Queen Victoria.
- *height 10cm*
- **£1,250** ● Hope & Glory

Jubilee Tile ▲
- *1887*

A tile commemorating Queen Victoria's Golden Jubilee with fragmented coat of Arms.
- *15.5cm square*
- **£75** ● Hope & Glory

Prime Minister ▲
- *circa 1941*

Pottery jug modelled as the Prime Minister of South Africa by J.C. Smutts.
- *height 13cm*
- **£98** ● P. Oosthuizen

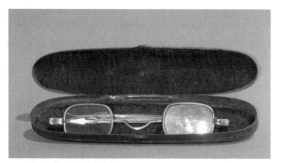

Powder Horn ▲
- *circa 1850*

American Civil War powder horn, made from horn with original bung tightly in place.
- *length 15.5cm*
- £75   • Gordon's Medals Ltd

Bronzed Imperial Eagles ▼
- *1914*

Two bronzed metal imperial eagles mounted on marble. Each with an iron cross 1914 2nd Cl., swinging from their beaks. Both fine unusual pieces, which would have been used in the officers mess as decoration.
- *height 14cm*
- £295   • Gordon's Medals Ltd

American Spectacles ▲
- *circa 1850*

Spectacles in original metal case, from the American Civil War period, with adjustable side-arm typical of the period and eye-hole ear pieces for attachment of cord.
- *length 10.5cm*
- £95   • Gordon's Medals Ltd

Porcelain Roundel ▲
- *1914*

German domed porcelain roundel, decorated with a coloured portrait of General Field Marshall Hindenburg shown in uniform.
- *diameter 7cm*
- £70   • Gordon's Medals Ltd

The Queen's Vesta Box ▼
- *1939*

The Queen's regiment vesta box with The Queen in relief.
- *width 5cm*
- £35   • Gordon's Medals Ltd

German Bronze Statue ▼
- *circa 1886*

Bronze statue of a German guards officer in uniform, standing with his left hand on hip and grasping sword in his right. Excellent patina and finely detailed modelling. Mounted on heavy granite base, with inset presentation plaque: 'to Hptm.Heinrich Esenbeck from the Officers of k.b.1 Inf Regt. Konig. 4.12.1886 to 11.12.1901'.
- *height 32cm*
- £725   • Gordon's Medals Ltd

Brass Shield Plaque ▼

- *1897*

Brass plaque of Queen Victoria in the shape of a shield to commemorate the Diamond Jubilee of Queen Victoria.

- *43cm x 32cm*
- **£175**   • **Hope & Glory**

Imperial Beer Stein ▼

- *1870*

Imperial half litre size beer stein with attractive painted enamelled panel of Ulanen, of the Imperial Lancers, hunting in a mountainous landscape. Inscribed with the following undamaged lettering: 'Zur Erinnerung an meine Dienstzeit'.

- *height 24cm*
- **£495** • **Gordon's Medals Ltd**

Blue and White Plaque ▲

- *1898*

Blue and white plaque of William Gladstone to commemorate his death. Maker Burgess and Lee.

- *39cm x 25.8cm*
- **£230**   • **Hope & Glory**

Gordon Highlanders ▲

- *1890*

One of a pair of Gordon Highlander commemorative plates. Decorated with a picture of a soldier standing guard, with the words 'Gordon Highlander' inscribed around the figure.

- *height 21cm*
- **£75**   • **Gordon's Medals Ltd**

Crown Devon Jug ▼

- *1937*

Crown Devon jug musical 'Super Jug' to commemorate the coronation of King George VI and Queen Elizabeth. Limited edition. With a lion handle.

- *height 30.5cm*
- **£2,250**   • **Hope & Glory**

German Knight ▼

- *1918*

German bronzed spelter figure of a knight in armour on a stained wood plinth, with a dedication plate on the side to Major Niemann from his brother officers of the 39 Field Artillery Regiment, 22 March to 16 November 1918.

- *height 45.5cm*
- **£325** • **Gordon's Medals Ltd**

Wall Plaque ◄

- *1938*

German black ash wall plaque with metal relief of Artillery crew serving their gun, and metal label reading: 'Res. battr. Opel 39.8.38. 11 10.38'.

- *23cm x 32.5cm*
- **£115**   • **Gordon's Medals Ltd**

Toby Jug ▲
- *circa 1939*
Small earthenware toby jug of
Neville Chamberlain, the handle
modelled as an umbrella.
Manufactured by Lancaster.
- *height 7.7cm*
- £65 ● Hope & Glory

Child's Teapot and Jug ▲
- 1937
Child's teapot and jug with
transfers showing Princess
Elizabeth and Princess Margaret
as children.
- *tea pot height 8.8cm*
- £70 ● Hope & Glory

Princess Diana Mug ▼
- 1996
Bone china by Chown. Limited
edition of 70 to commemorate
her 35th birthday and was her
last mug made before her death
and is rare.
- *height 9cm*
- £95 ● Hope & Glory

Wedgwood Plaque ▼
- 1974
Black basalt Wedgwood plaque to
commemorate the centenary of
the birth of Winston Churchill.
- *diameter 16.4cm*
- £65 ● Hope & Glory

Bone China Mug ▲
- 1937
Bone china mug by Hammersley
to commemorate the coronation
of King George VI and Queen
Elizabeth. Transfer with enamel
colours.
- *height 7.8cm*
- £75 ● Hope & Glory

Ovaltine Jubilee Mug ▲
- 1977
Ovaltine Jubilee mug inscribed
with the words, 'This was
presented to you by Ovaltine and
Woman's Own because you were
born in the week February 6th-
12th, 1977, The Silver Jubilee of
Queen Elizabeth II'.
- *height 10.7cm*
- £29 ● Hope & Glory

Expert Tips

*Check that the painting or
transfer has not been defaced in
any way by harsh cleaning or
chips on the porcelain. Also
check the provenance as this
conributes to the item's value.*

Ainsley Plate ◄
- 1953
An elaborate commemorative
plate by Ainsley in cobalt blue
with a gold border centred with a
portrait of the Queen.
- *diameter 26.4cm*
- £250 ● Hope & Glory

Ephemera

Wonder Woman ▼
- *2000*
Wonder Woman. An archive-
volume No. 9. By William
Mouton Marston & H.G. Peter.
- £38   • Gosh

Girl ▼
- *1951*
Girl . No.1. Published by Hulton
Press.
- £25   • 30th Century Comics

Courage ▲
- *circa 1950*
Courage. Vol.1. No.1. Published
by Miller & Son Ltd.
- £4   • 30th Century Comics

Look and Learn ◀
- *1962*
Look and Learn No.2, published
by Odhams.
- £2   • 30th Century Comics

The Amazing Spiderman ▲
- *1963*
The Amazing Spiderman, 'The
Enforcer' No.10, published by
Marvel Comics.
- £140   • Gosh

Rupert Weekly ▲
- *1983*
Rupert Weekly published by
Marvel Comics.
- £1.50   • 30th Century

Spivs' Gazette ▲
- *circa 1950*

Spivs' Gazette published by Clare
& Son Ltd.
- £3 • 30th Century Comics

Cheyenne ▼
- *1960*

Cheyenne, Exciting Adventure.
Published by Dell.
- £10 • Gosh

Mickey Mouse Weekly ▲
- *circa 1950*

Mickey Mouse Weekly published
by Odhams.
- £2.50 • 30th CenturyComics

Strange Sports Stories ▲
- *1963*

The Brave and the Bold presents
Strange Sports Stories.- No.48-
published by D.C.
- £10 • Gosh

Tales of Suspense ▲
- *1963*

Tales of Suspense approved by the
Comics code - No.37.
- £50 • Gosh

2000 AD Year Book 1992 ▲
- *1992*

2000 AD Year Book 1992
published by Fleetway.
- £5 • 30th Century Comics

Comic Cuts ▲
- *1955*

Comic Cuts No.2983. Published
by Amalgamated Press.
- £4 • 30th Century Comics

Teen Titans ▼
- *1967*

Teen Titans No.12 - published by
D.C.
- £7 • Gosh

Here Comes Daredevil ▲
- *1964*

Daredevil the Man Without Fear!
Published by Marvel.
- £45 • Gosh

The Flash ▲
- *1961*
The Flash featuring Superman
C.C. National Comics featuring,
'Flash of two worlds!' No.123.
- £120 • **30th Century Comics**

X-Men ▼
- *1966*
The X-Men – Holocaust.
Published by Marvel Comics
Group.
- £17.50 • **Gosh**

Blackhawk ◀
- *1956*
Blackhawk, The Delphian Menace.
A Quality Comic Publication.
- £35 • **Gosh**

Exciting Comics ▲
- *1947*
Exciting Comics featuring, The
Black Terror, Nemesis of Crime.
No.58, published by Better
Comics. Art Cover by Xela.
- £95 • **30th Century Comics**

The Fantastic Four ▲
- *1961*
The Fantastic Four, featuring the
Fantastic-Car, and Fantastic
Four's skyscraper hide-out!
Published by Marvel Comics.
- £300 • **30th Century Comics**

Iron Man & Captain America ▼
- *1965*
*Tales of Suspense featuring Iron
Man and Captain America.*
Published by Marvel.
- £65 • **Gosh**

Fantastic Four ▲
- 1963

Fantastic Four - the Living Bomb-burst. Published by Marvel Blastaar.
- £22   • Gosh

The Eagle ▲
- 1951

The Eagle ,Vol.2 No.3. Published by Hulton Press.
- £6   • 30th Century Comics

Tales of Suspense ▼
- 1962

Tales of Suspense -The Teenager who ruled the World!
- £75   • Gosh

Sensation ◄
- 1949

Sensation Comics featuring Wonderwoman, 'The End of Paradise Island!' No.104.
- £68   • 30th Century Comics

The Comet ◄
- 1958

The Comet published by J.B. Allen No.57.
- £5   • 30th Century Comics

Countdown ▲
- 1971

Countdown Dr. Who. Published by Sun Printers.
- £11   • 30th Century Comics

Film Fun Annual ◄
- 1938

Film Fun Annual. Published by Amalgamated Press.
- £25   • 30th Century Comics

Batman Year One ▲
- 1988

Batman Year One by Frank Miller and David Mazzucchelli with Richmond Lewis. Published by D.C.
- £8.99   • Gosh

X-Men

- 1963

The X-Men published by Marvel Comics Group.
- £175 • Gosh

Green Lantern

- 1959

Showcase presents *Green Lantern* published by D.C. No.23.
- £280 • Gosh

Wonder Woman ▶

- 1947

Wonder Woman No.22. 'Wonder Woman and the Color Thief!' published by D.C. Comics.
- £135 • 30th Century Comics

The Champion ▲

- 1949

'Johnny Fleetfoot gets' em guessing'. *The Champion.* No.1428 Vol.55.
- £4 • 30th Century Comics

Batman's Detective Comics ▲

- 1977

Batman's Detective Comics published by D.C. No.471.
- £7.50 • Gosh

The Amazing Spider-Man ◀

- 1966

The Amazing Spider-Man.
- £30 • Gosh

The Hotspur ▲

- 1950

The Hotspur No.699.
- £3 • 30th Century Comics

Star Spangled Comics ▲

- 1947

Star Spangled Comics - Batman's famed partner-in-peril Robin - the boy wonder in Solo Action! No.65.
- £160 • Gosh

X-Men ▼
- *1963*
The X-Men published by Marvel
Comics Group. No.1.
- £250   • 30th Century Comics

Love and Rockets ▲
- *1982*
Love and Rockets - No.1.
Published by Fantagraphics Books
Inc.
- £12   • Gosh

Mystery in Space ▲
- *1962*
*Mystery in Space- featuring The
Robot-Wraith of Rann!* Published
by D.C.
- £17   • Gosh

Superman ▼
- *1994*
Superman Archive - Vol.4, by Jerry
Siegel and Joe Shuster.
- £37.95   • Gosh

Aquaman ◄
- *1963*
*Aquaman featuring Aqualad and
The War of the Water Sprites!*
Published by D.C. No.10.
- £7.50   • Gosh

All Winners ►
- *1941*
*All Winners starring The Human
Torch, Captain America* No.3,
Winter Issue Timely.
- £650   • 30th Century Comics

Legion of Super-Heroes ▼
- *1973*
*Legion of Super-Heroes- The lad
who wrecked the Legion.* No.1.
- £7.50   • Gosh

Eagle Annual ▼
- *1951*
Eagle Annual No.1. Published by
Hulton.
- £15   • 30th Century Comics

Kabuki ▲
- **1999**

Kabuki published by Wizard
Entertainment.
- **£7.50** • Gosh

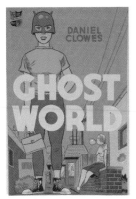

Ghost World ▲
- **2000**

Ghost World by Daniel Clowes -
published by Jonathan Cape
Random House Comic Books Inc.
- **£6.99** • Gosh

Essential Avengers ▼
- **2001**

Essential Avengers Vol.1,
published by Marvel Comics.
- **£11.50** • Gosh

The Beano Book ▼
- **1973**

The Beano Book. Published by
D.C. Thompson.
- **£20** • 30th Century Comics

League of Extraordinary Gentlemen ▶
- **2000**

*The League of Extraordinary
Gentlemen* published by America's
Best Comics Vol.1.
- **£18.99** • Gosh

Film Fun ◀
- **1958**

Film Fun published by
Amalgamated Press.
- **£13** • 30th Century Comics

X-Men ▲
- **1986**

X-Men published by Marvel. 25th
Anniversary.
- **£6** • Gosh

Batman Annual ▲
- **1964–5**

Batman Annual with Batman and
Robin also John Jones from Mars
and Congo Bill.
- **£20** • 30th Century Comics

Forbidden Worlds ▲
- *Sept–Oct 1951*
Forbidden Worlds Exploring the Supernatural. A.C.G. publications. Issue No.2.
- £120 • 30th Century Comics

Rangers Comics ▲
- *1944*
Rangers Comics featuring U.S. Rangers in Raider of Red Dawn. Fiction House Magazine No.17.
- £70 • 30th Century Comics

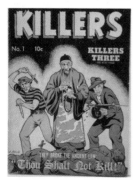

The Dandy ▼
- *1967*
The Dandy Book, published by D.C. Thompson.
- £30 • 30th Century Comics

Our Army at War ▼
- *1959*
Our Army at War No.1 by D.C. National Comics, including, 'The Rock of Easy Co.!' and other explosive Battle-Action Stories.
- £125 • 30th Century Comics

Sandman ▶
- *1988*
Sandman Master of Dreams published by D.C.
- £10 • Gosh

The Killers ◀
- *1947*
The Killer No.1, 'Killers Three Thou shalt not kill!', published by Magazine Enterprises, cover artist L.B. Cole.
- £200 • 30th Century Comics

The Fourth Man ▲
- *2001*
Planetary - The Fourth Man. Published by Wildstorm Productions.
- £18.95 • Gosh

Jimmy Corrigan ▲
- *2001*
Jimmy Corrigan and The Smartest Kid on Earth.
- £27.50 • Gosh

Drawn & Quarterly ▲
- 2000

Drawn & Quarterly Vol.3.
- £18.99 • Gosh

Soba ▲
- 1998

Soba, Stories from Bosnia by Joe
Sacco. No.1.
- £2.95 • Gosh

Justice League of America ▼
- 1960

Justice League of America -
published by D.C. No.23.
- £50 • Gosh

Beano ◀
- 1959

The Beano Book. Published by
D.C. Thompson.
- £70 • 30th Century Comics

The Essential Hulk ▲
- 1999

The Essential Hulk Vol.1.
Selections from Tales to
Astonish.
- £11.50 • Gosh

Superman ▼
- 1943

Superman No.20. Published by
D.C.
- £230 • 30th Century Comics

The Alchemist ▲
- 1998

Cartoon by Chris Riddel - *The Alchemist l.*
- £300 ● Gosh

Diana ▲
- 1968

'*Diana*' No.305, an English comic published by D.C. Thompson.
- £1 ● 30th Century Comics

Chris Riddell ▲
- *circa 1977–8*

Cartoon of John Bull by Chris Riddell.
- £80 ● Gosh

Sun ▼
- 1947

The Sun No.1. Published by J.B. Allen.
- £20 ● 30th Century Comics

Torso ▼
- 2000

Torso, a true crime graphic novel by Bendis/Andreyk.
- £18.99 ● Gosh

Steve Bell Cartoon ▼
- 1998

Cartoon of Prince Charles and General Pinochet by Steve Bell.
- £250 ● Gosh

Rhubarb and Custard ▲
- 2000

Cartoon of *Rhubarb and Custard* by Bob Godfrey.
- £250 ● Gosh

Rupert ▲
- 1979

Rupert the Daily Express Annual, published by Express Newspapers Ltd.
- £10 ● 30th Century Comics

Dennis the Menace ▲
- 1958

Dennis the Menace, published by D.C. Thompson.
- £15 ● 30th Century Comics

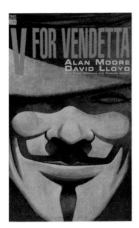

V for Vendetta ▲
- *1990*
V for Vendetta by Vertigo/D.C.
Comics.
- £14.95 • Gosh

Buster ▲
- *1960*
Buster No.1, published by
Fleetway.
- £30 • 30th Century Comics

Green Arrow ▼
- *2001*
Green Arrow – Quiver, Part one.
- £5 • Gosh

Ian Baker, *The Bar* ◄
- *1999*
Cartoon by Ian Baker entitled, "I
wish you'd stop playing hard to
get... Rid of !".
- £15 • Gosh

Cerebus ▲
- *1977*
Cerebus - the Aardvark Vol.l.
- £450 • Gosh

All Winners ▲
- *1941*
All Winners Comics starring
Captain America. Fall Issue No.2.
Published by Timely.
- £1,050 • 30th Century Comics

Mclachlan △
● *1998*
Cartoon of Eskimos by Mclachlan with the words, "Well, so much for solar panel heating".
● £180 ● Gosh

Bulletman ▽
● *1941*
Bulletman, a Fawcett Publication No.3.
● £160 ● 30th Century Comics

100 Bullets ▽
● *1999*
100 Bullets – Vertigo by D.C. Publications.
● £8 ● Gosh

Buffy ▶
● *2001*
Buffy the Vampire Slayer by Dark Horse Comics, featuring Angel.
● £9.99 ● Gosh

Rupert Adventure Book △
● *1955*
Rupert Adventure Book, published by Express Newspapers Ltd.
● £10 ● 30th Century Comics

Special Edition Comics ▽
● *1940*
Special Edition Comics featuring Captain Marvel, No.1. A Fawcett Publication.
● £400 ● 30th Century Comics

The Dandy ▲
• *1969*
The Dandy Book published by
D.C. Thompson.
• £30   • 30th Century Comics

Rupert ▲
• *1955*
Rupert The Daily Express Annual.
No.20.
• £40   • 30th Century Comics

Hunt Emmerson ▲
• *2000*
A biblical cartoon with reference
to Jesus and the story of the
loaves and fishes.
• £90   • Gosh

Bulletman ▶
• *1941*
*Bulletman featuring Bulletman and
Bulletgirl 'Be an American'*, No.1
by Fawcett.
• £475   • 30th Century Comics

Hellboy The Conqueror Worm ▲
• *2001*
Hellboy the Conqueror Worm by
Dark Horse. Maverick
Publications.
• £215   • Gosh

Planetary ▼
• *2001*
Planetary by Wildstorm
Publications.
• £175   • Gosh

The House of Secrets ▼
• *1971*
The House of Secrets No.92,
published by D.C. Artist:
Wrighton.
• £60   • Gosh

Do It Yourself ▲
• *1999*
Cartoon by Ian Baker entitled
'Do it Yourself'.
• £75   • Gosh

Gentlemen's Accessories

Top Hat ▲
- *circa 1940*

Grey top hat by Army and Navy, London.
- *height 14cm*
- £45   • Julian Smith Antiques

Shaving Brush ▲
- *1903*

Gentlemen's travelling silver shaving brush.
- *length 14.5cm*
- £400   • Bentleys London

Horn Beakers ▲
- *1873*

Nest of six horn beakers with hall marked solid silver collars in original leather case.
- *height of case 14,5cm*
- £2,000   • Bentleys London

Travel Clock ▲
- *1920*

Crocodile skin, 8-day movement travel clock, with Arabic numerals on a white enamel face.
- *height 10cm*
- £1,000   • Bentleys London

Travelling Cutlery Set ▲
- *1900*

Travelling cutlery set with ivory handles.
- *width 56cm*
- £550   • Bentleys London

Set of Razors ◄
- *circa 1880*

Set of ivory handled straight razors in an original silver and ivory box.
- *width 18cm*
- £1,000   • Bentleys London

Set of Horn Beakers ▶
• *1870*
Rare set of horn beakers, with hall marking (dated 1870) around the collar. They are all the same size and come with original leather case.
• *height 14.5cm*
• £3,500 • Bentleys London

Miniature Tool Kit ▲
• *1920*
Miniature travelling tool kit in a leather case with 'Bonsa' on flap.
• *width 14.5cm*
• £300 • Bentleys London

Grey Top Hat ▲
• *1930*
Grey top hat with original box by Herbert Johnson of New Bond St, London, W 1.
• *height 16cm*
• £75 • Julian Smith Antiques

Ironing Kit ▶
• *circa 1900*
Campaign officer's batman's ironing kit in original leather case, complete with board and a paraffin flask, a lighter and bright nickel-plated steel.
• *width 24cm*
• £1,000 • Bentleys London

Travelling Mirror ▲
• *1930*
Travelling mirror in original leather case with the letter H.R.B. inscribed on the lid.
• *diameter 23cm*
• £40 • Julian Smith Antiques

Bowler Hat ▼
• *circa 1930*
Black bowler hat with original box from James Lock & Co. Ltd., 6 St James Street, London SW1.
• *height 32cm*
• £45 • Julian Smith Antiques

Spirit Flasks ◀
• *1920*
Pair of silver-plated spirit flasks housed in original leather case.
• *height 15cm*
• £300 • Bentleys London

Handbags

Blue Beaded Bag ▼
- *circa 1940*
Blue beaded circular bag with an unusual gilt ball clasp, and generous beaded looped handle.
- *diameter 16.5cm*
- **£295** • **Beauty and the Beasts**

Bakelite Bag ▼
- *1950*
American silver grey bakelite bag with lucite top. With a flower and foliate design standing on ball feet.
- *height 15cm*
- **£265** • **Beauty and the Beasts**

Pink Sequinned Bag ▼
- *1960*
English baby pink beaded and sequinned small evening bag.
- *width 22cm*
- **£160** • **Beauty and the Beasts**

Two Owls Bag ▲
- *1930*
Brown leather bag with strap decorated with two owls with beaded glass eyes, surrounded by a foliate design.
- *width 21cm*
- **£145** • **Beauty and the Beasts**

Leather Handbag ▶
- *1930*
Brown leather handbag with chrome and orange bakelite clasp.
- *width 21cm*
- **£295** • **Beauty and the Beasts**

Cream Beaded Bag ▲
- *1880*
Victorian cream beaded bag depicting a basket of pink flowers with emerald green and pink beaded tassels, gilt clasp and chain handle.
- *height 21cm*
- **£695** • **Beauty and the Beasts**

Bakelite Bag ▲
- *1950-*
Light brown bakelite bag with
elaborate brass filigree clasp and
fittings to handle.
- *width 27cm*
- **£375** • **Beauty and the Beasts**

Black Beaded Bag ▲
- *circa 1920*
Black beaded bag with elaborate
gilded frame inset with diamante.
- *height 13cm*
- **£295** • **Beauty and the Beasts**

Venetian Evening Bag ▶
- *circa 1930*
Cream silk Venetian and
Chinoiserie design evening bag
with pagoda shaped clasp,
decorated with coloured enamels
and small white beads.
- *width 21cm*
- **£395** • **Beauty and the Beasts**

Silver Chain Bag ▶
- *1900*
Silver chain link bag with
butterfly design and blue stones.
With an oval mirror inside the
lid, and a chain handle.
- *height 10cm*
- **£165** • **Beauty and the Beasts**

Navy Chagrin Bag ▲
- *1930*
Navy chagrin bag with unusual
metal fittings and chain handle.
- *width 19cm*
- **£495** • **Beauty and the Beasts**

Bakelite Bag ◀
- *circa 1950*
Bakelite tortoiseshell bag with
metal clasp in the form of a flower
with a pearl in the centre.
- *height 17cm*
- **£290** • **Lynda Brine Antiques**

Art Nouveau Bag ▲
- *1900*
Art Nouveau white beaded bag
and frame, decorated with a floral
design of poppies, wild flowers,
with a gilt chain handle.
- *height 25cm*
- **£295** • **Beauty and the Beasts**

Red Snakeskin Bag ▼
• *1940*
Red snakeskin box shaped bag with a long carrying handle and brass fitting.
• *height 17cm*
• **£295** • **Beauty and the Beasts**

Sequinned Bag ▲
• *1930*
French aubergine sequinned bag with small gold beading, a blue enamel clasp with small cornflowers, and a gilt frame.
• *width 20cm*
• **£165** • **Beauty and the Beasts**

Square Perspex Bag ◄
• *circa 1950*
American square perspex handbag with brass design and fittings.
• *height 14cm*
• **£180** • **Lynda Brine Antiques**

Evening Bag ▼
• *circa 1950*
Cream silk evening bag with silver embroidery and beading with a chain handle.
• *height 17cm*
• **£49** • **Lynda Brine Antiques**

Leather Pochette ▲
• *circa 1930*
Small leather pochette decorated with two cartouches; one with a sleeping cat with a peony, and the other with a red Chinese bridge over a river.
• *width 16cm*
• **£125** • **Beauty and the Beasts**

Evening Bag ▲
• *circa 1950*
Evening bag with paste diamante.
• *width 20cm*
• **£29** • **Lynda Brine Antiques**

Victorian Bag ◄
• *circa 1890*
Victorian fine beaded green and gold bag with theatrical figures, and an unusual geometric design. Silver gilt frame with cherubs set with semi-precious stones and a gold beaded tassel.
• *height 24cm*
• **£695** • **Beauty and the Beasts**

Victorian Beaded Bag ▲

- 1890

Cream Victorian fine beaded bag with pink and yellow roses, with a silver gilt frame and pink and green glass beaded tussles.
- *height 25cm*
- **£495** • **Beauty and the Beasts**

Ken Lane Handbag ▲

- 1960

Ken Lane brown handbag with a dramatic coral circular diamante handle.
- *height 15cm*
- **£295** • **Beauty and the Beasts**

Floral Handbag ▲

- *circa 1940*

Petit point floral design bag with black enamel frame with gilt scalloped edge and gilt chain.
- *width 19cm*
- **£295** • **Beauty and the Beasts**

Clochette Evening Bag ▶

- *circa 1920*

Clochette shaped beaded evening bag, with rows of blue and pink with a black metal filigree clasp and silver and black handle.
- *height 18cm*
- **£395** • **Beauty and the Beasts**

Chain Link Bag ▼

- 1900

Gilt chain link bag with an Art Nouveau lady on the rim inset with sprays of berries inset with red stones and foliate design.
- *height 14cm*
- **£395** • **Beauty and the Beasts**

Velvet Bag ▼

- *circa 1860*

Victorian cream velvet evening bag with a silver filigree frame, and fine cut-steel looped fringing.
- *height 23cm*
- **£495** • **Beauty and the Beasts**

French Beaded Bag ▼

- *circa 1950*

French beaded bag decorated with pink roses and a gold and white beaded frame inset with enamel roses.
- *width 22cm*
- **£695** • **Beauty and the Beasts**

Silk Evening Bag ▲

- *circa 1920*

Black silk evening bag decorated with flowers in blue, red, and green with steel chips decoration.
- *height 18cm*
- **£295** • **Lynda Brine Antiques**

Black Beaded Bag ▼
- **1890**
Fine black beaded Victorian bag
with floral design of pink roses,
blue cornflowers and daisies, with
a filigree frame and paste jewels.
- *height 25cm*
- **£495** • **Beauty and the Beasts**

Clear Perspex Bag ▼
- *circa 1950*
Clear perspex American bag with
foliate design on the lid.
- *height 111cm*
- **£248** • **Lynda Brine Antiques**

Petit Point Handbag ▶
- *circa 1940*
A handbag with black petit point
background decorated with
flowers in a vase.
- *width 21cm*
- **£275** • **Beauty and the Beasts**

Moiré Silk Evening Bag ▲
- *circa 1940*
Brown moiré silk evening back
with a geometric gilt clasp by
Josef.
- *height 17cm*
- **£265** • **Beauty and the Beasts**

Wicker Bag ▼
- **1950**
Wicker bag made by Midas of
Miami, decorated with birds, and
green, orange and blue sequins.
- *width 37cm*
- **£135** • **Beauty and the Beasts**

Velvet Bag ▲
- *circa 1860*
Black velvet bag with cut steel
beading of a heraldic design.
With metal clasp and chain.
- *height 28cm*
- **£895** • **Beauty and the Beasts**

Red Plastic Bag ▲
- **1930**
Red plastic bag with a gold and
black geometrical design, with a
gilt chain handle.
- *width 19cm*
- **£395** • **Beauty and the Beasts**

Powder Compact Bag ▲
- *1930*
Black suede French bag inset with a powder compact. A Jeannes Bernard Paris creation.
- *height 11.5cm*
- **£245** • **Beauty and the Beasts**

Plastic Tyrolean Bag ▲
- *1950*
New York made Tyrolean plastic bag with brass filigree foliate design, a red and black plaid pattern and a red leather handle.
- *width 20cm*
- **£195** • **Beauty and the Beasts**

Art Nouveau Bag ▲
- *1890*
Brown leather Art Nouveau chatelaine bag with irises and leaves trailing along the brass clasp.
- *height 17cm*
- **£295** • **Beauty and the Beasts**

American Handbag ▼
- *circa 1950*
American clear perspex bag with geometric design on the lid.
- *height 11cm*
- **£245** • **Lynda Brine Antiques**

Gold and Silver Bag ▼
- *circa 1920*
Gold and silver beaded bag with geometric designs and gold fringing, with a metal filigree clasp.
- *height 26cm*
- **£595** • **Beauty and the Beasts**

Silver Chain Bag ▲
- *1900*
Silver chain link bag with Art Nouveau metal clasp inset with mother of pearl and pink enamel.
- *height 12.5cm*
- **£295** • **Beauty and the Beasts**

211

Beaded Bag ▲
- *circa 1920*
Gold metal beaded bag with pink lotus flowers and a green and pink geometric design, with a metal clasp and gold and silver looped fringing.
- *height 20cm*
- £395 • Beauty and the Beasts

Bulaggi Bag ▼
- *circa 1950*
Bulaggi plastic bag with gold metal fittings and handle, with the inscription Bulaggi on the right hand side.
- *width 17cm*
- £85 • Lynda Brine Antiques

English Handbag ▶
- *1831*
English leather handbag with floral design. Inside the inscription reads 'His Majesty King William the Fourth to his dutiful subject and servant John Singleton Lord Lyndhust AD 1831'.
- *width 19cm*
- £175 • Beauty and the Beasts

Brown Bakelite Bag ◀
- *1950*
America brown bakelite bag with lucite cover with faceted foliate design, made by Solar.
- *height 15cm*
- £395 • Beauty and the Beasts

Wicker Bag ▲
- *1950*
Simulated wicker bag with a fabric head of palomino horse made by Atlas of Hollywood.
- *width 32cm*
- £165 • Beauty and the Beasts

Metal Beaded Bag ▼
- *circa 1920*
Metal beaded bag with a blue, pink and gold floral design, and a gilt frame and chain.
- *height 22cm*
- £695 • Beauty and the Beasts

Petit Point Bag ◀
- *circa 1940*
Petit point bag decorated with figures on horseback outside a castle, with an opaline beaded and enamel frame.
- *width 21cm*
- £395 • Beauty and the Beasts

Kitchenalia

Coffee Mill ▼
- *circa 1950*
French coffee mill made from fruitwood with a metal and turned wooden handle.
- *height 11cm*
- **£50** • **Michael Laws Antiques**

Brass Jelly Mould ▼
- *1880*
Brass jelly mould with a hooped brass handle and fluted body.
- *height 19.5cm*
- **£45** • **Rookery Farm Antiques**

Chicoree Tin ▲
- *1950*
French Chicoree tin with a cream background and decorated with red flowers and a red and black geometric pattern.
- *height 21cm*
- **£17** • **Rookery Farm Antiques**

French Water Jug ▲
- *1880*
Large French enamel water jug with variegated blue and white base, decorated with pink flowers and green leaves.
- *height 37cm*
- **£78** • **Rookery Farm Antiques**

Bread Knife ▼
- *1940*
Bread knife with a turned wooden handle with the inscription 'BREAD'.
- *length 31cm*
- **£30** • **Michael Laws Antiques**

Enamel Allumettes ◀
- *1890*
Blue and white marbled wall hanging storage box, with the word 'Allumettes' in black writing.
- *height 20cm*
- **£48** • **Rookery Farm Antiques**

Copper Kettle ▼
- *1950*
Copper kettle of bulbous shape with four feet and a tortoiseshell coloured glass handle.
- *height 21cm*
- **£78** • **Rookery Farm Antiques**

English Sugar Jar ▲
• **1950**
English white porcelain sugar jar
with a circular wood lid with a
royal blue geometric design with
the words 'Sugar' in black.
• *height 17cm*
• **£28** • **Rookery Farm Antiques**

Porcelain Wall Box ▲
• **1950**
Porcelain wall box with wooden
lid and decorated with fruit and
blue banding with "Allumettes"
in gold writing.
• *height 15.5cm*
• **£45** • **Rookery Farm Antiques**

Bread Bin ▲
• **1890**
French enamel red and white
marbling bread bin with handles
each side and a handle on the
cover.
• *height 23cm*
• **£50** • **Rookery Farm Antiques**

Metal Salad Sieve ▲
• **1920**
Metal salad sieve with handles
and two feet.
• *height 24cm*
• **£15** • **Rookery Farm Antiques**

Ham Stand ▼
• **1910**
English white pottery ham stand.
• *height 20cm*
• **£45** • **Rookery Farm Antiques**

Enamel Utensil Rack ◄
• **1880**
French Royal and light blue
enamel wall hanging utensil rack,
with two ladles.
• *height 52cm*
• **£75** • **Rookery Farm Antiques**

Copper Kettle ▼
• **1850**
Large English rose copper kettle
with original patina.
• *height 30cm*
• **£125** • **Rookery Farm**

Rocket Ice Crusher ▶

- *1950*

American rocket ice crusher made from aluminium with red plastic handle and container. Made by Fortuna.
- *height 32.5cm*
- £150 • The Manic Antique

Enamel Coffee Pot ▲

- *1890*

French corn flour blue enamelled coffee pot with turned fruitwood side-handle.
- *height 22cm*
- £70 • Rookery Farm Antiques

Scales ▲

- *1920*

European cast iron weighing scales with copper pans and iron weights.
- *height 32cm*
- £45 • Michael Laws Antiques

Café and Chicorée Pots ▲

- *1920*

Café and chicorée, brown enamelled pots with white writing and banding.
- *height 20cm*
- £45 • Rookery Farm Antiques

Enamel Funnel ▶

- *1890*

French blue and white enamel funnel.
- *height 12cm*
- £12 • Rookery Farm Antiques

Wood Butter Pat ▲

- *1910*

Wood butter pat moulded one side with a handle.
- *length 19.5cm*
- £10 • Rookery Farm Antiques

Small Metal Mould ▲

- *1890*

Small metal mould in the shape of a fish.
- *length 9.5cm*
- £12 • Rookery Farm Antiques

French Storage Jar ▼

- *1920*

French hanging storage jar with a wood lid with red and white panels and the word 'Sel' in black.
- *height 27cm*
- £65 • Rookery Farm Antiques

Enamel Jug ▲
● *1880*
French enamel jug with a large group of irises with terracotta banding around the lip.
● *height 36cm*
● **£68** ● **Rookery Farm Antiques**

Bread Knife ▶
● *1920*
Bread knife with a wooden handle inscribed 'Hovis'.
● *length 30cm*
● **£22** ● **Rookery Farm Antiques**

Metal Weighting Scales ▼
● *1880*
Kitchen weighing scale with 'OK' and 'domestic use only' written on the base, four weights and a copper weighing scoop.
● *height 21cm*
● **£88** ● **Rookery Farm Antiques**

French Red Pot ▲
● *1920*
French red coffee pot with variegated panels of red and white and red handle and spout.
● *height 27cm*
● **£78** ● **Rookery Farm Antiques**

Copper Ice Bucket ▲
● *1940*
Copper ice bucket with foliate design.
● *height 13.5cm*
● **£15** ● **Rookery Farm Antiques**

French Utensil Rack ◀
● *1880*
French white enamel utensil rack with shaped top and a red and white check design to the centre with two ladles with red handles.
● *height 54cm*
● **£75** ● **Rookery Farm Antiques**

Fruitwood Flour Scoop ▶
- *1940*

Fruitwood flour scoop carved from one piece of wood with a turned handle.
- *length 28cm*
- £20 • Michael Laws Antiques

Enamel Casserole Dish ▲
- *1910*

French enamel casserole dish with painted cornflowers and variegated blue, white and turquoise, with white handles.
- *height 18cm*
- £68 • Rookery Farm Antiques

Green Thermos ▲
- *1950*

Green Vacwonder metal thermos painted with a selection of sportsmen including runners, cyclists, shot putters and swimmers, made to commemorate the Olympic Games.
- *height 27cm*
- £65 • The Manic Antique

Art Deco Allumettes ▲
- *1920*

Art deco allumettes storage box decorated with a purple floral and geometric design with red spots.
- *height 13cm*
- £45 • Rookery Farm Antiques

Peugeot Frères Coffee Grinder ▲
- *1950*

Wooden coffee grinder with the makers mark in brass, Peugeot Frères Valentigney (Doubs) with a large metal handle and wood knob.
- *height 19cm*
- £50 • Rookery Farm Antiques

Butter Press ▲
- *circa 1890*

Wooden butter press with an oak leaf mould.
- *height 19cm*
- £58 • Michael Laws Antiques

French Water Jug ▶
- *1880*

Large white French enamel water jug with red banding and a red pattern of squares and a central diamond with four gold bands.
- *height 29cm*
- £55 • Rookery Farm Antiques

Blue Enamel Candleholder ▶
- *1880*

French blue enamelled candleholder with gold banding on the handle.
- *diameter 16cm*
- £20 • Rookery Farm Antiques

Royal Blue Pot ▶

- *1920*

French enamel variegated blue coffee pot with noughts and crosses design.
- *height 27cm*
- **£60** • **Rookery Farm Antiques**

Oak Cutlery Box ▲

- *1880*

Oak cutlery tray with two compartments, divided by a central panel with a carved handle.
- *width 31cm*
- **£45** • **Michael Laws Antiques**

French Enamel Jar ▲

- *1930*

Royal blue wall storage jar with the word 'Sel' in gold with two rows of gold banding.
- *height 23cm*
- **£28** • **Rookery Farm Antiques**

Enamel Bread Bin ▶

- *1880*

French white enamel bread bin decorated with a delicate painting of birds and cherry blossom and on the cover coastal landscape with mountains in the background in a chinoiserie style.
- *height 33cm*
- **£95** • **Rookery Farm Antiques**

Knife Sharpener ▲

- *1880*

Knife sharpener with a brass inscription 'The Albert Knife Board J.& A Mc F. G.'
- *length 45cm*
- **£30** • **Michael Laws Antiques**

Aluminium Funnel ▼

- *1950*

Aluminium funnel manufactured by Stella.
- *height 15cm*
- **£3.50** • **Rookery Farm**

French Green Marbled Tin ▼

- *1890*

French enamel tin with green and white marbling and metal handle.
- *height 12.5cm*
- **£22** • **Rookery Farm Antiques**

Wood Bread Board ▲

- *circa 1940*

Circular wood bread board with a carved foliate design to the rim and the inscription 'BREAD'.
- *diameter 28cm*
- **£28** • **Michael Laws Antiques**

Enamel Coffee Pot ▼
- *1890*

White enamel coffee pot in two sections with purple flowers and red banding.
- *height 33cm*
- **£70** • **Rookery Farm Antiques**

Enamel Utensil Rack ▼
- *1890*

Enamel French utensil rack painted red and black with a shaped top and white tray.
- *height 54cm*
- **£65** • **Rookery Farm Antiques**

Metal Weighing Scales ▲
- *1890*

Metal kitchen weighing scales with metal base and copper scoop and weights, inscribed 'To weigh 2lbs'.
- *height 22cm*
- **£98** • **Rookery Farm Antiques**

Worcester Ware Cake Tin ▲
- *1950*

Worcester Ware cake tin with a red lid and 'Cakes' in red letters on the front and Worcester Ware made in England on the base.
- *diameter 22cm*
- **£28** • **Rookery Farm Antiques**

Copper Dish ▲
- *1920*

Medium size copper dish with cover with brass handles.
- *9cm x 22cm*
- **£58** • **Rookery Farm Antiques**

[image of small iron]

Small Iron ▲
- *circa 1920*

Small iron with a moulded base made by W. Cross and Son.
- *length 12cm*
- **£18** • **Michael Laws Antiques**

Sucre and Café Pots ◄
- *1920*

French enamel blue and white marbled pots printed in black with the words 'sucre' and 'café'.
- *height 23cm*
- **£45** • **Rookery Farm Antiques**

Flour Shaker ▲

- *circa 1940*

Green enamelled flour shaker
with the words 'Fine Flour' in
cream writing, decorated with
yellow banding.
- *height 12cm*
- **£10** • **Michael Laws Antiques**

Green French Candleholder ▼

- *1890*

French green enamel
candleholder with white trim and
scrolled handle.
- *diameter 16cm*
- **£15** • **Rookery Farm Antiques**

French Coffee Pot ▲

- *1890*

Orange enamel French coffee pot
decorated with a bunch of
cherries.
- *height 28cm*
- **£85** • **Rookery Farm Antiques**

Rolling Pin ▼

- *1880*

Turned wood rolling pin made
from fruitwood.
- *length 30cm*
- **£18** • **Michael Laws Antiques**

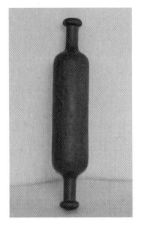

Brass Jelly Mould ▲

- *circa 1950*

Circular brass jelly mould with a
stepped pattern.
- *diameter 22cm*
- **£15** • **Michael Laws Antiques**

Harlequin Cups ▲

- *1950*

Harlequin melamine set of six
plastic cups and saucers. Argosy
Ware made by Melmex.
- *height 3cm*
- **£45** • **The Manic Antiques**

Art Deco Coffee Pot ▼

- *1920*

French enamel coffee pot with
angular design and variegated
brown and cream panels.
- *height 29cm*
- **£60** • **Rookery Farm Antiques**

Metal Weighing Scale ▶

- *1950*
Metal Hanson air mail weighing scale.
- *height 25cm*
- £55 • Rookery Farm Antiques

Storage Jar ▼

- *1930*
Hanging enamelled storage jar with a wooden lid and flue and white check design.
- *height 24cm*
- £38 • Rookery Farm Antiques

French Enamel Rack ▼

- *1890*
French pale blue enamel utensil rack with shaped top and blue and white sunshine border with two pale blue labels.
- *height 52cm*
- £70 • Rookery Farm Antiques

Porcelain Jars ▶

- *1910*
Five French cream pottery storage jars in three different sizes for cafe, sucre, farine and poivre, each one decorated in blue with wild flowers.
- *height 22cm*
- £95 • Rookery Farm Antiques

Enamel Storage Tin ▶

- *1890*
French enamel storage tin with yellow and blue marbled pattern.
- *height 15cm*
- £22 • Rookery Farm Antiques

Blue and White Coffee Pot ▲

- *1890*
French enamel coffee pot, white with blue banding and a white scrolling pattern.
- *height 29cm*
- £78 • Rookery Farm Antiques

Bread Board ▼

- *circa 1940*
Circular wood bread board with the inscription 'Bread' and a foliate design surrounding a central flower.
- *diameter 28cm*
- £28 • Michael Laws Antiques

Large Brass Kettle ▼

- *1920*
Oversized brass English kettle.
- *height 20cm*
- £68 • Rookery Farm Antiques

Luggage

Snakeskin Hat Box ◀
- *1912*

Lady's hardrock python snakeskin hat box with snakeskin handle, made in London for a family in Brunei.
- *23cm x 33cm*
- £1,500 • Julian Smith

Leather Suitcase ▼
- *1930*

Brown leather suitcase with leather straps.
- *width 73cm*
- £120 • Julian Smith

Gladstone Bag ▶
- *1930*

Lady's gladstone leather bag with brass fittings and leather handle.
- *width 37cm*
- £75 • Julian Smith

Army & Navy Hat Box ▼
- *1910*

Leather and canvas top hat box made by Army and Navy outfitters, comes with original top hat.
- *height 33cm*
- £200 • Julian Smith

Gentleman's Hat Box ▼
- *1910*

Leather gentleman's top hat box with leather handle, brass lock and leather strap.
- *height 23cm*
- £160 • Julian Smith

Crocodile Skin Case ▼
- *1930*

Indian crocodile skin case with handles each end and silver nickel locks.
- *32cm x 61cm*
- £450 • Julian Smith

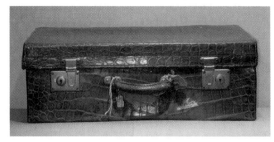

Crocodile Hat Box ▶

- *circa 1920*
Crocodile skin hat box with gilt over brass locks, with brown Moiré silk lining.
- *26cm x 41cm*
- **£4,000** • **Bentleys**

Crocodile Case ▲

- *circa 1900*
Small crocodile case with handle and nickle fittings, with the letters L.T. on the lid.
- *width 35cm*
- **£650** • **Bentleys**

Attaché Case ▲

- *circa 1900*
Rare moulded Norfolk hide attaché case with original brass fittings, a leather handle, and a green leather interior.
- *10cm x 47cm x 32cm*
- **£1,000** • **Bentleys**

Goyard Hat Case ▶

- *1920*
Goyard canvas hat case with a painted chevron pattern and a tan leather trim with small brass nails, leather handle and brass fittings.
- *25cm x 49cm*
- **£1,500** • **Bentleys**

Lady's Travelling Case ▶

- *circa 1930*
Lady's green leather travelling case in two separate sections, fitted with a silk interior incorporating a turquoise enamel brush set, boxes with silver gilt lids and a travelling clock.
- *width 32cm*
- **£600** • **Julian Smith**

Gladstone Bag ◀

- *1890*
Small leather Gladstone bag with brass fittings and leather handle.
- *24cm x 34cm*
- **£500** • **Bentleys**

Leather Briefcase ▲
- *circa 1920*
Leather brief case with circular
brass fitting and leather straps
and handle.
- *length 40cm*
- £500   • Bentleys

Louis Vuitton Case ▲
- *1920*
Louis Vuitton case with leather
trim and handle with brass
fittings.
- *width 70cm*
- £1,000   • Bentleys

Cricket Case ▼
- *1930*
Tan leather cricket case with
brass fittings and leather handle,
the interior fitted with leather
straps for holding a tennis racket,
by Finnigans of Bond Street,
London.
- *length 73cm*
- £800   • Bentleys

Dispatch Satchel ▲
- *circa 1900*
Leather dispatch satchel with a
good patina, one main leather
shoulder strap and three smaller
straps.
- *width 61cm*
- £800   • Bentleys

Tan Hat Box ▼
- *1930*
Tan leather hat box with nickel
fittings and a leather handle.
- *diameter 41cm*
- £700   • Bentleys

Hat Box ▶
- *circa 1890*
Tan leather top hat bucket with
brass fittings and leather handle.
- *height 23cm*
- £500   • Bentleys

Jewellery Case ▲
- *circa 1915*
Crocodile skin jewel case, with velvet and silk lining, with gilded brass fittings.
- *width 20cm*
- £950   • Bentleys

Gladstone Bag ▶
- *1960*
Gladstone python skin bag with brass fittings double bolt straps with stitched leather handle, in good condition.
- *width 42cm*
- £395 • Beauty and the Beasts

Wicker Picnic Case ▲
- *circa 1925*
Wicker motoring hamper. Well fitted with two white enamel sandwich boxes, and one large chrome sandwich box. A circular jam pot with leather strap, two wicker bottles and six glass holders, salt and pepper shakers, with place settings for six persons.
- *29cm x 57cm*
- £3,000   • Bentleys

Picnic Set ▲
- *circa 1925*
A leather cased picnic set with nickel-plated fittings and a setting for four people.
- *width 47cm*
- £1,800   • Bentleys

Louis Vuitton Trunk ▲
- *1905*
Louise Vuitton patterned trunk with beech wood rails leather binding solid brass fittings and handles each side.
- *54cm x 110cm*
- £7,200   • Bentleys

Louis Vuitton Trunk ◀
- *1920*
Rare leather covered Louis Vuitton trunk with brass fittings, copper rivets and leather handles.
- *70cm x 110cm*
- £9,000   • Bentleys

Mechanical Music

Rock-Ola Princess ▲
• *1946*
American Rock-Ola Princess No.1422, manufactured in 1946, plays 20, 78 R.P.M. records. In good original condition with pheonilic pilasters, and a central panel with decorative metal scrolling.
• *149cm x 54cm*
• **£5,200** • **Juke Box Services**

Eight Air Musical Box ▲
• *circa 2885*
Swiss eight air music box with five bells and drum by Paillard, in an inlaid rosewood case with brass handles each side standing on square ebonised feet.
• *23cm x 68cm*
• **£4,000** • **Vincent Freeman**

Singing Bird Autometer ▼
• *circa 1880*
Rare French singing bird autometer in a brass and gilded cage with moving chicks and singing bird. The cage with foliate design and gilded panelling around the base. Coin operated and in perfect working order.
• *58cm x 21cm*
• **£6,800** • **Vincent Freeman**

Heart Musical Box ▼
• *1950*
Heart shaped musical manicure box, lined with pink silk, with a circular mirror on the inside of the lid and a couple in evening dress dancing. Fitted with pink manicure set and two small circular metal boxes.
• *diameter 23cm*
• **£48** • **The Manic Antique**

Ami Continental ▲
• *1961*
American Ami Continental juke box, which has push button electric selection and plays both sides. In good working condition and fully restored.
• *170cm x 70cm*
• **£6,500** • **Juke Box Services**

Seeburg HF100R ▲
• *1954*
Seeburg H.F. 100R. Holds 60 records with push button electric selection. Plays both sides. Considered by many to be the best design of a series of jukeboxes made by Seeburg in the 50s and 60.
Made in the U.S.A.
• *158cm x 87cm*
• **£7,000** • **Juke Box Services**

American Music Box

- **1895**

Regina music box cased in light oak with two rows of beading. On the inside of the lid is a central figure of a lady surrounded by cherubs playing instruments.
- *28cm x 55cm*
- **£4,300** • **Vincent Freeman**

Zodiac

- **1971**

A Zodiac multi selector model 3500 phonograph, manufactured by the Wurlitzer Company, Tonawanda, New York, U.S.A. with the slogan 'Music for Millions'.
- *138cm x 74cm*
- **£1,000** • **Juke Box Services**

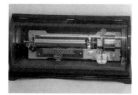

Swiss Music Box

- *circa 1890*

Unusual Swiss music box with convex glass lid by Mermod Freres.
- *27cm x 76cm*
- **£4,000** • **Vincent Freeman**

Rock-Ola 1454 ▼

- **1956**

Rock-Ola 1454 juke box in original condition. The cabinet styling is based on a Seeburg M100 from 1954.
- *143cm x 77cm*
- **£4,000** • **Juke Box Services**

Rock-Ola Princess ▼

- **1962**

Rock-Ola Princess stereophonic juke-box, Model 1493. Takes 50 records. Stereo and auto mix, (plays with or without centres). In original condition. Made in the U.S.A.
- *124cm x 76cm*
- **£4,000** • **Juke Box Services**

Swiss Music Box ▶

- *circa 1875*

Swiss music box playing 10 airs with sixteen reed organ by Bremond.
- *29cm x 69cm*
- **£5,000** • **Vincent Freeman**

Ami H ▲

- **1957**

American Ami H, one of the first of the car influenced style of jukebox with a wrap around glass. It holds 100 records, with orange and blue push button electric selection, and plays both sides. Fully restored and in original condition.
- *159cm x 80cm*
- **£7,000** • **Juke Box Services**

Singing Bird Autometer ▲

- *circa 1900*

French singing bird, sitting on a brass rail with white flowers in a brass cage. Standing on a circular base with foliate scrolling decoration.
- *height 53cm*
- **£4,600** • **Vincent Freeman**

Bal-Ami S100 ▲
• **1960**
The Bal-Ami Jukebox, made in
Britain by Balfoure. Engineering,
using *High Tech* parts
manufactured in the U.S.A by
Ami, to overcome import ban on
luxury goods after the Second
World War.
• *147cm x 80cm*
• **£3,500** • **Juke Box Services**

Key-Wind Musical Box ▲
• **1858**
Nicole Frères key-wind musical
box playing six operatic airs by
Bellini, in an inlaid rosewood
case. No.37625.
• *11cm x 56cm*
• **£2,600** • **Vincent Freeman**

Líepee Music Box ▲
• *circa 1880*
6 bell music box by Líepee,
playing 8 operatic airs contained
in an inlaid rosewood case.
• *22cm x 58cm*
• **£4,000** • **Vincent Freeman**

Ami J 200 ▼
• **1959**
Ami J.200. Holds 100 records.
With pink plastic push-button
electric selection, playing both
sides. Made in U.S.A. Fully
restored.
• *152cm x 83cm*
• **£5,800** • **Juke Box Services**

Birdcage Autometer ▼
• **1870**
French birdcage with two singing
birds in rustic setting with roses,
standing on a circular gilded base
with a leaf design and circular
feet. In perfect working order.
• *height 61cm*
• **£5,600** • **Vincent Freeman**

German Symphonion ▲
• **1895**
German symphonion in a rococo
walnut case carved with cherubs
and a courting couple on the lid,
with carved foliate design.
Standing on bracket feet.
• *height 30cm*
• **£6,000** • **Vincent Freeman**

Musical Jewellery Box ▲
• **1960**
Red plastic musical jewellery box
in the form of a radiogram with
turn-table that rotates when
music plays, Blue interior, red
drawers and a gold fleur de lys.
• *height 11cm*
• **£55** • **The Manic Antique**

Music Box ▲
• *circa 1875*
Music box by Nicole Frères
playing 8 operatic airs.
• *12cm x 58cm*
• **£2,500** • **Vincent Freeman**

Paperweights

Baccarat Millefiori ▲
- 1960

Millefiori closepack designed
paperweight with various
coloured and patterned canes.
- *diameter 7cm*
- £65   • London Antique

Whitefriars Paperweight ▲
- 1976

Whitefriars of London
hemispherical shape paperweight,
with six rings of composite
cogwheels of indigo, white, blue,
yellow and red, around a central
cane.
- *diameter 8cm*
- £195   • London Antique

Expert Tips

*Antique paperweights from the
major French factories of
Baccarat, Clichy and St Louis
are the most widely collected.
The finest can be dated to the
1840s. There are also good
examples attributed to the
Pantin factory.*

Wedgwood Paperweight ▼
- 1981

Wedgwood blue jasper and glass
paperweight, to commemorate
the marriage of the Prince of
Wales and Lady Diana.
- *diameter 9cm*
- £95   • London Antique

Cat Paperweight ▶
- 1970

Globular clear paperweight
mounted with a metal cat.
- *height 10cm*
- £45   • London Antique

Baccarat Prince Charles Paperweight ▼
- 1976

Baccarat sulphite paperweight in
facet form, with six lozenge cuts
and a bust of Prince Charles.
- *diameter 7.5cm*
- £195   • London Antique

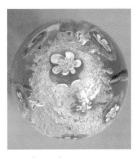

Circular Italian Paperweight ▲
- 1960

Circular Italian paperweight with
a silver bubble effect with stylised
pink and white flowers and a lime
green border.
- *diameter 7cm*
- £55   • London Antique

Whitefriars Paperweight ▲
- 1977

Whitefriars paperweight from a limited edition to commemorate the Silver Jubilee of Her Majesty Queen Elizabeth 1952-1977 No.418/1000.
- *diameter 8cm*
- £135   • London Antique

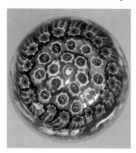

Multi coloured Paperweight ▲
- *circa 1950*

Closepack designed paperweight with emerald green, red, cobalt blue and turquoise canes.
- *diameter 7cm*
- £40   • London Antique

Jubilee Moonflower Paperweight ▼
- 1977

Jubilee moonflower using abstract techniques. Echoes the glitter and ceremony of the Silver Jubilee. Engraved on the base with the Royal Cipher, designed by Colin Terris No.2846.
- *diameter 7.5cm*
- £85   • London Antique

Paperweight ▼
- 1977

Crystal paperweight by Baccarat commissioned by Spinks. Limited edition of 500 to commemorate the Silver Jubilee of Queen Elizabeth II.
- *diameter 8.5cm*
- £245   • Hope & Glory

Purple Paperweight ▶
- *circa 1970*

Purple faceted paperweight with a central flower.
- *diameter 8cm*
- £55   • London Antique

Whitefriars Paperweight ◀
- 1976

English Whitefriars hexagonal faceted paperweight, with puce composite canes divided by six gauze tubes around a central turquoise cluster of canes.
- *diameter 7cm*
- £195   • London Antique

Prince Phillip Paperweight ▲
- 1976

Baccarat sulphite paperweight in facetop form, with six lozenge cuts and printed with a bust of Prince Phillip.
- *diameter 7.5cm*
- £179   • London Antique

Whitefriars Paperweight ▲
- 1970

Faceted paperweight by Whitefriars of London, cut with five roundels and moulded turquoise purple and white canes.
- *diameter 7.5cm*
- £195   • London Antique

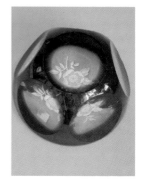

Photographs

Film Makers ▲

- **1960**

Three Italian neo-realist filmmakers, from l to r; Vittorio de Sica (1901-1974), Roberto Rossellini (1906-1977) and Federico Fellini (1920-1993) on the set of de Sica's film, 'Generale delle Rovere'. Black and white fibre, silver gelatin photograph. Limited edition: one of only 4 signed by the photographer Slim Aarons. Printed from original negative in Hulton Getty darkrooms.
- *length 25.4cm*
- **£1,500**   • Hulton Getty

Bacall and Bogart ▶

- **24th December 1951**

American actor Humphrey Bogart (1899 - 1957) with his wife Lauren Bacall and their son Stephen at their home in Beverly Hills in California on Christmas Eve. Black and white fibre, silver gelatin photograph from a limited edition: one of only 4 signed by the photographer Slim Aarons. Printed from original negative in Hulton Getty darkrooms.
- *length 61cm*
- **£1,500**   • Hulton Getty

Take It ▼

- *September 1970*

Painter Salvador Dali (1904 - 1989) in a characteristic pose with his trademark walking stick, with some of his works at Port Ligat, Costa Brava, Spain. Colour Lambda photograph. Limited edition: one of only 4 signed by the photographer Slim Aaron.
- *50.8cm x pro*
- **£2,400**   • Hulton Getty

Groucho Marx ▼

- *circa 1954*

American comic Julius 'Groucho' Marx (1895 - 1977), member of the Marx brothers, in bed with a joke cigar in Beverly Hills, California. Black and white, fibre silver gelatin photograph, from a limited edition: one of only 4 signed by the photographer Slim Aarons. Printed from original negative in Hulton Getty darkrooms.
- *length 61cm*
- **£1,500**   • Hulton Getty

Capucine ▲

- **1957**

French actress Capucine, (Germaine Lefebvre) (1933 - 90) fanning herself at a New Years Eve party held at Romanoffs in Beverly Hills. By Photographer Slim Aarons. Black and white fibre, silver gelatin photograph. Limited edition: one of only 4 signed by the photographer. Printed from original negative in Hulton Getty darkrooms.
- *length 50.8cm*
- **£1,500**   • Hulton Getty

Kings of Hollywood ▲

- **31st December 1957**

Film stars (left to right) Clark Gable (1901 - 1960), Van Heflin (1910 - 1971), Gary Cooper (1901 - 1961) and James Stewart (1908 - 1997) enjoy a joke at a New Year's party held at Romanoff's in Beverly Hills. A black and white, fibre silver gelatin photograph. Limited edition: one of only 250 signed by the photographer.
- *length 50.8cm*
- **£2,000**   • Hulton Getty

Jackie K ▼

- *circa 1959*

Jacqueline Kennedy (Jackie Onassis 1929 - 1994), wife of Senator Jack Kennedy at an 'April in Paris' ball. Colour Lambda photograph. Limited edition: one of only 4 signed by the photographer.

- *50.8cm x pro*
- **£2,400**   • **Hulton Getty**

Sea Drive ▶

- **1967**

Film producer Kevin McClory takes his wife and family out in an 'Amphicar' in the Bahamas. Colour Lambda photograph. Limited edition: one of only 4 signed by the photographer

- *length 152.4cm*
- **£3,500**   • **Hulton Getty**

The Rolling Stones ▼

- **January 1967**

British rock group The Rolling Stones; from left to right, Bill Wyman, Brian Jones (1942 - 1969), Charlie Watts, Keith Richards and Mick Jagger. Photographer: Keystone Collection. Modern black and white, fibre silver gelatin archival photograph printed in Hulton Getty Darkrooms. Limited edition: 300.

- *length 50.8cm*
- **£225**   • **Hulton Getty**

Man's Work ▲

- **1960**

Hugh Hefner working at his typewriter surrounded by 'bunny girls'. Publisher Hugh M Hefner at the Playboy Key Club in Chicago. He founded adult magazines, *Playboy*, *VIP* and *Oui*. Colour Lambda photograph. Limited edition: one of only 4 signed by the photographer.

- *length 50.8cm*
- **£2,400**   • **Hulton Getty**

Victoria Bridge ▲

- **1859**

Victoria Bridge - Special limited edition. A lone man sitting on the Victoria Railway Bridge over the St Lawrence River in Montreal, during its construction. Photographer: William England/London Stereoscopic Company. PLATINUM Photograph. Modern platinum print made from original glass negative by Studio 31. Platinum Limited edition: 10 only.

- *paper size: 40.7cm x 30.5cm image size: 23cm x 20.4cm*
- **£500**   • **Hulton Getty**

Hitchcock Profile ▼

- **July 1966**

Film director Alfred Hitchcock (1889 - 1980) during the filming of 'The Torn Curtain' by photographer Curt Gunther/BIPs Collection. Modern black and white, fibre silver gelatin archival photograph, printed in Hulton Getty Darkrooms. Limited edition: 300.

- *length 50.8cm*
- **£225**   **Hulton Getty**

Night Time New York ▼

- **1936**

Paramount Building in Times Square, New York, towers over Schenley's Chinese Restaurant. Photographer: Fox Photos Collection. Modern black and white, fibre silver gelatin archival photograph, printed in Hulton Getty darkrooms. Limited edition: 300.

- *length 50.8cm*
- **£225**   • **Hulton Getty**

Chrysler Building ▲
- **3rd May 1957**
The Chrysler Building in New York by Photographer: Phil Burcham, Fox Photos. Modern black and white, fibre silver gelatin archival photograph, printed in Hulton Getty darkrooms. Limited edition: 300.
- *length 50.8cm*
- **£225**   • Hulton Getty

Taylor Reclines ▲
- **1954**
American actress Elizabeth Taylor reclining in bed by the photographer Baron. Modern black and white, fibre silver gelatin archival photograph, printed in Hulton Getty darkrooms. Limited edition: 300.
- *length 50.8cm*
- **£225**   • Hulton Getty

John Lennon Profile ▼
- **26th June 1967**
John Lennon (1940 - 1980), singer, songwriter and guitarist with pop group 'The Beatles' by photographer Peter King, Fox Photos. Modern black and white, fibre silver gelatin archival photograph, printed in Hulton Getty darkrooms. Limited edition: 300.
- *length 50.8cm*
- **£225**   • Hulton Getty

Ali In Training ▼
- **August 1966**
American heavyweight boxer Muhammad Ali in training in London for his fight against Brian London. Photographer: R.McPhedran, Express Collection. Modern black and white, fibre silver gelatin archival photograph, printed in Hulton Getty darkrooms. Limited edition: 300.
- *length 50.8cm*
- **£225**   • Hulton Getty

Commissionaire's Dog ◀
- **22nd October 1938**
A hotel commissionaire talking to a small dog in London. Photographer: Kurt Hutton, Picture Post. Modern black and white, fibre silver gelatin archival photograph, printed in Hulton Getty darkrooms. Limited edition: 300.
- *length 40.7cm*
- **£185**   • Hulton Getty

The Beatles ▲
- **10th January 1964**
Paul McCartney, Ringo Starr, John Lennon (1940 - 1980) and George Harrison of British pop group, 'The Beatles'. Photographer: Terry Disney, Express Collection. Modern black and white, fibre silver gelatin archival photograph, printed in Hulton Getty darkrooms. Limited edition: 300.
- *length 50.8cm*
- **£225**   • Hulton Getty

Gorbals Boys ▲
- **31st January 1948**
Two boys in the Gorbals area of Glasgow. The Gorbals tenements were built quickly and cheaply in the 1840s. Conditions were appalling; overcrowding was standard and sewage and water facilities inadequate. The tenements housed about 40,000 people with up to eight family members sharing a single room, 30 residents sharing a toilet and 40 sharing a tap. By the time this photograph was taken 850 tenements had been demolished since 1920. Photographer: Bert Hardy, Picture Post. Modern black and white, fibre silver gelatin archival photograph, printed in Hulton Getty darkrooms. Limited edition: 300.
- *length 40.7cm*
- **£185**   • Hulton Getty

Snow in the Park ▼
- **1947**
A man trudging through Central Park West, New York City, in a blizzard by photographer: Nat Fein/ Courtesy of Nat Fein's Estate. Exclusive. Black and white, fibre silver gelatin archival photograph, printed from original negative in Hulton Getty darkrooms.
- *length 50.8cm*
- **£485**   • Hulton Getty

Fonda in Town ▼
- **1951**
Film star Henry Fonda (1905 - 1982) on a balcony overlooking a street in New York by photographer Slim Aarons. Black and white, fibre silver gelatin photograph, printed from original negative in Hulton Getty darkrooms. Limited edition: 300.
- *paper: 40.7cm x 30.5cm*
image: 30.5cm x 30.5cm
- **£185**   • **Hulton Getty Picture Gallery**

Walking in the Rain ▲
- *circa 1955*
A man and his dog walking in the rain in Central Park, New York City by photographer: Nat Fein/Courtesy Of Nat Fein's Estate. Black and white, fibre silver gelatin archival photograph, printed from original negative in Hulton Getty darkrooms. Exclusive.
- *length 40.7cm*
- **£415**   • Hulton Getty

Guggenheim Window ▲
- *circa 1955*
The Guggenheim Museum of Modern and Contemporary Art in New York. Photographer: Sherman, Three Lions Collection. Black and white fibre, silver gelatin photograph, printed from original negative in Hulton Getty darkrooms. Limited edition: 300.
- *length 61cm*
- **£250**   • Hulton Getty

Fair Fun ▲
- **8th October 1938**
Two young women enjoying themselves on a roller coaster at Southend Fair, England by the photographer Kurt Hutton, Picture Post. Modern black and white, fibre silver gelatin archival photograph, printed in Hulton Getty Darkrooms. Limited edition: 300.
- *length 50.8cm*
- **£225**   • Hulton Getty

Bright Lights ▲
- **1970**
Aerial view of the Manhattan skyline at night, looking southeast down Fifth Avenue, from the RCA Building Rockefeller Center, New York City by photographer: Lawrence Thornton. Modern black and white, fibre silver gelatin archival photograph, printed in Hulton Getty Darkrooms. Limited edition: 300.
- *length 50.8cm*
- **£225**   • Hulton Getty

Jazz Scooter ▶
- **1949**
Lucille Brown takes control of the Vespa scooter as her husband Louis Armstrong (1898 - 1971) displays his musical appreciation of the ancient Coliseum in Rome. Black and white fibre, silver gelatin photograph, from a limited edition of 300 by photographer Slim Aarons. Printed from original negative in Hulton Getty darkrooms.
- *length 50.8cm*
- **£225**   • Hulton Getty

Cary in Rain ▼
- 1957

British-born American actor Cary Grant (1904 - 1986) sheltering in a hotel porch as he waits for the rain to stop. Photographer: Express Collection. Modern black and white, fibre silver gelatin archival photograph, printed in Hulton Getty darkrooms. Limited edition: 300.
- *length 40.7cm*
- £185   • Hulton Getty

SS Arctees ▶
- 26th January 1934

The SS Arctees, designed by Sir Joseph Isherwood and christened by his wife. The ship was built to the 'Arcform' design of hull. This shot shows the unusual rudder design, before she was launched at Furness Shipbuilding Co's yard at Haverton-on-Tees, County Durham. Photographer: Douglas Miller, Topical Press Agency. Modern black and white, fibre silver gelatin archival photograph, printed in Hulton Getty Darkrooms. Limited edition of 300.
- *length 40.7cm*
- £185   • Hulton Getty

Great Loss of Life ▲
- 16th April 1912

Newspaper boy Ned Parfett selling copies of the Evening News telling of the Titanic maritime disaster. Photographer: Topical Press Agency. Modern black and white, fibre silver gelatin archival photograph, printed in Hulton Getty darkrooms. Limited edition: 300
- *length 40.7cm*
- £185   • Hulton Getty

Racing Yacht ▲
- 6th August 1935

Racing Yacht 'Candida' during a race at the Cowes Regatta. Photographer: E.Dean, Topical Press Agency. Modern black and white, fibre silver gelatin archival photograph, printed in Hulton Getty darkrooms. Limited edition: 300
- *length 61cm*
- £250   • Hulton Getty

Lying on Deck ▼
- 1st July 1939

The crew of a 12-metre racing yacht lying on the deck to lessen windage during a big race. Photographer: Kurt Hutton, Picture Post. Modern black and white, fibre silver gelatin archival photograph, printed in Hulton Getty darkrooms. Limited edition: 300.
- *length 50.8cm*
- £225   • Hulton Getty

Mike McKendrick ▼
- 1963

Black and white fibre, silver gelatin photograph of American banjo player Mike McKendrick performing in Chicago by the photographer Slim Aarons. Printed from original negative in Hulton Getty darkrooms from a limited edition of 300.
- *length 40.7cm*
- £185   • Hulton Getty

Lady Day ▼
● **1954**
American jazz singer Billie
Holiday (1915 - 1959) in the
spotlight during a performance by
photographer Charles Hewitt,
Picture Post. A modern black and
white fibre, silver gelatin archival
photograph, printed in Hulton
Getty Darkrooms. Limited
edition: 300.
● *length 40.7cm*
● **£185**   ● Hulton Getty

Early Aircraft ▼
● **11th April 1907**
Mr Guillon attempts to fly his
Guillon and Clouzy aeroplane on
the Epsom Downs, Surrey.
Photographer: Topical Press
Agency. Modern black and white
fibre, silver gelatin archival
photograph, printed in Hulton
Getty darkrooms. Limited
edition: 300.
● *length 40.7cm*
● **£185**   ● Hulton Getty

Twin Angels ▲
● *circa 1865*
A pair of baby twins lie sleeping
whilst a pair of twin angels watch
over them. Photographer:
London Stereoscopic Co. Black
and white fibre, silver gelatin
photograph, printed from original
negative in Hulton Getty
darkrooms. Limited edition: 300.
● *length 30.5cm*
● **£125**   ● Hulton Getty

Grand Central Light ▲
● *circa 1930*
Beams of sunlight streaming
through the windows at Grand
Central Station, New York by the
photographer Hal Morey, Fox
Photos. Modern black and white
fibre, silver gelatin archival
photograph, printed in Hulton
Getty darkrooms. Limited
edition: 300.
● *length 50.8cm*
● **£225**   ● Hulton Getty

Jimi Hendrix ▲
● *August 1970*
Rock guitar virtuoso Jimi
Hendrix (1942 - 1970) caught
mid guitar-break during his
performance at the Isle of Wight
Festival from the Evening
Standard collection.
Modern, black and white fibre,
silver gelatin archival
photograph, printed in Hulton
Getty darkrooms. Limited
edition: 300.
● *length 50.8cm*
● **£225**   ● Hulton Getty

Duke Ellington ▼
● *October 1958*
Modern black and white, fibre
silver gelatin, archival
photograph of American big band
leader and legendary jazz pianist
Duke Ellington (1899 - 1974)
from the Evening Standard
collection. Printed in Hulton
Getty darkrooms. Limited
edition: 300.
● *length 30.5cm*
● **£125**   ● Hulton Getty

Maynooth College ▲
- 1858

Maynooth College (the National College of Saint Patrick) seen through an arch. Founded in the year 1795, the college is situated in County Kildare, about twelve miles from Dublin by the photographer William England, LSC. Black and white fibre silver gelatin 'quad' photograph, printed from original negative in Hulton Getty darkrooms. Limited edition: 300.
- *length 61cm*
- £250   • Hulton Getty

Delivery after Raid ▲
- 9th October 1940

Delivery After Raid - A milkman delivering milk in a London street devastated during a German bombing raid. Firemen are dampening down the ruins behind him. Photographer: Fred Morley, Fox Photos. Modern black and white, fibre silver gelatin archival photograph, printed in Hulton Getty darkrooms. Limited edition: 300.
- *length 40.7cm*
- £185   • Hulton Getty

River Ottawa ▼
- 1859

Gentlemen contemplate the beauty of the Chaudiere falls on the River Ottawa by photographer William England, LSC. A black and white fibre, silver gelatin photograph, printed from original negative in Hulton Getty Darkrooms. Limited Edition: 300.
- *length 40.7cm*
- £185   • Hulton Getty

Power Station ▼
- circa 1935

Smoke belches from the famous chimneys of London's Battersea Power Station. This photograph was taken before the chimneys increased to four in number. Photographer: Fox Photos Collection. Modern black and white, fibre silver gelatin archival photograph, printed in Hulton Getty darkrooms. Limited edition: 300.
- *length 40.7cm*
- £185   • Hulton Getty

Stamford Bridge ◄
- circa 1925

Stamford Bridge, Chelsea Football Club's Stadium by the photographer A.H. Robinson. Black and white fibre, silver gelatin photograph, printed from original negative in Hulton Getty Darkrooms. Limited Edition: 300.
- *61cm x pro, panoramic format*
- £250   • Hulton Getty

Evening Dior ▲
- 4th September 1954

An evening ensemble of tight-waisted jacket with long fur trimmed sleeves worn over a full, ground-length skirt. Designed by Dior in Duchess satin. Photographer: John Chillingworth, Picture Post. Black and white toned fibre, silver gelatin photograph, printed from original negative in Hulton Getty darkrooms. Limited edition: 300.
- *length 30.5cm*
- £187   • Hulton Getty

Jessie's Hands ▲
- 1930

The hands of Jessie Matthews (1907 - 1981), dancer and film-star by the photographer Sasha. Black and white toned fibre, silver gelatin photograph, printed from original negative in Hulton Getty darkrooms. Limited edition: 300.
- *length 50.8cm*
- £337   • Hulton Getty

Sophia Loren ▲
• *April 1959*
Italian film actress Sophia Loren on the phone to her mother. Photographer: Keystone Photos. Modern black and white, fibre silver gelatin archival photograph, printed in Hulton Getty darkrooms. Limited edition: 300.
• *length 40.7cm*
• **£185**　　• **Hulton Getty**

Marilyn Monroe ▲
• *1953*
EXCLUSIVE. A portrait of actress Marilyn Monroe (1926 - 1962) surrounded by reporters and fans outside Grauman's Chinese Theater in Hollywood, California. Photographer: Murray Garrett. A black and white fibre, silver gelatin photograph, printed from original negative in Hulton Getty Darkrooms. Signed limited edition: 75 only signed by photographer.
• *length 40.7cm*
• **From £500**　　• **Hulton Getty**

Audrey's Funny Face ▼
• *7th July 1956*
Actress Audrey Hepburn (1929-1993) on the set of the Paramount musical 'Funny Face'. Costumes by Givenchy. Photographer: Bert Hardy, Picture Post. Modern black and white, fibre silver gelatin archival photograph, printed in Hulton Getty darkrooms. Limited edition: 300.
• *length 50.8cm*
• **£225**　　• **Hulton Getty**

Marilyn Monroe ▼
• *1954*
EXCLUSIVE. American actor Marilyn Monroe (1926 - 1962) emerges from a car, wearing a strapless white gown and white fur coat at the premiere of director Walter Lang's film 'There's No Business Like Show Business'. Photographer: Murray Garrett. A black and white fibre, silver gelatin photograph, printed from original negative in Hulton Getty Darkrooms. Signed limited edition: 75 only signed by photographer.
• *length 50.8cm*
• **From £500**　　• **Hulton Getty**

Street Games ▲
• *7th August 1954*
A young child wearing an Indian headdress hides in a coalhole as he takes aim under the watchful eye of a friend. By the photographer Thurston Hopkins, Picture Post collection. A black and white fibre, silver gelatin photograph, printed from original negative in Hulton Getty darkrooms. Limited edition: 300.
• *length 40.7cm*
• **£185**　　• **Hulton Getty**

Flooded Road ▲
• *August 1939*
A pedestrian attempts to leap across a flooded road near Hyde Park in London. Photographer: J.A. Hampton, Topical Press Agency, Hulton Getty Gallery, London. Modern black and white, fibre silver gelatin archival photograph, printed in Hulton Getty darkrooms. Limited edition: 300.
• *length 50.8cm*
• **£225**　　• **Hulton Getty**

Posters

From Russia with Love ▲
- 1963
"From Russia with Love", starring Sean Connery. Original U.K. quad.
- 76cm x 105cm
- £2,750   • Cine Art Gallery

Breakfast at Tiffany's ▲
- 1961
Colazione ad Tiffany.
- 27.5cm x 51cm
- £1,000   • Cine Art Gallery

The Ladykillers ▲
- 1955
"The Ladykillers" with Alec Guiness, Peter Sellers and Frankie Howard. Made at Ealing Studios. U K One Sheet.
- 40cm x 69cm
- £2,000   • Cine Art Gallery

Dial M For Murder ▼
- 1954
"Dial M for Murder" by Alfred Hitchcock.
- 36cm x 41cm
- £1,000   • Cine Art Gallery

The Prince and the Showgirl ▼
- 1957
"Prince and the Showgirl" U. S. half sheet. Starring Marilyn Monroe and Laurence Olivier.
- 22cm x 28cm
- £850   • Cine Art Gallery

The Graduate ◄
- 1967
"The Graduate", with Dustin Hoffman and Anne Bancroft (framed).
- 28cm x 36cm
- £350   • Cine Art Gallery

Apocalypse Now ◀

- 1979

"Apocalypse Now" with Marlon Brando. German double panel.
- 85cm x 118cm
- £1,300   • Cine Art Gallery

Way out West ▼

- 1937

"Way out West" with Laurel and Hardy.
- 28cm x36cm
- £650   • Cine Art Gallery

Ice Cold in Alex ▼

- 1958

"Ice Cold in Alex" with John Mills and Sylvia Syms. Directed by Bruce Robinson.
- height 102cm
- £350   • Cine Art Gallery

The Untouchables ▲

- 1987

"The Untouchables", with Kevin Costner, Sean Connery and Robert De Niro.
- 28cm x 36cm
- £75   • Cine Art Gallery

Bladerunner ▲

- 1982

"Bladerunner" with Harrison Ford.
- 104cm x 58cm

Sherlock Holmes Faces Death ▲

- 1951

"Sherlock Holmes faces Death". Spanish one sheet.
- 104cm x 29cm
- £450   • Cine Art Gallery

The Birds ▲

- 1963

"The Birds" by Alfred Hitchcock, with Tippi Hedren and Rod Taylor.
- 102cm x 79cm
- £500   • Cine Art Gallery

Goldfinger ▲

"Golfinger" starring Sean Connery.
- 28cm x 36cm
- £325   • Cine Art Gallery

Some Like it Hot ▲
- *1959*
"Some Like it Hot", with Marilyn Monroe, Tony Curtis and Jack Lemmon.
- *28cm x 36cm*
- £450 • Cine Art Gallery

Al Pacino ▲
- *1974*
"The Godfather Part II", with Al Pacino.
- *28cm x 36cm*
- £125 • Cine Art Gallery

Lawrence of Arabia ▲
- *1963*
"Lawrence of Arabia" with Peter O'Toole. Re-issue 1963 of 1962 film.
- *102cm x 56cm*
- £650 • Cine Art Gallery

The Odd Couple ▼
- *1968*
"The Odd Couple", with Walter Mattheau and Jack Lemmon.
- *28cm x 36cm*
- £140 • Cine Art Gallery

Vertigo ▼
- *1958*
"Vertigo", The International vision, by Alfred Hitchcock, with Kim Novak and James Steward.
- *83cm x 60.5cm*
- £2,500 • Cine Art Gallery

Le Samourai ▲
- *1967*
"Le Samourai", produced by Alain Delon, starring Nathalie Delon and François Perier.
- *height 76cm*
- £450 • Cine Art Gallery

Goldfinger ◀

- **1964**

"Goldfinger" poster with Sean Connery as James Bond and Honor Blackman as Pussy Galore.
- *76cm x 101cm*
- **£2,800**   • **Cine Art Gallery**

Withnail and I ▼

- **1987**

"Withnail and I" starring Richard E. Grant and Paul McGann.
- *height 103cm*
- **£400**   • **Cine Art Gallery**

The Godfather ▲

- **1972**

"The Godfather" and "Italian Photobusta".
- *45cm x 65cm*
- **£350**   • **Cine Art Gallery**

Alfie ▲

- **1966**

"Alfie", with Michael Caine.
- *28cm x 36cm*
- **£95**   • **Cine Art Gallery**

Brigitte Bardot ▲

- **1963**

"Le Mepris", with Brigitte Bardot.
- *height 158cm*
- **£1,500**   • **Cine Art Gallery**

Goldfinger ▼

- **1967**

"Goldfinger" with Sean Connery.
- *56cm x 102cm*
- **£1,200**   • **Cine Art Gallery**

High Society ▼

- **1956**

"High Society" with Frank Sinatra, Gene Kelly and Bing Crosby.
- *28cm x 36cm*

Love is My Profession ▼
- 1959
"Love is My Profession", starring Brigitte Bardot.
- 83cm x 60.5cm
- £350 • Cine Art Gallery

Revenge of the Creature ▲
- 1955
"Revenge of the Creature" U.K. Quad John Agar Laurie Nelson.
- 102cm x 60.5cm
- £850 • Cine Art Gallery

Psycho ▲
- 1962
"Psycho" 2962 re-issue US sheet.
- width 29cm
- £600 • Cine Art Gallery

Breakfast at Tiffany's ▼
- 1961
"Breakfast at Tiffany's", starring Audrey Hepburn.
- 28cm x 36cm
- £475 • Cine Art Gallery

My Fair Lady ▲
- 1965
"My Fair Lady" with Audrey Hepburn and Rex Harrison.
- 75cm x 137cm
- £450 • Cine Art Gallery

Manhattan ▼
- 1979
"Manhattan" Lobby Carl.
- 28cm x 36cm
- £95 • Cine Art Gallery

The Enforcer ▲
- 1977
"The Enforcer" with Clint Eastwood as Dirty Harry.
- 28cm x 36cm
- £95 • Cine Art Gallery

Gilda ▲
- 1946
"Gilda". U.S Insert.
- 92cm x 35cm
- £1,600 • Cine Art Gallery

Yellow Submarine ▶

- **1969**

"Yellow Submarine" with the Beatles. U.S. One sheet.
- *height 104cm*
- **£12,500** • **Cine Art Gallery**

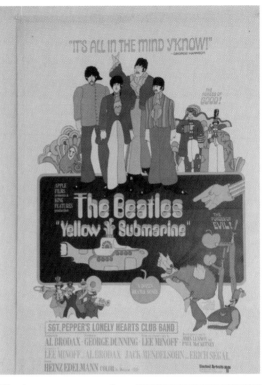

Thunderball ▲

- **1965**

"Thunderball" with Sean Connery.
- *41cm x 27cm*

Midnight Cowboy ▲

- **1969**

"Midnight Cowboy" with Dustin Hoffman. U K. Quad.
- *76cm x 102cm*
- **£190** • **Cine Art Gallery**

Expert Tips

If you are deciding to start collecting by buying posters, it is best to start with the posters that depict your favourite old films and stars. As an amateur antique collector, posters are a good starting point as their cost is fairly reasonable.

The Apartment ▶

- **1960**

"The Apartment" starring Jack Lemmon and Shirley McLaine.
- *28cm x 36cm*
- **£85** • **Cine Art Gallery**

Bullitt ▲

- **1969**

"Bullitt" with Steve McQueen. U. S. One sheet.
- *27cm x 21cm*
- **£680** • **Cine Art Gallery**

The Italian Job ▼

- **1969**

"The Italian Job" with Michael Caine. UK Mini Quad.
- *31cm x 41cm*
- **£5** • **Cine Art Gallery**

Radios

Wondergram Record Player ▶

• **1959**

Very rare Wondergram record player for 45R.P.M. and 33 and a third R.P.M. in anodised aluminium case, with folding legs. Made in England by Baird.

• *height 8.5cm*

• **£350** • The Manic Antique

Dansette Major de-luxe ▲

• **1960**

Dansette Major de-luxe with a red and cream case, sloping front gold grill and light up Dansette badge, with cream plastic handles each side for carrying.

• *height 27cm*

• **£75** • The Manic Antique

Dansette Conquest ▼

• **1959**

Dansette Conquest green and cream record player, standing on four black tapered legs on circular base. Holds ten records on stack. Fully restored and re-conditioned. With cream handles each side for carrying.

• *height 67cm*

• **£80** • The Manic Antique

H. M. V. Record Player ◀

• **1958**

His Master's Voice record player in a red and mottled grey case with red plastic carrying handles, with a Monarch deck.

• *height 25cm*

• **£75** • The Manic Antique

H. M. V. Record Player ▲

• **1957**

His Master's Voice record player in a chocolate brown case with cream interior and black handles.

• *height 27cm*

• **£75** • The Manic Antique

Expert Tips

Always buy a record player or radio in as near-perfect condition as possible, and purchase from a reputable dealer who has restored and re-wired the item, unless it is very rare, has the maker's name, or is extremely decorative.

245

Pye Record Player ▲

• **1955**
Pye record player in a bow
fronted teak case with cream
turntable. Holds ten records on
stack.
• *height 26cm*
• **£100** • The Manic Antique

Radio and T. V. Diary 1957 ▲

• **1957**
Radio and T. V. Diary for 1957
with photographs on each page of
actors and musicians. Showing a
photograph of David
Attenborough.
• *height 12cm*
• **£10** • The Manic Antique

E.A.R. Triple Four ◄

• **1958**
E. A. R. Triple four record player
in a blue and grey Rexine case
with cream piping and handles.
• *height 27cm*
• **£80** • The Manic Antique

P.Y. E. Record Player ▼

• **1955**
P. Y. E. record player in a grey
with white polka dot case, with
unusual curved sides, white
plastic carrying handles and a
black and gold sparkling grill.
• *height 25cm*
• **£75** • The Manic Antique

Perdio Transistor ►

• **1962**
Perdio Super Seven Transistor
radio, inscribed with 'Real
Morocco leather made in
England', on the back, with a dial
for an aerial and phone or tape,
and a large brass dial and gold
writing.
• *height 12.5cm*
• **£38** • The Manic Antique

Roberts Radio ▲

• **1958**
Roberts radio in original condition
with red Rexine case and handle
and brass dials and fittings.
• *height 15cm*
• **£68** • The Manic Antique

Hacker ▲

• **1964**
Hacker record player in a black
and grey case with metal fittings.
• *height 27cm*
• **£50** • The Manic Antique

Rock & Pop

Me and my Shadows ▲
- **1960**

"Me and my Shadows" Cliff Richard export copy in excellent condition.
- **£70** • Music and Video

Hollywood Blues ▲
- **1970**

"Johnny Almond Music Machine / Hollywood Blues" by Deram Records.
- **£60** • Music and Video

Happily Ever After ▲
- **1980**

The Cure, "Happily Ever After".
- **£45** • Music and Video

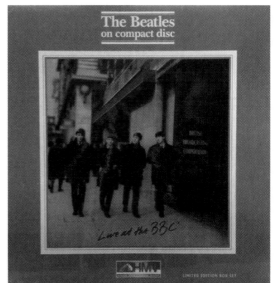

U.F. Orb ▲
- **1992**

"U.F. Orb" presented to Kris Weston to recognise sales in the United Kingdom of more than 60,000copies of the "Big Life/ Wau!" Mr Modo Album. U.F. Orb.
- **£265** • Music and Video

Michael Jackson Doll ▶
- **1997**

Michael Jackson doll wearing a red leather jacket with zippers and black trousers holding a microphone in original box and sings 'Beat It'.
- **£37** • Music and Video

The Beatles ▲
- **1994**

The Beatles- "Live at the BBC". The only existing Marquette for the proposed HMV box set edition-permission for which was refused by Apple as the delayed production was considered potentially detrimental to the 'Anthology' launch.
- **£4,995** • Music and Video

The Police Box ▼
- *1997–87*

"The Police Box" The Police (Sting. Stewart Copeland. Andy Summers) from 1977 to 1987.
- £150   • Music and Video

Elvis ▼
- *1971*

"You'll Never Walk Alone" by Elvis. Manufactured and Distributed by RCA Limited.
- £1,800   • Music and Video

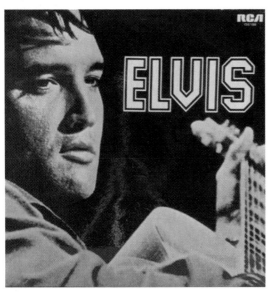

H. M. S. Donovan ▲
- *1971*

"H.M.S. Donovan" produced by Donovan Engineered by Mike Bobak at Morgan Studios London. All paintings by Patrick.
- £130   • Music and Video

Sticky Fingers: Rolling Stones ▲
- *1972*

"Sticky Fingers", an album by The Rolling Stones.
- £220   • Music and Video

Whitehouse Present Total Sex ▼
- *circa 1980*

Whitehouse present "Total Sex".
- £125   • Music and Video

The Velvet Underground ▼
- *circa 1967*

Andy Warhol presents the The Velvet Underground and Nico, original German Issue with Erice Emmerson Sleeve (No Banana).
- £248   • Music and Video

Roy Harper Sophisticated ▼
- *1966*

Roy Harper "Sophisticated Beggar" Strike JHL 105. Test pressing. W/Proff Sleeve in excellent condition.
- £550   • Music and Video

Captain Beefheart ▲

- *1975*

Trout mask replica Captain
Beefheart and his magic band.

- **£44**   • **Music and Video**

The Dixie Cups ◄

- *1962*

The Dixie Cups "Riding
High".

- **£47**   • **Music and Video**

The Gordon Beck Trio ▲

- *1968*

The Gordon Beck TrioTwin
Stereo MJ1 Jazz series.

- **£495**   • **Music and Video**

Brum Beat ▲

- *1964*

"Brum Beat" including The
Strangers, The Mountain Kings,
The Blue Stars, The Cavern Four.
Dave Lacey and The Corvettes.

- **£120**   • **Music and Video**

Rolling Stones Hologram ◄

- *1967*

Rolling Stones hologram "Their
Satanic Majesties Request" fully
signed on front cover.

- **£249**   • **Music and Video**

Bob Dylan ◄
- *1961*
Bob Dylan's first recording
produced by John Hammond.
- £735 • Music and Video

Beatles Lady Madonna ▲
- *1968*
"The Inner Light, Lady
Madonna" by The Beatles.
- £72 • Music and Video

Time Will Pass ▲
- *1977*
"Time Will Pass" by the Spriguns.
Distributed by The Decca Record
Company Limited, London.
- £175 • Music and Video

Equinoxe 4 ▼
- *1979*
"Equinoxe 4", an album by Jean
Michel Jarre, with a signed
autograph in black biro on front
cover.
- £60 • Music and Video

Yellow Submarine ▼
- *1960s*
The Beatles - "Yellow Submarine
and Eleanor Rigby".
- £72 • Music and Video

Agogo ▲
- *1963*
"Agogo", with Ray Charles, The
Supremes, Petula Clark, and The
Everly brothers.
- £35 • Music and Video

Status Quo ▲
- *1970*
"In my Chair / Gerdundula"
Status Quo.
- £72 • Music and Video

The Monkees ▲
- *1968*
The Monkees. Original motion
picture sound track "Head".
- £95 • Music and Video

Pat As I See Him ▲

- **1966**

"Pat As I See Him", a pen and ink portrait on an envelope by Joe Meek of his lover. Annotated in verso 'Pat was Meek's boyfriend and was present at the landlady's shooting and Meek's subsequent suicide'.

- **£5,250**   • Music and Video

Michael Jackson Doll ▼

- **1995**

A singing Michael Jackson doll wearing a white shirt and black trousers in original box.

- **£47**   • Music and Video

Stone Age ◄

- **1971**

"Stone Age" by The Rolling Stones.

- **£580**   • Music and Video

Instant Karma Lennon ▲

- **1971**

John Ono Lennon "Instant Karma" produced by Phil Spector.

- **£117**   • Music and Video

Andy Warhol ◄

- **1967**

Andy Warhol- "Andy Warhol's Index Box". First hardback edition-Random House USA complete and in working order including the velvet underground flexi-disc. Reed's eye has not even popped!.

- **£1,500**   • Music and Video

Wings "Back To The Egg" ◄
- 1979

Wings "Back to the Egg" Promo only picture disc manufactured for the MPL christmas party 1979 but delivered too late for use.
- £1,250   • Music and Video

Whitehouse Present Total Sex ▲
- circa 1980

Whitehouse present Total Sex.
- £125   • Music and Video

Cliff Richard and the Shadows ▼
- 1964

"A Forever Kind of Love" by Cliff Richard and the Shadows.
- £33   • Music and Video

Brenda Lee ▲
- 1950

Brenda Lee "Speak to Me Pretty".
- £27   • Music and Video

John Lennon-Signature Watch ▲
- 1991

John Lennon signature watch produced for Toshiba and given to visiting signees.
- £200   • Music and Video

Expert Tips

As music production moves forward with new advances in technology, start thinking about collecting items such as CDs; they may be modern now but in ten years time they could be as outdated as records.

Travelling Wilburys ▶
- 1990

"Travelling Wilburys", manufactured and distributed by Warner Bros. Records.
- £25   • Music and Video

Captain Beefheart ▲
- 1965

Captain Beefheart and his Magic Band/ "Mirror Man" with a broken mirror on the cover.
- £95   • Music and Video

Scripophily & Paper Money

Guatemala Note ◀

- *1895*

Guatemala Banco Americano five hundred pesos written in Spanish with two seated ladies surrounded by anvil, mallet wheel, fruit and parrot with a steamship in the background.

- **£270**   • **Yasha Beresiner**

Turkey Piastres ▲

- *1863*

Turkish Ottoman 200 Piastres 1279/1863.

- **£200**   • **Yasha Beresiner**

Cuban Note ▲

- *1896*

Cuban 50 Pesos 'Plata' El Banco Espanol de la Isla de Cuba with a coat of arms in the centre and a lady with a lion and a lamb in a cartouche to the left.

- **£90**   • **Yasha Beresiner**

Expert Tips

When framed some notes can make an interesting and decorative addition to a study, office or hallway.

Thailand Note ▼

- *1987*

Thailand 60 Baht, Government.

- **£9**   • **Yasha Beresiner**

Russian Note ▼

- *1819*

Blue Russian 5 Rubles note decorated with a two headed eagle in the centre.

- **£220**   • **Yasha Beresiner**

Bolivian Note ▶

- *350*

Bolivian, 10 Bolivianos, Proof obv. & re. with Mercury seated by the sea.

- **£350**   • **Yasha Beresiner**

Israel Shekel ▲

- *1975*

Israeli 100 Shekel with a picture of a building with the 'Bank of Israel' beneath.

- **£5**   • **Yasha Beresiner**

Mozambique Note ▲

- *1919*

Mozambique 5 Libras note Banco da beira.

- **£20**   • **Yasha Beresiner**

Rhodesian Pound Note
● **1952**
Southern Rhodesian pound note, showing Queen Elizabeth II.
● **£125** ● **Yasha Beresiner**

Barclays Cheque Palestine ▲
●
Cheque for Palestine Refugees. 'UNRWA' Barclays Bank (Dominion, Colonial and Oversea).
● **£35** ● **Yasha Beresiner**

Indo China Note ▲
● **1938**
Bank de Lindochine 1000 Francs 'Mille Francs' with painted with ladies and camels on one side and on the reverse a lady carrying a basket with the sea in the background.
● **£65** ● **Yasha Beresiner**

Uzbekistan Note ▲
● **1993**
Uzbekistan '5 sum' note with a decorative wreath and an eagle spreading its wings.
● **£1** ● **Yasha Beresiner**

Spanish Bank Note ▶
● **1857**
Spanish bank note 'Banco de Cadiz' 500 Reales Vellon with a central figure holding two lions.
● **£110** ● **Yasha Beresiner**

Romanian Bank Note ▲
● **1938**
Romanian bank note 500 Lei showing two seated Romanian women, one with a baby.
● **£15.** ● **Yasha Beresiner**

Portuguese Note ▲
● **1960**
Portuguese 50 Escudos.
● **£7** ● **Yasha Beresiner**

Argentian Note ▼
● **1859**
Argentinian 500 Pesos note 'Confederacion Argentina'.
● **£110** ● **Yasha Beresiner**

Zaire Note ▼
● **1992**
Banque du Zaire cinque millions Zaires.
● **£4** ● **Yasha Beresiner**

Chinese Government Treasury Notes ▲

• *1925/29*
Chinese Government 8 per cent 10 year. Treasury note for L100. Sterling.
• £50   • **Yasha Beresiner**

Bolivian Bond ▲

• *1887*
Bolivian note with the inscription: Compania Minera Nacional Anonima El Gallao Capital Bollivares.
• £36   • **Yasha Beresiner**

Chinese Bond ▲

• *1913*
'Banque Industrielle de chine' bond decorated with a picture of China and two dogs of Fo.
• £42   • **Yasha Beresiner**

Chinese Bond ▼

• *1920*
'Gouvernement de la Republique Chinoise bon du tresors 8per cent de 1921. Chemin de fer lung Tsing U Hai'.
• £15   • **Yasha Beresiner**

Polish Bond ▼

• *1928*
Polish Bond Banku Gospodarstwa Krajowego.
• £20   • **Yasha Beresiner**

Chinese Bond ▼

• *1920*
Chinoise don du tresors 8 per cent. Francs 50,000,000.
• £15   • **Yasha Beresiner**

Titanic Stock Certificate ▲

• *1919*
Titanic stock certificate, with the words 'International Mercantile Marine company' which owned the White Star Line, and showing the Titanic.
• £50   • **Yasha Beresiner**

Chinese Gold Loan ▲

• *1912*
Chinese Government gold loan of 1912 for L10,000,000 sterling.
• £30   • **Yasha Beresiner**

Mining & Railway Co.Ltd. ▲

• *1936*
The El Oro Mining & Railway Company, Limited.
• £52   • **Yasha Beresiner**

Expert Tips

Make sure the paper is not torn or stained, especially in early bonds or stock certifcates and treasury notes.

Quebec Railway Company Bonds ▼
• *1907*
The Atlantic Quebec and Western Railway Company. Five per cent. First mortgage debenture bonds for 9,050,000 dollars.
• £45   • **Yasha Beresiner**

Mexican Bond ▼
• *1921*
Mexican Bond Minas Pedrazzini. Gold and Silver Mining Co.
• £20   • **Yasha Beresiner**

Turkish Note ▲
• *1854*
Turkish note '10 Kurush, Ordu Kaimesi 6th Issue.
• £300   • **Yasha Beresiner**

Mexican Bond ▼
• *1921*
Mina Pedrazzini Gold and Silver Mining Co.
• £20   • **Yasha Beresiner**

Bank Note ▼
• *1800*
Peruvian bond that circulated as currency, 207 Pesos, Casa de Moneda.
• £210   • **Yasha Beresiner**

Gold Mining Share Certificate ▼
• *1900*
The road block Gold Mining Company of India Limited share certificate.
• £28   • **Yasha Beresiner**

White English Note ▼
• *1944*
Bank of England white five pound note.
• £70   • **Yasha Beresiner**

Sewing items

Ivory Needle Case
- *circa 1870*
Fine ivory needle case with original needle packets and the inscription 'T.H.' on the cover.
- *height 11cm*
- £495   • Arca

English Bodkin Case ▲
- *circa 1780*
English lilac enamel bodkin case in two sections with a bird cartouche.
- *length 15cm*
- £520   • Arca

Pig Pincushion ▲
- *circa 1880*
Ivory pig with brown velvet pincushion on the back.
- *height 3cm*
- £360   • Arca

Oval Tortoiseshell Case ▼
- *circa 1880*
Oval tortoiseshell sewing case, complete with gold scissors, thimble, pick needle case and pencil.
- *length 12.5cm*
- £950   • Arca

Gold Egg Sewing Case ▲
- *circa 1880*
French gold filigree case in the shape of an egg and lined with the original red velvet. With gold thimble scissors, needle case and pick.
- *height 8cm*
- £700   • Arca

Tortoiseshell Box ▲
- *circa 1880*
Tortoiseshell needle case, with hinged cover.
- *height 5cm*
- £330   • Arca

Bodkin Case ◄
- *circa 1780*
Purple bodkin case with white hexagonal spot design and six landscape cartouches, with gold banding.
- *length 15cm*
- £980   • Arca

Silver Boot Pincushion ▼
- *circa 1870*
Silver boot pincushion.
- *height 5cm*
- £280 • Arca

Silver Wool Winder ▼
- *circa 1780*
Silver wool winder in the shape of a ball made of fine foliate filigree, with small flowers on each leaf.
- *circumference 18cm*
- £850 • Arca

Gold Chatelaine ▼
- *circa 1780*
French gold five piece sewing chatelaine, with heavily engraved design of flowers in baskets, ribboning, and scrolling joined by linked chains to a central foliate scrolled hook.
- *length 18cm*
- £1,350 • Arca

Silver Scissors ◀
- *circa 1880*
Victorian silver case with scissors.
- *length 9.5cm*
- £260 • Arca

Gothic Chair Pincushion ▲
- *circa 1900*
Gothic silver metal chair the red velvet seat being a pincushion.
- *height 6.5cm*
- £135 • Arca

Walnut Sewing Case ▶
- *circa 1840*
French walnut sewing case in the form of a nut, lined with red satin and containing small scissors, thimble, needle case and pick.
- *width 5cm*
- £690 • Arca

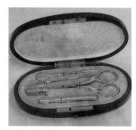

French Etui ▲
- *circa 1880*
French ebonised etui with silver gilt fitting.
- *length 12cm*
- £550 • Arca

Mouse Tape Measure ◀
- **1900**

Silver mouse tape measure, with tail used to wind the tape back into the mouse.
- *length 7cm*
- **£175**   • Arca

Pink Enamel Case ▼
- **1920**

Black ebonised case with pink enamel lid with a gold shield on the lid, and two silver line borders, complete with sewing items.
- *length 13cm*
- **£180**   • Arca

Bakelite Tape ▼
- *circa 1900*

Bakelite figure of a girl smiling and holding a red apple, on her right side is a tape measure.
- *height 5.5cm*
- **£225**   • Arca

Porcelain Thimble ▼
- *circa 1900*

Porcelain thimble with a painted robin and roses and gold banding.
- *height 2cm*
- **£210**   • Arca

Gold Thimble ▼
- *circa 1770*

Fine engraved gold thimble.
- *height 3cm*
- **£450**   • Arca

Ivory Sewing Case ▲
- *circa 1890*

Ivory sewing case inscribed with the name Enid on the top of the lid, complete with gold sewing implements.
- *length 7.5cm*
- **£495**   • Arca

Silver Needle Case ▼
- *circa 1880*

Oblong silver needle case with decorative flower design.
- *length 6cm*
- **£125**   • Arca

Japanese Sewing Case ▲
- *circa 1880*

Japanese ivory sewing case with raised gilt foliate and bird design with mother of pearl chrysanthemums, complete with silver scissors and thimble.
- *length 9cm*
- **£695**   • Arca

Musical Sewing Box ◄

- *circa 1850*

Palais Royale tortoiseshell and ivory faced musical sewing box with a reverse glass painted pastoral scene on the lid, enclosing original inkwells, needle case, screw top pencil, scissors, thimble and other sewing implements. Most with the Palais Royale insignia. The music box is in working order.

- *10cm x 19cm*
- £3,450   • J. & T. Stone

Silver Filigree Case ▶

- *circa 1780*

French silver filigree case enclosing pincushion and blue glass bottle.

- *length 5cm*
- £1,150   • Arca

Silver Bear Pincushion ▼

- *1908*

English silver articulated bear pincushion from Birmingham.

- *height 8cm*
- £850   • Arca

English Thimble ▲

- *circa 1880*

English mother of pearl thimble.

- *height 2cm*
- £220   • Arca

Filigree Scissor Case ▶

- *circa 1840*

Delicate silver filigree scissor case with scrolling.

- *length 6.5cm*
- £480   • Arca

Sewing Box ▶

- *circa 1820*

Chinese export black lacquer sewing box with a scene showing a family group with a pagoda and landscape in the background, with fitted interior, standing on gilt claw feet.

- *34cm x 23.5cm x 14cm*
- £2,000   • O.F.Wilson

Snuff Boxes & Smoking Equipment

Cigarette Case ◀
- *circa 1900*

Silver cigarette case with an enamel lady reclining with a large fan at her side.
- *length 9cm*
- £1,550   • Arca

Novelty Lighter ▼
- 1980

Novelty cigarette lighter, modelled as a roll of film with a picture of a model wearing Formula One overalls.
- *height 5cm*
- £10 • Jessops Classic Cameras

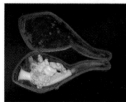

Lady's Meerschaum ▲
- *circa 1880*

Lady's meerschaum holder for cigar or cigarettes, with a lady standing beside a horse.
- *length 14cm*
- £235   • Arca

Ladies' Cigar Holder ▲
- *circa 1860*

Ladies' meerschaum cigar holder, with a reclining lady holding a spray of flowers.
- *length 13cm*
- £260   • Arca

Greyhound Meerschaum ▶
- *circa 1880*

Meerschaum holder in the form of a head of a greyhound.
- *length 22cm*
- £650   • Arca

Skull Meerschaum ▲
- *circa 1880*

Meerschaum pipe in the shape of a skull, with amber stem.
- *length 15cm*
- £300   • Arca

Chieftain Meerschaum ▲
- *circa 1880*

Meerschaum in the form of a chieftain with a large headdress, and plume.
- *length 19cm*
- £360   • Arca

Silver Gilt Snuff Box ▶

- *circa Louis XIV*

French silver gilt snuff box with
shell design on the top and a
pastoral scene with a bird at the
bottom.

- *length 8cm*
- £980   • Arca

Ebonised Snuff Box ▲

- *circa 1870*

Circular ebonised snuff box,
painted with a portrait of a
woman shown against a blue
background, by L. Fischer.

- *diameter 8.5cm*
- £980   • Arca

Circular Painted Snuff Box ▶

- *circa 1790*

Circular tortoiseshell painted
snuff box showing a lady seated
playing a harp.

- *diameter 8cm*
- £1,750   • Arca

French Gold Snuff Box ◀

- *circa 1750*

French oval snuff box with a
tooled striped pattern of gold over
tortoiseshell, and a roped effect
around the rim.

- *length 7cm*
- £1,980   • Arca

Burr Walnut Snuff Box ▲

- *circa 1870*

Burr walnut circular snuff box,
with a painted landscape scene
on the lid and gold banding.

- *diameter 6.5cm*
- £250   • Arca

Painted Snuff Box ▶

- *circa 1890*

English oval papier mâché
snuff box painted with the head
of a young man on a red
background.

- *length 7cm*
- £460   • Arca

Silver and Enamel Cigarette Case ▶

- *circa 1896*

Silver cigarette case with an enamel picture showing a circus ring, with a lady in a pink dress astride a white horse, with a clown turning towards her.
- *length 9cm*
- £1,350   • Arca

Tortoiseshell and Silver Snuff Box ▲

- *circa 1780*

An oval tortoiseshell snuff box with a silver floral and geometric design, with a mother of pearl background.
- *diameter 6.5cm*
- £240   • Arca

Japanese Cigar Box ▲

- *circa 1880*

Japanese export cigar box with a dragon and Japanese characters on the lid characterising longevity and good fortune.
- *5cm x 18cm*
- £120   • Younger

Satinwood Humidor ▲

- *circa 1910*

An elegant English rectangular satinwood humidor, with ivory banding and a fitted interior.
- *12.5cm x 23cm*
- £495   • A.I.G

Mother of Pearl Snuff Box ▼

- *circa 1750*

Small bulbous snuff box with mother of pearl sections and silver banding.
- *height 5cm*
- £750   • Arca

Dog Tobacco Jar ▲

- *circa 1900*

Carved mahogany tobacco jar in the shape of a comical dog with glass eyes, wearing a hat with a tassel and a bow tie.
- *height 18cm*
- £600   • Arca

Telephones

Bakelite Telephone ▶
- *circa 1950*
Black bakelite British GPO
telephone with ringing bell.
- *16cm x 24cm*
- £105 • Genie

Gecophone Telephone ▼
- *circa 1930*
Gecophone black bakelite
telephone with ringing bell.
- *18cm x 24cm*
- £185 • H. Duffed

Genie Telephone ▼
- *circa 1970*
Red 'Genie' designer telephone
by A. P. Besson manufactured by
British Telecom, with push
button dial.
- *11.5cm x 22cm*
- £65 • Old Cinema

Red Telephone ▲
- *circa 1960*
Red plastic British GPO
telephone.
- *13cm x 24cm*
- £45 • Genie

Pyramid Telephone ▼
- *circa 1930*
Black bakelite pyramid telephone
with drawer and ringing bell.
- *16cm x 23cm*
- £185 • H. Duffeld

Green Plastic Telephone ◀
- *circa 1960*
Green plastic British GPO
telephone. Slightly older than
telephone # 9965.
- *13cm x 24cm*
- £45 • Genie.

Expert Tips

*Bakelite telephones became very
popular in the 1950s with the
introduction of mass marketing.
Look out for chips on mouth
pieces and broken dials as these
can devalue the telephone.*

Ivory Telephone ▼
- *circa 1950*
Ivory bakelite telephone with drawer and ringing bell.
- *14cm x 25cm*
- £225   • H. Duffeld

GPO Pyramid Telephone ▲
- *circa 1930*
British Ivory bakelite GPO Pyramid telephone with ringing bell.
- *15cm x 24cm*
- £295   • H. Duffeld

British Telephone ▶
- *circa 1970*
British GPO plastic telephone with Warble ringing and adjustable volume.
- *12cm x 10cm*
- £48   • Genie

Black Bakelite Telephone ◀
- *circa 1950*
Black bakelite British GPO telephone with drawer and ringing bell.
- *16cm x 24cm*
- £135   • H. Duffeld

Lysell & Bloomberg Telephone ▲
- *circa 1957*
The first ever one piece telephone designed by Ralph Lysell & Hugo Bloomberg in cream with rotary dial underneath.
- *height 23.5cm*
- £100   • Old Cinema

GPO Telephone ▶
- *circa 1946*
Black bakelite British GPO telephone with function on/off switch for ringing.
- *16cm x 24cm*
- £175   • H. Duffeld

Two Toned Telephone ▶

- *circa 1970*

Two toned adjustable volume stone coloured British GPO telephone in plastic.
- *12cm x 10cm*
- £48   • Genie

English Telephone ▲

- *circa 1950*

Cream Bakelite telephone with nickel rotary dial and black numerals, inscribed Portobello 4559, rare in any colour but black.
- *height 15cm*
- £290   • Old Cinema

Belgian Desk Telephone ▼

- *circa 1950*

European ivory desk telephone with large numerals and clear plastic rotary dial.
- *height 12.5cm*
- £75   • Old Cinema

Candlestick Telephone ▲

- *circa 1920*

Candlestick telephone with steel handle with black bakelite top and brass and separate wood and brass ring box.
- *44cm x 15cm*
- £395   • H. Duffeld

Ericsson Telephone ◀

- *circa 1950*

Cream bakelite Ericsson telephone with original handset and cord and large rotary dial with black numerals
- *height 14cm*
- £185   • Old Cinema

Walking Sticks

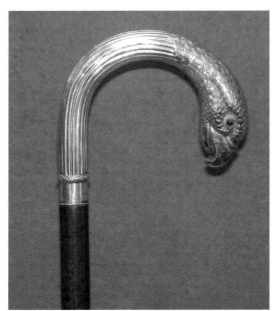

Crook-Handled Walking Stick ◄

● 1880

Fine crook-handled cane with a snakewood shaft surmounted by a finely moulded silver parrot's head with glass eyes.

● £1,300   ● Michael German

Russian Walking Stick ▼

● 1890

Russian ebonised hard wood walking stick, with a bridled horse head. Finely moulded, with architectural motifs.

● £1,100   ● Michael German

Silver Horse Walking Stick ▼

● 1890

Russian ebonised hard wood cane, surmounted by a fine silver handle moulded as a horse's head.

● £900   ● Michael German

Silver Walking Stick ▲

● 1880

Russian fine crook-handled walking stick, with an ebony shaft surmounted by a silver horses head.

● £1,000   ● Michael German

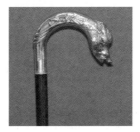

Rosewood Walking Stick ◄

● 1870

Rare and unusual cane, with a head of a wild boar in silver and a rosewood shaft.

● £950   ● Michael German

Ivory Tau Cane ▲
- 1880

Ivory tau shaped handled cane with a carved grotesque, mounted on a lacquered shaft.
- £800   • Michael German

Victorian Walking Stick ▲
- 1870

A Victorian cane with a finely carved ivory handle depicting an amusing dog seated with a hat and holding a stick, mounted on an ebony shaft, with a silver collar.
- £1,800   • Michael German

Japanese Stick ▼
- 1880

Fine Japanese ebonised cane fitted with a silver handle, with trailing foliate designs.
- £900   • Michael German

Victorian Greyhound Cane ▼
- 1870

Finely carved ivory Victorian greyhound with an engraved silver collar and ebonised shaft.
- £1,500   • Michael German

Russian Enamelled Cane ▲
- 1890

Russian cane with enamelled handle with floral designs and jewelling on an ebonised shaft.
- £1100   • Michael German

Mother of Pearl Cane ▲
- 1880

Elegant mother of pearl inlay handled cane, with delicate scrolling floral designs in gilt, mounted on a ebonised shaft.
- £480   • Michael German

Russian Cane ▼
- *1880*

Fine Russian cane with silver nelio tau shaped handle, mounted on a hardwood shaft.
- £650   • Michael German

Porcelain Handle Cane ▼
- *1820*

Fine early painted porcelain handle stick, with a silver collar and malacca shaft.
- £1,400   • Michael German

Porcelain Cane ▲
- *1840*

Porcelain painted head of a young gentleman, with a silver collar on an ebonised shaft.
- £800   • Michael German

Rock Crystal Cane ▲
- *1890*

Continental stick mounted with a rock crystal handle, inset with semi precious stones, hardwood shaft and silver collar.
- £1,300   • Michael German

Kingfisher Walking Stick ▼
- *1870*

Victorian stick with a well carved and painted handle, modelled as a kingfisher mounted on an ebonised shaft.
- £380   • Michael German

Whalebone Cane ▼
- *1850*

Whalebone cane with a finely carved whale tooth handle, modelled as a hand holding a bar.
- £1,250   • Michael German

Parrot Cane ▼

- *1870*

Oversized head of a parrot carved
from fruitwood, with fine detail,
mounted on a hardwood shaft,
with ornate gilt collar.

- **£850**   • **Michael German**

English Walking Stick ▼

- *1870*

Country walking stick with a
carved wood handle, modelled as
a hare with large glass eyes and
silver collar, mounted on a briar
wood shaft.

- **£580**   • **Michael German**

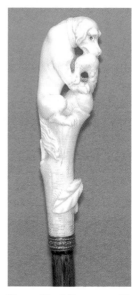

Ebony Cane ▲

- *1840*

Ebony cane with the handle
carved as the head of a Negro
with ivory teeth and boxwood hat
and collar, mounted on a
rosewood shaft.

- **£480**   • **Michael German**

Stag Horn Cane ▲

- *1860*

Country walking stick carved as a
grotesque with a beard and glass
eyes, mounted on a knotted wood
shaft, with a silver collar and an
antler handle.

- **£390**   • **Michael German**

Victorian Cane ▼

- *1860*

Elegant Victorian cane with a
well carved handle depicting a
hunting dog with a bird, mounted
on a partidge wood shaft, with a
gilt collar.

- **£1,100**   • **Michael German**

Hussar Head Cane ▼

- *1860*

A painted and carved wood cane
with the handle modelled as a
Continental hussar, with a
plumed helmet.

- **£950**   • **Michael German**

Victorian Porcelain Cane ▼
• *1870*
Victorian porcelain ball handle
stick, with an enamel portrait of a
young boy within a scrolled gilt
border.
• **£580**   • **Michael German**

Onyx Horn Cane ▼
• *1892*
Onyx horn cane with metal vesta
and hinged flap within the
handle. Monogrammed top
B.D.C. 1892.
• **£800**   • **Michael German**

Vesta Handled Cane ▲
• *1910*
Rare vesta handled cane with
silver whistle and hinged flap, on
a hardwood shaft with inlay.
• **£1,400**   • **Michael German**

Boar's Head Cane ▲
• *1890*
Rare and unusual Austrian cane,
with cold enamel boar's head
handle on an ebonised shaft.
• **£285**   • **Michael German**

Dice Handle Cane ▲
• *1900*
Amusing wooden dice handled
cane with ivory inlay.
• **£225**   • **Michael German**

Folk-Art Cane ▲
• *1840*
One piece country folk art cane
with carved heads and animals
along the shaft.
• **£1,200**   • **Michael German**

271

Folk Art Cane ▼
• *1860*
Oversized folk art cane carved from one piece of wood depicting a dwarf sitting on a tree stump, laughing .
• £1,400   • Michael German

Guardsman Cane ▼
• *1940*
Composition guardsman cane with silver collar mounted on an ebonised shaft .
• £220   • Michael German

German Cane ▲
• *1880*
German black forest cane with the handle carved as French pug, with glass eyes and a leather collar with a bell.
• £480   • Michael German

German Shepherd Cane ▲
• *1880*
A German walking stick with the handle comically carved as a german shepherd dog with glass eyes, and ivory teeth.
• £420   • Michael German

Ivory Cane ▼
• *1870*
A carved ivory handled cane, modelled as a tiger's head with glass eyes and and scrolled gilt collar, on an ebonised shaft.
• £1,200   • Michael German

Golfing Stick ▼
• *1890*
Rare Sunday golfing stick with silver cigarette case within the handle.
• £1,150   • Michael German

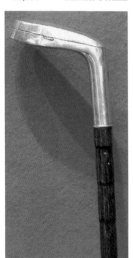

Decorative Arts

The term decorative arts is ambiguous and can be expressed by the modelling or carving of stone, wood and bronze.

The term 'decorative' applies to all art that is not detailed as 'fine art', such as paintings. The idea is that there is no practical use for the item – that it is made purely for decoration, in order to enhance the surroundings and give pleasure to the beholder.

The Victorian era heralded the time when decorative items became hugely popular, with the Victorians collecting and filling every nook and cranny, whether it was with a bust of a gentleman, a carving of an animal, or a stone bust of a girl, all their spaces were filled. The

demand for sculptures that had been growing since the second half of the nineteenth century continued in the 1920s and 30s with an emphasis on smaller figures, either carved in ivory, or cast in bronze.

Today many decorative items have enormous appeal to the interior designer and home owner. One special item may be a source of inspiration for the design of a room, an entrance hall, a public space or a garden.

This is an area of collecting which is in flux – there are no rules, just focus on buying what you really like.

Figures & Busts

Bust of Child ▲
- *circa 1910*
A good patinated bronze bust of a child with a rose in her hair by H. Jacobs, standing on an integral plinth inscribed 'H. Luppens & Cir Editeurs'.
- *height 56cm*
- £2,953   • Gavin Douglas

Marie Antoinette ▼
- *circa 1890*
A fine terracotta bust of Marie Antoinette, her head inclined to dexter and raised on a spreading square plinth.
- *65cm x 44cm*
- £950   • Westland & Co

Futurum ▶
- *circa 1900*
A classical bronze figure of a woman, entitled 'Futurum', by Henry Levasseur.
- *height 46cm*
- £2,475   • Gavin Douglas

Augustus Caesar ▼

• *circa 1850*
Italian marble bust of Augustus
Caesar raised on a marble plinth.
This is taken from the bronze
full-length figure of Augustus,
circa 20 BC in the Vatican
Museum. The breastplate is richly
carved with mythological and
historical scenes and the bust is
supported on a panelled and
moulded marble plinth of
tapering form.
• *height 208cm*
• **£9,800**   • **Anthony Outred**

Bronze Centaur ▼

• *circa 1850*
Italian bronze of a centaur
fighting a ram on marble.
• *height 17cm*
• **£895**   • **Gavin Douglas**

Pair of Maidens ▶

• *circa 1730*
A pair of white marble busts of
maidens in the antique manner,
attributed to Michael Rysbrach
(1694-1770). With finely carved
robes pinned at the shoulder with
a brooch, the hair flowing loosely
over one shoulder, supported on
later Portoro marble socles.
• *76cm x 36cm*
• **£33,000**   • **Anthony Outred**

Marley Horses ▲

• *circa 1880*
A small pair of French 'Marley
horses' after the model by
Costeau. On black marble bases
decorated with patinated friezes.
• *height 28cm*
• **£1,075**   • **Gavin Douglas**

Napoleon ▼

• *circa 1850s*
A fine well finished momento
mori of Napeleon in bronze from
the mid 19th century.
• *height 13cm*
• **£475**   • **Gavin Douglas**

Maternity ◀

• *circa 1880*
'Maternity', a fine patinated, cold
painted parcel gilt bronze of a
mother feeding an infant from
the breast while holding a
sleeping toddler, by Paul Dubois
(1829-1905). Cast by the F.
Barbedienne Foundry.
• *height 49cm*
• **£3,950**   • **Gavin Douglas**

Carved Oak Saint ▲
- *circa 1880*

Large carved oak ecclesiastical figure standing with hands in a praying position, mounted on a wood base.
- *height 163cm*
- **£2,800** • John Clay Antiques

Marble Head ▲
- *circa 1900*

A French statuary marble head of a woman after Rodin.
- *36cm x 30cm*
- **£1,250** • Westland & Co

Bronze Dog ▲
- *circa 1880*

Fine bronze dog front signed by G. Fontaine.
- *height 11.5cm*
- **£475** • Gavin Douglas

Ajax ▼
- *1893*

Fine bronze mounted onyx table thermometer surmounted by a figure of Ajax, signed and dated by Barnel.
- *height 36cm*
- **£1,150** • Gavin Douglas

Bronze Venus ▼
- *circa 1860*

Good patinated Italian bronze of the kneeling Venus after the antique. Set on a fine moulding.
- *height 56cm*
- **£3,500** • Gavin Douglas

Italian Bust ▲
- *circa 1800*

Good early 19th century Italian bust of a young woman with her hair tied high on her head in the classical style.
- *height 56cm*
- **£3,450** • Gavin Douglas

Marble Bust of Boy ▲
- *circa 1811*

Fine marble bust of a young boy standing on a grey marble base with gilt bronze frieze.
- *height 48cm*
- **£1,850** • Hatchwell Antiques

Italian Marble Figure ◄
- *circa 1890*

An Italian marble figure showing a slave girl sitting on a rug. Signed by Branlony.
- *height 60cm*
- **£3,850** • Gavin Douglas

Grand Tour Bronze ▲
• *circa 1860*
Unusual and small Italian grand tour bronze of a man about to use a sling.
• *height 12cm*
• £425   • Gavin Douglas

Marble Statue ▲
• *circa 1890*
An attractive Italian marble statue of a young girl leaning against a fountain playing a set of 'panpipes'. Signed 'Pittaluga'.
• *height 80cm*
• £8,750   • Gavin Douglas

Italian Bronze Boy ▶
• *1904*
A fine Italian bronze of a naked young boy playing with kittens. He holds one up while cuddling the other. The bronze is signed Marcuse, Roma 1904. On a chamfered marble base.
• *height 73cm*
• £5,950   • Gavin Douglas

Stone Roundels ▼
• *circa 1850*
A pair of Italian carved stone roundels in the Renaissance manner, each with a carved head, one depicting Benvenuto Cellini (1500-1571), Florentine sculptor, goldsmith and amorist. The other depicts Giulio Romano (1499-1546), painter and architect, one of the creators of mannerism, and chief assistant of Raphael.
• *diameter 102cm*
• £12,000   • Westland & Co

Bronze Bust ▼
• *circa 1880*
Fine pair of bronze busts of Albrecht Durer & Paul Romaine, with two colour patination, standing on bases of red and black reeded marble, after the style of Salmson.
• *height 40cm*
• £2,950   • Gavin Douglas

Beaux Art Figure ▲
• *circa 1890*
French 'Beaux Art' statuary marble figure of a young woman emblematic of spring. Signed F. Palla.
• *76cm x 23cm*
• £6,500   • Westland & Co

Venus ▲
• *circa 1860*
A Victorian re-constituted stone figure of Venus by the Farnley Co. Standing by a pillar in flowing chiffon, her hair dressed in a chignon, on a rectangular plinth.
• *134cm x 55cm*
• £750   • Westland & Co

Lighting

French Chandelier ▲

- *circa 17th–18th century*
Chandelier with ten large mainly
seventeenth century branches
and five smaller ones. With later
editions.
- *height 188cm*
- £6,800 • Augustus Brandt

Wall Sconces ▼

- *1890*
Fine quality gilt metal wall
sconces with shell decoration and
crystal drops.
- *height 65cm*
- £4,250 • Augustus Brandt

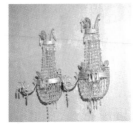

Four Light Colza Chandelier ▲

- *circa 1835*
A William IV period bronze four
light colza chandelier. The foliate
corona issuing four cast bronze
foliate chains attached to the
reservoir by applied leaf mounts,
intersected by four branches in
the form of duck heads supporting
clear glass storm shades. The
reservoir is surmounted by a bud
finial and is embellished by a
decorative pineapple pendant to
the base.
- *diameter 61cm*
- £15,500 • Anthony Outred

Giltwood Pickettes ▲

- *1860*
Pair of reeded and tapered
giltwood pickettes, with acanthus
leaf decoration, and 'M'
monogram, the whole standing
on three paw feet.
- *height 83cm*
- £1,000 • Augustus Brandt

French Brass Lanterns ◄

- *circa 1880*
One of a pair of large and
impressive French brass and
metal lanterns.
- *height 102cm*
- £12,500 • Anthony Sharpe

Italian Wall Sconces ▼

- *circa 1790*
One of a pair of Italian silver
plated three branch tin wall
sconces with a trailing leaf design
and cut glass drops.
- £1,850 • Mora Upham

Farroday & Son Table Lamp ▼

- *circa 1899*

Farroday & Son English table lamp fitted with transfer printed lampshade. With F&S stamped on the bottom.
- *height 34cm*
- £600　• Turn On Lighting

Brass Library Lamp ▼

- *1880*

French library brass and tôle lamp with lever movement and brass fittings, standing on an oval brass base, in original condition.
- *height 55cm*
- £550　• Augustus Brandt

Gilt Candlesticks ▲

- *1880*

One of a pair of large gilt candlesticks with foliate and vine leaf decoration, standing on lion heads and paw feet.
- *height 79cm*
- £900　• Goodison Paraskeva

Chromed Cast Table Lamp ▼

- *1899*

Victorian table lamp with an opal glass bowl shaped shade standing on a chromed cast column, and circular base.
- *height 56cm*
- £895　• Turn On Lighting

Wall Obliques ▼

- *circa 1895*

One of a pair of silver bronze three branch, heavily scrolled wall obliques, made in New York by Caldwell.
- £4,500　• Mora Upham

'Go To Bed' Candlestick ▲
- *circa 1850*
'Go to bed' Victorian Tunbridge Ware and rosewood candlestick, and taper holder. The lid rises to reveal storage for candles and tapers.
- *height 11cm*
- £365   • Period Pieces

Italian Gilded Candlesticks ▲
- *circa 1880*
A pair of Italian gilded bronze candlesticks, with three foliate scrolled branches.
- *height 74cm*
- £2,950   • Poppets

Victorian Table Lamp ▼
- *1880*
Victorian brass pedestal lamp with a pink and glass shade with a cherry blossom painted design.
- *height 49cm*
- £895   • Turn On Lighting

French Student Lamp ▼
- *circa 1899*
French highly decorative adjustable library lamp with a frosted glass shade, standing on a reeded Corinthian column with laurel leaf decoration, standing on a rouge royale marble base.
- *height 65cm*
- £1,200   • Turn On Lighting

French Chandelier ◄
- *circa 1880*
French ormolu and cut glass bag and waterfall eight branch chandelier.
- £2,400   • Mora Upham

Victorian Bijou Lamp ▲
- *1880*
Victorian adjustable reading lamp with a pink glass tulip shade, metal rim and a curved brass stand, on a circular wooden base.
- *height 24cm*
- £700   • Turn On Lighting

Silver Plated Table Lamp ▲
- *circa 1895*
Late Victorian silver-plated table lamp, fitted with feathered white glass lampshade, standing on a moulded silver column and base.
- *height 36cm*
- £895   • Turn On Lighting

Foliate Design Lamp

- *1870*
Green tôle lamp with 19th century base with gilt scrolling, and dark green shade with foliate design
- *height 78cm*
- £580   • Augustus Brandt

Cast Brass Table Lamp

- *circa 1899*
English decorative cast brass table lamp stamped Hinks. Fitted with a cut glass lampshade.
- *height 56cm*
- £1,300   • Turn On Lighting

French Giltwood Candlesticks

- *1870*
Pair of French giltwood prichet with foliate carved column standing on carved scrolled feet.
- *height 73cm*
- £800   • Heytesbury

Glass Table Lamps

- *1899*
One of a pair of English pressed glass table lamps of ovoid form, with a petal design.
- *height 24cm*
- £900   • Turn On Lighting

Cast Brass Table Lamp

- *1895*
English cast brass table lamp fitted with a blue vaseline glass lampshade, standing on an elegant shaped brass tripod base.
- *height 52cm*
- £1,100   • Turn On Lighting

Spanish Ormolu Chandelier

- *circa 1880*
Spanish ormolu hour-glass shape chandelier.
- £3,800   • Mora Upham

Gas Ceiling Pendant ▼

- *circa 1880*

Decorative Victorian two branched gas ceiling pendants in brass fitted with opal and clear glass shades

- *height 80cm*
- £1,100
- Turn On Lighting

Mongolfier Chandelier ▼

- *circa 1800*

A fine French crystal and gilt bronze Mongolfier chandelier with four patinated bronze putti in the Louis XVI style.

- *drop 152cm*
- £12,500
- Westland & Co

Victorian Lanterns ▼

- *circa 1899*

Copper oxidised late Victorian ceiling pendants fitted with frosted glass covers.

- *height 33cm*
- £750
- Turn On Lighting

English Lanterns ▲

- *circa 1895*

One of a pair of copper oxidised English lanterns fitted with blue vaseline glass shades.

- *height 26cm*
- £1,500
- Turn On Lighting

Italian Chandelier ▲

- *circa 1790*

A rare late 18th century Italian giltwood and twisted glass forty branch chandelier of large size.

- *drop 180cm*
- £26,000
- Westland & Co

English Desk Lamp ▲

- *circa 1899*

English silver plate on brass adjustable desk lamp.

- *height 43cm*
- £895
- Turn On Lighting

English Wall Lamp ◄

- *circa 1870*

One of a pair of decorative cast brass gas wall lamps fitted with lime feather glass shades.

- *height 33cm*
- £1,500
- Turn On Lighting

Bronzed Gas Wall Light ▼

- *circa 1865*

An important English bronzed gas wall light fitted with opal glass gas shade with decorative motives.
- *height 45cm*
- **£1,200** • Turn On Lighting

French Chandeliers ▼

- *circa 1890*

A pair of gilt brass French Gothic revival chandeliers.
- *62cm x 91cm*
- **£3,500** • Westland & Co

Three Light Ceiling Pendant ▶

- *circa 1899*

Edwardian three light ceiling pendant in brass, fitted with acid edged cranberry glass shades.
- *height 43cm*
- **£1,500** • Turn On Lighting

Wall Appliques ▲

- *circa 1860*

A pair of gilt brass Neo-Classical wall appliqués.
- *length 81cm*
- **£1,500** • Westland & Co

Brass Wall Lamp ▲

- *circa 1880*

One of a pair of English decorative gas brass wall lamps fitted with cut and acid edged glass shades.
- *height 20cm*
- **£995** • Turn On Lighting

French Candelabra ▼

- *circa 1840*

One of a pair of French four branch ormolu candelabra with a snake circling a tapered column, with scrolled acanthus leaf and shell decoration and a flame finial, the whole on a solid platform base.
- *height 60cm*
- **£3,850** • O. F. Wilson

15 Branch Chandelier ▲
- *circa 17th–18th century*
Chandelier with ten large branches and five smaller ones from the seventeenth century with some later editions.
- *height 186cm*
- £6,800   • Augustus Brandt

French Prichet Sticks ▲
- *1780*
One of a pair of French prichet sticks standing on three feet.
- *height 55cm*
- £950   • Heytesbury

Black Tôle Lamp ▲
- *1870*
Black tôle lamp with gilt vases and floral swags around the base, and sprays of corn around the central column, with original patination.
- *height 74cm*
- £580   • Augustus Brandt

Victorian Ceiling Pendant ▼
- *circa 1889*
Victorian gas ceiling pendant in brass fitted with two branches with acid edged cranberry glass shades.
- *height 90cm*
- £1,100   • Turn On Lighting

Cast Brass Table Lamp ▼
- *circa 1890*
English cast brass table lamp fitted with a hand painted glass lampshade decorated with a scene of birds and trailing foliage, supported by brass arms.
- *height 48cm*
- £1,100   • Turn On Lighting

English Gas Wall Lamps ▲
- *circa 1875*
One of a pair of decorative glass brass wall lamps fitted with acid edged glass shades.
- *33cm*
- £995   • Turn On Lighting

Victorian Wall Lamps ▲
- *circa 1895*
One of a pair of Victorian gas wall lamps fitted with moulded peach coloured glass shades.
- *34cm*
- £895   • Turn On Lighting

Electric Wall Lamps ▲
- *circa 1900*
One of a pair of decorative cast brass electric wall lamps fitted with blue vaseline glass shades.
- *20cm*
- £895   • Turn On Lighting

Wall Lamp ▶
- *circa 1890s*
Pair of English bronzed electric wall lights. Fitted with cut crystal glass shades.
- *height 28cm*
- £1,800   • Turn On Lighting

French Silver Plated Obliques ▲
- *circa 1860*
French silver plated three branch wall obliques with cut glass storm shades, mounted on a silver stylised shield with scrolled shell design.
- £3,400   • Mora Upham

English Wall Lamp ▲
- *circa 1880*
One of a pair of English decorative cast brass gas wall lamps fitted with acid edged glass shades.
- *35cm*
- £995   • Turn On Lighting

Gas Wall Lamp ▲
- *circa 1875*
One of a pair highly decorative cast glass gas wall lamps fitted with cut glass shades.
- *22cm*
- £995   • Turn On Lighting

Expert Tips

Try to buy from a reputable dealer who will have rewired the gas lamp fittings with new electric cables, and check that the shades are not broken.

Edwardian Ceiling Lights ◀

- *circa 1901*

Pair of Edwardian cast brass flash ceiling lights fitted with frosted glass covers.
- *height 20cm*
- £1,600 • Turn On Lighting

Victorian Table Lamp ▼

- *circa 1890*

A highly decorative Victorian, cast brass table lamp fitted with acid edged glass lampshade, standing on a tripod base.
- *height 44cm*
- £895 • Turn On Lighting

English Electric Wall Lamp ▼

- *circa 1890s*

One of a pair decorative cast brass electric wall lamps fitted with hobnail glass shades.
- *27cm*
- £1,500 • Turn On Lighting

Ceiling Pendant ▼

- *circa 1895*

Late Victorian three branch ceiling pendant in brass, fitted with three green vaseline shades.
- *height 42cm*
- £1,200 • Turn On Lighting

French Candelabra ▼

- *circa 1830*

Pair of large gilt ormolu candelabra, with four gilt scrolling branches and a gilt finial, on a central reeded column standing on three bent goat legs with cloven hooves.
- *height 66cm*
- £4,500 • O. F. Wilson

'Palmer & Co.' Lamp ▼

- *circa 1850*

Victorian 'Palmer & Co' lamp with original glass shade and an emerald green column with gilt foliate design.
- *height 78cm*
- £2,200 • O. F. Wilson

Metalware

French Tôle Lilies ▼
• *circa 1880*
One of a pair of French metal tôle lilies in their own brown metal pots.
• *height 58cm*
• £2,100 • Anthony Sharpe

George III Candelabra ▼
• *circa 1800*
A fine pair of late 18th century English George III three branch candelabra. On white marble bases with ormolu caps, the two opposing patinated bronze children hold up the candelabra tops.
• *height 66cm*
• £5,750 • Gavin Douglas

Bronze and Ormolu Cassolettes ▲
• *circa 1800*
Good pair of French or English patinated bronze and ormolu cassolettes. They can be used either as urns or as candleholders, with fine quality chasing.
• *height 38cm*
• £9,250 • Gavin Douglas

English Candelabra ▲
• *circa 1790*
A fine pair of English George III patinated bronze, ormolu and marble figural candelabra. The marble bases in white and grey marble. The two opposing young boys are a well known model and have their original patination. They appear to have original chains.
• *height 67cm*
• £8,950 • Gavin Douglas

French Tôleware ▼
• *circa 1880*
French tôleware painted floral wall appliqués with oak leaf decoration and candle holder.
• *height 29cm*
• £480 • Anthony Sharpe

French Candelabra ▼
• *circa 1880*
A good pair of French late 19th century ormolu and rouge marble candelabra. In superb condition with original gilding and finial. In the manner of Barbedienne.
• *height 84cm*
• £5,250 • Gavin Douglas

French Empire Candlesticks ▼

- *circa 1815*

A fine pair of French Empire patinated bronze, ormolu and marble figural candlesticks. The two young boys holding candle holders in the form of standards.
- *height 28cm*
- **£2,450**　• Gavin Douglas

Bronze Boys ▲

- *circa 1870*

Pair of bronze boys playing with a hoop and stick.
- *height 22cm*
- **£2,300**　• John Clay

Patinated Bronze Females ◀

- *circa 1890.*

A fine quality pair of naked classical females in patinated bronze on marble bases. The bronzes well executed and finished and with the feel of a Levantine slave market. Probably French
- *height 38cm*
- **£4,950**　• Gavin Douglas

Regency Candelabra ▲

- *circa 1820*

A pair of Regency porcelain, ormolu and cut glass candelabra. With triform porcelain base with gilt enriched salmon pink circular urns and scrolled arms cast with Amorini, terminating in hob nail cut drip pans, surrounded with cast foliate corona suspending cut glass lustres.
- *34cm x 24cm*
- **£5,250**　• Gavin Douglas

Gilded Ormolu Candelabra ▲

- *circa 1840*

A fine pair of early 19th century mercury gilded ormolu candelabra from a design by Pierre Gouthiere. The four branch candelabra lift out leaving a pair of candlesticks.
- *height 56cm*
- **£12,000**　• Gavin Douglas

Bronze Horse ◀

- *circa 1880*

A fine quality 19th century French bronze figure of a stallion. Signed Vidal.
- *32cm x 39cm*
- **£1,995**　• John Riordan

287

Ormolu Ewers ▲
- *circa 1795*
A pair of French Directoire
period patinated bronze and
finest original ormolu ewers. Of
slender ovoid form, the sinuous
lip continuing to an SOR-scroll
arm with finely chased griffin and
satyrs mask terminal, on a
circular base with stiff leaf and
engine turned decoration, resting
on a square plinth.
- *height 38cm*
- **£11,250** • Gavin Douglas

Ormolu Tazza ▼
- *circa 1815*
A fine quality fire gilded ormolu
tazza or dish set on a porphry
base. Almost certainly Swedish
from early 19th century. With
fine quality work to tazza and
original ormolu.
- *25cm x 25cm.*
- **£2,250** • Gavin Douglas

Bronze Dolphins ▼
- *1880*
A pair of English stylized bronze
dolphins with mounted seashells
resting on their tails, on a
rectangular marble base.
- *height 16cm*
- **£1,650** • Heytesbury

Bronze Lady ▼
- *circa 1880*
Bronze lady with a pensive
expression, one arm over a chair
and the other at her spinette.
- *height 53cm*
- **£720** • John Clay

Gothic Revival Splint Holders ▲
- *circa 1850*
An attractive pair of gothic
revival splint holders in the style
of Pugin. With fine original
ormolu in superb condition.
Probably French.
- *height 20.5cm*
- **£1,750** • Gavin Douglas

Bronze Girl with Dragonfly ▲
- *circa 1880*
Painted spelter figure of a young
laughing girl with a bow in her
hair, one arm outstretched and
the other holding a bowl with a
dragonfly. Standing on a foliate
rustic mound and circular wood
base.
- *height 49cm*
- **£220** • John Clay

Expert Tips

*Get to know your metals! Can
you tell the difference between
spelter and bronze, or ormolu
and brass? If you can't, this
could be an expensive gap in
your knowledge.*

French Empire Candlesticks ▼

• *circa 1815*
A fine pair of patinated bronze and original ormolu French Empire candlesticks. In the form of a classically draped vestal standing holding an oil lamp in her arms, with a very well formed candleholder on her head, with round ormolu socle.
• *height 38cm*
• **£3,950**   • **Gavin Douglas**

Reclining Nude Plaque ▲

• *circa 1880*
Reclining nude with her head resting on her hand and an angel at her feet.
• *width 51cm*
• **£275**   • **John Clay**

Bronze Young Girl ▼

• *circa 1880*
Bronze classical figure of a young girl semi-clad, holding her robe in one hand.
• *height 52cm*
• **£1,320**   • **John Clay**

Boy Water Carrier ▲

• *circa 1870*
Gilt on bronze boy carrying two ewers on a yoke, standing on a circular bronze base and signed Moreau.
• *height 23cm*
• **£1,250**   • **John Clay**

Orient ▶

• *circa 1900*
A good quality early 20th century French bronze bust of a woman inscribed 'ORIENT', and stamped: E VILLANIS.
• *51cm x 34cm*
• **£2,750**   • **John Riordan**

Bronze Figures ▲

• *circa 1870*
Very attractive pair of patinated bronze figures of negro slaves carrying produce. Produced and signed by Susse Frères from models by Charles Cumberworth an American born artist working in Paris. On reeded onyx bases.
• *height 50cm*
• **£4,750**   • **Gavin Douglas**

Bacchante ▼

- *circa 1880*
A fine quality 19th century
French bronze figure of
Bacchante. Signed Clodion. Also
stamped with the Barbedienne
foundry stamp.
- *55cm x 54cm*
- **£2,995**   • John Riordan

The Kiss ▶

- *circa 1875*
A superb 19th century French
bronze bust of a couple kissing.
Signed Houdon.
- *46cm x 39cm*
- **£4,950**   • John Riordan

Celinius ▼

- *circa 1800*
Bronze figure of Celinius and the
infant Bacchus.
- *height 59cm*
- **£3,750**   • John Riordan

Robert the Bruce ▼

- *circa 1890*
Impressive spelter figure of
Robert the Bruce wearing armour
and holding a shield, standing on
a square green marble base.
- *height 83cm*
- **£1,500**   • John Clay

Bronze of David ▼

- *circa 1880*
Bronze figure of David with the
head of Goliath. Stamped and
signed A. Mercie Barbedienne
foundry.
- *height 70cm*
- **£4,950**   • John Riordan

Bronze Chinese Roe Deer ◀

- *circa 1880*
Bronze study of a Chinese Roe
deer from the Chiurazzi foundry,
Naples.
- *height 56cm*
- **£7,800**   • Wakelin Linfield

Furniture

The chest or coffer is the earliest form of furniture, made from planks and sometimes reinforced with iron bandings.

The best way to learn about furniture is to handle it by turning the piece over, opening drawers, examing the method of construction and observing signs of wear and tear. Colour and patina also play a large part: for example, when buying a walnut table it is important that the item has not been polished in such a way that the natural grain and patina has been lost, so often a piece of furniture has been over French polished. The quality of the wood can also be as important as style, so always go to a reputable dealer. The introduction of

machine cut veneering started a decline in quality in much of the nineteenth century furniture, however, the best Victorian and Edwardian furniture is highly collectable. Furniture needs taking care of and protecting from the damaging effects of damp and direct sunlight, which can cause pigments and inlays to fade. Before purchasing an item of furniture make sure you are informed about the main buying criteria including style, materials, method of construction, period and manufacturer, as these influence its value.

Beds

Polonaise Day Bed ▼
- *circa 18th century*
Fine Polonaise day bed with carved head and footboard, original washed pink paintwork, with curved pillars and oval cover, with wreath and floral carving.
- *height 280cm*
- £10,000   • **Augustus Brandt**

French Empire Bedroom Set ▲
- *circa 1890*
French empire burr walnut bedstead with ormolu mounts and bow front with matching bedside cabinets and dressing table.
- *width 153cm*
- £10,500   • **Sleeping Beauty**

Brass French Bedstead ▲
- *circa 1880*
French brass 'chapeau gendarme' with unusual oval plaques on the head and foot board with three playful cherubs and garlands of flowers.
- *length 179cm*
- £3,500   • **Sleeping Beauty**

Edwardian Bedsteads ◄
- *1910*
A pair of Queen Anne style Edwardian moulded single bedsteads in burr walnut, standing on cabriole legs.
- *width 111cm*
- £4,500   • **Sleeping Beauty**

French Empire Bedstead ▼
- *circa 1870*
French empire flame mahogany bedstead with pilaster moulding, cross banded and inlaid designs with ormolu mounts.
- *width 153cm*
- **£6,500**   • Sleeping Beauty

French Mahogany Bedstead ▼
- *circa 1880*
French mahogany Louis XVI bed with a moulded headboard with a gilt torchière in the centre with two cherubs below, and gilt finials.
- *length 178cm*
- **£5,500**   • Sleeping Beauty

Mahogany French Bedstead ▶
- *circa 1860*
Flame mahogany Louis XV bedstead with highly decorative floral and ribbon ormolu mounts.
- *width 137cm*
- **£6,000**   • Sleeping Beauty

Expert Tips

If you come across a pair of period bed posts for a four poster bed, snap them up. It is simple to make your own bed as long as you have the geniune posts.

French Louis XV Bedstead ▲
- *circa 1880*
French Louis XV solid walnut single bed with moulded and carved headboard and footboard.
- *length 184cm*
- **£4,200**   • Sleeping Beauty

Bow Fronted Bedstead ▼
- *19th century*
Upholstered bow fronted and padded Louis XV bedstead with original green paintwork.
- *148cm*
- **£1,295**   • Sleeping Beauty

Walnut Louis XVI Bedstead ◀
- *circa 1880*
Large French solid walnut Louis XVI bed with a carved ribboning on the headboard, and floral swags footboard, with fluted posts.
- *length 179cm*
- **£6,750**   • Sleeping Beauty

Louis XV Bedstead ▲
- **19th century**
Upholstered Louis XV pink velvet button backed bedstead with solid walnut frame and bow fronted base, standing on cabriole legs.
- *length 222cm*
- **£1,495**   • Sleeping Beauty

Louis XV Bedstead ▲
- **1880**
Painted, padded and upholstered Louis XV bedstead with original gilding to headboard and base.
- *length 185cm*
- **£4,500**   • Sleeping Beauty

Walnut Louis XV Bedstead ▲
- **circa 1880**
French solid walnut Louis XV bedstead with carved floral swag and moulded decoration.
- *width 153cm*
- **£4,200**   • Sleeping Beauty

Renaissance Style Bedstead ▶
- **circa 1880**
Extended Renaissance style walnut bedstead with wreath and torchière ormolu mounts.
- *width 222cm*
- **£6,950**   • Sleeping Beauty

Victorian Bedstead ▼
- **1895**
Victorian brass and black painted iron bedstead with unusual tubular brass top and central linked plaques on both the headboard and base.
- *length 222cm*
- **£2,500**   • Sleeping Beauty

Cottage Bedstead ▼
- **1880**
Victorian hand forged black iron cottage bedstead.
- *length 222cm*
- **£1,495**   • Sleeping Beauty

Victorian Bedstead ▲
- **1885**
Victorian black cast iron bedstead with brass rail and ball finials.
- *length 222cm*
- **£1,295**   • Sleeping Beauty

Spanish Bedstead. ▲
- **1850**
A Spanish hand forged iron bedstead with large ornate cast brass ornamentation.
- *length 183cm*
- **£2,600**   • Sleeping Beauty

Iron Bedstead ▼
- *1890*

Victorian black cast iron and
brass bedstead with urn shaped
finials.
- *length 183cm*
- £1,950   • Sleeping Beauty

Walnut Bedstead ▼
- *19th century*

Solid walnut carved Louis XV
bedstead with a central scroll to
the moulded headboard.
- *length 222cm*
- £1,400   • Sleeping Beauty

French Walnut Bedstead ▼
- *circa 1770*

French walnut Louis XV bed with
a carved cochial head and
footboard.
- *length 178cm*
- £3,495   • Sleeping Beauty

Brass Bedstead ▲
- *1885*

Victorian black cast iron bedstead
with brass rails and brass ball
finials.
- *length 183cm*
- £1,500   • Sleeping Beauty

French Child's Bed ▼
- *circa 1880*

French four poster child's bed,
with turned and fluted columns
and hand-painted decoration.
- £3,250   • Serendipity

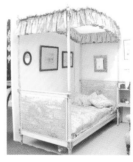

Louis XV Bedstead ◄
- *19th century*

Solid walnut hand carved Louis
XV bedstead with a moulded
apron to footboard, on cabriole
legs.
- *length 185cm*
- £3,495   • Sleeping Beauty

Bonheurs du Jour

Bonheur du Jour ▼
• *circa 1890*
Bonheur du jour with pierced brass rail and two small drawers, flanked by cupboards with circular inlay panels and a gallery single drawer, standing on slender tapering legs.
• *104cm x 73cm*
• £1,150 • The Swan

Victorian Dressing Table ▼
• *circa 1870*
Fine quality Victorian burr walnut dressing table and mirror supported by scrolled carving.
• *height 174cm*
• £2,800 • Hill Farm

George IV Bonheur du Jour ▼
• *circa 1825*
George IV rosewood writing table in solid and veneered rosewood. With pierced gallery drawers and moving writing slide supported by twist columns.
• *height 122cm*
• £7,800 • Gerald Brodie

Sheraton Bonheur du Jour ▼
• *circa 1790*
Fine Sheraton period bonheur du jour, with harewood inlay fold-over tops, enclosing a rising nest of drawers and pigeonholes.
• *89cm x 114cm*
• £22,500 • John Bly

Victorian Dressing Table ▼
• *circa 1880*
Victorian mahogany dressing table with central mirror and drawer, flanked by eight small drawers.
• *height 167cm*
• £2,350 • C. Preston

Bonheur du Jour ▼
• *circa 1890*
Late Victorian mahogany bonheur du jour with satinwood stringing, a roll top cover, the interior fitted with five pigeonholes and a central small drawer, above a pull out writing slope and two drawers, the whole on straight legs.
• *103cm x 72cm*
• £1,500 • Macnaughton-Smith

Chippendale Style Bonheur du Jour ▼
• *circa 19th century*
Chippendale style bonheur du jour in the style of Angelica Kauffman, decorated with floral designs and classical scenes in the finest satin wood. Shield style bevelled glazed mirror with urn finial, standing on delicate turned legs.
• *165cm x 107cm*
• £24,500 • J. & T. Stone

Bookcases

George IV Mahogany Bookcase ▲

- *circa 1825*

A George IV cream-painted and parcel-gilt mahogany bookcase in the manner of William Kent. The rectangular moulded cornice above an egg and dart dentilled lower cornice above a foliate swagged frieze centred by a female mask and flanked by shells, with four glazed panelled doors below between Ionic pilasters. The base section with four panelled doors between plain panelled uprights, each enclosing an adjustable shelf.

- *308cm x 210cm*
- £48,000 • **Anthony Outred**

Mahogany Bookcase ▲

- *circa 1840*

Fine flame mahogany secretaire bookcase with two glazed doors and fitted interior and two cupboards below on a square base.

- *236cm x 104cm*
- £10,500 • **Butchoff**

Mahogany Bookcase ▼

- *1880*

Unusually large breakfront bookcase with mahogany and satinwood cross-banded decoration, swan neck pediment, galleried and moulded designs, raised on a plinth base.

- *233cm x 313cm*
- £28,000 • **Butchoff**

Glazed Bookcase Cabinet ▼

- *circa 1760*

An early George III mahogany glazed bookcase cabinet. With a broken, moulded dentil work pediment, each door composed of two astragal glazed octagonal panels with glazing bars connecting to the door frames, the interior lined and fitted with glass shelves. The cabinet with figured timber, the doors each with a shaped fielded panel defined by ribbon and flower-head moulding. The cabinet fitted with a moulded lip at the base above.

- *232.5cm x 117cm*
- £24,500 • **Anthony Outred**

Victorian Walnut Bookcase ▲

- *circa 1880*

Victorian walnut bookcase with moulded flat top pediment, glazed doors enclosing five shelves, two deep drawers above two moulded doors, standing on moulded bracket feet.

- *height 251cm*
- £2,850 • **Hill Farm**

Secretaire Bookcase ▲

- *circa 1820*

Regency secretaire bookcase with Gothic glazed upper section, the fall opens to reveal a well fitted interior above matched flame veneer doors, the whole raised on splayed feet with shaped apron.

- *262cm x 120cm*
- £18,750 • **Serendipity**

Irish Bookcase ▼
- *circa 1830*
Irish flame mahogany bookcase of four arched doors with brass grills standing on a square straight base, stamped Strahan Co. Dublin
- *height 168cm*
- £12,500 • Fred E. Anderson

Lacquered Bookcase ▼
- *circa 1870*
Three tier hanging bookcase finished in black lacquer with gold banding and flower designs.
- *height 83cm x 70cm*
- £675 • John Clay

Victorian Bookcase ▼
- *circa 1890*
A late Victorian open bookcase with three shelves with carved leaf moulding to the sides, standing on a plain straight base.
- *110cm x 97cm*
- £595 • Clarke & Denny

Ebonised Bookcase ▲
- *circa 1850*
Victorian well proportioned ebonized bookcase of inverted breakfront outline, leading to egg and dart ormolu mounts above a central panelled frieze, with an ebonised panelled back, flanked by crisp ormolu patera with a bead and flower moulding below and three adjustable ebonised shelves The whole supported on an inverted breakfront base.
- *117cm x 127cm*
- £7,500 • Anthony Outred

Painted Bookcase ▲
- *circa 1840*
Small painted bookcase with three shelves, a moulded top and two panelled cupboards, standing on turned legs.
- *163cm x 67cm*
- £1,500 • John Owen

George III Secretaire Bookcase ▼
- *circa 1810*
George III secretaire bookcase with a well fitted interior, in excellent flame mahogany. With Gothic glazing bars to the upper section and cupboard to base.
- *221 x 101.5cm x 58.5cm*
- £14,500 • Wakelin Linfield

Mahogany Bookcase ▼
- *circa 1880*
Mahogany bookcase with moulded pediment, pillared sides and one long single drawer at the base, standing on turned feet.
- *250cm x 125cm*
- £1,760 • John Riordan

297

George II Mahogany Bookcase ▲

- *circa 1750*
George II mahogany bookcase, the bold swan neck pediment with foliate and rosette carving, above two astragal glazed doors opening to reveal a fitted interior. The lower section with sloping fall opening to reveal a finely fitted interior. The whole on bracket feet.
- *228cm x 100cm*
- **£27,500** • **Wakelin Linfield**

Regency Bookcase ▲

- *circa 1810*
English Regency period two door chiffoniere/bookcase in a mixture of pine and fruit wood with galleried and turned designs.
- *107cm x 63cm*
- **£2,950** • **Wakelin Linfield**

George III Bureau Bookcase ▼

- *circa 1765*
George III mahogany bureau bookcase, the astragal glazed doors enclosing adjustable shelves with fall front and well fitted interior of tulip wood. With letter slides and drawers.
- *width 109cm*
- **£7,900** • **Salem Antiques**

Satinwood Secretaire Bookcase ▼

- *circa 1780*
Excellent secretaire bookcase of small elegant proportions. The whole veneered in satinwood heightened with cross banding in tulip wood, with shaped cornice and urn finials surmounting a corbelled frieze above two doors with moulded gothic glazing bars retaining their original glass.
- *194cm x 52cm x 23cm*
- **£85,000** • **Wakelin Linfield**

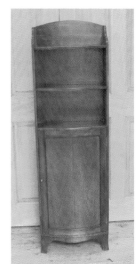

Victorian Mahogany Bookcase ▲

- *circa 1880*
One of a pair of mahogany bookcases with open shelves and storage cupboards below, enclosed by bow fronted doors.
- *135cm x 13cm*
- **£1,850** • **R.S. Antiques**

Regency Bookcase ▲

- *circa 1835*
Regency rosewood bookcase with glazed doors and two panelled doors below, standing on a plinth base.
- *193cm x 84cm x 36cm*
- **£3,250** • **The Swan**

Boxes

Parchment Box ▲
- *circa 1890s*
Ex-Shanghai rectangular leather red lacquered parchment box, the top and sides finely painted in gilt showing a cartouche of children playing games.
- *7cm x 32cm*
- £360　　• Eastern Interiors

Wedding Basket ▼
- *circa 1880*
Red lacquered circular box with a half-moon shaped lid secured with brass lockplate arched handle depicting two magpies facing each other, symbolising marital bliss.
- *height 25cm*
- £260　　• Eastern Interiors

Dutch Bible Box ▶
- *18th century*
Dutch colonial Bible box, heavily carved with scrolled designs, with fine pierced and engraved mounts.
- *15.5cm x 23cm*
- £850　　• Younger

Leather Hatbox ▲
- *circa 1860*
Single leather Shanghai pyramid hat box cover with leaf shaped, lockplate ruyi form head-mounts.
- *height 30cm*
- £385　　• Eastern Interiors

Large Tapestry Box ▼
- *circa 1870*
Large box covered in a wine red tapestry with cornflowers and wheatsheafs.
- *70cm x 65cm*
- £675　　• Drummonds

Ballot Box ▼
- *circa 1860*
Ebonised ballot box with red banding, inscribed with the words, 'For and Against' in gold letters each side of a metal postal opening.
- *height 28cm*
- £300　　• The Lacquer Chest

Satinwood Tea Caddy ◀
- *circa 1820*
Satinwood tea caddy, crossbanded with tulipwood, boxwood and ebony.
- *16cm x 27.5cm*
- £375　　• A.I.G.

Wig Box ▶

• *circa 1780*
French wig box with a domed lid
hand painted with floral garlands
centred by a classical folly in a
heart shaped cartouche, flanked
by a lady to the right and a
gentleman to the left.
• *16cm x 30cm*
• £1,050   • O. F. Wilson

Document Box ▲

• *circa 1880s*
Late Meiji period sugi wood
cabinet for documents, in six
sections.
• *71cm x 46cm*
• £1,395   • Gordon Reece

Box on Stand ▼

• *circa 1870*
Leather lacquered box on stand
with original brass lockplate with
'ruyi' head mounts and fittings.
Ex- Shanxi.
• *36cm x 48cm*
• £570   • Eastern Interiors

Jewellery Case ▲

• *circa 1880*
Black lacquered jewellery box
with a red interior and
polychrome paintings of flora and
fauna. Inside the lid is a folding
mirror. Ex Fuzhou.
• *20cm x 24cm*
• £390   • Eastern Interiors

Blackwood Box ▼

• *circa 1870*
Small box with a mirror fitted
under the lid, with double
handles, chrysanthemum shaped
mounts and brass lockplate
fashioned as a butterfly. Ex
Shanghai.
• *10cm x 24cm*
• £280   • Eastern Interiors

Chinese Hat Box ▼

• *circa 1880*
Red lacquered cylindrical
Chinese hat box with original
brass fittings, the interior fitted
with two sandalwood plates for
the storage of hats.
• *41cm x 34cm*
• £430   • Eastern Interiors

Tea Tin

- *1880*

One of a set of four black metal tea tins with a central cartouche of two birds perched on a cherry blossom branch.
- *height 44cm*
- **£1,500** • Goodison Paraskeva

Games Compendium

- *circa 1860*

Victorian walnut games compendium comprising: solid board for chess and backgammon, ivory cribbage and score board, ivory hand counters, lower drawer containing; playing cards, shakers and tiddlywinks and counters.
- *width 23cm*
- **£5,950** • J.& T.Stone

Jewel Casket ▶

- *circa 1860*

French lustre tortoiseshell jewel casket with bowed panels, extensive ormolu decorative mounts and original silk lined interior.
- *height 25cm*
- **£9,500** • J.& T. Stone

Oak Box ▲

- *circa 1880*

Oak box with silver-plated mounts of cherubs holding a plaque, with mermaids each side of the escutcheon plate.
- *10cm x 25cm*
- **£350** • A.I.G.

Teapot Holder ▲

- *circa 1890s*

Ex-Fukien teapot holder. The lid secured with finely carved inverted scroll handles and dragons heads under clouds.
- *height 22cm*
- **£260** • Eastern Interiors

Japanese Travelling Box ▲

- *circa 1880*

A small Japanese Kiri-sugi wood, tansu storage box for travelling salesmen, from the Meiji period.
- *30cm x 52cm*
- **£995** • Gordon Reece

Regency Tea Caddy ▲

- *circa 1820*

Regency rosewood tea caddy of sarcophagus form with brass bun feet and double ring handles hanging from lion mask mounts.
- *30cm x 25cm*
- **£295** • A.I.G.

Mahjong Set ▲

- **1920**

Impressive and imposing Mahjong set of the highest quality in a solid oak case with extensive brass work decoration to the sides and top. With solid brass handle and sliding front panel revealing five similarly decorated drawers containing solid ivory tiles, game sticks and dice. Provenance: The Right Honourable The Viscount Leverhulme, K. G. of Thornton Manor.
- *29cm x 32cm*
- **£5,950**   • **J. & T. Stone**

Apothecary Box ▲

- **circa 1830**

Georgian mahogany apothecary box with an almost complete set of original bottles, some with original contents. With lower drawer with original scales, weights, mortar, pestle and key.
- *13cm x 19cm*
- **£1,950**   • **J. & T. Stone**

Tortoiseshell Tea Caddy ▶

- **circa 1775**

Exceptional red tortoiseshell tea chest with ivory stringing, silver ball feet and top handle; the interior with three original glass canisters with silver plate lids and original key.
- *height 14cm*
- **£29,500**   • **J. & T. Stone**

Georgian Knife Boxes ▼

- **circa 1790**

One of a pair of superb flame mahogany Georgian knife boxes with original interiors, silver plate ring pulls and escutcheons.
- *height 48cm*
- **£6,950**   • **J. & T. Stone**

Regency Chinoiserie Box ▼

- **circa 1820**

English Regency penwork box with trailing floral designs around a central panel depicting a group of hand painted Chinese figures.
- *height 16cm*
- **£1,650**   • **O. F. Wilson**

Scholar's Parchment Box ▲

- **19th century**

Scholar's leather parchment box embossed with the design of the Buddhist swastika, the cover designed with the character of 'long life'. Ex-Shanghai.
- *18cm x 28cm*
- **£465**   • **Eastern Interiors**

Tea Tins ▲

- **1880**

Set of six cylindrical tea tins with covers and a central cartouche of a classical ruin surrounded by a foliate design, each with a gilt shield and numerals.
- *height 48cm*
- **£2,500** • **Goodison Paraskeva**

Ash Tea Caddy ▶

- *circa 1850*

Tea caddy made from Mongolian ash, with lead receptacles and an oval enamel plaque with a painted cherub. This was a wedding present in 1869, and at that date tea cost 10/- per lb.

- *height 11cm*
- £2,800 • J.& T. Stone

Red Merchant's Trunk ▼

- *circa 1880*

Lacquered merchant's trunk with a moulded hinged lid over a conforming body, decorated with intricate brass-work of faceted and smooth rounded nails. The front lock is a large stylised butterfly - the symbol of longevity. Ex-Fuzhou.

- *27cm x 24cm*
- £400 • Eastern Interiors

Tortoiseshell Tea Caddy

- *circa 1800*

Rare George III red tortoiseshell single tea caddy with ebony line stringing. The cover and interior lid have the original silver plated ball handles, with original silver plated lock and hinges.

- *height 10cm*
- £5,580 • Period Pieces

Expert Tips

A tortoiseshell tea caddy is worth more if it is not restored. Sometimes slight wear and tear at the corners makes the tea caddy more valuble.

Regency Rosewood Tea Caddy ▶

- *circa 1810*

Regency rosewood tea caddy with brass foliate inlay, with a cushion moulded cover on a tapering body. Standing on brass ball feet. The interior is fitted with the original cut glass mixing bowl and two brass inlaid tea containers.

- *height 21cm*
- £1,325 • Period Pieces

Tortoiseshell Box ▼

- *circa 1760*

Tortoiseshell Anglo Dutch box with ivory stringing and silver mounts, on silver bun feet.

- *16cm x 28cm x 20cm*
- £3,000 • O. F. Wilson

Satinwood Tea Caddy ▼

- *circa 1790*

A George III oval satinwood tea caddy with bats wing pattern to the front and cover and original axe head handle to lid.

- *height 12cm*
- £1,950 • Period Pieces

George III Cutlery Urns ▲

- *circa 1790*

One of a pair of George III mahogany cutlery urns, with chequered line stringing and barbers pole edging. The stepped lid with ivory finial rises to reveal the original fitted interior for twelve place settings. Standing on a platform base with barber's pole stringing.

- *height 66cm*
- £10,980 • Period Pieces

George III Tea Caddies ▼

- *circa 1790*

Pair of square George III tea caddies with canted corners, in quartered mahogany veneers, with boxwood rosewood and ebony line inlays and box and hare-wood pattern to front and cover. It is unusual to find a matching pair.

- *height 11.5cm*
- £5,860 • Period Pieces

Tortoiseshell Tea Caddy ▲

- *circa 1820*

Very rare Regency pressed tortoiseshell tea caddy with ribbed and bowed front panel, dome top, silver stringing, insignia plate, escutcheon and top ball finial.

- *height 22cm*
- £9,450 • J. & T. Stone

Victorian Coromandel Wood Box ▲

- *circa 1870*

Unusual Victorian coromandel wood jewel box with gilded ormolu decoration and hand painted ivory miniature of an Eastern Princess on the lid.

- *6cm x 9cm*
- £995 • J. & T. Stone

Pear Shaped Tea Caddy ▶

- *circa 1800*

Fine pear shaped George III tea caddy made from fruitwood, comprising two sections with brass fitting and stem.

- *height 19cm*
- £5,350 • Period Pieces

Pen Work Tea Caddy ▲

- *circa 1825*

Regency pen work double tea caddy with extensive Chinoiserie scenes of a festive parade. The whole standing on brass lion's paw feet, with matching side ring handles.

- *12cm x 14cm*
- £4,750 • J.& T. Stone

Voting Box ▼

- *circa 1880*

Victorian oak voting box inscribed with the brass letters 'Y' and 'N', with two small drawers and a central hole with emerald green satin.

- *28cm x 25cm*
- £495 • A.I.G.

Regency Tea Caddy ▼

- *circa 1820*

Tortoiseshell tea caddy with twin compartments, chamfered corners, a Pagoda cover and mother of pearl inlay depicting thistles and roses, standing on silver plated ball feet.

- *height 14cm*
- £4,980 • Period Pieces

Victorian Coromandel Dressing Case ▶

- *circa 1851*

Victorian quality coromandel wood lady's dressing case with thirteen, London 1851, hall marked silver topped jars and containers, the lower lockable drawer for jewellery and sewing, complete with four mother of pearl bobbins, a waxer, tape, pin cushion and needle case. Signed, Mechi, maker, London.
- *height 25cm*
- **£4,950**   • J. & T. Stone

George III Tea Caddy ▲

- *circa 1790*

George III square burr, yew and parquetry inlaid tea caddy with chamfered angles. Boxwood and chequer strung, with oval striped hare wood paterae.
- *height 14cm*
- **£2,950**   • J. & T. Stone

Hendserson Tea Caddy ▼

- *circa 1810*

Regency tortoiseshell tea caddy by Henderson, a reputed tortoiseshell box maker. With mother of pearl diamond inlay, twin compartments and a ripple serpentine front, standing on small mahogany bun feet. With maker's label.
- *height 12.5cm*
- **£3,500**   • Period Pieces

Ebony Casket ▲

- *circa 1860*

Ebony casket inlaid with ivory, mother of pearl flowers and various fruitwoods.
- *10cm x 32cm*
- **£595**   • A.I.G.

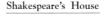

Rosewood Tea Caddy ▲

- *circa 1820*

Regency 'sarcophagus' rosewood tea caddy, with double ring handles, on bun feet.
- *20cm x 17cm*
- **£375**   • A.I.G.

Shakespeare's House ◀

- *circa 1920*

Whimsical novelty jewel box in the form of a model of Shakespeare's house, inset with a clock and barometer on the side. Probably a tourist item.
- *height 18cm*
- **£2,950**   • J. & T. Stone

Chinese Lacquer Box ▼

- *circa 1800*

Black Chinese lacquer games box, gilded with scenes of pagodas, willows, boats, animals and figures.
- *10cm x 29cm*
- £980   • Younger

Charles Stiven Tea Caddy ▼

- *circa 1800s*

Tartan ware rectangular tea caddy by Charles Stiven, Laurencekirk. Enclosing three wooden hinged tops decorated with ink drawings of scenes from Sir Walter Scott Waverley.
- *13cm x 24cm*
- £16,500   • J. & T. Stone

Mahogany Tea Caddy ▲

- *circa 1870*

Mahogany tea caddy with two compartments, with inlaid and cross banded decoration.
- *11cm x 21cm*
- £475   • A.I.G.

George III Tea Caddy ▲

- *circa 1790*

Ivory George III tea caddy with tortoiseshell stringing, silver shield inscribed 'E.H.', surrounded by a mother of pearl garland. The interior has the original floating lid.
- *height 10cm*
- £4,860   • Period Pieces

Rolled Paper Tea Caddy ◀

- *circa 1800*

George III rolled paper tea caddy with satinwood banding, inlaid with brass circular designs and stars, around a central floral cartouche, with original brass handle.
- *height 12cm*
- £2,960   • Period Pieces

Satinwood Knife Box ▼

- *circa 1790*

Satinwood George III knife box with a serpentine front with fluted inlaid satinwood pillars, rosewood crossbanding on the sloping lid, and a harewood oval shell pattern. Silver shield and keyhole with interior taking twelve place settings.
- *height 36cm*
- £2,480   • Period Pieces

Porcupine Box ▼

- *circa 1800*

Unusual porcupine Georgian work box with a hinged horn handle, standing on small bun feet.
- *height 9cm*
- £750   • Younger

Tuscan Ebony Casket ▶
- *circa 1680*
Extremely rare Tuscan ebony casket with inset marble and ivory panels, the interior lined at a later date with red silk, complete with original key.
- *26cm x 46cm*
- £6,500 • J. & T. Stone

George III Knife Boxes ▲
- *circa 1790*
One of a pair of fine quality George III mahogany serpentine fronted knife boxes. With ebony and boxwood line stringing. The interior has the original fittings for twelve place settings and carving implements. It is unusual to find a pair of such fine quality.
- *height 37cm*
- £6,500 • Period Pieces

Papier Mâché Tea Caddy ▲
- *circa 1785*
Papier mâché single tea caddy with gilt leaf decoration to lid and bottom edge matched with Greek key pattern border. Probably from the factory of Henry Clay.
- *height 9cm*
- £4,950 • J. & T. Stone

Georgian Tea Caddy ▼
- *circa 1790*
Georgian oval hare wood single tea caddy with marquetry inlaid urns and swags.
- *height 12cm*
- £2,6 50 • J.& T. Stone

Masonic Tea Caddy ▼
- *circa 1790*
Rare George III Masonic mahogany tea caddy with canted corners, ebony and box line stringing, and kingwood cross banding, profusely inlaid with harewood and boxwood, with the moon and sun symbols and various other Masonic imagery.
- *height 14cm*
- £4,880 • Period Pieces

War Decoration Tea Caddy ▲
- *circa 1780*
Fine George III oval tea caddy with unusual decoration showing articles of war, cannonballs, anchor, musket, flags, sabre and epaulettes. Possibly referring to the American War of Independence.
- *height 12cm*
- £2,950 • J. & T. Stone

Black Lacquer Tea Caddy ▲
- *circa 1880*
Victorian black lacquer papier-mâché tea caddy with ivory inlay and painted floral sprays of red roses, with floral gilt designs.
- *15.5cm x 30.5cm*
- £800 • Younger

Bureaux

Queen Anne Bureau ▼
- *circa 1710*
Queen Anne Irish walnut bureau bookcase with double domed top, the drawer and door fronts with elm herringbone cross banding.
- *width 88cm*
- £110,00 • John Bly

Burr-Walnut Secretaire ▼
- *circa 1880*
French burr walnut fall front secretaire with central pillared cupboard flanked by five drawers and two below.
- *height 142cm*
- £2,950 • The Swan

Biedermeier Bureau ▲
- *circa 1830*
Swedish birch Biedermeier bureau commode.
- *100cm x 106cm*
- £5,900 • Rupert Cavendish

William & Mary Bureau ▲
- *circa 1700*
A transitional William and Mary English writing bureau in well figured veneered walnut, the top fall and drawer fronts strung with double feather banding, with a fully fitted interior with drawers and well pelmeted pigeonholes, the whole on bracket feet.
- *99cm x 97cm x 51cm*
- £17,000 • Wakelin Linfield

English Elm Bureau ▶
- *circa 1700*
English veneered bureau in well figured elm with good patination, the fall front with good stepped interior above two short and two long drawers, the whole raised on turned bun feet.
- *106cm x 92cm x 53cm*
- £16,500 • Wakelin Linfield

George III Bureau ▼
- *circa 1800*
A fine George III mahogany cylinder bureau with fitted interior, eight pigeonholes and three small drawers with ivory handles, the whole on slender tapered legs on brass castors.
- *142cm x 123cm*
- £10,500 • Westland & Co

George II Walnut Bureau ▼
- *circa 1740*
George II walnut bureau with fall front and a well fitted interior, the fall above four graduated drawers with original brass fittings, the whole raised on moulded bracket feet.
- *99cm x 84cm x 47cm*
- £19,500 • O. F. Wilson

French Bureau Plat ▶

- *circa 1850*

French ebony, tortoiseshell and brass inlaid bureau plat. The antique leather top with a massive moulded gilt bronze edge, above a large recessed central drawer flanked by two smaller drawers. Supported on four cabriole legs. mounted above the knees with a satyr's mask, and terminating in hoof feet. With chased and gilt bronze mounts. The central drawer is mounted with a large mask of Bacchus.
- *79cm x 202cm*
- **£65,000**   • Anthony Outred

Regency Secretaire ▲

- *circa 1805*

A Regency mahogany secretaire cabinet enclosed by a pair of astragal glazed doors. Fitted with a secretaire drawer and an arched frieze drawer below, on square tapering legs terminating in spade feet.
- *160cm x 75cm*
- **£12,500**   • Great Grooms

Swedish Bureau ▼

- *1780*

Swedish bureau with original paintwork and fall front with stepped interior above three long drawers, standing on original scrolled bracket feet.
- *104cm x 94cm x 54cm*
- **£6,200**   • Heytesbury

French Secretaire ▼

- *circa 1810*

Secretaire desk with serpentine front, original paint, three long drawers with oval iron handles, brass escutcheon plates and a fall front enclosing fourteen small drawers, the whole raised on gilded feet.
- *108cm x 121cm*
- **£9,000**   • Augustus Brandt

Druce of London Bureau ▲

- *circa 1880*

George III style mahogany bureau with fall front, fitted interior and original brass fittings, standing on moulded bracket feet, with a brass plate bearing the inscription, 'Druce & Co, Baker St, London', inside the top drawer.
- *height 113cm*
- **£3,500**   • Hill Farm

Walnut Secretaire ▲

- *circa 1880*

Fine Swedish secretaire, heavily carved with a burr walnut veneer. The fall front enclosing an architectural fitted interior, above three long drawers.
- *147cm x 109cm*
- **£6,500**   • Hatchwell

Cabinets

Goncalo Alvez Wood Chiffonier ▲

• *circa 1820*

Regency period Goncalo Alvez wood chiffonier. The use of ionic capitals on this piece is both rare and appealing. With a finely figured rectangular top above a moulded lip. Two doors each with a pleated green moire silk panel, columns with ionic capitals and turned bases.

• *93cm x 130cm*
• **£9,500**   • **Anthony Outred**

Rosewood Specimen Cabinet ▲

• *circa 1850*

An unusual rosewood specimen cabinet with panelled doors fitted with wire grilles and pleated silk. Each corner fitted with cantered brass cornering, with pigeonholes in the interior above a fall front satinwood drawer leading to rosewood and satinwood panelled doors enclosing ten graduated drawers with a further fourteen of various sizes. The whole raised on a stand with barley twist supports and stretchers.

• *137cm x 78cm*
• **£3,750**   • **Anthony Outred**

Japanese Lacquer Cabinet ▼

• *circa 1705*

Queen Anne period black lacquer and gilt Japanese cabinet on English base. Decorated with a relief landscape on the exterior, the pair of doors revealing an arrangement of eight drawers. Raised on a stand with cabriole legs and pad feet.

• *135cm x 76cm*
• **£8,500**   • **Anthony Outred**

Dutch Display Cabinet ▼

• *circa 1830*

Dutch marquetry display cabinet with serpentine moulded cornice, centred with a crisply carved finial, above two glazed doors with shelving. The base consisting of three tiers of drawers, raised on scrolled feet.

• *239cm x 168cm*
• **£22,000**   • **Butchoff**

Ebony and Tortoiseshell Cabinet ▲

• *circa 1680*

Fine 17th century ebony and tortoiseshell cabinet on later stand with architectural designs and gilt ormolu mounts.

• *142cm x 107cm*
• **£12,500**   • **Butchoff**

Display Cabinet ▲

• *circa 1900*

One of a pair of fine mahogany Chippendale style display cabinets of cylindrical form, with gallery cornice above glazed doors, with a heavily carved and molded base concealing two double doors.

• *203cm x 81cm*
• **£15,000**   • **Butchoff**

Regency Cabinet ▼
- *circa 1825*

Regency linen press with two arched moulded panelled doors with ebony inlay and three drawers, standing on turned feet.
- *width 110cm*
- £5,800
- C. Preston

Italian Petite Commode ▼
- *circa 1830*

One of a pair of Italian walnut and boxwood inlay commodes, with stylised swan pillar and original grey marble tops.
- *78cm x 60cm*
- £8,750
- C. Preston

French Vitrine ▲
- *circa 1870*

Fine quality kingwood and ormolu mounted Louis XV style bombe display cabinet, with fine floral and swag ormolu mounts.
- *202cm x 112cm*
- £12,500
- Butchoff

Rosewood Chiffoniere ▲
- *circa 1840*

Rosewood Regency chiffoniere with gallery single drawer and cupboards below standing on a straight square base.
- *height 157cm*
- £2,850
- C. Preston

Painted Cabinet ◀
- *circa 1840*

Austrian pine painted cabinet with floral octagonal cartouches and a dark blue background, with an arched moulded pediment over a single door, standing on a raised base.
- *height 280cm*
- £6,500
- Denzil Grant

Victorian Cabinet ▼
- *circa 1880*

Small bedside cabinet with brass gallery with mirror below, single cupboard with scrolled carving panel ebony inlay and brass handles each side, standing on turned legs,
- *height 100cm*
- £875
- C. Preston

Mahogany Chest on Chest ▼
- *circa 1760*

Flame mahogany chest on chest, with three small drawers at the top and four variegated below, four further drawers resting on moulded bracket feet.
- *width 39cm*
- £18,500
- C. Preston

Georgian Corner Cupboard ▲
- *circa 1780*
Georgian pine corner cupboard with astragal glazed doors and two moulded panel doors below with porcelain handles.
- *204cm x 105cm*
- £1,250 • Drummonds

Camphor Wood Cabinet ▼
- *circa 1900*
Late Qing Dynasty Chinese black lacquer camphor wood cabinet, in three parts with gilded carvings, and a couplet in Chinese characters. Man celebrates four seasons with festivals and self-attainment for all in quiet meditation.
- *75cm x 28cm*
- £1,680 • Younger

Florentine Cabinet ◄
- *circa 1580*
Florentine ebony and rosewood cabinet with ivory and geometric inlay to the sides. Contains nine small and two long drawers, and one small cupboard with ivory stringing.
- *28cm x 62cm*
- £2,350 • W. John Griffiths

William IV Cabinet ▲
- *circa 1830*
William IV mahogany cabinet with eight glazed pillared doors and a single drawer, standing on moulded legs.
- *197cm x 78cm*
- £11,500 • Fred E Anderson

Empire Secretaire ▲
- *circa 1820*
Swedish mahogany empire secretaire with central foliate ormulu mount flanked by lion's head ring handles, with a fall front with fitted interior and three long drawers, with a shaped base.
- *141cm x 126cm*
- £9,500 • Rupert Cavendish

Regency Sideboard ◄
- *circa 1815*
An important English Regency mahogany and ebony inlaid sideboard, attributed to Gillow of Lancaster. The cabinet work is of the highest order, as one would expect with Gillow furniture making.
- *134.5cm x 74.5cm*
- £16,500 • Freshfords

Victorian Cabinet ▼
- *circa 1890*

Victorian walnut and plane-wood bedside cabinet, with moulded cupboard doors, raised on a plinth base.
- *height 85cm*
- £450 • Hill Farm Antiques

Chinese Medicine Cabinet ▶
- *circa 19th century*

One of a pair of black lacquer Chinese medicine cabinets with forty-five drawers with circular ring handles.
- *height 206cm*
- £1,800 •Younger

English Corner Cupboard ▲
- *1780*

English painted wall mounted, corner cupboard, with carved moulded door panels and original blue paintwork
- *108cm x 81cm*
- £2,800 • Heytesbury

Continental Painted Cabinet ▼
- *circa 1880*

Continental fruitwood display cabinet with circular moulded pediments, two glazed doors, flanked by bevelled glass, below two cupboard doors painted with ribbons and flowers, surmounted with a pierced brass rail, standing on small cabriole legs.
- *175cm x 135cm*
- £3,500 • Hill Farm

Walnut Bedside Cabinet ▼
- *circa 1880*

One of a pair Louis XV style walnut bedside cabinets with one single drawer above a carved and moulded cupboard door, raised on cabriole legs
- *height 88cm*
- £1,650 • Hill Farm Antiques

Small Chinese Cabinet ◀
- *1880*

Small Chinese cabinet from Zhejiang Province, decorated with carvings of a phoenix and lotus plants.
- *81cm x 55cm*
- £550 • Lotus House

George III Demi-Lune Commode ▼

- *circa 1790*

George III demi-lune commode decorated with fine marquetry veneers in the manner of John Linnell.

- *86cm x 73cm*
- **£135,000**
- • John Bly

George III Satinwood Cabinet ▼

- *circa 1775*

George III period mahogany and satinwood cabinet designed by John Linnell. The upper doors framed in satinwood, the lower doors with a circular panel of satinwood within quartered mahogany veneers.

- *width 101cm*
- **£165,000**
- • John Bly

Expert Tips

Always use a good wax polish and do not use aerosol sprays on wood, as these can destroy the patina.

Empire Style Vitrine ▲

- *circa 1890*

A late 19th century empire style vitrine with gilt banding, a brass gallery and one glass door enclosing two shelves, standing on turned legs.

- *146cm x 70cm*
- **£1,895**
- • John Riordan

Walnut Chest on Chest ▲

- *circa 1780*

Fine walnut chest on chest with unusual indented shell moulding on the bottom drawer.

- *width 101cm*
- **£48,500**
- • John Bly

William IV Cupboard ▶

- *circa 1830*

A William IV mahogany bedside cupboard with turned supports.

- *76cm x 43cm*
- **£525**
- • Great Grooms

Chinese Cabinet ▼

- *1890*

Chinese cabinet in red and black lacquer with carvings of birds and foliage and Chinese characters from the Fujian Province, South Eastern China.

- *151cm x 90cm x 43cm*
- **£2,500**
- • Lotus House

Cabinet from Fujian ▼

- *1880*

Chinese lacquer cabinet from Fujian Province, South East China, with a couplet on the doors stating, 'The Dragon rises to the morning sun with a canopy, the phoenix breathes calligraphy into the evening clouds.'

- *140cm x 84cm*
- **£1,380**
- • Lotus House

Dutch Walnut Display Cabinet ▲

- *circa 1780s*

A slim Dutch walnut display cabinet profusely decorated with floral and foliate motifs in marquetry, the shaped cornice above shaped glazed doors and canted corners to the upper section. The lower section of bombe form, the whole on turned and ebonised bun feet.

- 236.5cm x 170cm
- £22,500   •Wakelin Linfield

Dutch Display Cabinet ▲

- *circa 1780*

Dutch walnut display cabinet with foliate inlay with glass panels to front and doors.

- height 85cm
- £4,850   • Paul Hopwell

Japanese Lacquer Cabinet ▶

- *circa 1880*

Japanese lacquer cabinet with two doors decorated with mother of pearl floral inlay, two small drawers and one long drawer inlaid with boxwood.

- 39cm x 29cm
- £450   • Younger

Mahogany Chiffonier ▼

- *circa 1840*

Flame mahogany chiffonier with single long drawer, above two gilt brass grills with doors silks, flanked by turned pilasters, raised on turned feet.

- 93cm x 91.5cm x 41cm
- £3200   • O. F. Wilson

Two Part Kortan Cabinet ▼

- *circa 1800*

A kortan cabinet of two parts made from elm, with four drawers above two cupboard doors with brass mounts.

- 145cm x 105cm
- £2,950   • Wakelin Linfield

George IV Display Cabinet ▲

- *circa 1825*

George IV mahogany display cabinet, the top section with two glazed doors, above a lower section with four octagonal tapering legs decorated with stylised palmetto.

- 191cm x 94cm
- £8,750   • Wakelin Linfield

Swedish Mahogany Cupboard ▲

- *circa 1890s*

Swedish Louis XVI style mahogany cupboard with two doors, above one long single drawer, with moulded apron with gilt ormulu mounts, on tapering slender legs.

- 106cm x 59cm
- £1,950   • Rupert Cavendish

315

Mahogany Chiffonier ▼

- *circa 1880*

Victorian flame mahogany chiffonier with scrolled carved moulded back, a single shelf supported by pillars, one single long drawer and two enclosed cupboards.

- *93cm x 84cm*
- **£1,700** • Salem Antiques

Biedermeier Secretaire ▲

- *circa 1830*

Swedish Biedermeier secretaire in masur birch and birchwood.

- *116cm x 107cm*
- **£6,700** • Rupert Cavendish

Biedermeier Cabinet ▲

- *1815-1820*

Danish Biedermeier mahogany cabinet with satinwood inlay. The curvaceous shape of the door and its satinwood inlay, with griffins symbolising the 'vigilant guardian'. characteristics shared by Danish and north German Biedermeier furniture.

- *118cm x 54cm*
- **£4,900** • Rupert Cavendish

Bedside Cupboard ▶

- *1830*

Mahogany bedside cupboard with gallery and single cupboard with small turned handle, standing on slender tapering legs.

- *height 79cm*
- **£550** • Salem Antiques

Bow Front Corner Cupboard ▼

- *1780*

Bow front corner cupboard with two doors and herringbone banded edging.

- *width 78cm*
- **£1,450** • Salem Antiques

Walnut Credenze ▲

- *circa 1860*

Victorian walnut credenze decorated with ormolu mounts and crossbanding and profusely inlaid with kingwood, harewood and boxwood.

- *109cm x 164cm*
- **£3,950** • The Swan

Regency Chiffonier ▼
• *circa 1820*
Regency mahogany chiffonier
with silk panel doors, a pierced
gallery and one long mirror, with
two Corinthian columns, lions
head ring handles and brass
ormulu mounts.
• *118cm x 100cm*
• **£1,650** • **R. Macklin Smith**

Mahogany Corner Cupboard ▼
• *circa 1890*
Mahogany corner cupboard with
double moulded panel doors,
above three drawers with turned
knob handles.
• *width 116cm*
• **£1,585** • **The Swan**

Victorian Cabinet ▲
• *circa 1880*
Victorian mahogany cabinet with
two panelled doors, enclosing two
small drawers with turned
handles, raised on a plinth base.
• *width 134cm*
• **£1,175** • **The Swan**

George III Dressing Stand ▲
• *circa 1795*
George III mahogany gentleman's
dressing stand with original
mirror, and brass fittings.
• *89cm x 51cm*
• **£825** • **The Swan**

Mahogany Chiffonier ▼
• *circa 1880*
Victorian mahogany chiffonier,
with one long single drawer
above two moulded panelled
doors, flanked with carved
pilasters.
• *105cm x 114cm*
• **£1,350** • **The Swan**

Biedermeier Style Cupboard ▼
• *circa 1899*
Danish Biedermeier style
cupboard in birchwood, with a
central oval inlay in rosewood
and satinwood of an urn with a
spray of flowers.
• *128cm x 55cm*
• **£5,600** • **Rupert Cavendish**

Swedish Sideboard ◄
• *circa 1800*
Louis XVI Gustavian painted
pine sideboard with two centrally
carved diamond panels on the
doors.
• *98cm x 107cm*
• **£4,500** • **Rupert Cavendish**

Regency Sideboard ▶

• *circa 1800s*
Regency mahogany and
satinwood cross banded
sideboard, with two drawers and
cupboards, and gilt handles.
• *81cm x 121cm*
• **£1,495**   • **Vale Antiques**

Chinese Lacquer Cabinet ▼

• *circa 1900*
Lacquer cabinet from Eastern
China with a couplet in Chinese
characters on the doors; Research
in the art of craft. Writing on
cookery skill.
• *height 154cm*
• **£980**   • **Younger**

Regency Cabinet ▼

• *circa 1820*
Regency mahogany side cabinet,
with maple amboyna veneer and
one long and two small drawers
above a central cupboard, flanked
by two long cupboards.
• *92cm x 108cm*
• **£2,750**   • **W. John Griffiths**

Gesso Side Cabinet ▶

• *circa 1860*
A pair of Napoleon III ebonised
gilt-bronze and painted gesso side
cabinet. The black porta marble
tops with a panelled central door
decorated in the Louis XVI taste.
• *110cm x 144cm*
• **£9,500**   • **Westland & Co**

George III Corner Cupboard ▼

• *circa 1818*
George III corner cupboard with
mahogany banding and swan
neck pediment with brass rosettes
over astragal glazed door.
• *109cm x 74cm*
• **£1,350**   • **W. John Griffiths**

Gustavian Style Cabinets ▲

• *circa 1890s*
One of a pair of Swedish
Gustavian style cabinets signed:
'AFI' and 'S&E'. Made in the
style of Louis XVI.
• *72cm x 42cm*
• **£3,400**   • **Rupert Cavendish**

Canterburies

Mahogany Canterbury ▶
• *circa 1830s*
Early Victorian mahogany
galleried and tiered dumb waiter,
with turned supports and single
drawer with turned handles, the
whole standing on bulbous turned
legs with brass castors.
• *100cm x 38cm*
• £2,200　　• **Old Cinema**

Rosewood Canterbury ▼
• *circa 1790*
Mahogany canterbury comprising
four sections with a single side
drawer with circular ring handle,
raised on square tapered legs with
original brass casters.
• *height 39cm*
• £1,950　　• **John Clay**

Walnut Canterbury ▶
• *circa 1880*
Victorian walnut canterbury with
four sections with heavily carved
and pierced floral designs, turned
handles, and a single side drawer,
the whole raised on turned legs
with brass castors.
• *height 54cm*
• £1,295　　• **The Swan**

Mahogany Canterbury ◀
• *circa 1870*
Victorian mahogany canterbury
with three compartments. The
side drawer with turned knob
handles, finials and supports, with
original porcelain castors.
• *height 62cm*
• £995　　　　　　• **A.I.G.**

Victorian Canterbury ▲
• *circa 1880*
Victorian walnut canterbury of
four sections, with pierced
scrolled decoration above a lower
shelf, on upturned scrolled legs.
• *height 55cm*
• £1,195　　• **The Swan**

Chairs

Gothic Dining Chairs ◄

- *circa 1860*

A set of six English carved walnut and oak Gothic dining chairs after the Venetian influence. Two large and four side chairs, each with intricately carved Gothic tracery backs, finials and front legs.

- *height of large chair 121cm*
  height of sidechairs 90cm
- £8,500   • Westland & Co

Walnut Armchair ▼

- *circa 1890*

Walnut open armchair with carved top rail and arm supports, button upholstered back and seat, raised on cabriole legs, with original casters.

- *76cm x 70cm*
- £695   • The Swan

George III Armchair ▶

- *circa 1790*

A fine mahogany George II armchair. The moulded serpentine top rail above a pierced splat with Athemion carving. The shaped seat on square tapered legs.

- *height 93cm*
- £1,250   • Westland & Co

French Side Chairs ▼

- *circa 1880*

One of a pair of French side chairs, with carved back and original padded seat cover, raised on cabriole legs, with escargot feet.

- *height 89cm*
- £575   • The Swan

Chinese Elmwood Chair ▲

- *circa 1890*

One of a pair of Chinese elmwood lacquer chairs from Zhejiang Province, Eastern China.

- *height 96cm*
- £980   • Younger

Mahogany Child's Chair ▼

- *circa 1890*

Unusual child's mahogany corner chair, with heavily carved floral decoration.

- *height 60cm*
- £425   • The Swan

Rosewood Chairs ▶

- *circa 1800*
A rare pair of French rosewood chairs with undecorated rectangular backs with square section upright supports. The shaped arms with low relief carved decoration to the upper surface, terminating in very well carved rams heads above scrolled supports with low relief carved decoration to the front. With a straight seat rail above an apron.
- *100cm x 59.5cm*
- £15,500 • Anthony Outred

Regency Mahogany Chair ▼

- *circa 1810*
Regency mahogany elbow chair, with curved arms and turned legs and leather seat.
- *height 89cm*
- £995 • Old Cinema

Elbow Chair ▼

- *1890*
One of a pair of mahogany elbow chairs with foliate carving on slender turned legs with cane back and set
- *height 97cm*
- £1,450 • Old Cinema

Victorian High Chair ▲

- *circa 1860*
Victorian ash and elm child's high chair, with turned decoration.
- *height 99cm*
- £395 • The Swan

French Walnut Chair ▲

- *1890*
French Walnut chair with carved mask decoration, standing on a cross stretcher base.
- *height 87cm*
- £595 • Old Cinema

Child's Chippendale Chair ▼

- *circa 1890*
Chippendale style mahogany child's chair, with pierced back splat, serpentine top rail and raised on straight tapered legs..
- *height 78cm*
- £475 • The Swan

Victorian Nursing Chair ▼

- *1880*
Victorian Nursing chair with a circular padded seat and a padded back.
- *height 74cm*
- £550 • Old Cinema

Arts & Crafts Chair ▼
● *1890*
Arts and Crafts chair with curved
arms and turned legs, with
pressed brass inlay back.
● *height 115cm*
● **£550**   ● Old Cinema

Rosewood Chair ▼
● *1860*
One of a pair of Victorian
Rosewood chairs with shaped
carved top rail.
● *height 82cm*
● **£795**   ● Old Cinema

Library Chairs ▲
● *1880*
One of a pair of library chairs
with a hooped back, ten shaped
spindles, circular seat, horseshoe
stretcher base and fluted legs.
● *height 76cm.*
● **£725**   ● Old Cinema

Berger Chair ▲
● *1880*
One of a pair of French chairs
with a shaped tall cane back with
padded shaped seat, and gilt
shells carved at the top of the
legs, standing on a pad foot.
● *height 108cm*
● **£725**   ● Old Cinema

Oak Country Chair ▼
● *1810*
One of a pair of oak ladder-back
chairs with a rush seat, standing
on turned legs and pad feet.
● *height 104cm*
● **£495**   ● Old Cinema

Chippendale Style Carver ▼
● *1880*
One of a set of Chippendale style
mahogany chairs with swept
arms, carved back splat and ball
feet, with six dining chairs and
two carvers.
● *height 105cm*
● **£6,500**   ● Old Cinema

Folding Campaign Chair ▲
• *circa 1860s*
Victorian folding campaign chair made from mahogany with cane seat.
• *70cm x 37cm*
• £395   • **Old Cinema**

Hepplewhite Carver ▲
• *1880*
One of a set of eight mahogany Hepplewhite style, dining chairs including two carvers.
• £11,000   • **Butchoff**

Arts & Crafts Chair ▶
• *circa 1890*
Russian Arts & craft chair of triangular outline, with a tablet back, profusely inlaid with numerous wood specimens including walnut, mahogany, satinwood and hare wood in geometric patterns. Above a shaped back splat decorated with inlaid woods, with decorated arms issuing from tablet back, leading to an overstuffed shaped brown leather seat. Raised on turned legs of alternate specimen woods.
• *86.5cm x 58.5cm*
• £3,400   • **Anthony Outred**

Oak Elbow Chair ▼
• *circa 1890*
Late Victorian oak elbow chair, with padded and buttoned top rail.
• *90cm x 55cm*
• £395   • **Old Cinema**

Regency Chair ▼
• *circa 1830*
Regency rosewood chair with scrolled top rail, splayed back legs and turned front legs.
• *84cm x 51cm*
• £980   • **The Lacquer Chest**

Oak Dining Chair ▲
• *circa 1890*
One of a set of four late Victorian oak dining chairs, in the Chippendale style, raised on square straight legs.
• *100cm x 50cm*
• £695   • **Old Cinema**

Windsor Armchair ▲
• *circa 1810*
Beechwood Windsor armchair with elm seat, hooped back and arms, standing on turned legs.
• *87cm x 55cm*
• £435   • **The Lacquer Chest**

Laburnham Wood Chairs ▲
- *circa 1840*
One of a pair of laburnham wood ladder back chairs with concave seats, raised on straight square legs.
- *96cm x 51cm*
- £780 • The Lacquer Chest

Giltwood Chair ▲
- *circa 1890*
Small giltwood French chair, delicately carved with roses and torchiere motifs, with original upholstered padded seat.
- *height 75cm*
- £595 • A.I.G.

Library Chair ▼
- *1870*
Light oak library chair with circular back scrolled arms and turned legs, with a circular padded green leather seat.
- *height 78cm*
- £1,695 • A.I.G.

William IV Chair ▼
- *1830*
One of a pair of William IV mahogany hall chairs, with circular turned back with scrolled supports, raised on turned front legs.
- *height 81cm*
- £975 • A.I.G.

Rococo Chair ◄
- *1730–1760*
One of a set of six Rococo chairs, of simple design, with carved back splat, raised on cabriole legs with scrolled decoration and hoof feet.
- *height 103cm*
- £9,500 • Augustus Brandt

Victorian Rosewood Chair ▲
- *circa 1860*
Victorian rosewood spoon back armchair, finely carved with floral designs and raised on scrolled legs fitted with casters..
- *height 96cm*
- £1,895 • A.I.G.

William IV Chairs ▲
- *1830*
One of a set of six mahogany William IV dining chairs, with shaped top rail and carved stretcher, raised on turned front legs.
- *height 85cm*
- £2,995 • A.I.G.

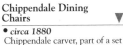

Hepplewhite Chair ▼

- *circa 1780*
Cherrywood hepplewhite elbow-chair, with shaped arms standing on square straight tapered legs, and padded horse hair covered seat.
- *height 92cm*
- £995
- A.I.G.

French Mahogany Side Chairs ▲

- *circa 1860*
One of a pair of French mahogany side chairs with brass finials on the top rail.
- *height 95cm*
- £3,250
- Serendipity

Chippendale Dining Chairs ▼

- *circa 1880*
Chippendale carver, part of a set of eight chairs with carved and pierced splats and cabriole legs standing on claw and ball feet.
- *height 96cm*
- £8,750
- Serendipity

Chippendale Dining Chairs ▼

- *circa 1880*
One of a set of ten mahogany style dining chairs with a pierced back splat.
- *height 92cm*
- £7,500
- Serendipity

Chippendale Dining Chairs ◄

- *circa 1880*
One of a set of eight mahogany Chippendale style chairs with carved and pierced splats, cabriole legs, and standing on claw and bell feet.
- *height 96cm*
- £8,750
- Serendipity

Georgian Wing-Back Armchair ◀

- *circa 1760*

Georgian mahogany wing-back armchair, raised on square chamfered legs, with an H stretcher, upholstered in a woven silk damask.
- *height 119cm*
- £3,450   • R.S. Antiques

Regency Armchair ▲

- *circa 1880*

Regency revival armchair with mahogany frame carved with honeysuckle and harebell motifs, raised on moulded bun feet.
- *83cm x 54cm*
- £1,395   • R.S. Antiques

Georgian Fruitwood Chair ▼

- *circa 1760*

Georgian fruitwood chair of the Chippendale period, with unusual rosewood splat and square chamfered legs. Original colour and patina.
- *height 95cm*
- £485   • R.S. Antiques

French Walnut Bergère ▼

- *circa 1880*

French 2nd Empire bergère with a heavily carved walnut frame incorporating floral swags and fruit motifs, raised on cabriole legs.
- *height 101cm*
- £2,200   • O. F. Wilson

Italian Walnut Chair ▲

- *circa 1740*

One of a pair of Italian armchairs. The walnut framwork carved with scrolled and moulded decoration, raised on cabriole legs with escargot feet.
- *height 114cm*
- £14,000   • O. F. Wilson

Windsor Chair ▲

- *circa 1860*

Oak Windsor chair, with carved vase shaped back splat, turned supports and shaped seat.
- *height 107cm*
- £750   • Poppets

Victorian Lacquered Chair ▲

- *circa 1860*

Small Victorian black lacquered chair with mother of pearl inlay, wicker back and seat and elongated arms, standing on turned legs with brass castors.
- *height 75cm*
- £995   • Serendipity

Painted Fauteuils ▼
- *circa 1880*

One of a pair of fauteuils with painted decoration to the entire frame work of the chair, with carved and turned decoration to the arm supports and front legs.
- *height 86cm*
- £3,750   • O. F. Wilson

Walnut and Beech Fauteuils ▼
- *circa 1760*

One of a pair of walnut and beech fauteuils, with finely carved floral designs, scrolled arm supports and serpentine moulded apron front, Stamped 'ROVAMAION'.
- *height 110cm*
- £25,000   • O. F. Wilson

Louis XVI Chairs ▶
- *circa 1780*

One of a pair of lyre backed, Louis XVI chairs, with a carved oval seat rail and pale green paint, raised on turned legs .
- *height 92cm*
- £8,500   • O. F. Wilson

Hepplewhite Armchair ▲
- *circa 1780*

Ebonised hepplewhite armchair with shield back, curved arm supports and straight tapered legs with hand painted designs of trailing foliage and ribboning.
- *height 96.5cm*
- £4,450   • O. F. Wilson

Louis XV Style Bergères ▲
- *circa 1880*

One of a pair of large Louis XV style bergères, with a high arched back and moulded decoration, centred with a carved and gilded floral design.
- *99cm x 71cm*
- £5,250   • O. F. Wilson

French Fauteuils ▼
- *circa 1870*

One of a pair of Louis XV fauteuils stamped 'BOVD', with carved top rail and front rail, scrolled arm supports and hand painted decoration, raised on cabriole legs,.
- *height 89cm*
- £5,500   • O. F. Wilson

Walnut Master's Chair ▼
- *circa 1835*

A walnut master's chair with carved foliate, scrolled and scalloped crest surmounted by a recumbent lion. The arms composed of a series of S-scrolls and C-scrolls headed by imposing carved lion heads, these surrounded by a carved mane above a scallop motif. Standing on shaped front legs with paw feet and substantial rear legs on brass castors.
- *150cm x 84cm*
- £18,500   • Anthony Outred

Painted Fauteuils ▼
- *circa 1760*
One of a pair of beechwood
fauteuils with oval backs and gilt
foliate designs over cream paint.
Stamped 'Premy'.
- *height 83cm*
- £7,800   • O. F. Wilson

Regency Chairs ▼
- *circa 1820*
One of a pair of Regency faux
rosewood chairs, with turned and
gilded designs, raised on sabre
legs.
- *height 82cm*
- £2,750   • O. F. Wilson

Ebonised Beechwood Chairs ▲
- *circa 1880*
One of a pair of ebonised
beechwood chairs with rush seats,
influenced by William Morris.
- *height 84cm*
- £220   • O. F. Wilson

French Louis XV Fauteuils ▲
- *circa 1760*
Pair of Louis XV fauteuils with
curved top rail, inverted arm
supports and serpentine front rail,
raised on cabriole legs.
- *height 84cm*
- £5,250   • O. F. Wilson

Mahogany Armchair ◄
- *1880*
One of a pair of mahogany
Chippendale style armchairs,
with a heavily carved serpentine
top rail and pierced back splat,
raised on carved cabriole legs.
- *height 95cm*
- £8,800   • Butchoff

Directoire Armchair ▼
- *circa 1795*
Fine directoire mahogany
armchair, with scrolled top rail,
pierced back splat, and turned
arm supports.
- *height 86cm*
- £2,500   • O. F. Wilson

Empire Bergère ▼
- *circa 1815*
Mahogany Empire bergère, with
turned top rail and curved,
padded arms.
- *height 94cm*
- £2,8501   • O. F. Wilson

Expert Tips

*When buying antique furniture
always try to buy the item in
pristine condition and from a
good dealer, as restoration costs
could be a shock.*

- *circa 1890*
Elm and beech kitchen chair.
- *height 97cm*
- £65　　• Nicholas Mitchell

English Bamboo Chairs ▲
- *circa 1830*
A set of four English faux bamboo chairs, with cane seats, and splayed front legs.
- *85.5cm x 44.5cm x 38cm*
- £2,750　　• O. F. Wilson

French Walnut Chair ▼
- *circa 1780*
French walnut open bergère standing on cabriole legs, one of a pair.
- £3,800　　• Mora & Upham

lst Empire Chair ▲
- *circa 1810*
French lst Empire, giltwood chair in the manner of dellenge, with carved stylised floral decoration.
- £3,800　　• Mora & Upham

Mahogany Hall Chairs ◄
- *circa 1775*
One of a pair of English mahogany hall chairs inspired by designs from Chippondalev Alt's pattern books, the circular carved and pierced backs in the form of spoked wheels, the dished seats shaped to reflect this pattern, the turned front legs decorated with ring turning.
- *95cm x 35cm*
- £10,500　　• Wakelin Linfield

Louis XV Fauteil ▲

• *circa 1750*
Louis XV French giltwood fauteil, with carved floral designs raised on cabriole legs.
• £1,250   • Mora Upham

Swedish Armchair ▲

• *circa 1880*
Swedish armchair, with gilded floral decoration to the back rail, carved and gilded supports to the arms and original neutral paint. Part of a set comprising a sofa, armchair and four single chairs.
• *height 106cm*
• £18,500 set • Wakelin Linfield

Six Mahogany Chairs ▼

• *circa 1870*
Set of six mahogany and brass inlaid dining chairs in the manner of Gillows.
• £3,200   • Mora Upham

Swedish Dining Chair ▼

• *circa 1880*
Swedish dining chair, with lyre shaped back, gilded with floral designs, raised on straight tapered front legs, with swept back legs.
• *height 83cm*
• £18,500   • Wakelin Linfield

English Hepplewhite Chairs ◀

• *circa 1780*
English Hepplewhite oval back chairs, with three Prince of Wales peacock feathers carved into the back splat, above a shaped front rail, raised on elegant cabriole legs, with floral and shell motifs.
• *height 84cm*
• £5,500   • Mora Upham

Directoire French Chairs ▲

• *circa 1880*
One of a pair of French, mahogany directoire style open armchairs with carved finial decoration, raised on tapered, reeded legs.
• £1,850   • Mora Upham

George I Walnut Chair ▲

• *circa 1715*
One of a pair of George I walnut side chairs with vase shaped splats, the front cabriole legs and back legs united by a turned wavy stretcher.
• *height 96cm*
• £6,800   • Wakelin Linfield

George IV Hall Chairs ▼
- *circa 1825*
A pair of George IV, mahogany hall chairs, with original painted armorials to the shaped and reeded backs, raised on reeded front legs with outswept rear legs.
- *85cm x 42.5cm*
- £4,950   • Wakelin Linfield

Tub/Desk Chair ▶
- *circa 1880*
French flame mahogany clysmos shaped tub/desk chair, the downswept arms decorated with gilt ormolu palmettos and supported by winged swans, raised on square tapered legs.
- *109cm x 68cm*
- £4,500   • Wakelin Linfield

English Regency Chair ▲
- *circa 1830*
English Regency mahogany chair, with a shield back and a 'klismos' shaped seat, with carved and reeded designs.
- £3,500   • Mora Upham

Set of Dining Chairs ◀
- *circa 1835*
A set of eight William IV period mahogany dining chairs. Stamped: J. Porter, Cabinet Chairs & Sofa Manufacturer, Upholsterer, 166 High Street Camden Town. Each consisting of a panelled klismos tablet back, supported by shaped uprights which are in the form of stylised ionic columns with leaf motifs to capitals. With turned reeded legs and saber back legs.
- *89.4cm x 44cm*
- £16,500   • Anthony Outred

George I Dining Chairs ▲
- *circa 1720*
Set of walnut George I dining chairs, with shaped top rail, vase shaped back splat and moulded seat and rail, raised on cabriole legs, with turned cross rails.
- *97cm x 47cm*
- £14,000   • Wakelin Linfield

William IV Library Chair ▲
- *circa 1835*
Outstanding William IV gentleman's library chair. The massive mahogany frame heavily carved with C scrolls and acanthus leaf designs. Supported on large brass castors.
- *102cm x 98cm*
- £7,950   • Wakelin Linfield

Queen Anne Desk Chair ▼
- *circa 1705*

Queen Anne walnut single desk chair with interesting and boldly shaped front legs and back splat.
- *102cm x 40cm*
- £1,750 • Wakelin Linfield

French Fauteuil ▼
- *circa 1840*

A well proportioned French fauteuil. The carved beech frame retaining traces of original painted decoration
- *100cm x 73cm*
- £5,500 • Wakelin Linfield

Ash Dining Chairs ▲
- *18th century*

One of a set of ten ash dining chairs, decorated with floral marquetry and birds. The shaped top rail over a serpentine splat with shaped serpentine fronted seat rails and cabriole legs with pad feet.
- *92cm x 51cm*
- £22,50 • Wakelin Linfield

English Windsor Chair ▲
- *circa 1750s*

Unusual rustic, mid 18th century, Windsor chair made from elm, with turned supports and solid seat, with good warm patina.
- *100cm x 53cm*
- £3,85 • Wakelin Linfield

Venetian Chair ◄
- *1820*

Venetian Rococo style carved fruitwood armchair, in original condition.
- *104cm x 84cm*
- £8,000 • Augustus Brandt

Directoire Side Chair ▼
- *1780*

One of a set of four French giltwood directoire dining chairs, with original cream paintwork and gilt pastel pink covers.
- *89cm x 43cm*
- £6,800 • Augustus Brandt

Elm Elbow Chair ▼
- *circa 1890s*

One of a pair of late 19th century elbow chairs in elm from southern China, of sculptural 'oxbow' form, from a good merchant's house.
- *125cm x 60cm*
- £6,000 • Wakelin Linfield

Ladder Back Chair ▲
- *circa 1780*

Well proportioned 18th century ladder back chair made from elm with rush seat and good patina.
- *106cm x 57cm*
- £1,750 • Wakelin Linfield

English Elbow Chairs ▲
- *circa 1900*

Stylish pair of English elbow chairs in an Egyptian style, with carved heads and paw feet and hand worked signed tapestry upholstery in the Regency manner.
- *95cm x 62cm*
- £4,500 • Wakelin Linfield

Country Armchair ▶
- *circa 1700*

A rare traditional English country arm chair, the back with two vase shaped splats, with down swept arms on two turned supports, solid seat and turned front legs.
- *120cm x 55cm*
- £7,850 • Wakelin Linfield

Chinese Armchairs ▼
- *circa 1850s.*

One of a pair of Chinese arm chairs in padouk wood with original seats, from the Meiji period.
- *height 90cm*
- £3,950 • Wakelin Linfield

Yew-wood Rocking Chair ▼
- *circa 1820s*

Yew-wood early 19th century rocking chair, with carved and turned decoration.
- *105cm x 49cm*
- £1,750 • Wakelin Linfield

Blade & Gilt Dining Chair ▲
- *circa 1840*

One of a set of eight Harlequin blade and gilt japanned dining/salon chairs, with shaped seat rails, turned baluster legs, the black ground with pil work depicting flowers, foilage and birds.
- *90cm x 46cm*
- £5,800 • Wakelin Linfield

Hepplewhite Chair ▲
- *1785*

Hepplewhite mahogany chair. The shield back with pierced decoration above a concave leather upholstered seat, raised on square tapered legs.
- *98cm x 57cm*
- £26,000 • Wakelin Linfield

Wing Chair ▼

- *circa 1899*

19th century William & Mary style wingchair, with generous scrolled arm rests, raised on turned legs.

- *125cm x 105cm*
- **£5,950**   • Wakelin Linfield

Mahogany Armchair ▼

- *circa 1840*

Mahogany Chippendale armchair and three singles, with unusual pierced back splat.

- *height 96cm*
- **£1,500**   • John Clay

Georgian Armchair ▲

- *circa 1750*

Georgian armchair with shaped top rail and unusually carved willow tree splat, standing on square straight legs, and single bar stretcher.

- *96cm x 52cm*
- **£1,500**   • John Clay

Lamp Hanger Armchairs ◀

- *1830*

Pair of Chinese high backed lamp hanger armchairs with carved central slat.

- *110cm x 72cm*
- **£1,450**   • Gordon Reece

Walnut Armchairs ▼

- *circa 1880*

One of a pair of French armchairs in walnut with carved decoration depicting gothic cruettes and medieval masks.

- *150cm x 70cm*
- **£7,800**   • Wakelin Linfield

Rope Back Oxford Chairs ▼

- *circa 1880*

One of a pair of rope back Oxford chairs, with turned legs and shaped seat.

- *height 88cm*
- **£170**   • John Clay

Swedish Rococo Armchairs ◀

- *1780*

One of a pair of Swedish Rococo armchairs with moulded frame, out turned arms, cabriole legs and padded seat. In original condition.

- *height 96cm*
- **£8,000**   •Heytesbury

George III Dining Chairs ◀

• *circa 1810*

A set of twelve, George III, Sheraton period mahogany dining chairs, including two armchairs. These elegant chairs retain good colour and patination, with crisp carving and dramatically figured veneers to the tablet shaped top-rails. The chairs bear the influences of Edinburgh furniture maker William Trotter. Provenance: originally purchased by Dr. Archibald Lyle-Galbraith.

• *height 92.5cm*
• **£47,500**   • **Freshfords**

Horse Shoe Shaped Chairs ▼

• *circa 1850*

A pair of very low Chinese horseshoe shaped back rail chairs.

• *82cm x 57cm*
• **£1,480**   • **Gordon Reece**

Victorian Oak Chair ▼

• *circa 1870*

Victorian oak country chair with shaped back and tuned supports, above a solid seat, raised on turned legs, with good patina.

• *height 87cm*
• **£450**   • **Hill Farm**

Regency Dining Chairs ▼

• *circa 1820*

One of a set of five Regency, flame mahogany dining chairs, the back rest with carved architectural supports, raised on turned legs with reeded decoration.

• *height 82cm*
• **£2,500**   • **Hill Farm**

Mahogany Dining Chair ▲

• *circa 1820*

One of a set of five Regency mahogany dining chairs, with carved back rest and supports, raised on tapering, turned legs, with carved decoration.

• *height 82cm*
• **£2,300**   • **Hill Farm**

Chinese Horseshoe Chairs ▲

• *19th century*

A pair of Chinese horseshoe backed chairs.

• *103cm x 64cm*
• **£1,600**   • **Gordon Reece**

Hat Armchair ▼

• *circa 1850s*

A pair of Chinese official's hat armchairs with filigree carved central splat,

• *107cm x 63cm*
• **£1,720**   • **Gordon Reece**

Court Chairs ▲
- *circa 1810*

Pair of Chinese court chairs of simple elegant form
- *100cm x 61cm*
- £3,100 • Gordon Reece

Italian Chair ▲
- *circa 1870*

One of a pair of Italian walnut chairs, heavily carved with depictions of Pan, ram's heads, and griffins, raised on claw feet.
- *height 154cm*
- £18,000 •Hatchwell

Horseshoe Shaped Chair ▲
- *circa 1800*

A single low horseshoe shaped back rail chair. Originally low in construction
- *82cm x 57cm*
- £1,480 • Gordon Reece

Syrian Folding Chair ▲
- *circa 1890*

Attractive and decorative, folding, Syrian chair with inlaid ivory stars, profusely carved with scrolled, foliate designs throughout.
- *height 105cm*
- £485 • Elyot Tett

Ladder Back Chair ▲
- *circa 1820*

One of a pair George IV ash and elm ladder back chairs, with domed top rail above four graduated ladders, on turned legs standing on pad feet.
- *height 94cm*
- £1,075 • Great Grooms

Regency Dining Chairs ◄
- *circa 1820*

One of a set of eight Regency mahogany dining chairs, with pierced back splats, raised on turned legs.
- *height 84cm*
- £12,000 • Barry Cotton

Hepplewhite Armchair ▼
- **1785**
Hepplewhite mahogany armchair, with shield back and shaped arm rests with scrolled terminals on wavy supports, the whole raised on square tapered legs
- *98cm x 57cm*
- **£26,000** • Wakelin Linfield

Court Chairs ▼
- *circa 1810*
One of a pair of Chinese court chairs of simple elegant form
- *100cm x 61cm*
- **£3,100** • Gordon Reece

Victorian Mahogany Chair ▶
- *circa 1860*
Victorian mahogany button back chair, with scrolled arms and cabriole legs.
- *height 110cm*
- **£1,350** • In Vogue

French Desk Chair ▲
- *circa 1880*
French mahogany desk chair in the Louis XV style, with gilt ormolu mounts and carved front rail.
- *height 95cm*
- **£1,950** • Hatchwell

Horse Shoe Back Chairs ▲
- **18th century**
One of a pair of Chinese antique horseshoe back chairs, each bearing a moon symbol.
- *97cm x 24cm x 18cm*
- **£2,680** • Gordon Reece

Elmwood Chairs ▼
- **19th century**
A pair of Chinese elmwood chairs.
- *102cm x 56cm*
- **£890** • Gordon Reece

Lancashire Spindle Back Chairs ▼
- *circa 1880*
One of a set of ten Harlequin Lancashire rush seat spindle back chairs.
- *height 98cm*
- **£6,750** • Gerald Brodie

French Louis XV Suite ▼
- **1870**
French Louis XV suite with two armchairs and one sofa.
- *106cm*
- **£10,500** • Butchoff

Recumbent Easy Chair ◀

- *circa 1830*

One of a pair of rare matched English Regency 'Daws' patent 'Recumbent Easy Chairs', both bear the maker's stamp, with one chair bearing an original label for 'Bantings of Pall Mall'.
- *height 79cm*
- £18,500   • Freshfords

Small Swedish Chair ▶

- *1780*

Small Swedish pine nursing chair in original condition with moulded oval back, standing on turned legs.
- *height 92cm*
- £850   • Augustus Brandt

Oak Hall Chair ▼

- *1870*

Victorian oak hall chair with an architecturally carved back, raised on turned legs with good patina.
- *height 84cm*
- £375   • Elyot Tett

French Fauteuils ▲

- *circa 1870*

One of a pair of fine French fauteuils, with a high padded back and wings, with carved and gilded foliate decoration to the back and arms, raised on turned legs.
- *height 149cm*
- £1,850   • Elyot Tett

Regency Mahogany Bergères ▶

- *circa 1820*

A fine pair of Regency mahogany bergères decorated with ebony mouldings and turnings, with later cane and hide coverings.
- *width 66cm*
- £21,500   • Freshfords

Hall Chair ▼

- *1890*

One of a pair of mahogany hall chairs, with carved shield back and oval padded insert, raised on cabriole legs.
- *height 87cm*
- £875   • Elyot Tett

Walnut Armchair ▲

- *circa 1880*

George I, Chippendale style walnut armchair with pierced back rest with scrolled designs, supported by shaped, scrolled arms above a serpentine front rail, with scalloped motifs, raised on cabriole legs with claw and ball feet.
- *height 95cm*
- £1,600   • Elyot Tett

George II Irish Armchair ▲▲

- *circa 1730*

A rare George II Irish mahogany armchair of outstanding quality and design, the chair is beautifully carved throughout and in exceptional condition for its age.
- *height 98cm*
- £6,500   • Freshfords

Walnut Chair ▲

- *1880*

One of a pair of fine, George I style walnut chairs with pierced back splat and scrolled back, raised on cabriole legs with scalloped designs and claw and ball feet, with original leather and good patina.
- *height 95cm*
- £1,750   • Elyot Tett

William IV Rosewood Armchair ◄

- *circa 1830.*

William IV colonial rosewood armchair; formerly the property of Major Arthur Annesley.
- *height 89cm*
- £3,850   • Freshfords

339

Chaises Longues & Day Beds

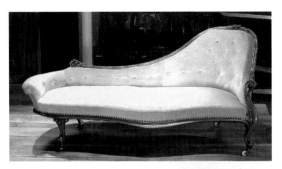

Victorian Chaise Longue ▶
- *circa 1860*
Victorian mahogany chaise longue with curved button back and scrolled arm, standing on turned legs with original brass castors.
- *length 150cm*
- **£1,375**   • **The Swan**

Mahogany Chaise Longue ▲
- *circa 1840*
Victorian mahogany chaise longue with feather padded button back, gold damask upholstery and carved, turned decoration.
- *length 189cm*
- **£1,650**   • **The Swan**

French Chaise Longue ▶
- *circa 1900*
Mahogany walnut Louis XVI style meridienne.
- *length 84cm*
- **£1,650**   • **French Room**

Rosewood Chaise Longue ◀
- *circa 1860*
Mid Victorian rosewood chaise longue, with finely carved rose decoration, scrolled arms, moulded serpentine apron and original porcelain castors.
- *length 186cm*
- **£2,800**   • **Drummonds**

Victorian Chaise Longue ▲
- *circa 1870*
Recently upholstered chaise longue dating from the Victorian period. Presented with original marble castors and brass fittings.
- *length 2.13m*
- **£1,900**   • **Gabrielle de Giles**

Louis XVI Chaise Longue ▲
- *circa 1890*
Double-ended chaise longue in Louise XVI style.
- *length 1.7m*
- **£2,700**   • **North West 8**

Chests of Drawers & Commodes

Mahogany Chest of Drawers ▲
- *circa 1890s*
Louis XVI style Swedish mahogany chest of four long drawers with tapered legs and ormulu mounts and a marble top.
- *83cm x 77cm*
- £2,900   • Rupert Cavendish

Miniature Chest of Drawers ▲
- *circa 1890*
Miniature rustic oak chest, with six small drawers and original turned wooden handles.
- *30cm x 38cm*
- £160   • The Lacquer Chest

William & Mary Chest of Drawers ▲
- *circa 1690*
Excellent and rare William & Mary chest of drawers with two short and three long drawers, the top, sides and drawer fronts decorated with reserves of floral marquetry on well figured walnut.
- *93cm x 96cm x 59cm*
- £48,000   • Wakelin Linfield

Plum Chest of Drawers ◄
- *circa 1840*
Unusual plum chest of four deep drawers with a fan holly-wood inlay to each corner turned handles, standing on turned legs.
- *height 120cm*
- £5,850   • Denzil Grant

Victorian Mahogany Chest ▲
- *circa 1880*
Victorian mahogany chest of drawers. The upper section with six small drawers above three long drawers, with turned wooden handles, standing on a straight base, with small raised feet.
- *118cm x 110cm*
- £1,250   • Old Cinema

Chest of Drawers ◄
- *circa 1890*
One of a pair of burr walnut veneered pedestal chest of four drawers.
- *height 89cm*
- £1,750   • The Swan

Venetian Commode ▶

- *circa 1760*

Superb Venetian commode with a
trailing foliate painted design
overall, two deep drawers large
metal handles painted marble
top, with moulded carved apron
on cabriole legs.
- *35cm x 101cm*
- **£18,750**   • **C. Preston**

Gustavian Commode ▲

- *circa 1800*

Louis XVI Swedish Gustavian
commode with three long drawers
and original brass handles,
standing on square legs.
- *86cm x 103cm*
- **£6,700**   • **Rupert Cavendish**

Indian Brass Chest ▲

- *circa 1890*

An Indian Repoussé and
engraved, floral, banded design
brass chest with teak interior.
The slightly domed lid decorated
with studded bands interspersed
with repoussé floral stripes,
flanked by stripes decorated with
diamonds. The lid with brass
inscribed catch; the front panel of
grid design with repoussé
decorated squares within a
banded frame, standing on
concealed wooded wheels.
- *70cm x 97cm*
- **£3,500**   • **Anthony Outred**

Ash Cupboard ▶

- *1870*

Small Hungarian pair of pot
cupboards, disguised as a chest of
drawers.
- *height 66cm*
- **£1,995**   • **A.I.G..**

George III Chest ▲

- *circa 1750*

George III mahogany chest of
drawers, of small proportions,
with four graduated drawers and
original brass handles, raised on
bracket feet.
- *86cm x 77cm*
- **£4,950**   • **Barry Cotton**

Small Chest of Drawers ▼

- *circa 1780*

George III small chest of oak two
small and two long drawers
standing on moulded bracket feet.
- *height 50cm*
- **£5,500**   • **Paul Hopwell**

Japanese Chest ▼

- *circa 1880*

Large standing Meiji period
Japanese chest, possibly for futon
storage.
- *171cm x 180cm*
- **£4,995**   • **Gordon Reece**

Mahogany Chest of Drawers ◄

- *circa 1890*
One of a pair of small Victorian mahogany chest of four drawers.
- *height 93cm*
- £1,380 • The Swan

Bombe Commode ▲

- *circa 1890*
Swedish serpentine fronted, walnut bombe commode, with cross banded designs and gilt brass mounts raised on splayed legs.
- *82cm x 92cm x 20cm*
- £2,250 • Hatchwell

Biedermeier Tallboy ▲

- *1842-1843*
Biedermeier birchwood tallboy with a gentleman's chest interior signed and dated: Carl Christian Hoff, Trondhjem, Norway.
- *140cm x 118cm*
- £8,800 • Rupert Cavendish

Kusuri Dansu ▼

- *circa 1890s*
A Japanese Kusuri Dansu (storage chest) with small drawers, from the Meiji period.
- *50cm x 43cm*
- £1,495 • Gordon Reece

Burr Walnut Tall Boy ►

- *circa 1740*
A good George II period burr-walnut tall-boy with original metalwork. The top surmounted with a canted concave cornice above three short drawers and three graduated long drawers, all drawers having herringbone inlay and cross banded with panels of distinctively figured walnut and fitted with open brass plate handles, with fluted canted corners terminating in an ogee point. The lower section with moulded lip above three long graduated drawers flanked by canted fluted corners headed and terminating in ogee points.
- *191cm x 109cm*
- £25,500 • Anthony Outred

Satinwood Commode ▶

- *circa 1899*
A pair of satinwood marquetry demi lune George III style commodes, with exceptional marquetry inlay.
- *94cm x 149cm*
- £30,000   • Butchoff

Georgian Chest of Drawers ▲

- *circa 1780*
Georgian chest of drawers with two small and three long graduated drawers, with brass ring handles, supported on bracket feet.
- *95cm x 95cm x 51cm*
- £1,450   • Vale Antiques

Choba Dansu ▶

- *19th century*
A Japanese Meiji period Choba Dansu (document chest), made from kiri wood with good markings and original metalwork.
- *93cm x 76cm*
- £2,995   • Gordon Reece

Mahogany Chest of Drawers ▲

- *circa 1890*
Mahogany chest of four drawers with small turned handles, on splayed bracket feet.
- *108cm x 105cm*
- £1,650   • C. Preston

Scandinavian Chest of Drawers ▼

- *circa 1880*
Scandinavian serpentine fronted chest of drawers with moulded top and three long drawers with large foliate brass handles and lockplates. With original lilac paint, standing on bracket feet.
- *height 83cm*
- £6,800   • Augustus Brandt

Miniature Chest of Drawers ▼

- *circa 1880*
Victorian mahogany miniature chest of drawers.
- *24cm x 21cm*
- £295   • Amandini

George II Chest of Drawers ▲

- *circa 1730*
George II chest of three drawers with original brass handles.
- *height 88cm*
- £8,750 • **Paul Hopwell**

George III Chest of Drawers ▲

- *circa 1790*
Fine George III mahogany bow front chest of drawers with moulded top over a brushing slide with cross banding, standing on small swept feet with.mahogany lined drawers.
- *86cm x 104cm*
- £3,850 • **Gerald Brodie**

Georgian Chest of Drawers ▼

- *circa 1750s*
Georgian mahogany bow front chest of two small and three long drawers, with original fittings and ebony stringing, standing on slay bracket feet.
- *105cm x 98cm*
- £1,425 • **The Swan**

Swedish Chest of Drawers ▼

- *circa 1790*
Swedish painted commode with four long drawers, in original condition with pillared sides.
- *107cm x 121cm x*
- £5,850 • **Anthony Sharpe**

Georgian Chest of Drawers ▶

- *circa 1760s*
Georgian chest with four graduated drawers, with original paint and turned handles, standing on moulded bracket feet.
- *90cm x 86cm*
- £1,700 • **Heytesbury**

Storage Chest ▲

- *circa 1820s*
A pair of early 19th century red and black lacquer storage chests with original paintwork. The doors have a circular motif inside which are idyllic scenes of the countryside rendered in black and gold.
- *173cm x 112cm*
- £12,500 • **Gordon Reece**

William & Mary Chest of Drawers ▲

- *circa 1690*
William & Mary chest of two short and three long drawers on turned bun feet, the whole in oyster laburnum with broad cross banding to the side, top and drawer fronts.
- *84cm x 94cm x 26cm*
- £24,500   • Wakelin Linfield

Mahogany Chest of Drawers ▲

- *circa 1860*
Flame mahogany, marble topped, chest of drawers with good colour and patination, one long single drawer above three deep drawers, standing on scrolled bracket feet.
- *92cm x 74cm*
- £1,850   • Drummonds

Himalayan Kist ▶

- *circa 17th century*
Fine Himalayan pine chip slab Kist (chest) with deeply carved designs, from the Indian state of Himachal Pradesh.
- *56cm x 130cm*
- £780   • Gordon Reece

French Commode ▲

- *1880*
French marquetry commode of small proportions, with serpentine top and fine gilt ormolu mounts.
- *79cm x 74cm*
- £5,500   • Butchoff

Biedermeier Tallboy ▶

- *1820-1830*
A rare narrow Swedish mahogany Biedermeier tallboy with one narrow and five wider drawers with ormulu mounts, standing on gilt paw feet.
- *136cm x 67cm*
- £4,500   • Rupert Cavendish

Wellington Chest ▼

- *circa 1835*
Unusually tall rosewood Wellington chest and with finely figured rosewood, the rectangular top with moulded lip, with eight drawers with wooden pulls, with hinged and locking stile, the whole raised on a plinth.
- *56.5cm x 53cm*
- £5,500   • Anthony Outred

Oak and Elm Chest of Drawers ▲

• **1680**
Oak and elm chest of three long
drawers. The elm over a scratch
carved dentil cornice, the drawers
surrounded by a split baluster.
• *78cm x 89cm*
• **£2,400**   • **Rushlight**

Oak Chest of Drawers ▲

• *circa 1670*
Walnut, sandalwood and
fruitwood chest of drawers, of two
part construction, with carved
and moulded decoration, raised
on turned bun feet.
• *102cm x 1150cm*
• **£8,750**   • **Wakelin Linfield**

Regency Chest of Drawers

• *circa 1810*
Small Regency chest of
exceptional quality and patina
with two small and two long
drawers on a moulded apron with
bracket feet.
• *height 84cm*
• **£1,950**   • **C. Preston**

William IV Chest of Drawers ▼

• *circa 1835*
William IV mahogany miniature
apprentice chest of drawers.
• *34cm x 34cm*
• **£1,995**   • **Amandini**

Victorian Chest ▶

• **1870**
Victorian mahogany bedside
cabinet with long drawer,
standing on a straight square
base.
• *height 84cm*
• **£495**   • **A.I.G.**

Maltese Commode ▼

• *circa 1760*
A fine and rare, serpentine
fronted, Maltese commode made
from olivewood, with four
graduated long drawers, fine gilt
handles, standing on unusual
shaped legs.
• *110cm x146cm*
• **£18,500**   • **Hatchwell**

Georgian Chest of Drawers ▲

• *circa 1800*
Georgian mahogany chest of
drawers, with four drawers, with
original brass swan neck handles,
standing on moulded feet.
• *height 98cm*
• **£1,495**   • **Vale Antiques**

Regency Bow Chest of Drawers ▲

- *circa 1820*

Regency mahogany bow fronted chest of two small drawers and three long, standing on curved bracket feet and moulded apron.
- *107cm x 105cm*
- **£1,950**   • C. Preston

Victorian Chest of Drawers ▼

- **1890**

Victorian mahogany chest of drawers, with pull out writing slop, above four tiered drawers, fine painted floral decoration and brass ring handles, raised on shaped bracket feet.
- *82cm x 86cm*
- **£6500**   • Butchoff

Victorian Chest of Drawers ◀

- *circa 1880*

Victorian mahogany chest of drawers with two short and four long drawers with original turned mahogany handles, standing on bracket feet.
- *126cm x 86cm*
- **£1,200**   • Hill Farm

Ryobaki ▲

- *circa 1860*

A very fine high quality Ryobaki (chest on chest) with fine copper strapping and lock. The top door reveals red lacquer drawers and a similar treatment of the locking safe and batch of drawers. With Kiri wood throughout.
- *114.5 cm x114.5cm*
- **£7,495**   • Gordon Reece

George III Oak Chest ▼

- *circa 1818*

George III oak chest on chest in original condition with good patination, original swan neck handles and key plates, standing on moulded bracket feet.
- *width 99cm*
- **£2,995**   • The Swan

Demi-Lune Commode ◀

- *circa 1810*

An English demi-lune commode in veneered satinwood, the top and side panels cross-banded in kingwood and strung in ebony and boxwood. With painted decoration to the front and four cedar lined drawers.
- *91cm x 104cm*
- **£12,950**   • Wakelin Linfield

Arcile Chest ▶

- **17th century**

Italian, Bologna walnut Arcile chest of heavy construction with good colour and patinaton. The top, front and side panels inset with brass roundels and rosettes.
- *140cm x 190cm*
- **£16,500** • **Wakelin Linfield**

Swedish Chest of Drawers ▲

- *circa 1830*

Swedish birchwood Biedermeier style chest of four long drawers standing on carved scrolled feet.
- *94cm x 92cm*
- **£4,500** • **Rupert Cavendish**

Swedish Pine Chest of Drawers ▲

- *circa 1760*

Swedish painted pine chest of drawers with serpentine moulded top and four long drawers with foliate ormolu handles and lockplates, standing on short cabriole legs.
- *height 88cm*
- **£8,600** • **Augustus Brandt**

Italian Commode ▶

- *circa 1760*

Fine Italian serpentine front walnut commode with olive wood inlay, carved and scrolled foliate moulded apron, standing on cabriole legs.
- *88cm x 109cm*
- **£8,750** • **C. Preston**

French Directoire Commode ▼

- *circa 1880*

French directoire style mahogany and marble topped commode with three long drawers, square elongated handles and interesting gilt ormolu mounts.
- *87cm x 112cm*
- **£5,400** • **Anthony Sharpe**

Mahogany Chest of Drawers ▲

- *circa 1870*

Figured mahogany chest of drawers with two short and three long drawers, with original brass handles and curved apron, supported by moulded bracket feet.
- *height 97cm*
- **£1,250** • **R. S. Antiques**

Mahogany Chest of Drawers ◀

- **1790**
One of a pair of small mahogany chest of drawers with three drawers with ebony moulding, brass handles, standing on bracket feet.
- *height 66cm*
- **£1,750**
- • A.I.G.

Chest on Chest ▼

- *circa 1760*
Fine George III beautifully figured mahogany chest on chest, with dentil moulded cornice above an upper section of two short and six long drawers, supported on ogee bracket feet.
- *195cm x 102cm*
- **£12,750**   • Wakelin Linfield

Georgian Chest of Drawers ▲

- *circa 1790*
Georgian chest of two short and three long drawers, with swan neck handles, standing on bracket feet,
- *1,127cm x 98cm*
- **£1,475**   • The Swan

Walnut Chest of Drawers ▲

- *circa 1820*
Walnut chest of four drawers standing on bracket feet, with original handles.
- *height 98cm*
- **£4,800**   • Denzil Grant

French Mahogany Commode ▲

- *circa 1840*
French flame mahogany commode with original marble top and one long and three deep drawers on a straight base with small plain bracket feet.
- *width 112cm*
- **£2,250**   • C. Preston

Dutch Chest of Drawers ▷

- *circa 1725*
An excellent early 18th century
Dutch chest of drawers of
serpentine form, with four
graduated long drawers. The top
quarter veneered and walnut
strung. This is an exceptionally
small example of this type of
furniture.
- *75cm x 79cm*
- **£18,750** • **Wakelin Linfield**

Collector's Chest ▲

- *circa 1880*
Mahogany collector's chest of
eight small drawers with wooden
bar with lock and key.
- *28cm x 33cm*
- **£170** • **The Lacquer Chest**

Louis XV Style Commode ▲

- *circa 1880*
Louis XV style bombe commode,
with violet marble top with three
long drawers, veneered in
rosewood and mahogany with
marquetry panels, profusely gilded
with foliate bronze ormolu
mounts.
- *102cm x 115cm*
- **£5,500** • **Hatchwell**

George III Oak Chest of Drawers ▷

- *circa 1817*
George III chest of drawers with
two short and three long drawers,
with boxwood banding and brass
handles, standing on shaped
bracket feet.
- *90cm x 88cm*
- **£1,425** • **Rushlight**

English Mahogany Chest of Drawers ▽

- *circa 1780*
Fine English Mahogany chest of
two small and three long drawers
standing on plain bracket feet.
- *height 106cm*
- **£2,550** • **C. Preston**

Oak Coffer ▲

- *circa 1780*
George III oak chest with carving
to the front standing on square
straight legs.
- *height 56cm*
- **£6,850** • **Paul Hopwell**

Mahogany Chest of Drawers ▲

- *circa 1880*
Georgian mahogany chest of
drawers, consisting of three deep
drawers with original brass swan
neck handles, on low bracket
feet.
- *85cm x 115cm*
- **£1,500** • **Drummonds**

Davenports

Victorian Davenport ▶
- *circa 1870*

An unusual Victorian burr walnut rising top davenport, enclosing a fitted interior and pull out ratcheted writing slope.
- 90cm x 60cm
- £4,350   • Amandini

Regency Davenport ▲
- *circa 1820*

A Regency style faux rosewood davenport with pen drawer to right hand side and a removable fire screen.
- 98cm x 51cm
- £995   • Clarke & Denny

Walnut Davenport ▲
- *circa 1860*

Fine Walnut Victorian davenport with original leather, inlaid with satinwood, with four side drawers, pierced brass rail and maple interior.
- *height 88cm*
- £1,950   • Old Cinema

Burr Walnut Davenport ▼
- *circa 1860*

Burr walnut davenport with piano lid, central cupboard flanked by eight small side drawers with turned wood handles.
- 98cm x 62cm
- £3,750   • The Swan

Rosewood Davenport ▼
- *circa 1820*

Small Regency rosewood davenport, with pierced brass gallery and pen drawer to the side of a writing slope with unusual side action.
- 88cm x 34cm
- £3,995   • W. John Griffiths

Expert Tips

The name davenport came from an entry in the book of Captain Davenport in the 1790s. Look out for the following:

fine vaneer in walnut
panelled back
original inkwells
pen trays
mother of pearl escutcheons
secret drawers

Up to 1840 their style was quite plain, but after 1840 davenports tended to be more feminine, with scrolled supports.

Walnut Davenport ◀
- *circa 1840*

An English figured walnut davenport with stunning matched sunburst veneers. The sliding top is fitted with a hinged pen and inkwell drawer raised above four graduated drawers and four dummy panel drawers supported on a shaped plinth base.
- 79cm x 46cm
- £7,500   • Freshfords

Desks

Roll Top Desk ▲

- *circa 1880*

Flame mahogany roll top kneehole desk. The fitted interior with pigeonholes, eight small drawers and leather adjustable book rest, above a kneehole flanked by eight drawers with turned wood handles.

- *121cm x 135cm*
- **£5,250**   • Drummonds

Walnut and Ormolu Writing Desk ▼

- *circa 1860*

Walnut and ormolu mounted writing desk in the manner of Gillows, with serpentine top above a central drawer flanked by two side drawers. The whole raised on cabriole legs with fine ormolu mounts.

- *width 137cm*
- **£16,500**   • Butchoff

English Library Desk ▶

- *circa 1840*

A rare and sought-after English 19th century burr-walnut, kidney-shaped Library desk in the manner of Gillow. The top with original brass gallery is fitted with three frieze drawers with a bank of four graduated drawers either side of the kneehole, with the opposing side fitted with bookshelves. This desk relates to a design by Gillows recorded in their 'Estimate Sketch Book' of 1840.

- *76.2cm x 122cm*
- **£43,500**   • Freshfords

Biedermeier Mahogany Desk ▼

- *1830–1840*

Swedish flame mahogany Biedermeier desk. The top, with rope twist and beaded rim, with three short drawers, above a kneehole with three figured mahogany panelled doors.

- *87cm x 83cm*
- **£4,900**   • Rupert Cavendish

Italian Walnut Desk ▶

- *1760*

North Italian walnut desk with a rectangular thumb moulded top centred by a geometric radiating petal design, cross-banded walnut with boxwood stringing. Above a writing slide, leading to a long drawer flanked by three short drawers to the left, and three to the right. The whole raised on four square tapered legs.

- *76cm x 94cm*
- **£12,500**   • Anthony Outred

Kidney Shaped Desk ▲

- *1880*

Lady's kidney shaped desk in the manner of Gillows, with satinwood, box and ebony stringing and cross banding. On original gilt-brass castors.

- *82cm x 120cm*
- **£8,750**   • Gerald Brodie

Expert Tips

One point to remember is that the interior of a period drawer should have a totally untouched, almost dry, unpolished look.

Louis XVI Desk ▲

- *circa 1800*
Louis XVI Swedish Gustavian
desk, with long drawer with, plain
gilt ring handle, raised on slender
tapered legs.
- *75cm x 80cm*
- **£1,950**   • Rupert Cavendish

Mahogany Partner's
Desk ▲

- *circa 1825*
A historically important George
IV mahogany partner's desk by
Robert Lawson for Gillows of
Lancaster. With a central drawer
above the kneehole flanked by a
bank of four drawers. Each
pedestal with vertical reeded
pilasters. The pedestals supported
on plinth bases with gilded
casters, all locks original.
- *79cm x 183cm*
- **£95,000**   • Anthony Outred

Louis XV Bureau Plat ▲

- *circa 1900*
Fine French Louis XV style
mahogany bureau plat with gilt
bronze mounts.
- *80cm x 145cm x 76cm*
- **£9,500**   • Hatchwell

Satinwood Writing Table ▼

- *1870*
Satinwood and ormolu writing
table. The top with egg and dart
moulded rim, above two side
drawers, raised on four reeded legs
on original brass castors, by
Wright & Mansfield.
- *74cm x 110cm*
- **£10,500**   • Butchoff

Satinwood Desk ▼

- *circa 1890*
Sheraton revival high quality
Victorian inlaid satin wood
pedestal desk with two side
compartments. The base
containing single drawer, stamped
'Maple & Co.
- *124cm 104cm*
- **£12,500**   • J. & T. Stone

Georgian Mahogany
Desk ▶

- *circa 1820s*
Georgian kneehole mahogany
desk with leather top, two long
and two small drawers, original
laurel wreath brass handles.
- *79cm x 101cm*
- **£1,350**   • Old Cinema

George II Partner's Desk ▲

- *circa 1755*
George II ebony-inlaid mahogany
partners pedestal desk with a rich,
untouched patina. The
rectangular leather inset top
above three mahogany-lined
frieze drawers to each side and
two simulated drawers with
carrying-handles to each. Raised
on a plinth base.
- *80.5cm x 139.5cm*
- **£68,000**   • Anthony Outred

Birchwood Desk ▲

- *circa 1890s*
Swedish free standing veneered
Biedermeier style birchwood
desk. The top with leather insert
and three drawers, above two
pedestals with panelled doors.
- *76cm x 143cm*
- **£5,900**   • Rupert Cavendish

Dining Tables

Mahogany Dining Table ▶

- *circa 1860s*

A mid-Victorian mahogany circular dining table. The moulded top in two halves, on a large ring-turned shaft with gadrooned stem, on an X-frame base with scrolled feet and countersunk brass castors. Provenance: by repute, William Hesketh Lever, 1st Viscount Leverhulme (d.1925).
- *75cm x 274.5cm*
- £80,000   • Anthony Outred

English Dining Table ▼

- *circa 1880*

Mahogany circular dining table. With finely figured mahogany tilt top, cross-banded, with a gadrooned edge above a cross-banded frieze, raised on a tri-form, panelled pedestal, with large scrolled feet.
- *height 75cm*
- £32,000   • Anthony Outred

Regency Dining Table ▼

- *circa 1825*

A late regency mahogany dining table with excellent figuring. The top with rounded corners and a reeded moulded edge, incorporating five identically sized leaves. The top supported on a mahogany concertina bearer mechanism, on eight slender reeded legs.
- *length 364cm*
- £28,500   • Anthony Outred

Mahogany Extending Dining Table ◀

- *circa 1820*

Regency mahogany extending dining table by Thomas Wilkinson of London. The scissor-action, 'lazy-tongs' mechanism for extending the table was covered by the King's patent.
- *length 379cm*
- £32,000   • Freshfords

355

Expert Tips

When buying an extending table do make sure you have the action demonstrated. Also check the full extendability of the table, that the casters are unbroken and in good condition and that all the legs and wood are matching.

George IV Dining Table ▲
- *circa 1825*
An exceptional George IV extending dining table in the manner of Gillow. With a well-figured top and an ogee moulded edge, raised on four tapering, fluted and turned legs. The leaves sit on a solid mahogany telescopic bearer mechanism.
- *75cm x 300cm*
- **£38,000** • **Anthony Outred**

Victorian Dining Table ◄
- *circa 1860*
An imposing Victorian mahogany dining room table, the moulded rectangular top on ring-turned, tapering and reeded legs, with brass caps and castors.
- *length 364cm*
- **£6,599** • **Westland & Co**

William IV Extending Dining Table ▼
- *circa 1835*
A William IV period extending dining table. The well figured mahogany top, raised on six turned and fluted legs on original brass castors. The seven leaves with relaid surfaces, which retain a good colour and figure.
- *76cm x 138cm*
- **£45,000** • **Anthony Outred**

Mahogany Dining Table ▼
- *circa 1825*
Mahogany dining table attributed to Gillows of Lancaster. The well-figured mahogany top with a moulded edge, four large leaves and one smaller leaf when fully extended. Raised on four tapering, fluted and turned legs at each corner and with four smaller inset legs, all with original brass castors.
- *length 414cm*
- **£48,000** • **Anthony Outred**

Doors

Studded Panelled Door ▲
- *1880*

English gothic six panelled pine door, with carved gothic tracery to the top panels, large rustic iron handle and door furniture.
- *200cm x 114cm*
- £3,200 • Drummonds

Italian Double Doors ▲
- *circa 1790*

A pair of gilt wood and ivory painted double doors from an Italian Palazzo. The moulded gilt wood decoration centred by a Jasper panel.
- *295cm x 71cm*
- £15,000 • Westland & Co

Revolving Doors ▼
- *circa 1900*

Revolving oak doors, within a cylindrical housing with moulded frames, glazed panels and brass door furniture.
- *236cm x 190cm*
- £6,625 • Drummonds

Linen Fold Door ▼
- *circa 1640*

Oak door with four panels, the upper and lower sections carved with linen fold designs.
- *177cm x 77cm*
- £820 • Drummonds

Victorian Glazed Door ▲
- *circa 1870*

Victorian mahogany door with glazed oval panel of etched glass engraved with floral design flanked by royal blue, red and yellow glass panels with etched corner sections.
- *231cm x 101cm*
- £1,075 • Drummonds

George II Door Surround ▲
- *circa 1790*

A large and imposing George III carved pine door surround. The arched top with an egg and dart cornice together with an Anthemion frieze centred by a wrought iron fan light. The fluted pilasters with Ionic capitals with Anthemion carving.
- *354cm x 221cm*
- £15,500 • Westland & Co

Gothic Oak Door ▲
- **1880**

Gothic oak paneled door and surround with a glazed panel with gothic mouldings, with iron letter box and handle.
- *280cm x 87cm*
- **£875** • Drummonds

Oriental Door Frame ▼
- *circa 1860*

Oriental door within a deep surround with a panel set over the door, carved with amorphous designs.
- *200cm x 104cm*
- **£2,100** • Drummonds

Stone Door Surround ▼
- **1880**

Victorian door with stone surround, incorporating a gothic arch with stone coining, housing a grey painted door with cast iron fittings.
- *211cm x 105cm*
- **£4,250** • Drummonds

Set of Twelve Mahogany Doors ◄
- *circa 1900*

Set of twelve flame mahogany five panelled doors with brass door furniture.
- *221cm x 91cm*
- **£3.300 each** • Drummonds

Queen Anne Doorcase ▲
- *circa 1710*

A rare Queen Anne carved pine Baroque doorcase with a projecting canopy on scrolled brackets. The central frieze carved with the attributes of war flanked by fluted Tuscan pilasters.
- *308cm x 189cm*
- **£14,500** • Westland & Co

Georgian Style Door ▲
- **1870**

Georgian style oak door and surround. The arch with wood mouldings and the surround with lead glazing bars.
- *300cm x 124cm*
- **£1,580** • Drummonds

Neo-Classical Doors ▲
- *circa 1890*
A set of three pairs of carved neo-classical doors, together with matching frames in the Louis XVI manner.
- *239cm x 100cm*
- **£3,500**   • Westland & Co

Oak Panelled Door ▲
- *circa 1880*
English oak door with two central panels.
- *204cm x 88cm*
- **£1,190**   • Drummonds

French Glass Panelled Doors ▼
- *circa 1880*
Pair of French mahogany doors with six glass panels backed with brass plaques, with classical figures and stylized leaf designs.
- *203cm x51cm*
- **£1,285**   • Drummonds

Flamed Mahogany Door ▼
- *circa 1910*
One of a pair of fine quality six panelled, flamed mahogany doors, with egg and dart moulding and fine interior pencil beading.
- *201cm x 94cm*
- **£2,400**   • Drummonds

Carved Doors ▲
- *17th century*
A pair of 17th century Oriental doors with a carved geometric design, and twenty-eight panels.
- *180cm x 93cm*
- **£1,980**   • Gordon Reece

Art Nouveau Door ▲
- *circa 1920*
Mahogany door frame in Art Nouveau style with glass panels within organic styled mouldings, with brass door furniture.
- *220cm x 74cm*
- **£1,400**   • Drummonds

French Double Doors ▲

- *circa 1880*

Pair of French pine and oak double doors consisting of four large and two oblong moulded panels.
- *225cm x 68cm*
- **£2,225**   • Drummonds

English Circular Doors ▲

- *circa 1770*

Unusual pair of tall English oak curved doors, carved with asymmetric scrolled mouldings, with fine original brass locks and fittings.
- *340cm x 155cm*
- **£5,800**   • Drummonds

Oriental Door and Frame ▼

- *circa 1860*

Oriental door and frame with heavily carved surround, inset with a frieze incorporating interlaced dragons with scrolled, foliate tracery.
- *225cm x 124cm*
- **£2,900**   • Drummonds

Adelphi Door ▼

- *1920*

Pine Aldephi door, painted yellow with brass door furniture, circular foliate design on handle and the head of Pan on the door plate.
- *160cm x 89cm*
- **£950**   • Drummonds

Oak Panelled Door ▲

- *circa 1780*

Oak door with six long and one oblong panel with canted edges.
- *192cm x 94cm*
- **£620**   • Drummonds

Arched Oak Door ▲

- *circa 18th century*

Oak arched door with clear glass panel, decorative foliate carving within the arch and pillars and scrolled ionic capitals, from Dunstan Hall.
- *260cm x 90cm*
- **£2,875**   • Drummonds

Dressers

Oak Dresser Base ▶

- *circa 1780*

George III oak dresser base with central panelled door flanked by two sets of three long drawers with original brass handles, and standing on bracket feet.

- *height 110cm*
- **£14,750** • **Paul Hopwell**

George II Oak Dresser ▲

- *circa 1750*

George II oak dresser with panelled back, two shelves with three small drawers with turned handles and two cupboards below standing on straight square legs.

- *height 245cm*
- **£11,750** • **Paul Hopwell**

Victorian Sideboard ▲

- *circa 1880*

Impressive sideboard with a deep central drawer, centered with a raised ivory classical plaque, flanked by two deep large cupboards, standing on two pedestals with bun feet.

- *90cm x 198cm*
- **£4,850** • **Drummonds**

George III Plate Rack ▲

- *circa 1780*

George III open oak plate rack with pierced rail and architectural side columns.

- *height 102cm*
- **£3,750** • **Paul Hopwell**

Pine Open Dresser ◀

- *circa 1880*

Open back pine dresser with four shelves. The base with three long drawers above three paneled cupboard doors, with alloy handles and fittings.

- *275cm x 170cm*
- **£850** • **Drummonds**

French Dresser ▼

- *circa 1820*

French provincial fruitwood galleried four shelf dresser with two long drawers and cupboards below.

- *width 127cm*
- **£3,850** • **C.Preston**

Breakfront Sideboard ▲

- *circa 1800*

Mahogany Breakfront D Shaped sideboard, one cellaret drawer and a shallow centre drawer over a linen drawer. Raised on four front finely reeded legs and two turned back legs.
- *94.5cm x 168cm x 66.5cm*
- £16,500   • Wakelin Linfield

George III Oak Rack ▲

- *circa 1790*

George III oak wall mounted dresser with moulded and shaped cornice and three shelves flanked either side with additional shelving.
- *height 97cm*
- £3,250   • Paul Hopwell

Oak Dresser Base ▲

- *circa 1786*

George III oak dresser base. Carved drawers with geometric designs, with brass drop handles, the whole raised on turned front legs.
- *height 97cm*
- £22,500   • Paul Hopwell

Pine Glazed Dresser ▲

- *circa 1840*

Pine dresser with three glazed doors enclosing three shelves, with two long drawers and cupboards below with brass knob handles.
- *235cm x 170cm*
- £1,600   • Drummonds

Pine Dressers ▶

- *circa 1820*

One of a pair unusual narrow pine dressers or bookcases with panelled backs and adjustable shelves.
- *width 67cm*
- £3,350   • C.Preston

Miniature Dresser ◀

- *circa 1890*

Miniature English oak dresser with moulded gallery, turned supports all above carved panel doors and turned bun feet.
- *height 47cm*
- £225   • Great Grooms

Oversized Dresser ▲

- *circa 1840*

Large pine dresser painted pea green, with moulded pediment and two central cupboards flanked by four deep long drawers with brass handles, standing on a straight base.
- *height 425m*
- £3,650   • Drummonds

Dumb Waiters & Whatnots

Mahogany Whatnot ▶
- *circa 1880*
Mahogany whatnot with five
graduated serpentine tiers with
turned finials and barley twist
supports.
- *height 125cm*
- £350   • The Swan

William IV Dumbwaiter ▲
- *1825*
Pair of mahogany William IV
dumbwaiters with brass gallery,
three well figured shelves, raised
on carved supports with bun feet.
- *117cm x 124cm*
- £16,500   • Butchoff

Brass Cake Stand ▼
- *1890*
Victorian lacquered brass cake-
stand with two circular tiers
embossed with an organic
repeating design, raised on
scrolled legs with hoof feet.
- *height 88cm*
- £295   • A.I.G.

Oriental Cake Stand ▶
- *1880*
Oriental cake stand with three
circular tiers carved with six leaf
shaped receptacles, around a
central circular design, within a
carved frame.
- *height 82cm*
- £110   • Poppets

George II Washstand ▲
- *circa 1750*
George II mahogany two tier
washstand with fan carving to the
sides, and a small drawer standing
on slender legs and pad feet.
- *height 85cm*
- £3,850   • John Bly

Walnut Whatnot ▼
- *1880*
Victorian burr walnut whatnot
with, pierced gallery and turned
finials, three well figured tiers,
with turned supports the lower
section with single drawer and
wood knob handles, on turned
legs with original castors.
- *height 122cm*
- £2,200   • Salem Antiques

Four Tier Walnut Whatnot ▲

- *circa 1880*

Four tier walnut corner whatnot inlaid with boxwood and burr walnut, acorn finial and turned supports.
- *height 137cm*
- £875　　　　● The Swan

Satin Birch Whatnot ▲

- *circa 1840*

English Satin birchwood whatnot with three shelves, the lower section with a single drawer with barley-twist supports, stamped Mills Cabinet makers, raised on gadrooned feet with original brass casters.
- *99cm x 53cm x 39.5cm*
- £4,250　　　● O. F. Wilson

George III Whatnot ◄

- *circa 1790*

Unusual mahogany George III whatnot. The rising with ratcheted bracket and four shelves below. The whole on square section legs and square caped castors.
- *height 114cm*
- £6,500　　　● John Bly

Cake Stand ▲

- *circa 1880*

Mahogany cake stand with satin wood banding, incorporating three graduated circular shelves, within wood frame, open at one side, surmounted by a ball finial, raised on splayed legs.
- *height 93cm*
- £280　　　　● John Clay

Walnut Whatnot ◄

- *circa 1870*

Victorian walnut three tier whatnot with carved scrolled pierced gallery, on turned supports.
- *height 132cm*
- £1,950　　　● The Swan

Walnut Whatnot ▼

- *circa 1870s*
Victorian walnut whatnot, the scrolled gallery with turned finials, above four graduated triangular tiers, with carved apron and turned supports.
- *130cm x 57cm*
- £550   ● Old Cinema

Regency Rosewood Whatnot ▲

- *circa 1825*
English Regency rosewood whatnot of small proportions with three well-figured tiers, raised on finely turned supports, the middle tier having a fitted drawer with small brass circular handles.
- *102cm x 38cm*
- £4,650   ● Freshfords

Mahogany Washstand ▲

- *circa 1860*
Mahogany washstand inset with a circular pink marble top and two shelves, supported by pillared turned legs on a triangular base, raised on shallow bun feet.
- *85cm x 32cm*
- £980   ● The Lacquer Chest

Teak Whatnot ▼

- *1890*
Victorian corner whatnot made from teak with scrolled gallery, above four graduated tiers, supported by turned Solomonaic columns.
- *height 127cm*
- £450   ● Salem Antiques

Mahogany Plant Stand ▲

- *circa 1870s*
Fine Victorian mahogany plant stand, with a slender baluster column on three curved legs with drop turned finial.
- *90cm x 29cm*
- £495   ● Old Cinema

French Etagère ▲

- *1890*
French etagère with pierced brass gallery, single narrow drawer with brass handle and two shelves below, on ebonised shaped legs.
- *height 94cm*
- £675   ● Vale Antiques

Mirrors

Venetian Wall Mirror ▲
- *circa 1860*
A fine oval Venetian wall mirror.
- *122cm x 102cm*
- **£2,600**   • Westland & Co

French Oval Mirror ▼
- *circa 1850s*
Louis Philippe small French oval
mirror with original bevelled plate.
- *56cm x 46cm*
- **£785**   • Looking Glass

Giltwood Mirror ▲
- *circa 1750*
An important giltwood mirror in
the manner of Gaetano Quadro
with bold intertwined C-scrolls
embellished with carved low
relief husk and C-scroll
ornament, the waist flanked by
draped carved floral branches.
- *63cm x 94cm*
- **£123,000** • Anthony Outred

Louis Seize Mirror ▶
- *circa 1780*
Small giltwood Louise Seize
mirror, surmounted by carvings of
broken arrows and a flower,
arranged at the base of a laurel
wreath, in original green
paintwork.
- *height 67cm*
- **£1,500**   • Augustus Brandt

English Convex Mirror ▲
- *circa 1870s*
Victorian circular convex mirror
with a repeating stylised floral
border and beaded rim.
- *68.5cm x 58.5cm*
- **£1,750**   • Looking Glass

Italian Giltwood Mirror ▲

- *circa 1820s*

Italian giltwood mirror with carved and moulded frame and trailing floral designs.

- *43cm x 35.5cm*
- £475 • Looking Glass

Victorian Bow Mirror ▲

- *circa 1890s*

Victorian oval giltwood mirror with a trailing foliate design terminating in a bow.

- 142.4cm x 94cm
- £5,600 • Looking Glass

Georgian Mirror ▼

- *circa 1800*

Georgian mahogany dressing mirror with three drawers and ebony stringing, standing on bracket feet.

- *52cm x 51cm*
- £440 • Salem Antiques

Seahorse Mirror ▼

- *1860*

Circular bevelled plate mirror, within an architectural frame. The pediment gilded with a gilt lyre flanked by seahorses, with gilt ormolu butterfly mounts.

- *107cm x 87.3cm*
- £2,800 • Looking Glass

Giltwood Oval Mirror ◄

- *circa 1890*

Giltwood oval mirror with two candle holders with scrolled floral decoration, raised on splayed legs.

- *height 87cm*
- £895 • Drummonds

Watergilt Mirror ▲

- *circa 1850s*

Oval watergilt mirror with four corner acanthus scrolls.

- *73.6cm x 58.4cm*
- £1,850 • Looking Glass

Victorian Giltwood Mirror ▲

- *circa 1870s*

Victorian gilded oval mirror with foliate carving and flowers, with scrolling and crest above.

- *135cm x 82.5cm*
- £4,230 • Looking Glass

Expert Tips

The condition and thickness of the plate glass provide a useful guide for distinguishing a genuine period mirror from a fake. Look out for pitted rust and dampness. The colour of old plate is greyer than colourless modern glass and gives a softer reflection.

Giltwood Oval Mirrors ▲
- *circa 1840*
One of a pair of finely carved oval English mirrors with carved giltwood vine leaves and grapes with bead and red moulding, and original plate glass.
- *108cm x 90cm*
- £8,000   • O. F. Wilson

French Giltwood Mirror ▲
- *circa 1890s*
Oval French giltwood mirror with carved roses placed intermittently on a moulded wood frame.
- *82cm x 51cm*
- £1,300   • Looking Glass

Regency Overmantle Mirror ▲
- *circa 1820*
Regency giltwood overmantle mirror, with architectural designs, surmounted by a frieze depicting the procession of Jupiter.
- *length 139cm*
- £3,500   • Great Grooms

Regency Toilet Mirror ▼
- *circa 1810*
Regency mahogany toilet mirror with three drawers, cross-banded in satinwood with boxwood and ebony stringing.
- *height 68cm*
- £1,150   • Barry Cotton

French Mirror ▶
- *circa 1860*
A fine French gilt wood and Gesso looking glass in the Louis XV manner. The arched framed headed by a foliate and shell cresting.
- *194cm x 132cm*
- £1,950   • Westland & Co

French Oval Mirror ▼
- *circa 1850*
Small oval French mirror with elaborate carved foliate and acorn border.
- *53.4cm x 46cm*
- £1,400   • Looking Glass

Victorian Mirror ▶
- *circa 1870*
Victorian oval gilt framed mirror with triple candle sconce and beaded rim, surmounted by a scrolled finial.
- *height 75cm*
- £685   • The Swan

Mercury Plate Mirror ▲
- *circa 1800s*
Rectangular Austro/Hungarian water-gilt mirror with a scrolling floral border and original plate glass.
- *96.5cm x 81cm*
- £5,350   • Looking Glass

Scalloped Giltwood Mirrors ▼

- *circa 1860s*
Square giltwood mirror with a floral border, surmounted with shell and scrolled carving.
- *84cm x 83.4cm*
- £1,500 • Looking Glass

Parcel Gilt Mirrors ▼

- *circa 1790s*
Italian giltwood mirror with arched plate and scrolled conforming carved borders and gilded beading.
- *69cm x 28cm*
- £655 • Looking Glass

Gilded Girondoles ▲

- *circa 18th century*
One of a pair of gilded papier-mâché girondoles, with carved floral and C-scroll decoration, surmounted by a palm leaf and an urn at the base.
- *35cm x 17cm*
- £12,500 • O. F. Wilson

Venetian Mirror ◄

- *circa 1800s*
Highly ornate, oval Venetian mirror, etched with trailing sprays of folia and flowers.
- *122cm x 73.6cm*
- £5,900 • Looking Glass

369

Regency Mirror ▲
- *circa 1830*
A small gilt wood Regency mirror of rectangular shape.
- *51cm x 113cm*
- **£1,850**   • **Westland & Co**

William & Mary Mirror ▲
- *circa 1690*
Fine William & Mary cushion frame mirror, decorated with floral and bird motifs including stained ivory.
- *109cm x 92cm*
- **£22,500**   • **Wakelin Linfield**

Giltwood Mirror ▼
- *1870*
French carved giltwood mirror on red bouille, with moulded rim.
- *height 117cm*
- **£650**   • **Augustus Brandt**

Victorian Gilt Mirror ▲
- *circa 1860s*
Victorian circular mirror verre eglomise with swept arch, surmounted by a large carved eagle.
- *89cm x 43cm*
- **£1,750**   • **Looking Glass**

Adam Style Gilt Mirror ◄
- *circa 1880*
English Adam style gilt mirror surmounted by an urn finial above a strung lyre, flanked by foliate swags. The base with swept berried and bunched laurel bracket.
- *156cm x 71cm*
- **£12,800**   • **Anthony Outred**

Italian Carved Mirror ▲
- *circa 1810*
Giltwood mirror with a carved, scrolled floral border, surmounted by a scallop shell and a head of a young girl at the base.
- *99cm x 68.5cm*
- **£3,600**   • **Looking Glass**

Regency Convex Mirror ▲
- *circa 1820s*
Fine Regency giltwood convex mirror with ebonised slip and ball-encrusted frame, surmounted by an eagle suspending a ball on a columned finial.
- *99cm x 56cm*
- **£3,950**   • **Looking Glass**

Regency Mirrors ▲

- *circa 1820s*
One of a pair of Regency pagoda mirrors surmounted by a pineapple, flanked by Corinthian columns.
- *109cm x 37cm*
- **£4,200** • **Looking Glass**

Regency Mirror ▲

- *circa 1820s*
Fine Regency giltwood mirror with central ivory plaque of a bird with flowers, with reeded columns, on a straight base.
- *82.5cm x 51cm*
- **£2,250** • **Looking Glass**

Queen Anne Mirror ▶

- *circa 1710*
Small Queen Anne maroon lacquered mirror with original plate.
- *60cm x 29cm*
- **£1,500** • **O. F. Wilson Ltd**

Venetian Mirror ▼

- *circa 1610*
Venetian Moorish style mirror, flanked by two elongated narrow mirrors, within a carved wood frame with spires, finials, and a raised floral carving.
- *height 117cm*
- **£5,800** • **Augustus Brandt**

William IV Giltwood Mirror ▲

- *circa 1835*

William IV period giltwood and gesso convex mirror with a carved frame depicting acorns and foliage, surmounted by a crest in the form of a seated deer upon a rocky ground, the mirror fitted with sconces in the form of serpents.
- *112cm x 76cm*
- **£7,500** • **Anthony Outred**

Irish Mirror ▶

- *circa 1850s*

Irish oval mirror with a blue and gold strip border on the mirror.
- *71cm x 46cm*
- **£2,500** • **Looking Glass**

Venetian Giltwood Mirror ▲

- *circa 1780*

Venetian giltwood mirror with lion, armorial crest and trophies, with trailing foliate designs to the rim, with original plate glass.
- *84cm x 47cm*
- **£3,800** • **O. F. Wilson**

Italian Giltwood Mirror ▼

- *circa 1780*

Italian giltwood swept mirror with carved scrolling, decorated with trailing ivy and small pink roses.
- *49cm x 44cm*
- **£650** • **Augustus Brandt**

Venetian Mercury Plate Mirror ▼

- *circa 1850s*

Small mid 19th century Venetian blue oval glass mirror, etched with floral sprays, with original mercury plate mirror.
- *56cm x 43cm*
- **£2,250** • **Looking Glass**

Regency Girandole Mirror ▲

- *circa 1820s*

Regency giltwood convex mirror, with ebonised slip surrounded by ropework design, surmounted by a giltwood deer and grapevines, at the base stylised leaf designs flanked by two scrolled candle holders of candle holders.
- *104cm x 56cm*
- **£4,250** • **Looking Glass**

Victorian Mirrors ▲

- *circa 1870s*

One of a pair of rectangular giltwood mirror with arched top surmounted by a stylised acanthus leaf, flanked by giltwood urn finials, and a carved border with foliate swag decoration.
- *94cm x 53cm*
- **£3,250** • **Looking Glass**

Miscellaneous

Library Steps ▼
• *1770*
French library steps made from
walnut consisting of four steps,
with turned and carved
decoration.
• *99cm*
• **£4,850**   • **Augustus Brandt**

Music Stand ▼
• *circa 1825*
Regency rosewood music stand
with lyre shaped design. The
reeded column with turned and
gadrooned decoration raised on a
tripod base with bun feet.
• *height 108cm*
• **£3,600**   • **O.F. Wilson**

Tôle Plant Holder ▲
• *1850*
One of a pair painted English
tôle plant holders decorated with
hand painted chrysanthemums
and peonies. With pierced gilt
foliate rail around the top,
flanked by brass lion handles.
• *height 34.5cm*
• **£1,250** • **Goodison Paraskeva**

Victorian Washstand ▼
• *circa 1870*
Victorian burr-walnut washstand
with a grey and white marble top
above three drawers and a
moulded cupboard, standing on a
straight moulded base.
• *85cm x 124cm*
• **£850**   • **Hill Farm**

Chinese Pot Stand ▼
• *18th century*
One of a pair of simple boldly
executed pot-stands of country
craftsman construction, from
Southern China.
• *81cm x 50cm*
• **£2,950**   • **Gordon Reece**

Towel Rail ◄
• *circa 1870*
Victorian satin birchwood towel
rail with carved and turned
decoration.
• *height 90cm*
• **£220**   • **Nicholas Mitchell**

Knife Cleaner ▲
• *circa 1900*
Circular pine knife sharpener,
with the maker's name 'Kent's',
on cast iron frame support, with
a wood and metal handle.
• *120cm x 75cm*
• **£475**   • **Drummonds**

Birdcage ▲

• *circa 1850s*
Mid 19th century French
birdcage, modelled on the Notre
Dame of Paris.
• *210cm x 110cm*
• £6,950　　• Wakelin Linfield

Cast Iron Trivet ▲

• *circa 1830s*
Early Victorian cast iron trivet
with a scrolled design within a
lattice border.
• *26cm x 42cm*
• £295　　　• Old Cinema

French Plant Holder ▲

• *1880*
Dark green French circular tôle
plant holder, standing on gilt paw
feet with a laurel wreath design
around the lip, and a cartouche of
a hand painted classical scene.
• *height 49cm*
• £495　• Goodison Paraskeva

Georgian Tray ▼

• *circa 1820*
Georgian oval tray, with
fruitwood inlay around the rim,
brass handles and a central shell
design.
• *length 54cm*
• £275　　• Salem Antiques

Mahogany Piano Stool ▼

• *circa 1880s*
An ornate Victorian mahogany
piano stool with a music
compartment under seat with
turned and scrolled decoration.
• *56cm x 51cm*
• £550　　　• Old Cinema

Luggage Rack ▼

• *circa 1870*
Yew-wood luggage rack, standing
on four tapered square legs with
shaped apron.
• *45cm x 72cm*
• £1,250　　　• John Clay

Rosewood Music Stand ▲

• *circa 1820s*
Early 19th century rosewood
music stand with candle holders,
supported by a turned column on
a tripod base with scrolled feet.
• *height 150cm*
• £2,200　　　• Old Cinema

Torchère Stand ▲

• *circa 1890*
A Regency style torchère stand
decorated with three female
busts, with stylized acanthus leaf
designs, surmounted by a black
marble top on a tripod base
standing with gilt paw feet.
• *height 114cm*
• £450　　　• Vale Antiques

Screens

Louis XV Screen ◀

- *circa 1760*

Louis XV period six fold painted canvas screen, showing children playing the game of leapfrog, hoops and flying kites, within a pastoral setting.
- *length 198cm*
- £8,500   • O. F. Wilson

Mahogany Pole Screen ◀

- *circa 1770*

George III mahogany pole screen with well drawn base and earlier needlework banner.
- *height 156cm*
- £4,250   • John Bly

Pole Screen ▲

- *circa 1840*

Regency rosewood pole screen with original silk embroidery.
- *height 147cm*
- £535   • Macnaughton-Smith

Dutch Leather Screen ▶

- *circa 1720*

Dutch leather panel screen, with a Japanese influenced painting showing birds, bamboo, water lilies and pink chrysanthemums.
- *153cm x 200cm*
- £5,800   • Anthony Sharpe

Victorian Screen ◀
- *1870*

A good size painted leather four fold screen in the 18th century style, painted with floral arrangements.
- *160cm x 153cm*
- **£4,200**   • Butchoff

Chinese Fire Screen ▲
- *circa 1860*

Chinese fire screen embroidered with peonies, chrysanthemums, butterflies and birds, in silk with gold threads. Supported by a mahogany stand.
- *78cm x 62cm*
- **£385**   • Younger

Soolmaker Screen ▲
- *1690*

Dutch six fold screen by Soolmaker, with a painted romantic landscape of an impression of Italy.
- *126cm x 244cm*
- **£3,800**   • Butchoff

Expert Tips

Original needlepoint or tapestry must be in good condition and there should not be any wear or tears on the picture.

Victorian Beadwork Screens ▼
- *circa 1840*

One of a pair of excellent Victorian pole screens in walnut carved frames containing fine examples of beadwork of the period.
- *height 140cm*
- **£4,500**   • Wakelin Linfield

Regency Rosewood Screen ▲
- *circa 1820*

Regency rosewood pole screen with floral tapestry panel, on a turned pedestal and tri-partite platform base.
- *height 143cm*
- **£545**   • R. S. Antiques

Settees & Sofas

Beechwood Canapé ▼

- *circa 1890s*

A grey painted and carved
beechwood canapé in the style of
Louis XVI.

- *105cm x 173cm*
- **£1,500**   • Westland & Co

Swedish Sofa ▲

- **1730**

Swedish pine sofa in original
condition, with carved scrolling
to apron and on the moulded back,
standing on reeded turned legs.

- *84cm x 260cm*
- **£14,500**   • Augustus Brandt

Regency Mahogany Sofa ▲

- *circa 1824*

A Regency mahogany double
ended sofa raised on turned legs
with original brass castors and
maker's name and date on top
back rail.

- *95cm x 220cm*
- **£1,950**   • Old Cinema

Mahogany Hall Bench ▼

- *circa 1800*

Mahogany hall bench with
scrolled reeded back with applied
reeded roundels, central oval
frame and mahogany panel,
standing on moulded square
tapering legs.

- *85cm x 105cm*
- **£5,850**   • Wakelin Linfield

Birchwood Sofa ▲

- *circa 1890*

Swedish birchwood Biedermeier-
style sofa showing an architectural
influence, with a central black
plaque of an angel in a chariot
below an arched pediment, the
whole on square legs.

- *97cm x 211cm*
- **£3,900**   • Rupert Cavendish

Victorian Two Seat Settee ▲

- *circa 1880*

Elegant Victorian settee with a
brass rose in the centre of the
moulded top rail, six rail splats
and moulded arms terminating
with a brass rose, standing on
shaped and tapered legs.

- *89cm x 99cm*
- **£825**   • Drummonds

High Back Settee ▼
- *circa 1880*
Victorian mahogany high back settee with scrolled high arched and sides, standing on cabriole legs.
- *107cm x 88cm*
- £3,200 • John Clay

French Sofa ▲
- *circa 18th century*
French sofa with a high back and curved sides, standing on turned doric legs on ball feet, with a straight stretcher.
- *height 118cm*
- £8,800 • Augustus Brandt

Gustavian Style Sofa ▲
- *circa 1899*
Swedish Louis XVI style Gustavian style birchwood sofa, upholstered in calico with noticeable carved and scrolled arm rests and moulded back, the whole resting on carved scrolled feet.
- *135cm x 158cm*
- £3,400 • Rupert Cavendish

High Back Oak Settee ▼
- *circa 1840*
Oak high back four panelled settee with moulded arms and padded seat, standing on cabriole legs with pad feet.
- *82cm x 189cm*
- £1,875 • Drummonds

Biedermeier Sofa ▲
- *circa 1820*
Biedermeier birchwood sofa with serpentine back and front and carved decoration to the apron, on turned and fluted legs.
- *95cm x 199cm*
- £5,600 • Rupert Cavendish

Expert Tips

Always check that the legs are in good condition, especially on a Victorian chaise longue or day bed, where the delicate sabre legs are often broken through heavy wear and tear. Check that the back is secured firmly to the base as often these have been broken and not restored correctly.

Regency Sofa ▲

- *circa 1810*

Regency beech wood faux
rosewood sofa with double scroll
arms and a carved moulded back
with scrolling, inlaid with brass
decoration.
- *93cm x 195cm*
- £5,250   • R. S. Antiques

Walnut Sofa ▶

- *circa 1890s*

Small late Victorian sofa with
arched padded button back and
carved walnut frame with small
scrolled arms, the whole on
slender turned legs.
- *94cm x 133cm*
- £1,200   • John Riordan

High Button Back Sofa ▲

- *circa 1860*

Victorian rosewood button back
sofa with moulded top rail, sides
and arms, curved apron and four
cabriole legs below, and four
splayed legs to the rear.
- *length 156cm*
- £2,400   • Drummonds

Chesterfield Sofa ▼

- *circa 1860*

Victorian Chesterfield sofa
upholstered in Venetian damask,
with padded moulded back and
seat, standing on turned legs.
- *length 197cm*
- £1,950   • The Swan

French Louis XVIII Sofa ▲

- *circa 1780*

French Louis XVIII sofa with
painted and moulded carved
wooden frame, curved back and a
padded seat and small padded arm
rests, above a carved apron of
fluted cariole legs, by D. Julienne.
- *82cm x 191cm*
- £6,200   • Augustus Brandt

Italian Hallbench ▶

- *circa 1790*

Italian pine hall bench with a
straight back swept arms, heavily
carved apron and short cabriole legs.
- *82cm x 193cm*
- £4,700   • Anthony Sharpe

Stools

Gothic Gallery Seats ◀

- *circa 1860*

A pair of American carved polychrome and gilded Gothic gallery seats, labelled Ketcham & Rothschild Inc, Makers Chicago, USA. With scroll arms to each end, the frames polychrome and parcel gilt, carved along the apron with rope twist moulding and trefoil arcading interspersed with stylised leaves in the spandrels. The ends carved with heavy rope twist moulding and acanthus leaves.

- *84cm x 168cm*
- **£33,000** • Anthony Outred

Miniature Stool ▼

- *circa 1820s*

Early 19th century fruit wood miniature stool with turned stretcher and legs.

- *19cm x 18cm*
- **£395** • Wakelin Linfield

Empire Style Window Seats ▲

- *circa 1880*

Pair of mahogany Empire style window seats with scrolled arms and gilded dolphin supports, raised on swept feet.

- *height 70cm*
- **£2,800** • Mora Upham

Wicker Seated Stool ▲

- *circa 1880*

Louis XVI style stool with cane seat with turned and fluted legs, with X frame stretcher.

- *height 49cm*
- **£485** • The Swan

French Giltwood Stool ▶

- *circa 1840*

French giltwood stool, the legs carved with a rope twist design terminating on tassel feet.

- *height 42cm*
- **£4,000** • Augustus Brand

Expert Tips

When examining a stool check for hessian under the seat as it was never used before 1840 and is often used to conceal an alteration.

Louis XVI Footstool ▼
- *circa 1780*
Louis XVI giltwood footstool
with carved acanthus moulding
and foliate legs.
- *height 14cm*
- £2,900   • O. F. Wilson

Walnut Footstool ▼
- *circa 1880*
Small walnut footstool with
circular re-upholstered padded top
,standing on small cabriole legs.
- *width 36cm*
- £290   • Salem Antiques

Rustic Stool ▼
- *circa 1840*
Rustic oak child's stool standing
on four turned legs.
- *20cm x 31cm*
- £85   • The Lacquer Chest

Tapestry Stool ▶
- *1880*
Fine walnut tapestry Queen
Anne style stool raised on
cabriole legs carved with
acanthus leaf designs, with claw
and ball feet.
- *48cm x 51cm*
- £3,500   • Butchof

Birchwood Stools ▲
- *1820–1830*
One of a pair of Swedish
Biedermeier birchwood stools
raised on splayed legs.
- *39cm x 35cm*
- £3,400   • Rupert Cavendish

Mahogany Stool ◀
- *circa 1880*
Mahogany oblong country oak
stool standing on square straight
legs, with scrolls at each corner.
- *56cm x 34cm*
- £495   • Macnaughton-Smith

Mahogany Stool ▶

- *circa 1890*
Miniature mahogany stool
fashioned as a small table.
- *22cm x 33cm*
- **£89**   ● The Swan

Piano Stool ▲

- *circa 1830s*
William IV piano stool on
adjustable reeded and carved
column, on a platform base with
scroll end feet and original
tapestry seat.
- *height 54cm*
- **£495**   ● The Swan

George I Walnut Stool ◀

- *circa 1720*
George I walnut stool with
cabriole legs, carved at each knee
with a carved shell.
- *height 54cm*
- **£22,500**   ● John Bly

Piano Stool ▲

- *circa 1880*
Walnut revolving piano tool with
circular padded seat on cabriole
legs with claw feet.
- *height 49cm*
- **£500**   ● Nicholas Mitchell

Ebonised Stool ◀

- *circa 1860*
Ebonised stool with a rush seat,
with faux bamboo designs and
gilding with curved rails
connected by gilded balls.
- *42cm x 40cm*
- **£220**   ● The Lacquer Chest

Gustavian Bench ▲

- *circa 1800*
Louis XVI Swedish Gustavian
pine bench seat painted white
with carved arms, raised on
turned feet.
- *37cm x 109cm*
- **£2,900**   ● Rupert Cavendish

Chinese Stools ◄

- *18th century*
A pair of Chinese hardwood
stools with caned seat, hump back
stretcher and horse hoof feet.
- *45cm x 35cm*
- £1,600   • Gordon Reece

French Painted Stool ▼

- *circa 1870*
French window seat with carved
frame and two arms traditionally
re-upholstered in cream striped
fleur de lys fabric.
- *height 64cm*
- £795   • R. S. Antiques

Miniature Oak Stool ▲

- *circa 1810*
Miniature rustic oak stool for a
child standing on four legs.
- *height 95cm*
- £95   • The Lacquer Chest

Pair of Tabourets ▼

- *circa 1790*
One of a pair of Tabourets with
painted decoration, fluted tapered
legs and a carved frieze.
- *14.5cm x 30.5cm x 25cm* •
£2,600   • O. F. Wilson

Victorian Piano Stool ▲

- *circa 1870*
Victorian mahogany adjustable
piano stool with a circular seat
and a tripod carved base.
- *height 61cm*
- £395   • A.I.G.

Piano Stool ▲

- *1870*
Victorian rosewood revolving
piano stool on a carved column
and scrolled feet.
- *height 59cm*
- £480   • Salem Antiques

Tables

Huan Huali Sofa Table ▲
- *circa 1810*
Rare Anglo-Chinese Huan Huali sofa table with a rectangular solid huan-huali wood top flanked by drop leaves with rounded corners, above a frieze with two short drawers flanking one long drawer, each decorated with ebony stringing and fitted with macassar ebony knobs, having dummy drawers to the reverse. Raised on trestle-end supports with ebony stringing terminating in brass sabots and castors.
- *74cm x 148cm*
- **£16,500**   • **Anthony Outred**

Victorian Writing Table ▲
- *circa 1870*
Victorian writing table/workbox, standing on cabriole legs and stretcher base.
- *84cm x 70cm*
- **£5.500**   • **The Swan**

Dutch Lowboy ▼
- *1740*
Dutch walnut lowboy with a serpentine front with foliate inlaid marquetry, moulded shaped apron standing on slender cabriole legs, with ball and claw feet.
- *71cm x 72cm*
- **£7,500**   • **Butchoff**

Regency Tables ▼
- *1820*
Regency set of four tables, attributed to Gillow, with ebonised stringing. The well figured mahogany top with side flaps above two short drawers with turned knob handles. The whole raised on carved supports with reeded, splayed legs.
- *76cm x 56cm*
- **£14,000**   • **Butchoff**

Regency Library Table ◀
- *circa 1815*
Regency library table in veneered rosewood with shaped top over a frieze supported on shaped end standards quarter beaded plinth, supported on rosettes and acanthus carved scrolled feet.
- *74cm x 140cm x 74cm*
- **£10,800**   • **Wakelin Linfield**

French Games Table ▲
- *circa 1890s*
French Provincial walnut games table with four counter corners and two drawers standing on cabriole legs with small hoof foot.
- *height 72.5cm*
- **£3,400**   • **Augustus Brandt**

Sheraton Card Table ▲
- *circa 1790*
Sheraton mahogany demi-lune card table with boxwood stringing, raised on square tapered legs.
- *72cm x 92cm*
- **£2,950**   • **Barry Cotton**

Games Table ▲
- *1880*
Victorian rosewood games table with inlaid chess
- *height 78cm*
- **£695**   • **A.I.G**

Victorian Mahogany Table ▼

- *circa 1850*
Victorian mahogany circular table on a turned baluster stand, raised on a tripod base, with splayed legs on circular ball feet.
- *height 84cm*
- £850   • Hill Farm

French Side Table ▼

- *circa 1860*
French provincial side table with pine top, two long drawers and a serpentine apron, the whole standing on straight square legs.
- *73cm x 123cm*
- £1,250   • Anthony Sharpe

Kingwood Table ▼

- *1880*
French Kingwood two tier oval marquetry table, cross-banded with gilt ormolu mounts above a solid inlaid stretcher.
- *height 110cm*
- £5,800   • Butchoff

Cricket Table ▲

- *circa 1870*
Fine rustic elm cricket table, with good original patina, raised on three turned legs.
- *height 78cm*
- £3,750   • Gerald Brodie

Mahogany Sofa Table ▲

- *circa 1880s*
Empire-style mahogany Swedish sofa-table with side flaps on a cylindrical support, raised on a quatral base with lion paw feet.
- *76cm x 92cm*
- £2,900   • Rupert Cavendish

Folding Card Table ▲

- *circa 1880*
Mahogany folding card table, with hinged flap and legs.
- *height 70cm*
- £950   • John Clay

Mahogany Sutherland table ▼

- *circa 1898*
A late Victorian mahogany Sutherland table with serpentine top and swing legs.
- *68cm x 68cm*
- £440   • Old Cinema

Victorian Tea-Poy ▼

- *circa 1870*
Victorian burr-walnut hexagonal shaped tea-Poy with a turned pedestal and carved tripod base.
- *height 74cm*
- £1,295   • A.I.G.

Expert Tips

Burr walnut is a tightly knotted grain from the base of the tree, and was used to decorative effect in veneers. Parquetry refers to a geometrical pattern of small pieces of veneer.

Russian Centre Table ▲

● *circa 1790*

A fine Russian oval centre table, the cobalt blue glass top surmounted by a three quarter brass gallery above a brass reeded edge. The frieze fitted with a drawer and decorated with fluted panels alternating with brass-edged square panels and lozenges on fluted turned tapering legs with beaded collars and sabots.

● *81cm x 93cm*
● **£28,500**   ● **Anthony Outred**

Victorian Occasional Table ▲

● *circa 1860s*
A Victorian rosewood and marquetry inlaid occasional table.
● *64cm x 50cm*
● **£440**   ● **Old Cinema**

William IV Table ▼

● *circa 1830s*
William IV mahogany table with brass drop handles and single drawer, raised on turned, tapering, candy twist legs.
● *76cm x 56cm*
● **£750**   ● **Macnaughton-Smith**

Louis XVI NightTable ▼

● *circa 1790*
Louis XVI night table with a pierced brass rail and three small drawers in purple heart and satinwood banding.
● *height 86cm*
● **£4,250**   ● **O. F. Wilson**

Light Oak Side Table ◄

● *circa 1870*
Victorian light oak side table with moulded back and scrolled designs, with side drawers, standing on turned tapering legs.
● *height 110cm*
● **£950**   ● **Hill Farm**

Tilt Top Table ▲

● *circa 1890*
Mahogany tilt top table with turned support raised on a tripod base with splayed legs.
● *height 83cm*
● **£295**   ● **Great Grooms**

Regency Pembroke Table ▲

● *circa 1810*
Fine quality Regency period mahogany and ebony inlaid Pembroke table. Standing on a twin double C- scrolled supports joining out swept legs, with brass caps and castors.
● *73cm x 104cm x 51cm*
● **£10,950**   ● **Wakelin Linfield**

Mahogany Writing Table ▲

● *circa 1870s*
19th century mahogany writing table with tooled leather writing surface and reeded, turned and tapered legs.
● *75cm x 110cm*
● **£1,675**   ● **Shirley Knight**

Victorian Washstand ▼
- *circa 1840*

Victorian mahogany washstand with two drawers with turned handles and side table, in excellent original condition.
- *width 98cm*
- £595　　　• The Swan

Side Table ▼
- *circa 1880*

Mahogany table with moulded serpentine top supported by two turned columns, joined by a turned stretcher above heavily carved legs with leaf designs.
- *height 89cm*
- £695　• Macnaughton-Smith

Mahogany Serving Table ▶
- *circa 1795*

English serving table,of breakfront D-shaped form, surmounted by the original brass gallery, the frieze fitted with a long oak lined drawer, with a finely flamed mahogany front. The rounded corner panels and side panels of the frieze finished in a similar manner each panel flanked by finely carved urns heading the six elegant fluted tapering legs.
- *82cm x 290cm*
- £28,000　• Anthony Outred

Sewing Table ▲
- *1870*

Victorian rosewood sewing table with single drawer standing on a pedestal base with turned feet.
- *88cm x 84cm*
- £1,995　　• Flower Antique

Mahogany Jardinière ▲
- *1830*

Rare William IV mahogany occasional table stamped Freemans on a carved and turned column raised on a tripod base, resting on bun feet.
- *76cm x 44cm*
- £4,500　　　• Butchoff

Victorian Tilt Top Table ▼
- *circa 1880*

Victorian mahogany tilt top table with turned baluster pedestal base, raised on splayed legs.
- *height 74cm*
- £580　　• Nicholas Mitchell

Mahogany Side Table ▼
- *circa 1830*

Mahogany side table with square top single long drawer with brass handle, standing on four straight square legs.
- *height 82cm*
- £475　　　　• John Clay

Oak Library Table ▶
• *circa 1835*
Medieval revival library table in the manner of Richard Bridgens. The top with rounded corners and decorated with a border of an interlocking band design defined on each side by a string inlay of ebony and with stylized motifs at each corner. The whole on stepped moulded feet.
• *74cm x 150cm*
• £28,000 • Anthony Outred

Games/Sewing Table ▲
• *circa 1810*
Miniature Pembroke sewing/games table with three tiered drawers with ring handles from mask decoration, raised on ring turned legs, terminating on brass castors.
• *73cm x 35cm*
• £5,250 • Wakelin Linfield

Birchwood Oval Table ▼
• *circa 1890s*
Swedish birchwood Biedermeier-style oval table of small proportions, cross-banded, and inlaid with central drawer, raised on square tapered legs
• *70cm x 69cm*
• £2,450 • Rupert Cavendish

Surprise Table ▼
• *circa 1920*
Inlaid satin wood surprise table on tapered legs and castors, with some original Baccarat glass and replacements.
• *72cm x 65cm extended*
• £5,950 • J. & T. Stone

Small Bouillotte Table ▲
• *circa 1890*
Small inlaid bouillotte table with a pierced brass gallery with a small circular drawer with brass knob, raised on square tapered legs with lower shelf.
• *height 76.5cm*
• £3,500 • O. F. Wilson

Regency Table ▲
• 1820
Regency rosewood worktable with oval folding top one single drawer small turned handles, standing on four moulded tripods and arched legs with brass castors.
• *height 48cm*
• £1,695 • A.I.G.

Rosewood Card Table ▲
• *circa 1820s*
Early 19th century well figured rosewood sabre leg card table, on a turned support, raised on four carved legs with brass lion paw casters.
• *75cm x 90cm*
• £1,695 • Old Cinema

Mahogany Console Table ▼

- *circa 1810*

A console table with a rectangular top with an ebonised moulded edge over a frieze inlaid with repeated brass sunburst motifs on an ebonised background, raised on a pair of columns joined to the panelled back with an arcaded profile. The whole raised on a concave plinth base leading to gilt paw feet, the front two facing forward, the back two to the side.

- 89cm x 95cm
- £9,800 • Anthony Outred

George III Table ▼

- *circa 1800*

George III small mahogany birdcage table, with well shaped baluster tri-pod support on splayed legs.

- *height 79cm*
- £2,500 • Great Grooms

Victorian Table ▶

- *circa 1870*

Victorian walnut and marquetry table on a pedestal base with carved gadrooned decoration and carved splat legs, by Taylor & Son, Dover St, London.

- *height 137cm*
- £9,800 • Butchoff

Peachwood Centre Table ▲

- *circa 1820*

A rare peachwood centre table with turned legs and bamboo skirting.

- *81cm x 175cm*
- £8,200 • Gordon Reece

Oval Table ▲

- *circa 1800s*

Small oval table with a George III tray with a scalloped edge on four splayed legs joined by a X frame stretcher.

- *height 56cm*
- £695 • Old Cinema

Rosewood Table ▲

- *circa 1835*

William IV rosewood sewing/games table with trestle supports and bun feet.

- 73cm x 61cm
- £2,600 • Salem Antiques

Victorian Dressing Table ▲

- *circa 1885*

Victorian mahogany dressing table with an oval mirror with heavily carved decoration, above fitted drawers and turned front legs.

- *height 1.3m*
- £4,500 • Sleeping Beauty

Victorian Games Table ▲

- *circa 1850*

Victorian mahogany inlaid walnut games table with inlaid chessboard and heavily turned column, standing on a tripod base with carved legs.

- *height 82cm*
- £875 • Hill Farm

Expert Tips

During the middle of the 18th century the tea gardens around London were regarded as vulgar, and it therefore became fashionable to invite friends to drink tea at home. Cabinet makers turned their attention to designing suitable ornamental tables for the occasion.

Italian Occasional Table ◀
- *circa 1880*
Superb Italian giltwood
occasional table with superb
inlaid top, raised on a heavily
carved support with C scroll legs
with stylized leaf carving with
drop finial.
- *height 105cm*
- £39,500   • Hatchwell

Console Table ▼
- *circa 1890*
Satinwood painted and parcel gilt
console table, raised on turned
and carved legs joined by a
carved stretcher with pineapple
finial.
- *88cm x 122cm*
- £7,800   • Butchoff

Regency Side Table ▲
- *circa 1850*
Regency side table with straight
moulded top with beading, on
straight supports joined by a
turned stretcher.
- *height 79cm*
- £850   • Hill Farm

Parquetry Top Table ▼
- *circa 1840*
Occasional table with an inlaid
parquetry octagonal top table
with central pedestal and
standing on a tripod base on ball
feet.
- *height 78cm*
- £995   • A.I.G.

Mahogany Worktable ▲
- *circa 1800*
Fine English mahogany worktable
with eboy inlay on carved
supports raised on four shaped
legs joined by a solid inlaid
stretcher.
- *72 cm x 53cm x 39cm*
- £4,200   • O. F. Wilson

Victorian Marquetry Table ▲
- *1870*
Victorian mahogany and
marquetry two tier table with
inlaid top, and a removable tray
with pierced top rail and carrying
handles.
- *height 88cm*
- £995   • Old Cinema

Sofa Table ▲
- *1810*
Mahogany Regency end support
sofa table in the manner of
Gillow.
- *73cm x 98cm*
- £11,000   • Butchoff

Oak Table ▼

- *circa 1840*
Oak country corner table with triangular top standing on three straight square legs, and straight stretcher.
- *85cm x 54cm*
- £1,100 • The Lacquer Chest

Rosewood Occasional Table ▶

- *1835*
A William IV Rosewood occasional table signed James Piggott, Richmond, raised on a turned support, with a tripod base resting on turned feet.
- *76cm x 65cm*
- £4,500 • Butchoff

Library Tables ▲

- *circa 1880*
A pair of mahogany library tables with two side drawers raised on turned reeded legs with brass castors.
- *72cm x 122cm*
- £750 • Westland & Co

Dutch Commodes ◀

- *circa 1820*
One of a pair of Dutch commodes with a pink marble top with fine ormolu mounts. The whole with marquetry inlay, raised on square tapered legs.
- *80cm x 65.5cm*
- £18,500 • Wakelin Linfield

Mahogany Side Table ▲

- *circa 1870*
French mahogany table with pierced brass rail, pink marble top and single long drawer. With brass and gilt banding.
- *84cm x 70.5cm x 35cm*
- £4,850 • O. F. Wilson

Biedermeier Tables ▲

- *1830-1840*
Pair of Swedish birchwood Biedermeier tables raised on a baluster turned column with a solid, shaped base, with four scrolled feet.
- *70cm x 58cm*
- £4,900 • Rupert Cavendish

Consol Table ◄

- *circa 1825*

One of a pair George IV mirror backed console table in rosewood. The marble tops above a rococo carved frieze supported by carve and giltwood acanthus decorated S scroll uprights.

- 96cm x 75cm x 36cm
- £18,750   • Wakelin Linfield

Cricket Table ▼

- *1790*

Oak cricket table with circular top standing on three splayed legs, joined by a square, panelled sretcher.

- 59cm x 66cm
- £1,275   • Rushligh

Burr Walnut Table ▲

- *circa 1880*

Victorian burr-walnut table with a circular top inlaid with boxwood foliate design and carved leaves around the rim, with a turned pedestal standing on a tripod base.

- height 69cm
- £875   • A.I.G

Games Table ▲

- *circa 1860*

Victorian mahogany games table with inlaid chess board on a circular top, pedestal column three splat legs.

- height 75cm
- £1,200   • The Lacquer Chest

Empire Writing Table ▶

- *1810-1820*

Swedish mahogany Empire writing/ console table. The top with fitted drawers and gallery, above a central drawer, raised on four turned columns, with a solid stretcher base.

- 72cm x 74cm
- £3,700   • Rupert Cavendish

Console Table ▲

- *circa 1870*

Empire style console figured maple wood table with a pink marble top, central winged brass motif, on a single drawer flanked by ebonised pillars with oriental busts.

- 91cm x 92cm
- £2,400   • Old Cinema

Drum Table ▲
- *1810*

Regency mahogany drum table with fitted short drawers on a turned pedestal base with splayed legs.
- *75cm x 87cm*
- **£13,500** • **Butchoff**

Regency Table ▲
- *circa 1820*

Regency mahogany fold over tea table, with U support and platform with brass beading, and flared legs standing on brass claw feet and castors.
- *height 83cm*
- **£3,350** • **Vale Antiques**

Demi-Lune Table ▼
- *circa 1810*

Demi-lune mahogany table
- *height 87cm*
- **£950** • **Old Cinema**

Sutherland Table ▼
- *1870*

Satin birchwood Sutherland table with two folding flaps and a stretcher base, on porcelain castors.
- *height 71cm*
- **£1,100** • **Old Cinema**

Louis XV Rafraichissoir ▲
- *circa 1760*

Louis XV rafraichissoir fitted with rouge royale marble top, brass handles and savots with copper fitting for ice/bottles.
- *65.5cm x 44.5cm x 28.5cm*
- **£4,000** • **O. F. Wilson**

Mahogany Card Table ▼
- *circa 1870*

Unusual Victorian mahogany card table, on a turned pedestal column, scroll feet and swivel top (re-baized).
- *84cm x 83cm*
- **£850** • **The Swan**

George I Lowboy ◄
- *circa 1720*

Very pretty and exceptionally small George I lowboy, the top with quartered veneers in well figured walnut, herringbone stringing and cross banding.With shaped frieze, one shallow and two deep drawers.
- *69cm x 68cm*
- **£17,500** • **Wakelin Linfield**

Mahogany Night Table ▲
● *1800*
Dutch mahogany night table with tambour front, and small brass round handles and brass handles each side.
● *66cm x 47cm*
● £995   ● A.I.G.

Sutherland Table ▲
● *circa 1835*
Walnut Sutherland table with satinwood and boxwood inlay.
● *height 72cm*
● £450   ● The Swan

Rosewood Occasional Table ▼
● *circa 1860s*
A good quality Victorian rosewood occasional table with a barley twist column.
● *73cm x 45cm*
● £550   ● Old Cinema

Mahogany Tripod Table ▼
● *circa 1760*
Mahogany tilt-top, birdcage table with turned support raised on splayed legs.
● *height 69.5cm*
● £4,800   ● O. F. Wilson

Burr-Walnut Card Table ▲
● *circa 1870*
Burr-walnut Victorian card table with marquetry inlay, serpentine basket base and scrolled legs with upturned finial.
● *height 87cm*
● £3,750   ● The Swan

Oak Side Bookstand ▲
● *circa 1890s*
Late Victorian oak side table/bookstand with carved scrolled supports
● *63cm x 57cm*
● £695   ● Old Cinema

Irish Side Table ◄
● *circa 1890*
Irish mahogany side table with a gadrooned edge above a plain frieze, the decorative, shaped apron centred by a lion-head mask within a rope twist border, flanked by stylised birds with feathered wings and foliate decoration. Raised on cabriole legs with handsome ball and claw feet decorated at the knees with low relief carved decoration of stylised birds.
● *81cm x 157.5cm*
● £12,500   ● Anthony Outred

Tripod Table ▶

- *circa 1860*
Circular table with figured
mahogany top, pedestal column
standing on three splayed legs.
- *65cm x 52.5cm*
- **£530** • **The Lacquer Chest**

Regency Table ▲

- *circa 1820*
Adjustable Regency mahogany
table, with a central tan hide top,
standing on a tall central pedestal
and a tripod base.
- *height 104cm*
- **£1,395** • **A.I.G**

Oak Cricket Table ▲

- *circa 1860*
Oak cricket table with circular
top, single shelf, standing on
three turned pillared legs.
- *70cm x 38cm*
- **£780** • **The Lacquer Chest**

Walnut Table ▼

- *1880*
Small octagonal shaped Victorian
walnut table, on a heavily
moulded cross-banded stretcher.
- *height 55cm*
- **£595** • **Old Cinema**

Small Tripod Table ▼

- *circa 1780*
Small rustic oak table with inlaid
flower in the centre standing on a
tripod base.
- *57cm x 40cm*
- **£395** • **The Swan**

Table with Ormolu Mounts ▼

- *1870*
Two tier mahogany table with
inlaid shaped top, with ormolu
pierced mounts and curved legs.
- *height 88cm*
- **£1,395** • **Old Cinema**

Portuguese Rosewood Table ▼

- *circa 1700*
A solid rosewood table, the top
with a decorative bead moulded
edge, the frieze with chevron
pattern decoration, raised on
spiral-twist legs with disks and
bulbous turnings, with similar
stretchers, joined at the corners
with decorative pegs.
- *79cm x 112cm*
- **£6.800** • **Anthony Outred**

Expert Tips

*The forerunners of the tripod
table were the small round
topped tables designed to
support a lantern or candlestick,
which were popular during the
second half of the 17th century.
These tables were an English
phenomenon. They were also
popular in America, but not on
the Continent.*

Regency Games Table

- *circa 1815*

Games table in faded rosewood, raised on turned trestle end supports, the top with hinged flaps to either side, the reversible slide inlaid with a chessboard, concealing a well fitted for backgammon. The frieze of the table is inset with a vertically reeded panel, and the whole is raised on swept sabre feet, with brass paterae and original brass castors.

- *79cm x 56cm*
- £12,500   • Anthony Outred

Tray Top Work Table

- *circa 1850s*

Victorian mahogany and marquetry inlaid tray top work table.

- *69cm x 54cm*
- £995   • Old Cinema

Regency Mahogany Table ▼

- *circa 1815*

Regency mahogany Pembroke rosewood cross-banded table with two drawers, four sabre legs, brass claw feet and original brass castors.

- *height 87cm*
- £3,950   • Old Cinema

Sheraton Style Demi-Lune Table ▲

- *circa 1815*

Sheraton style satinwood demi-lune table, cross-banded with king wood, standing on square tapered legs.

- *height 85cm*
- £3,950   • Old Cinema

Tilt Top Table ▲

- *circa 1890*

Mahogany circular tilt top occasional table on a turned baluster support with three splayed legs.

- *85cm x 17cm*
- £485   • Vale Antiques

Victorian Inlaid Card Table ▲

- *circa 1860*

Victorian figured walnut card table with moulded inlaid top raised on cabriole legs.

- *75cm x 83cm*
- £1,495   • W. John Griffiths

Wardrobes

Architectural Breakfront Wardrobes ▶

- *circa 1850*

A pair of ebonised wardrobes designed by Anthony Salvin for Peckforton Castle. Each with ogee moulded cornice above a central cupboard, revealing five slides, with ebonised facia, over two short and two long drawers. Flanked by lined hanging compartments each with brass rail fixtures. Each door with decorative panelling, and arts and crafts inspired brass strap hinges, engraved with an asymmetric design, the escutcheons follow the same design.

- *221cm x 258cm*
- **£28,000** • Anthony Outredd

Georgian Display Cupboard ▲

- *circa 1780*

Georgian cupboard with two doors enclosing an arched and pillared interior, and two cupboards below.

- *height 240cm*
- **£1,850** • Drummonds

Victorian Wardrobe ▶

- *circa 1880*

Victorian single door wardrobe with central mirror, moulded pediment and one long deep drawer with turned handles, the whole standing on a moulded square base.

- *height 207cm*
- **£995** • Old Cinema

Lacquer Corner Cupboard ◀

- *circa 1770*

Dutch black lacquered corner cupboard, with a raised gilt Chinoiserie design of figures, pagodas and birds, with brass butterfly hinges.

- *height 110cm*
- **£3,950** • O. F. Wilson

Dutch Corner Cupboard ◀

- *circa 1850*

Dutch Chinoserie painted corner cupboard with stylised butterflies, birds, and figures, with three green painted interior shelves, and original brass butterfly hinges, and a moulded base.

- *92cm x 59.5cm x 40cm*
- **£5,500** • O. F. Wilson

Expert Tips

Features to look for in wardrobes and tallboys include: original handles, feather banding to drawers, canted corners to top section and cross banding decoration.

397

Louis XVI Cupboard ▲

- *1800–1810*
Swedish Louis XVI Gustavian
cupboard in two sections, with
architecturally styled pediment
and doors to top chest, and the
lower chest with two panelled
door, the whole standing on small
bracket feet.
- *188cm x 113cm*
- **£2,700** • **Rupert Cavendish**

Mahogany Linen Press ▲

- *circa 1780*
Mahogany linen press with
moulded dentil course and two
doors with inlaid oval panels
concealing original trays. The
lower section with two short and
two long drawers.
- *212cm x 122cm x 58cm*
- **£10,950** • **Wakelin Linfield**

Indian Linen Press ▼

- *circa 1880*
Indian linen press, with panelled
doors carved with central pleated
medallions and corner spandrels,
above two long drawers raised on
bracket feet.
- *height 175cm*
- **£2,500** • **Hatchwell**

French Provincial Cupboard ▼

- *circa 1780*
French painted Provincial
cupboard in three parts, with
heavily panelled doors on the top
cupboard fitted with two
serpentine shelves, and elongated
hinges.
- *223cm x 172cm*
- **£4,300** • **Anthony Sharpe**

Black Lacquer Cupboard ▶

- *1880*
Small Chinese black lacquer
cabinet, with fitted interior of
one long and seven other
drawers. With brass fittings at
each corner with curved edges.
Flanked by brass carrying handles.
- *37cm x 40cm x 28.5cm*
- **£2,250** • **O. F. Wilson**

Mahogany Wardrobe ▲

- *circa 1880*
Fine Victorian figured mahogany
moulded two-door wardrobe, with
scrolled moulding below a
moulded pediment. Standing on a
straight base.
- *height 206cm*
- **£1,850** • **Hill Farm**

George III Commode ▲

- *circa 1790*
George III mahogany tambour
door commode with square
tapering legs.
- *79cm x 53cm x 49cm*
- **£3,450** • **Serendipity**

William IV Linen Press ▲

- *circa 1835*

William IV mahogany linen press retaining its old trays, with two finely figured panelled doors decorated with beading. The lower section with figured drawer fronts and original handles. The whole raised on turned and gadrooned feet.

- *214cm x 120cm x 50cm*
- **£8,750** • **Wakelin Linfield**

Pedestal Cupboard ▲

- *circa 1810*

Swedish Louis XVI Gustavian cream painted pine pedestal cupboard with two doors and square moulded and painted green base.

- *147cm x 107cm*
- **£2,900** • **Rupert Cavendish**

Flame Mahogany Wardrobe ▶

- *circa 1890*

Flame mahogany Victorian wardrobe with central pediment above bow fronted doors, with four drawers flanked by long cupboards with oval mirrors.

- *width 240cm*
- **£2,650** • **Drummonds**

Linen Press ▲

- *circa 1800*

Elegant mahogany linen press in original condition, with oval panels of matching veneers and satinwood cross banded doors.

- *height 225cm*
- **£8,950** • **Barry Cotton**

Corner Cupboard ▼

- *circa 1790*

George III bow fronted mahogany corner cupboard fitted with four shelves and two small drawers, with shell inlay to frieze and Greek key moulded cornice.

- *height 105cm*
- **£2,450** • **Serendipity**

Mahogany Linen Press ◀

- *circa 1860*

Mahogany linen press, having two arched panelled door enclosing three sliding drawers and two long and two short drawers below.

- *width 125cm*
- **£2,450** • **The Swan**

Expert Tips

Georgian bookcases were usually made in pine when they were going to be gessoed; gesso is a plaster-like substance applied to carved furniture before gilding. The bookcase would then be painted to complement the decor in the room or library.

Glass

Glass has been undervalued until recently but is now highly treasured for its decorative beauty and fragility.

Glass has myriad uses and throughout history has been shaped, coloured and moulded for a variety of purposes, from the stained glass windows in a cathedral to the ordinary drinking vessel used in the home. The Ancient Egyptians produced coloured glass including blue, green, violet, black and red, to imitate semi-precious stones. In England on the other hand coloured glass was rare until the early nineteenth century with the introduction of 'Bristol' glass products ranging from luxury items such as

scent bottles to tablewares which included jugs, fingerbowls and decanters. The most popular colour was blue, closely followed by deep green and amethyst.

Nailsea is a generic term given to a range of nineteenth- century glass objects, for example bottles and jugs, in shades of green and often incorporating flecks of white glass. Nailsea derived from a factory near Bristol in England, and was also produced in America during the nineteenth century.

Tall Bohemian Blue Vase ▼
- *circa 1880*

Tall slender cobalt blue vase engraved with an interlaced stylized leaf pattern, raised on a domed foot.
- *height 42cm*
- £290　　　　　● Mousa

Green Wine Glass ▲
- *1760*

Green wine glass with elegant air twist stem.
- *height 18cm*
- £3,000　　　● Somervale

Glass Match Striker ▼
- *circa 1890*

Circular glass match container with silver mounts. The body incised with a grooved pattern which functions as a striking surface.
- *height 8cm*
- £160　　　● H. Gregory

Amethyst Spirit Bottles ▲
● *circa 1839*
A fine pair of amethyst coloured
spirit bottles, with silver mounts
and stoppers with elaborate
chasing of bunches of grapes.
● *height 36cm*
● **£980**   ● **Somervale**

Tall Bohemian Vase ▲
● *circa 1890*
Tall elegant Bohemian dark red
vase with a conical neck and
splayed lip, engraved with trailing
bunches of vine and fruit,
supported on a splayed foot.
● *height 51cm*
● **£750**   ● **Mousa**

Green Drinking Glass ▼
● *1840*
Dark green drinking glass, with a
plain ring stem on a splayed foot.
● *height 12cm*
● **£65**   ● **Somervale**

Victorian Silver Tantalus ▼
● *circa 1860*
Victorian silver plated tantalus
with three decanters.
● *height 32cm*
● **£650**   ● **Barry Cotton**

Blue Spirit Bottle ▲
● *1890*
Blue tapering spirit bottle with
flute cutting and a cut spire
stopper.
● *height 34cm*
● **£480**   ● **Somervale**

Wine Glasses ▼

● *1860*
Two green Bristol glass wine glasses.
● *height 12cm*
● **£45** ● **Somervale**

Bristol Spirit Decanter ▼

● *circa 1825*
Bristol blue spirit decanter inscribed with 'Brandy' in gilt lettering, with a lozenge shape stopper.
● *height 28cm*
● **£400** ● **Somervale**

Green Wine Glasses ▲

● *1825*
Set of bowl shaped green wine glasses with raspberry encrustation applied to the stems, raised on circular bases.
● *height 17cm*
● **£600 set of three** ● **Somervale**

Toasting Glass ▲

● *circa 1700*
Toast master's glass with bell shaped bowl, large circular knop stem with enclosed tear drop.
● *height 12cm*
● **£1,800** ● **Somervale**

Cream Skimmer Bowl ▲

● *circa 1800*
Large shallow glass cream skimmer bowl with central boss and moulded rim.
● *diameter 51cm*
● **£500** ● **Somervale**

Tall Bohemian Vase ▼

● *circa 1880*
Tall fluted vase with borders of red overlay heavily engraved with gilt scrolled decoration, raised on a domed foot with a shaped edge.
● *height 42cm*
● **£480** ● **Mousa**

Bohemian Decanter with Bowl ▼

● *circa 1880*
Bohemian bottle shaped decanter and dish with jewelled decoration of pink and blue stylised flowers with red beading and gilding.
● *height 28cm*
● **£600** ● **Mousa**

French Vase ◀

- *circa 1880*

French white porcelain vase of baluster form, with a gilt cartouche of pale pink roses, poppies and cornflowers, surrounded by trailing pink wild roses, possibly by Baccarat.
- *height 44cm*
- £1,050 • Mousa

Baluster Wine Glass ▼

- *circa 1720*

Wine glass with bell shape bowl on an angular and true inverted baluster stem, with air twists and folded conical foot.
- *height 16cm*
- £1,100 • Somervale

Glass Rolling Pin ▼

- *1860*

Amethyst glass rolling pin with gilt inscription 'Forget me not', a gift from a soldier going to war.
- *length 41cm*
- £160 • Somervale

Blue Spirit Decanters ▲

- *1800*

Pair of blue octagonal spirit decanters, inscribed 'Brandy' and 'Rum' within gilt labels, with faceted stoppers and fluted rims.
- *height 20cm*
- £800 • Somervale

Bristol Blue Spirit Decanters ▲

- *1790*

A pair of blue spirit decanters with the gilt inscriptions 'Hollands' and 'Brandy' hanging from gilt ribbons around the neck, within a silver stand with handle.
- *height 28cm*
- £700 • Somervale

Bohemian Glass Bottle ▲

- *circa 1860*

Opaque bohemian bottle chased in gilt with butterflies, birds and pale pink and blue flowers.
- *height 20.5cm*
- £750 • Mousa

Nailsea Rolling Pins ▲
- *1860*
Two glass Nailsea rolling pins in blue and red.
- *length 41cm*
- £180   • Somervale

Decanter with Geometric Cutting ▲
- *circa 1780*
Decanter with tapered body with geometric cutting design, the body engraved with stars.
- *height 30cm*
- £400   • Somervale

Wine Glass ▼
- *circa 1745*
Wine glass with trumpet bowl prawn stem with multiple spiral air twist stem on a folded conical foot.
- *height 18cm*
- £500   • Somervale

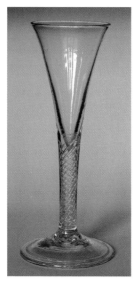

Claret Decanter ▼
- *circa 1780*
Decanter with mallet shaped body engraved with 'Claret' within a moulded cartouche with floral and grape design, and bevelled edge disc stopper.
- *height 30cm*
- £880   • Somervale

Pink Glass Bottle ▲
- *1850*
A dark pink glass bottle decorated with white shell scrolling around the globular base and elegant fluted neck.
- *height 19cm*
- £180   • Somervale

Bohemian Green Vase ▲
- *circa 1880*
Bohemian castellated green vase with gilt star pattern and white overlay panels with gilt flowers, supported on a knop stem with white panels and gilding.
- *height 34cm*
- £300   • Mousa

Glass Twisted Canes ▼
- *circa 1830*
Three assorted glass barley twist canes.
- *length 110cm*
- £150   • Somervale

Green Spirit Decanters ▼
- *1790*
Pair of green spirit decanters of ovoid form inscribed 'Rum' and 'Brandy' within gilt cartouches in the shape of a label, supported by gilt ribboning around the neck.
- *height 22cm*
- £1,200   • Somervale

Amber Vase ▲
- *circa 1850*
Amber vase with cover, engraved with stags and deer running through a forest and a trailing foliate design around the cover, with an octagonal base.
- *height 57cm*
- £5,800   • Mousa

Irish Oval Fruit Bowl ▼
- *circa 1790*
Fine Irish oval fruit bowl with panels of raised diamond design, knopped stem and radial moulded dual scalloped foot.
- *height 22cm*
- £2,600   • Somervale

Cut Glass Goblet ▼
- *circa 1810*
Large goblet engraved with the words 'London to Bath' and a scene showing a horse and carriage, with knop to stem and a square heavily cut base.
- *height 17cm*
- £1,500   • Somervale

Pink and Amber Goblet ▼
- *circa 1880*
Bohemian raspberry-coloured goblet with gilt trophy cartouche within a foliate border, raised on a topaz leaf-shaped base.
- *height 18cm*
- £460   • Mousa

Red Bohemian Glass Vase ▼

- *circa 1880*

Red Bohemian glass vase with white panels painted with bull rushes, above a knoped stem raised on a splayed foot decorated with panels of bullrushes within gilt borders.

- *height 31cm*
- £380 • Mousa

Blue and Gold Bohemian Bottle ▼

- *circa 1890*

Bohemian azure blue glass bottle with gilt floral and leaf designs, surmounted by an oversized lozenge-shaped stopper.

- *height 27cm*
- £490 • Mousa

Bohemian Centrepiece ▲

- *circa 1880*

Bohemian red glass centrepiece, with a circular clear glass dish supported on a red stem engraved with a trailing foliate pattern.

- *height 38cm*
- £1,400 • Mousa

Red Glass Candlesticks ▲

- *circa 1880*

Red Bohemian glass candlesticks with a scalloped rim, tapered stem on a circular star-cut base with a shaped edge.

- *height 23cm*
- £650 • Mousa

Amethyst Cream and Sugar Bowl ▲

- *1800*

Amethyst baluster cream and sugar bowls, with gilt writing.

- *height 12cm*
- £600 • Somervale

French Opaline Bottle ▼

- *circa 1880*

French opaline bottle and stopper, gilded, with a moulded rim. The body decorated with trailing roses and turquoise foliate designs, raised on a circular base.

- *height 25cm*
- £300 • Mousa

Bohemian Glass Bowl ▲

- *circa 1880*
Bohemian amber coloured glass
bowl.
- *height 18cm*
- £200 ● Sharif

English Vase ▲

- *circa 1870*
English clear cylindrical glass
vase engraved with birds amongst
foliage and geometric designs,
with a star cut base.
- *height 38cm*
- £680 ● Mousa

Red Sweet Dish ▼

- *circa 1890*
Red Bohemian sweet dish painted
with alternating panels of
portraits and white diamond
patterns, within gilt foliage,
supported on a white overlay
stem with a circular base.
- *height 34cm*
- £1,300 ● Mousa

Blue Decanter ▼

- *circa 1880*
Bohemian bottle shaped glass
decanter with blue overlay,
painted with red and yellow
designs amongst clear glass
flowers, made for the Middle
Eastern market.
- *height 25cm*
- £370 ● Mousa

Bohemian Red Candle Vase ▲

- *circa 1880*
Red Bohemian chalice shaped
vase, with white overlay and a
gilt band painted with a floral
frieze, above a knopped stem
supported on a splayed foot with
gilt banding.
- *height 27cm*
- £580 ● Mousa

Bohemian Style Vases ▲

- *circa 1880*
One of a pair of green Bohemian
style English vases of baluster
form with an asymmetric rim,
decorated with gilding, with a
clear glass shield cartouche.
- *height 30.5cm*
- £780 ● Mousa

J. Jacobs of Bristol Bowl ▶

- *circa 1810*

Bristol blue bowl and dish with gilt key pattern design around the rim of the bowl, and a gilt stag in the centre of the plate. Signed on the base of each J. Jacobs, Bristol, in gilt.
- *height of bowl 9cm*
- £1,000
- Somervale

Amethyst Cream Jug ▲

- *1820*

Pear shaped amethyst cream jug with 'Be canny with the cream' inscribed on the body, trails of gold enamelling, a loop handle, splayed lip and plain base.
- *height 14cm*
- £300
- Somervale

Newcastle Goblet ▼

- *circa 1750*

Newcastle goblet with a finely engraved foliate design, central air bedded and ball knops to the stem, and domed foot.
- *height 19cm*
- £1,800
- Somervale

German Liquor Set ▲

- *circa 1890*

German Moser hexagonal decanter and four glasses chased with gilt paisley designs surrounding clear red glass windows, surmounted by a spire shaped stopper.
- *height 24cm*
- £580
- Mousa

Jacobite Wine Glasses ▼

- *circa 1750*

Fine pair of Jacobite wine glasses with engraved bowls showing the Jacobite Rose and two buds, on double knopped, multiple spiral air twist stems, and domed bases.
- *height 16cm*
- £2,200
- Somervale

Cordial Glass ▲

- *circa 1720*

A cordial wine glass with flared trumpet bowl, knopped stem and air folded conical foot.
- *height 17cm*
- £800
- Somervale

Nailsea Glass Cloche ▲

- *circa 1800*

Clear glass bell shaped garden cloche by Nailsea.
- *height 34cm*
- £400
- Somervale

Green Wine Glasses ▲
- *circa 1830*

One of a set of twelve green wine glasses, with conical shaped bowls, bladed knob stems and a circular base.
- *height 11cm*
- £896   • Somervale

Bohemian Vases for Candles ▲
- *circa 1880*

One of a pair of dark green Bohemian candle holders with white overlay panels, painted with pink roses within gilt borders, raised on a conical stem and circular base.
- *height 34cm*
- £980   • Mousa

Posset Pot ▼
- *circa 1740*

Posset pot with a trumpet bowl with a carved spout flanked by two scroll handles, on a plain conical foot.
- *height 7cm*
- £995   • Somervale

Nailsea Container ▼
- *circa 1860*

Nailsea double container of clear glass with white pull up decoration, with emerald green rims.
- *height 21cm*
- £160   • Somervale

Mallet Shaped Decanter ▲
- *circa 1780*

Mallet-shaped decanter engraved with 'Port' within an oval cartouche, flanked by trailing vine and grapes.
- *height 31cm*
- £1,000   • Somervale

Amber Glass Cane ▼
- *circa 1810*

Amber glass barley twist cane with knob.
- *length 100cm*
- £150   • Somervale

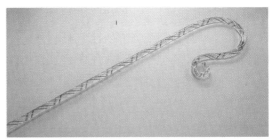

Glass Shepherd's Crook ▲
- *circa 1830*

Clear glass shepherd's crook with blue and white barley twist.
- *length 118cm*
- £150   • Somervale

Amber Bohemian Beaker ▲
- *circa 1880*

One of a set of six Bohemian amber beakers, with cut and moulded decoration and a central gilt foliate cartouche of flowers.
- *height 13cm*
- £380   • Mousa

Tapered Decanter ▼
- *circa 1780*

Tapered decanter with flute and pendant slice, and well cut lozenge stopper.
- *height 30cm*
- £450   • Somervale

Nailsea Jug ▲
- *circa 1810*

Dark olive green bulbous shape Nailsea jug with white inclusions.
- *height 18.5cm*
- £380   • Somervale

Blue Rum Decanter ▲
- *1790*

Bristol blue decanter with the inscription 'Rum' in gilt lettering within a cartouche of trailing grapes and vine leaves and a gilt 'R' on the stopper.
- *height 27cm*
- £380   • Somervale

Green and White Bohemian Vases ▲
- *circa 1880*

Pair of Bohemian green vases with turret shape rim and a white diamond design within gilded arches, raised on a knopped stem with a large splayed foot.
- *height 30cm*
- £780   • Mousa

Glass Twisted Cane ▼
- *circa 1810*

Turquoise twisted glass walking stick.
- *length 100cm*
- £150   • Somervale

Glass Barrel Decanters ▼
- *1820*

Set of three Bristol blue glass barrel decanters inscribed with 'Rum', 'Whiskey' and 'Brandy' in gilt lettering within gilt banding. Each decanter has a gilt ball stopper.
- *height 20cm*
- £1,400   • Somervale

Bristol Rum Decanter ▼
- *1800*

Rum decanter inscribed with 'Rum' in gilt lettering on the body and 'R' on the lozenge shape stopper.
- *height 28cm*
- £280   • Somervale

Victorian Epergné ▲
- *circa 1890*

One of a pair of Victorian epergnés, with a central flute flanked by matching hanging baskets, suspended on spiral branches.
- *height 48cm*
- £2,200   • Sinai

French Opaline Vase ▲
- *circa 1880*

Opaline pink glass vase with jewelled beading and gilt decoration with an eastern inspiration.
- *height 48cm*
- £850   • Sinai

Jacob Sang Wine Glass ▼
- *circa 1759*

Composite air twist stem wine glass, engraved with a scene showing the Customs House in Amsterdam and cargo being unloaded, marked 'Jacob Sang 1759', on the foot.
- *height 23.5cm*
- £8,000   • Somervale

Ale Glass ▼
- *circa 1760*

Ale glass with a round funnel bowl engraved with hops and barley and a double series twist stem, standing on a plain foot.
- *height 21cm*
- £580   • Somervale

Bohemian Bottles ▼

- *circa 1880*

Pair of Bohemian bottles with a white bulbous body with pink roses and blue cornflowers, orange flowers painted over red glass, with a slender fluted neck with a red lozenge-shape stopper and gilding.
- *height 22cm*
- £780 • Mousa

Large Green Goblet ▲

- *circa 1800*

Large dark green goblet with cup shaped bowl.
- *height 19cm*
- £1,200 • Somervale

Bristol Blue Oil Bottle ▼

- *1840*

Bristol blue bottle inscribed with 'Oil' in gilt lettering within a gilt foliate cartouche, with a painted chain around the neck.
- *height 12cm*
- £200 • Somervale

Set of Spirit Bottles ▲

- *1840*

A fine set of spirit bottles in amethyst, blue and green glass, with silver foliate bands around the neck and grape finials, resting in a pierced silver stand on three leaf shaped feet.
- *height 36cm*
- £980 • Somervale

Bohemian Lustres ▲

- *circa 1880*

One of a pair of Bohemian green lustres with white overlay with gilt borders, decorated with clear, cut glass hanging pendants.
- *height 30cm*
- £1,000 • Mousa

William III Glass ▲

- *circa 1780*

Irish wine glass with a cigar shaped stem and engraved with the figure of King William on horseback with the inscription 'The Glorious Memories of William III'.
- *height 15.5cm*
- £4,000 • Somervale

Newcastle Glass Goblet ▼
- *circa 1810*

Large bowl shaped goblet
engraved with a horse and
carriage, scrolling foliate and
grape design and the words
'Newcastle to York', on a domed
base.
- *height 24cm*
- £800 • Somervale

Baluster Cream Jug ▼
- *circa 1800*

Blue baluster cream jug with
pinched lip and barley twist
design.
- *height 12cm*
- £155 • Somervale

Bohemian Vases ▲
- *circa 1870*

A pair of Bohemian cranberry
glass vases with gilt leaf
decoration and central cartouches
showing portraits of a lady in a
wedding dress and a lady in
country dress.
- *height 39.5cm*
- £5,500 • Sinai

Match Holder ▼
- *circa 1890*

Ovoid match holder with a silver
rim and etched glass body.
- *height 8cm*
- £150 • H. Gregory

Blue Decanter ▼
- *circa 1790*

Club shape Bristol blue spirit
decanter with a plain lozenge
shape stopper.
- *height 32cm*
- £220 • Somervale

Jewellery

It is interesting to note that jewellery from any period can be worn today without appearing strange or dated.

The demand for jewellery is as strong now as it has been since the time of Cleopatra. The wide range of necklaces, rings and brooches available today embraces most styles and periods from history. Victoriana is extremely popular amongst collectors, especially lockets and pendants which were produced in vast numbers and often set in 9ct gold with garnets and pearls, or other gemstones, and usually designed with matching earrings.

Art Deco jewellery is very popular and can be distinguished by its elegance and the innovative and artistic use of materials and design, which was a reaction against Edwardianism. This led to the birth of a new freedom in style and experimentation which resulted in different techniques being used such as enamelling with silver. Horn was popular, with its light translucent colours often being coupled with softly coloured gems such as moonstones. It could be carved in fine detail and shaped into hair combs.

Early Victorian Diamond ▼
- *circa 1840*
Early Victorian rock crystal and diamond earrings set in silver and gold.
- *length 3cm*
- £2,850 • Wimpole Antiques

Victorian Gold Earrings ▶
- *circa 1875*
Victorian 15ct gold Etruscan revival style earrings with an applied globular design.
- *length 2cm*
- £875 • Wimpole Antiques

Salvador Dali Brooch ▼
- *1950*
18ct gold stylised leaf in the form of a hand with red painted nails signed Dali on the right-hand leaf.
- *length 6.5cm*
- £3,750 • N. Bloom

Sapphire and Diamond ▶

- *circa 1910*

Sapphire and diamond earrings set in a flower head design of platinum and gold.
- *length 3cm*
- £4,850   • Wimpole Antiques

Diamond Earrings ▲

- *1920*

Pair of diamond earrings with oval, circular and rectangular diamonds within gold settings.
- *length 2.5cm*
- £4,400   • N. Bloom

Gold Victorian Earrings ▲

- *circa 1875*

Victorian Etruscan revival 15ct gold earrings with a central wheel motif.
- *width 1cm*
- £875   • Wimpole Antiques

Diamond Leaf Earrings ▼

- *circa 1925*

Mille grain set in platinum diamond earrings in the form of a leaf.
- *length 2cm*
- £3,475   • Wimpole Antiques

Victorian 15ct Earrings ▲

- *circa 1880*

15ct gold Victorian articulated lozenge shaped earrings.
- *length 5cm*
- £1,295   • Wimpole Antiques

Expert Tips

Bear in mind that the majority of items of jewellery are second hand and will have been subject to some wear and tear.

Silver Gilt Brooch ▼

- *1940s*

American large silver gilt and cut glass sapphire floral brooch.
- *7cm x 6cm*
- £95   • Linda Bee

French Pearl and Diamond Earrings ▼

- *circa 1875*

French enamel, gold and platinum earrings set with diamonds and natural pearls.
- *length 3cm*
- £2,650   • Wimpole Antiques

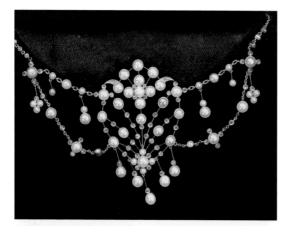

Pearl and Diamond Necklace ◄

- *circa 1905*
Edwardian pearl and diamond necklace with droplets and swag designs.
- *length 6cm*
- **£3,950** • Wimpole Antiques

Victorian Gold Bracelet ▼

- *circa 1880*
Victorian gold bracelet in the Etruscan revival style with architectural designs, set with pearls.
- **£2,250** • Wimpole Antiques

Gold Brooch/Pendant ▼

- *circa 1875*
Victorian 15ct gold brooch/pendant with natural pearls and floral enamel designs.
- *length 8cm*
- **£1,275** • Wimpole Antiques

Pearl Necklace ▲

- *circa 1900*
15ct gold necklace with half pearls and a second row of swagged pearls between floral droplets.
- *length 4cm*
- **£2,955** • Wimpole Antiques

Art Deco and Diamond Clasp ▶

- *1920*
Art Deco jade and diamond clasp together with a re-strung twisted cultured pearl necklace.
- *clasp 4cm*
- **£3,950** • N. Bloom

American Gold Bracelet ◄

- *1950*
American heavy textured gold link bracelet with geometric engraving on some of the links.
- *4cm/link size*
- **£3,300** • N. Bloom

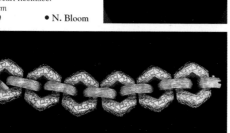

Mixed Gem Stones Earrings ▶

- *circa 1910*

Pendulous set of earrings set in gold with mixed gem stones of garnet, sapphire, zircon, and citrine.
- *length 6.5cm*
- £985　• Wimpole Antiques

Italian Glass Necklace ▲

- *circa 1990*

Italian glass necklaces, made up of blue, turquoise, lilac, indigo and clear glass beads linked by gold metal beads.
- *length 37cm*
- £85 each　• Francesca Martire

Peridot and Pearl Necklace ▲

- *circa 1900*

Peridot and pearl Edwardian necklace set in 15ct gold with graduated pearls and two lozenge shaped peridots.
- £795　• Wimpole Antiques

Diamond Brooch ▶

- *circa 1900*

Exceptional diamond brooch with a central diamond within a ring and ribbon design, with four diamonds, within an octagonal border, encrusted with diamonds set in platinum with bow, 4.5ct of diamonds.
- *width 3.5cm*
- £9,750　• Wimpole Antiques

Corsage Brooch ▼

- *1940*

Flower corsage brooch styled as two exotic flower heads with leaves.
- *13cm x 6cm*
- £65　• Linda Bee

Suffragette Brooch/ Pendant ◀

- *circa 1910*

Edwardian half pear, peridot and pink tourmaline pendant incorporating the colours white, green and pink of the Suffragette movement.
- *length 7cm*
- £1,975　• Wimpole Antiques

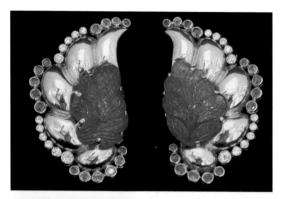

Pair of Ruby Clasps ◄
- *1940*

Pair of ruby and diamond clasps set in stylised gold leaf.
- *length 5cm*
- **£2,500** • N. Bloom

Austrian Violet Brooch ▼
- *1950*

Austrian violet brooch with diamonds and jade leaves, set in silver.
- *height 6.5cm*
- **£1,650** • N. Bloom

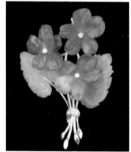

Glass Italian Necklace ▼
- *circa 1990*

Hand blown glass necklace, made from, blue, gold red, green and clear glass squares.
- *length 37cm*
- **£135** • Francesca Martire

Edwardian Jade Earrings ▲
- *1910*

Edwardian circular jade earrings set in plain gold with two bands of roping.
- *width 1.5cm*
- **£1,200** • N. Bloom

Pearl and Diamond Earrings ▼
- *circa 1925*

Pendulous natural pearl and diamond earrings set in 18ct gold and platinum.
- *length 3.5cm*
- **£3,785** • Wimpole Antiques

Emerald Pearl Pendant ▲
- *circa 1890*

French polished emerald set in 18ct gold with floral and swag designs, with diamonds and a single pearl.
- *length 8.5cm*
- **£1,975** • Wimpole Antiques

French Art Deco Bracelet ◄
- *1920*

French Art Deco sapphire and diamond bracelet by Trabert and Hoeffer, Mauboussin.
- *length 19cm*
- **£44,500** • N. Bloom

Deco Lapiz Bracelet ▶
- **1950**
Art Deco bracelet with circular
lapis lazulai discs with gold links
and rectangular enamels with
dragon designs.
- *length 19cm*
- **£4,500** • N. Bloom

Swiss Balainot Bracelet ◀
- **1960**
Swiss gold bracelet by Balainot
from the 'Sheet Range'.
- *height 6cm*
- **£3,950** • N. Bloom

Snake Bracelet ▼
- **1930**
Gilt bracelet styled as a coiled
serpent with a spiralled chain
link, body and scale design to the
head and tail.
- *8cm x 8cm*
- **£85** • Linda Bee

Coral and Diamond
Earrings ▼
- *circa 1910*
Carved coral ball and lozenge
shape earrings set in platinum
and 18ct gold with a diamond
bow linking the upper and lower
sections.
- *length 5.5cm*
- **£2,475** • Wimpole Antiques

Bear Claw Belt Buckle ▲
- **1950**
Bear claw set in silver foliate
design with two flowers with
coral and turquoise. Stamped E.
King and found on an Apache
reservation.
- *diameter 7cm*
- **£699** • Wilde One's

Expert Tips

*It is advisable to test all joints in
bracelets and necklaces for play,
and brooch clasps for security,
whilst ring shanks should not be
too thin as they can snap.*

Jade Earrings ▼
- **1930**
Carved flower jade earrings set in
14ct gold.
- *width 2.5cm*
- **£1,150** • N. Bloom

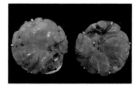

French Jade Brooch ▶
- **1940**
French jade carved dragon bar
brooch set in gold with gold
scrolling.
- *length 9cm*
- **£2,400** • N. Bloom

Art Deco Feather Pin ◄
- *1920*
Art Deco peacock feather pin encrusted with diamonds each side.
- *length 8cm*
- £4,500   • N. Bloom

Zuni Cuff ▼
- *1950*
'Sleeping Beauty' Zuni cuff with 33 turquoise stones set in silver in a traditional design.
- *diameter 9cm*
- £1,200   • Wilde One's

Zuni Turquoise Pin ▼
- *1920*
Zuni pin flower design with 30 turquoise stones, set on a silver base.
- *diameter 8cm*
- £799   • Wilde One's

English Silver Brooch ▼
- *1940s*
English silver and enamel brooch modelled as a butterfly.
- *6.5cm x 3cm*
- £125   • Linda Bee

Sterle Coral Earrings ▲
- *1960*
Coral earrings set in gold with gold balls.
- *height 8cm*
- £6,600   • N. Bloom

Vic Blister Pearl Heart ▼
- *1920*
Vic Blister heart-shaped pearl pendant set with diamonds.
- *width 2cm*
- £2,950   • N. Bloom

Gold 15ct Bracelet ◄
- *circa 1870*
Gold 15ct linked bracelet with a design of bars with chain link borders.
- *length 15cm*
- £1,475   • Wimpole Antiques

Berlin Necklace ▲

- *1870*
Berlin 'iron-work' necklace with 8 plaques.
- *length 3cm*
- £3,750 • N. Bloom

Night and Day Pin ▲

- *1950*
Gold metal flower 'night and day' brooch made by Warner, USA.
- *6cm x 4cm*
- £85 • Linda Bee

Bakelite Brooch ▶

- *1930s*
French bakelite black and white brooch, with an incised feather design.
- *8cm x 4cm*
- £65 • Linda Bee

Navajo Bull Bracelet ▼

- *1960*
Navajo silver sand-cast bracelet with two large silver bull's heads on a scrolling border, flanked by turquoise stones.
- *height 6cm*
- £499 • Wilde One's

Navajo Bracelet ▲

- *1950*
Navajo coral and turquoise set on a circular engraved base, signed P.M.
- *diameter 6cm*
- £499 • Wilde One's

Mic-Mak Indian Belt ▲

- *1920*
Glass Mic-mak 'Morning Star' Indian belt made from glass beads with butterflies and geometric blue and black design with a cream background, lined with antique pink material with floral design.
- *length 87cm*
- £399 • Wilde One's

Gold Collar ▲

- *circa 1875*
Victorian 15ct. gold collar engraved linkages.
- £3,750 • Wimpole Antiques

Navajo Shadow Box Bracelet ◀

- *1960*
Navajo silver shadow box bracelet set with five large coral pieces stamped by the artist P. Benally.
- *length 17cm*
- £699 • Wilde One's

Peridot Necklace ▼
- *circa 1900*

Peridot and pearl Edwardian necklace set in 15ct gold with lozenge and circular peridots linked by pearls.
- **£1,785** • Wimpole Antiques

Boucheron Diamond Pin ▲
- *1920*

Diamond-encrusted pin in the shape of a tie by Boucheron.
- *length 4cm*
- **£11,500** • N. Bloom

American Earrings ▲
- *1950*

American turquoise glass earrings by Tiffany, modelled as flower petals within gold settings.
- *3.5cm x 3.5cm*
- **£85** • Linda Bee

Amethyst Necklace ▶
- *circa 1890*

Large lozenge shape amethyst stones of graded size set in 15ct gold, with gold double linkages.
- *length 47cm*
- **£3,550** • Wimpole Antiques

Gold 18ct Bracelet ◀
- *circa 1940*

Gold 18ct double chain link bracelet with light and dark gold linkages.
- *length 15cm*
- **£1,350** • Wimpole Antiques

Opal and Ruby Necklace ▼
- *circa 1900*

Opal and ruby necklace with oval opals set in 15ct gold, hanging from a gold chain with ruby linkages.
- *length 47cm*
- **£3,985** • Wimpole Antiques

Austrian Bracelet ▼
- *1920*

Austrian art deco diamond bracelet set with a large central diamond surrounded by emeralds.
- *length 16cm*
- **£15,00** • N. Bloom

Zuni Pendant and Chain ▲
- *1920*
Circular silver pendant set with
18 stones surrounded by silver
scrolling, and a silver necklace.
- *diameter 6cm*
- £699　　　• Wilde One's

Indian Ring ▶
- *1980*
Indian blue lapis ring with large
amber stone set in gold.
- *length 2cm*
- £8,880　　　• N. Bloom

Bow Brooch ▲
- *1930*
Rhinestone and black enamel
brooch fashioned as a bow tie.
- *4cm x 12cm*
- £85　　　• Linda Bee

Navajo Coral Bracelet ▶
- *1920*
Navajo cast silver scrolled
bracelet with a natural coral set
in the centre.
- *length 16cm*
- £599　　　• Wilde One's

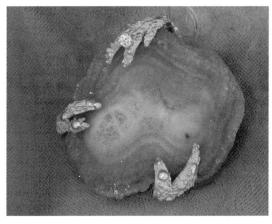

English Jewellery Set ◀
- *circa 1940s*
English jewellery set with silver
gilt top hat pin with faux pearl
and earrings.
- *8cm x 3cm*
- £120　　　• Linda Bee

Brooch by Andrew Grima ▲
- *1967*
Andrew Grima asymmetric
crystal brooch with three gold
leaves set with diamonds.
- *diameter 5cm*
- £1,850　　　• N. Bloom

Zuni Butterfly ▲
- 1960

Butterfly with a black and mother of pearl head and turquoise coral and mother of pearl body and wings, set in silver.
- *width 6cm*
- £599   • Wilde One's

Navajo Ring ▲
- 2000

Navajo natural coral from the 1920s, designed with a turquoise stone in a heavy silver setting with scrolling, by Rowan Horse.
- *length 4cm*
- £399   • Wilde One's

Navajo Bear Claw Necklace ▼
- 1970

Rare necklace with six bear claws set in silver with five large 'Sleeping Beauty' turquoise nuggets from the Arizona mine.
- *length of claw 4cm*
- £1,899   • Wilde One's

Turquoise Concho Belt ◄
- 1980

Turquoise Zuni 'concho' belt on black leather with nine large turquoise flowers, set in silver. Highly collectable due to the large size. Made by J. W. and M. S.
- *diameter 8cm*
- £3,999   • Wilde One's

Zuni Belt ▼
- 1930

Zuni delicate turquoise flower belt set in silver on brown leather.
- *diameter 2.5cm*
- £1,200   • Wilde One's

Art Deco Diamond Necklace ▼
- circa 1925

Art Deco necklace with an alternating design of bar and circular cut diamonds, set in 8ct, platinum.
- *length 47cm*
- £9,750   • Wimpole Antiques

Ruby and Emerald Pendant ▶

- **1950**
French ruby and emerald flower pendant with diamonds and pearls.
- *length 9.5cm*
- **£19,500**   • N. Bloom

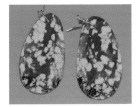

Santa Domingo Earrings ▲

- **1960**
Oval Santa Domingo rare turquoise and black earrings from Arizona.
- *length 4cm*
- **£129**   • Wilde One's

Navajo Green Bracelet

- **1930**
Navajo silver bracelet with two rosettes each side of a large green stone.
- *length of stone 6cm*
- **£459**   • Wilde One's

Metal Enamel Pin ▲

- *circa 1930*
English metal enamel pin by Dismal Desmond, with a seated black dog with a purple bow around its neck.
- *7.5cm x 2.5cm*
- **£75**   • Linda Bee

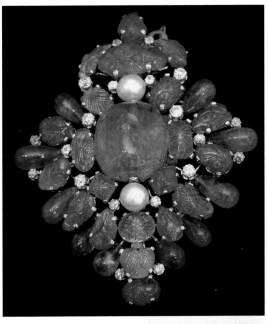

Ruby Heart Locket ▼

- **1850**
Ruby enamelled heart shaped locket with central gold star with diamonds and a single pearl in the centre, surrounded by scrolling set with diamonds with gold ring clasps on a velvet neck ribbon.
- *width 2.5cm*
- **£8,950**   • N. Bloom

Zuni Ceremonial Ring ▲

- **1920**
Lady's Zuni traditional ceremonial ring set with 17 turquoise stones in a flower design.
- *diameter 5cm*
- **£269**   • Wilde One's

Expert Tips

Recently, with the return of retro design in both fashion and furniture, jewellery from the 1960s and 1970s has become popular.

Amethyst Necklace ▶

- *1950*
Amethyst necklace consisting of
25 lozenge amethysts of varying
sizes set in gold with a nine-stone
amethyst flower design pendant.
- *size of pendant 6cm*
- **£2,750**   • **N. Bloom**

Czechoslovakian Brooch ▼

- *1930s*
Czechoslovakian shield brooch
with numerous cut glass stones
within gilt metal settings.
- *7.5cm x 5cm*
- **£85**   • **Linda Bee**

Pig Earrings ▶

- *1930s*
English mother of pearl earrings
styled as little pigs.
- *2.5cm x 2cm*
- **£95**   • **Linda Bee**

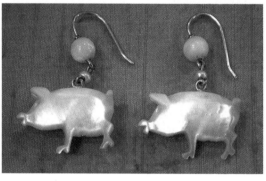

Silver Necklace ▼

- *1960s*
Silver heart necklace with a
bridle link chain.
- *length 30cm*
- **£65**   • **Linda Bee**

Spider Brooch ◀

- *1940s*
Gilt metal spider brooch with two
cut glass amethysts.
- *5cm x 5cm*
- **£45**   • **Linda Bee**

Diamond and Garnet Brooch ▼

- *1850*

Large Victorian oval gold filigree pendant with a central ruby surrounded by medium and smaller diamonds, three ruby lozenge shaped droplets, mounted by a diamond-encrusted platinum ribbon.

- *length 9cm*
- £16,000   • N. Bloom

French Gold Necklace ▼

- *1960*

Fine French gold necklace with a graduated design of icicles.

- *length of largest drop 4cm*
- £2,400   • N. Bloom

Snake Brooch ▲

- *circa 1900*

English gilt brooch modelled as a snake with stone settings.

- *6cm x 3cm*
- £150   • Linda Bee

Venetian Earrings ▲

- *1950s*

Venetian glass earrings modelled as sugared oranges and lemons.

- *2.5cm x 2.5cm*
- £45   • Linda Bee

Necklace and Bracelet Set ▼

- *1930s*

Rare interlinked diamante necklace and bracelet set by DRGM, Germany.

- *necklace length 36cm*
  bracelet length 18cm
- £350 for the set   • Linda Bee

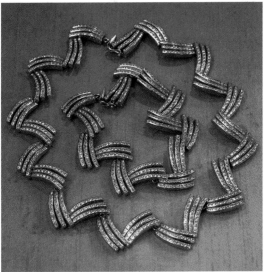

Jade Pendant ▶

- 1930

Carved green flower jade pendant with gold leaf ring fittings and an amethyst drop.
- *width 3cm*
- £1,250   • N. Bloom

Plane Pin ▲

- 1940s

Unusual metal pin in the shape of a plane with a map of south-west United States.
- *5cm*
- £85   • Linda Bee

Czechoslovakian Necklace ▲

- 1930

Czechoslovakian glass necklace made up of 18 triangular emerald glass segments.
- *length 33cm*
- £95   • Linda Bee

Coral Zuni Earrings ▲

- 1950

Coral diamond fashioned Zuni earrings, with a smaller diamond inside.
- *length 8cm*
- £169   • Wilde One's

Rhinestone Bracelet ▼

- 1938

Metal and rhinestone banded bracelet by DRGM, Germany.
- *length 20cm*
- £120   • Linda Bee

French Earrings ▼

- 1930s

Early French Egyptian revival glass earrings.
- *7cm x 2cm*
- £95   • Linda Bee

Lapis and Crystal Brooch ◀

- 1912

Lapis and moulded panel brooch with bands of diamonds set in platinum, made in San Francisco, USA.
- *width 4.5cm*
- £3,300   • N. Bloom

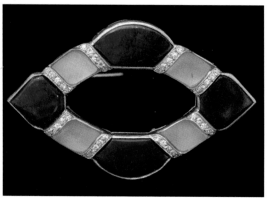

Marine Items

Star globes for nautical and instructional use are not subject to condition as some slightly worn globes are very popular.

Marine items have always been popular amongst collectors, with chronometers, sextants, models of boats, compasses and barometers being the most highly sought after in today's marketplace. Hand held telescopes were commonly used by seamen, along with the earliest refracting telescopes, and the examples one can find today are usually eighteenth-century, with vellum-covered card body tubes, often tooled in gilt with ivory and ebony mounts. The outer tubes can be covered in chagrin.

A vast quantity of surveying instruments were made from brass, copper, silver and platinum and unfortunately were often consigned to the melting pot as scrap. Today that is no longer the case, as the fine workmanship and mathematical precision of these instruments designed by engineers is now increasingly appreciated.

Other marine items that are collectable include posters, ship's decanters in boxes, models of boats, globes on stands, ship's wheels, back staff books and anchor lamps.

Atlas Globe ▶
- *circa 1920*
Bronze figure of Atlas supporting a globe with brass supports.
- *height 53cm*
- £1,250 ● Langfords Marine

Dwarf Sextant ▲
- *1820*
Dwarf sextant signed 'G. Whitbread, London', and housed in its original mahogany travelling case, with further pieces and accessories.
- *19cm*
- £2,500 ● T. Philip & Son

Dwarf Sextant ▶
- *circa 1835*
Dwarf sextant by Troughton & Simms. The instrument is housed in its original mahogany box with accessories. This would be used for navigation and surveying. Edward Troughton went into partnership with Simms in 1826.
- *height 13.5cm*
- £5,750 ● T. Philip & Son

Cornish Skiff ▼
- *circa 1910*
Model of 'The Vengeance', a Cornish fishing skiff.
- *height 24cm*
- £480 ● Langfords Marine

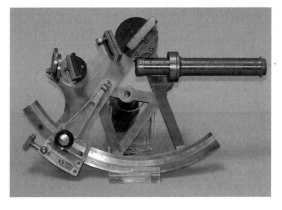

Sextant by Whitbread ▲
- *circa 1850*
Sextant by G. Whitbread, in original oak box with brass fittings.
- *width 27cm*
- £1,650 • Langfords Marine

Celestial Globe ▲
- *circa 1950*
Celestial globe with brass fittings, and original oak box carrying handle.
- *height 28cm*
- £1,280 • Langfords Marine

Octagonal Telescope ▲
- *circa 1780*
Fine octagonal fruitwood telescope with brass single draw and lens housing.
- *length of case 31cm*
- £800   • Langfords Marine

Marine Chronometer ▲
- *circa 1840*
Fine 2-day marine chronometer by Parkinson & Frodsham, Change Alley, London 1705. Housed in a mahogany double-tier case.
- *height 16cm*
- £7,000   • T. Philip & Son

Steam Yacht ▼
- *circa 1910*
Model steam yacht complete with planked hull, working steam engine, brass funnel prop and lights, and eight portholes.
- *length 100cm*
- £8,000   • Langfords Marine

Chinese Dish from the Ship Diana ▼
- *circa 1817*
Chinese porcelain blue and white dish from the ship 'Diana' which sank near Malacca on 4 March 1817.
- *diameter 28cm*
- £185   • Langfords Marine

Weichert Chronometer ▼
- *circa 1860*
Two-day chronometer by Weichert, in a coromandel box with brass inlay and handles.
- *height 20cm*
- £4,300   • Langfords Marine

Tulip Frame Sextant ▶

- *circa 1860*
Tulip frame sextant in original
oak box lined with green base,
with brass handle and fittings.
- *width 28cm*
- £1,250 • **Langfords Marine**

Pond Yacht ▲

- *circa 1900*
Pine pond yacht with three sails
and brass fittings modelled as a
pilot cutter.
- *width 164cm*
- £1,500 • **Langfords Marine**

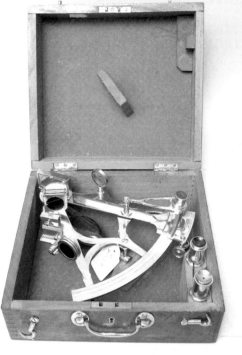

Bone Beaker Aberdeen Schooner ▲

- *circa 1880*
Bone beaker with the inscription;
'Succefs to the Aberdeen
Schoone Proto', below an
engraved schooner in full sail.
- *height 9.5cm*
- £320 • **Langfords Marine**

Dry Land Compass ▼

- *circa 1800*
Gimballed dry land compass in
brass case.
- *diameter 11.5cm*
- £1,150 • **Langfords Marine**

Georgian Coconut Cup ▲

- *circa 1810*
Georgian coconut cup with silver
mounts raised on splayed legs
with paw feet.
- *height 13.5cm*
- £690 • **Langfords Marine**

Half-Boat ◀

- *circa 1900*
Half-boat racing yacht, made
from fruitwood for use as a boat-
builder's model.
- *width 87cm*
- £1,600 • **Langfords Marine**

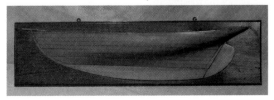

Small Brass Barometer ▶

- *circa 1800*
Barometer H. M. S. Britannia
Prize, by Coomes Devenport in
original leather box.
- *diameter 5.5cm*
- **£850** • **Langfords Marine**

Model of S.S. 'Rallus' ▲

- *circa 1900s*
A builder's scale model of the
S.S. 'Rallus', which was built for
the Cork Steam Ship Co Ltd,
Cork, Ireland by Swan Hunter &
Wigham Richardson Ltd. Masts,
derricks and rigging with scale
ivorine and nickel plated blocks,
deck details including anchor
winches, fairleads, bollards,
ventilators, deck rails, hatches,
and deck winches. The
superstructure with lifeboats.
- *67cm x 234cm*
- **£9,500** • **Anthony Outred**

Nelson's Last Signal ◀

- *circa 1910*
Nelson's last signal, 'England
expects that every man shall do
his duty.'
- *38cm x 57cm*
- **£430** • **Langfords Marine**

Parallel Brass Rule ▲

- *circa 1920*
Brass parallel rule
- *length 46cm*
- **£120** • **Langfords Marine**

Model of the Queen Mary ◀

- *circa 1940*
Model of the Queen Mary by
Bassett-Lowke, with display case.
- *width 32cm*
- **£400** • **Langfords Marine**

Model Yacht ◀
- *circa 1910*
Model yacht inscribed, 'Marine
d'autrefois Gildas de Kerdrel, 80
Avenue des Ternes, Paris'.
- *height 27cm*
- **£750** • **Langfords Marine**

Ebony Octant ▼
- *circa 1840*
Ebony and brass octant in
original oak box with label and
the inscription, 'W. Hughes,
Instrument Maker, 40 Fenchurch
Street, London'.
- *width 28cm*
- **£785** • **Langfords Marine**

Nautical Chandelier ▼
- *circa 1900*
Unusual German oak nautical
chandelier. The corona in the
form of a ship's wheel, each arm
decorated with an iron anchor,
with further chains linked to
three finely carved life-boats,
each with a carved watchman
holding a lantern over the bow of
the boat. The chandelier centred
by a carved lighthouse with a
pendant light fitting.
- *height 81.5cm*
- **£3,400** • **Anthony Outred**

Chinese Porcelain
Cup and Bowl ▼
- *circa 1817*
Blue and white Chinese cup and
bowl salvaged from the ship
'Diana', a trading ship working
the India-China route, which
sank near Malacca on 4 March
1817. Found in December 1993.
- *diameter of bowl 17cm*
- **£250** • **Langfords Marine**

Expert Tips

*Early compasses can be found
in fitted mahogany boxes.
Signatures are important but
not mandatory. It is best to
avoid the temptation to purchase
an instrument that has been
over-zealously polished.*

433

Edinburgh & Leith Ship's Glass ◀

- *circa 1930*
Edinburgh & Leith ship's glass from the Aberdeen suite, consisting of a wine jug, decanters, water glasses, wine glasses, liqueur glasses, fruit cups, fruit saucer and seafood dishes.
- *height 33cm*
- £4,600 • Langfords Marine

Chinese Porcelain Bowl ▲

- *circa 1817*
Chinese blue and white porcelain, from the ship 'Diana', which sank near Malacca on 4 March 1817 on the India-China route.
- *diameter 17.5cm*
- £220 • Langfords Marine

Nautical Match Holder ▲

- *circa 1920*
Porcelain match holder painted with a sailing yacht in a seascape.
- *diameter 8cm*
- £365 • Langfords Marine

Pond Yacht ▲

- *circa 1910*
A pond yacht named 'Bassett Lowke Britannia'.
- *length 60cm*
- £1,600 • Langfords Marine

Bone Model of a Boat ▶

- *circa 1940*
Bone Prisoner of War Model ship with three masts and the rigging made from hair, standing on a maple wood stand with satin wood inlay
- *height 36cm*
- £8,600 • Langfords Marine

Musical Instruments

Even new instruments are highly collectable because of their individuality and quality.

Before you begin to collect musical instruments it is worth researching the various makers, as it can be very expensive to not know what you are buying. Quality of materials, craftsmanship and musical quality are all very important factors to take into consideration before making your purchase. A good maker's name can also considerably enhance the value of the instrument, for example, a Steinway concert grand piano can fetch astronomical sums.

The provenance of the musical instrument also plays a huge part in the value of the item, for example, a piano that was once owned by Elton John fetched a price at auction that was out of reach of most ordinary buyers. The signature of a famous player on an instrument can also add to its value, which they often do for charity.

Gibson Guitar ▼
- *1964*
Gibson. Model: ES335TDC. Cherry finish. Original case. S/N 66236
- *height 104cm*
- £5,500   • **Vintage Guitars**

Gibson Guitar ▲
- *1960*
Gibson Model: Switchmaster. Blonde finish, with original case. S/N A 33343
- *height 105cm*
- £7,500   • **Vintage Guitars**

Gibson Guitar ▲
- *1962*
Make: Gibson. Model: ES350TN. Blonde finish with original case. S/N 80935
- *height 105cm*
- £4,250   • **Vintage Guitars**

Gretsch Guitar ▼
- **1957**

Gretsch guitar. Mode: 6120, with original white cowboy case. S/N:22080
- *height 105cm*
- **£5,545** • **Vintage Guitars**

Gibson Guitar ▼
- **1953**

Gibson Model SJ200. Sunburst finish. S/N A17263.
- *height 105cm*
- **£5,850** • **Vintage Guitars**

Gibson Guitar ▲
- **1960**

Gibson. Model Les Paul Special. Finish TV Yellow. S/N O 1432.
- *height 100cm*
- **£3,850** • **Vintage Guitars**

Gibson Guitar ▲
- **1960**

Gibson. Model: ES330. Sunburst finish. Dot neck. Factory order # R29523.
- *height 99cm*
- **£2,850** • **Vintage Guitars**

Fender Guitar ▼
- **1959**

Fender. Model: Esquire. Blond finish. S/N 40511.
- *height 95cm*
- **£5,500** • **Vintage Guitars**

Fender Guitar ▼
- **1959**

Fender. Model: Jazzmaster. Sunburst finish. Original tweed case. S/N 31596
- *height 104cm*
- **£2,095** • **Vintage Guitars**

Fender Guitar ▲
- *1952*
Fender. Model: Esquire with original thermometer case. S/N 4047
- *height 98cm*
- **£7,500** • **Vintage Guitars**

Gibson Guitar ▲
- *1949*
Gibson. Model: SJ200. Maple back and sides stained and a new scratch guard added by Gibson in the mid 60's. S/N A3487.
- *height 105cm*
- **£4,950** • **Vintage Guitars**

Epiphone Guitar ▼
- *1958*
Epiphone. Model: Coronet. Refinished in black.
- *height 96cm*
- **£1,895** • **Vintage Guitars**

Martin Guitar ▼
- *1965*
Martin. Model: D28. Brazilian rosewood. Replaced fingerboard. S/N 201923
- *height 103cm*
- **£2,300** • **Vintage Guitars**

Martin Guitar ▲
- *1965*
Martin. Model: O18. S/N: 208 916
- *height 99cm*
- **£1,895** • **Vintage Guitars**

Epiphone Guitar ▲
- *1967*
Epiphone. Model: casino. Long scale model. Near mint condition. Original card case.
- *height 108cm*
- **£2,500** • **Vintage Guitars**

Concert Grand Piano ▶

- *1935*

Model D. concert grand in a very
unusual mahogany high gloss
polish (most concert grands are
black). Fully rebuilt by Steinway
and Sons.
- *length 270cm*
- £58,500   • Steinway

Mahogany Cased Organ ▲

- *1805*

Rare organ by Broderip &
Wilkinson, London, in full
working order, complete with six
barrels each with up to eight
different tunes.
- *height 226cm*
- £24,500   • Anthony Outred

Rickenbacker Guitar ▲

- *1967*

Rickenbacker. Model: 365.
Fireglow finish. S/N GC1415.
- *height 98cm*
- £1,895   • Vintage Guitars

Fender Guitar ▼

- *1969*

Fender. Model: Jazzbase. Sunburst
finish. Original case. S/N 283918.
- *height 115cm*
- £2,250   • Vintage Guitars

Gretsch Guitar ▲

- *1962*

Gretsch. Model: 6120. Original
case. S/N 67410.
- *height 109cm*
- £2,500   • Vintage Guitars

Rosewood Satin Piano ◀

- **1906**

Model K. rosewood satin piano with inlay veneer. Fully rebuilt by Steinway & Sons. Made in Hamburg.
- *height 135cm*
- **£21,500**   • Steinway

Fender Guitar ▼

- **1963**

Fender. Model Stratocaster. Refinished in white. Some changes. S/N 95781
- *height 99cm*
- **£2,995**   • Vintage Guitars

National Guitar ▼

- **1929**

National. Model Style 2 . Irish rose Tenor. Very rare. Original case .S/N 684.
- *height 89cm*
- **£2,250**   • Vintage Guitars

Epiphone Guitar ▲

- **1967**

Epiphone. Model: Texan. Natural finish. S/N 875125
- *height 108cm*
- **£1,895**   • Vintage Guitars

Ebonised Piano ▶

- **1958**

Model B. black ebonised piano in a high gloss finish, fully rebuilt by Steinway & Sons.
- *length 208cm*
- **£39,500**   • Steinway

Silver & Pewter

**Some of the earliest spoons recorded date back to the Middle Ages.
Scottish spoons exist from the end of the sixteenth century.**

The advantage of collecting silver and pewter is that the hallmarks guarantee their quality and provide information on the maker, date and place of manufacture. A good maker's name is usually indicative of quality and can have an enormous bearing on the value of an item, with some pieces fetching very high prices. The serious collector would not need to look at the marks first, as their experience would enable them to identify the maker through the style of the object. Silver from the late seventeenth century by important silversmiths such as Nelme and Pyne is highly sought after and includes practical items such as beakers, tankards, bowls and candlesticks, which are of a much simpler design than those of the eighteenth and nineteenth centuries, by makers such as Gilpin, Hemming, Wakelin, Bateman, Chawner and Schofield, which have more ornamentation.

Silver Condiment Set ▲
- *1964*
Silver condiment set consisting of a salt, mustard and pepper pot. Made in Sheffield, England.
- *height 8cm*
- £400
   - S. Kalms

Liberty Silver Vase ▲
- *circa 1900*
English silver Tudric Liberty bomb vase.
- *height 19cm*
- £800
   - Victor Arwas

Barmaid's Measure ▶
- *circa 1860*
English pewter barmaid's half-pint measure tankard with waisted body, ear shaped handle and banded design.
- *11cm x 8cm*
- £55
   - Jane Stewart

Liberty Bulb Vase ▲
- *circa 1900*
Tudric pewter Liberty bulb vase with a hammered finish and five conical necks.
- *height 22cm*
- £480
   - Victor Arwas

Tulip Vase ▼

- *circa 1900*
Silver Art Nouveau Tudric tulip
vase with foliate style handles on
a circular base.
- *height 21cm*
- **£680**   ● **Victor Arwas**

Japanese Silver Mirror ▼

- *19th century*
Japanese silver mirror centered
with a jade panel carved with
apple blossom, within a silver
embossed border with natural cut
jade and amethysts, and a carved
jade handle.
- *length 22cm*
- **£500**   ● **Barrett & Towning**

Art Nouveau Butter Dish ▶

- *circa 1900*
Silver Art Nouveau butter dish
with cut glass liner and lid with
tulip design, standing on bracket
tulip feet, by W. M. F.
- *12cm x 7cm*
- **£500**   ● **Victor Arwas**

Hip Flask by
St. George Unite ▲

- *circa 1890*
Faceted glass flask with silver
mounts, hinged stopper and base
by St. George Unite, made in
Birmingham.
- *height 16cm*
- **£275**   ● **Barrett & Towning**

Silver Hair Comb ▼

- *1870*
Tortoiseshell hair comb with
silver inlay grip with original
fitted box.
- *length 15cm*
- **£250**   ● **Tagor**

Viennese Silver
Jardinières ▼

- *1875*
Solid silver Austrian jardinière,
one of a pair, the body finely
chased, handles with cast figures.
Made in Vienna by Klincosch.
- *width 40cm*
- **£8,750 the set**   ● **Percy's**

Archibald Knox Candlesticks ◄

• *circa 1900*
One of a pair of pewter candlesticks by Archibald Knox for Liberty, with a tulip design, on a large circular base.
• *height 19cm*
• **£3,000**   • **Victor Arwas**

Silver Cruet Set ▲

• *circa 1880*
Silver cruet set with salt, mustard and pepper pot with lobbed lower bodies and gadrooned borders.
• *height 11cm*
• **£190**   • **H. Gregory**

French Liquor Set ▼

• *1880*
French liquor set of twelve silver cups with foliate scrolling and matching tray, engraved with the initials J. C.
• *height of cup 5cm*
• **£575**   • **Tagor**

Loving Cup ▲

• *circa 1900*
Tudric pewter loving cup with double handles with 'honesty flower' design and a cartouche with the inscription 'For Old Times Sake', by Veysey for Liberty.
• *height 20cm*
• **£650**   • **Victor Arwas**

Silver Centrepiece ▲

• *1865*
A silver centrepiece with finely chased figures of 'romantic' children by The Barnards. Fully hallmarked.
• *height 33cm*
• **£5,750**   • **Percy's**

Silver Salts ▶

• *circa 1760*
Pair of Georgian silver salts with beaded decoration and blue glass liners.
• *height 7cm*
• **£675**   • **Barrett & Towning**

Victorian Silver Cruet ◄
- **1867**

A fine solid silver cruet comprising ten items, with pierced scrolled sides and scrolled central handle, by G Angel, London.
- *25cm x 30cm*
- **£3,750**   • Percy's

Art Nouveau Frame ▲
- *circa 1900*

Silver and enamel Art Nouveau picture frame by William Connell.
- *height 23cm*
- **£2,800**   • Victor Arwas

Silver Teapot with Bee ▶
- *circa 1900*

Silver teapot with unusual foliate and insect design with a bee finial, and stylised bamboo spout and handle.
- *height 16cm*
- **£1,500**   • Tagor

Continental Pewter Plate ▼
- *circa 1790s*

Continental pewter plate with a rifle stamp on the border with a single reeded rim.
- *25.5cm*
- **£70**   • Jane Stewart

Tudric Jug ▲
- *circa 1900*

Tudric Liberty pewter 'fish and the sea' jug with brass handle, and the inscription U. C. C.
- *height 19cm*
- **£680**   • Victor Arwas

Liberty Biscuit Tin ▲
- *circa 1900*

Pewter tudric box by Archibald Knox with floral design.
- *height 12.5cm*
- **£1,200**   • Victor Arwas

Expert Tips

On most coasters one must look out for hallmark on the lower rim, which overlaps the wooden base.

Art Nouveau Sauce Boat ▶

- *circa 1900*
German Art Nouveau pewter
sauce-boat with fixed base
designed by Orovit.
- *height 12cm*
- £300 • **Victor Arwas**

Salts with Shell Feet ▲

- *1913*
Pair of silver circular salts with
a serpentine scalloped rim,
standing on three scalloped
feet.
- *diameter 7.5cm*
- £395 • **Barrett & Towning**

Scrolled Silver Box ▼

- *1840*
Oblong silver box with embossed
scrolling and floral designs and a
cartouche inscribed with the
name 'Hilda'.
- *length 13cm*
- £175 • **Barrett & Towning**

Silver Pepper Caster ▲

- *circa 1860*
Silver pepper caster of baluster
form with a pierced and engraved
cover surmounted by a finial lid.
- *height 19cm*
- £325 • **Barrett & Towning**

Silver Milk Jug ▶

- *circa 1940*
Silver milk jug with a lobbed
body, engraved and embossed
decoration and a reeded handle.
- *height 11cm*
- £300 • **Barrett & Towning**

Silver Tea Set ◀

- *circa 1851*
Three piece silver tea set with
large scrolled handle standing on
small paw feet.
- *height teapot 17cm*
- £540 • **H. Gregory**

Pewter Ice Bucket ◀

- *circa 1920*

Pewter ice bucket with tulip pattern, designed by Orivit.
- *20cm x 21cm*
- **£700**   • **Victor Arwas**

Silver Snuff Box ▲

- *circa 1939*

Small silver snuff box made in Sheffield, England.
- *6cm square*
- **£110**   • **Barrett & Towning**

Cigarette Case ▲

- *circa 1920*

Silver cigarette case with canted corners and diamond pattern design within plain borders.
- *length 14cm*
- **£68**   • **H. Gregory**

Silver Tea Infusion ▲

- *circa 1919*

Rare silver tea infuser in the form of an egg, of two sections with silver chain.
- *length 9.5cm*
- **£485**   • **Barrett & Towning**

Piped Tankard ▼

- *circa 1850*

English 'bucket'-type tankard with piped decoration and scrolled handle.
- *12cm x 14cm*
- **£70**   • **Jane Stewart**

Silver Fish Servers ▼

- *circa 1886*

Silver serving fish knife and fork in a presentation box from Frazier and Haws, Garrards, London.
- *length 28cm*
- **£595**   • **Barrett & Towning**

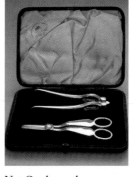

Nut Cracker and Grape Peeler ▲

- *circa 1904*

Silver nut cracker and grape peeler, made in Sheffield, in original silk lined and blue velvet box.
- *length 14cm*
- **£675**   • **Barrett & Towning**

Silver Mustard Pot ▼

- *circa 1896*

Silver mustard pot with hinged
lid and blue liner with a circular
scrolling pattern about the body.
- *height 6cm*
- **£225** • **Barrett & Towning**

Circular Mustard Pot ▼

- *circa 1929*

Mustard pot of drum design with
blue glass liner, hinged lid,
scrolled handle and scalloped
thumb piece.
- *height 5.5cm*
- **£248** • **Barrett & Towning**

Liberty Pitcher ▼

- *circa 1910*

Liberty green glass pitcher with a
pewter lid, handle and base.
- *height 21cm*
- **£1,200** • **Victor Arwas**

Palm Centrepiece ▲

- *circa 1880*

Silver palm centrepiece
supporting a glass oval dish. Part
of a set of three, by Bradbury of
England.
- *height 34cm*
- **£6,000** • **S. Kalms**

Dutch Water Urn ◄

- *circa 1780*

Dutch pewter pear shaped water
urn with scrolled handle, on
cabriole legs and round feet.
- *38cm x 23cm*
- **£250** • **Jane Stewart**

Silver Teapot with Bee ◀
- *circa* 1900

Silver teapot with unusual foliate and insect design with a bee finial, and stylised bamboo spout and handle.
- *height 16cm*
- £1,500   • Tagor

Silver Postal Weighing Scale ▼
- *1909*

Rare silver postal weighing scale with blue enamel, made in Birmingham.
- *height 7cm*
- £750   • Evonne Antiques

Silver Sugar Castor ▼
- *1906*

Silver sugar castor of baluster form made in Chester, with banded decoration a finial lid.
- *height 23*
- £395   • S. Kalms

Tudric Pewter Tankard ▲
- *1903*

Tudric pewter tankard with two large scrolled handles. Designed by David Veazey for Liberty & Co.
- *height 32cm*
- £995   • Liberty

Silver Shovel ▼
- *1872*

Miniature silver shovel with bone handle with an engraved foliate design made in Birmingham.
- *length 12cm*
- £375   • S. Kalms

Archibald Knox Bowl ◀
- *circa* 1900

Archibald Knox tudric pewter bowl designed for Liberty with a pierced frieze.
- *diameter 32cm*
- £1,500   • Victor Arwas

French Silver Bowl ◀

- *circa 1890*

Silver punch bowl/wine cooler with elaborate chasing and foliate designs, four scrolled handles, acanthus leaf swags and ribboning.
- *height 47cm*
- £32,500   • S. Kalms

Silver and Glass Jar ▶

- *1945*

Glass cosmetic container with a silver cover and a bone moon shaped thumb piece, made in London.
- *height 9cm*
- £150   • Evonne Antiques

Silver Bon-Bon Dish ▼

- *1901*

Liberty & Co. cymric silver bon-bon dish designed by Oliver Baker. Hallmarked 'Birmingham 1901'.
- *9cm x 10.5cm*
- £1,500   • Liberty

Art Nouveau Mirror ▲

- *circa 1930*

Art Nouveau silver mirror with elaborate scrolling and a young lady holding a light in the shape of a lily.
- *height 59cm*
- £4,500   • S. Kalms

Condiment Set ▲

- *1911*

Condiment set comprised of two glass bottles with faceted stoppers, on a silver stand with extended ring handle, supported on silver ball feet.
- *height 21cm*
- £240   • Evonne Antiques

Galleon Decanter ▶

- *1890*

Silver galleon, standing on wheels decorated with fruit and foliate designs, with small figures drinking and climbing the rigging, made by Bernard Muller.
- *66cm x 60cm*
- **£45,000**   • **S. Kalms**

George III Candlesticks ▼

- *1770*

A pair of English silver candlesticks of classical design with corinthian columns, standing on a raised plinth base with beading and floral designs, by Richard Rugg, London.
- *height 34cm*
- **£3,850**   • **Percy's**

Silver Blotter ▼

- *1921*

Silver blotter of plain design with chalice-shaped thumb piece.
- *length 17cm*
- **£280**   • **Evonne Antiques**

Silver Bed Pan ▶

- *circa 1780*

Rare English late Georgian silver bed pan of looking glass form, with a wide border and handle with banded decoration.
- *length 45cm*
- **£2,240**   • **Jane Stewart**

Quaiche ▼

- *1894*

Small glass quaiche with silver mounts and scrolled double handles.
- *diameter 11cm*
- **£150**   • **Evonne Antiques**

Birmingham Silver Rim ▲

- *1899*

Small glass match striker with silver rim, made in Birmingham.
- *height 7cm*
- **£180**   • **Evonne Antiques**

Dutch Urn ▼

- *circa 1800*

A Dutch urn and cover with an embossed floral leaf design and a wood knob finial.
- *13cm x 10cm*
- £65   • Jane Stewart

Pewter Ladle ▼

- *circa 1780*

English pewter soup ladle with shallow bowl and plain thumb piece.
- *length 32cm*
- £50   • Jane Stewart

Pot by Kayserzinn ▲

- *circa 1900*

German pewter Art Nouveau butter dish on raised feet, with foliate and tulip designs, by Kayserzinn.
- *height 13cm*
- £300   • Victor Arwas

Silver Salt and Pepper Pot ▲

- *circa 1923*

Matching silver salt and pepper pot, of octagonal baluster form with finial lid, from E. Johnson & Son Ltd., Derby.
- *height 9cm*
- £240   • Barrett & Towning

Continental Pewter Bowl ▼

- *18th century*

Continental pewter deep dish, with floral engraving to the centre, with a single reeded rim.
- *23cm*
- £70   • Jane Stewart

Cigarette Case ▼

- *circa 1920*

Silver cigarette case with meshed effect and lines of gold inlay.
- *length 12cm*
- £65   • H. Gregory

Pewter Continental Bowl ▼

- *circa 1900s*

Continental pewter bowl with a wide border and moulded rim.
- *Diameter 30cm*
- £120   • Jane Stewart

Silver Bowl ◄

- *1930*

Silver 'Crumpled Paper' bowl with fruit decoration.
- *height 16cm*
- £1,100   • S. Kalms

Set of Pewter Measures ◀

- *circa 1840*
Rare set of English pewter
tankards from quarter gill to quart
measure.
- *14cm x 14cm*
- **£3,250 a set** • **Jane Stewart**

Glass Decanter ▶

- *1881*
Glass decanter with silver
mounts, chain attached to silver
rim and cover with finial, by H.
W. Wilkinson, Sheffield,
England.
- *height 27cm*
- **£1,350** • **S. Kalms**

Conical Silver Vases ▼

- *circa 1930*
Two tall conical vases with
chased scrolling and cartouches
of cherubs, musicians, dancers
and revellers, surrounded by
foliage birds and flowers, standing
on a circular base, made in
Germany.
- *height 61cm*
- **£5,500** • **S. Kalms**

Half-Pint Pewter Tankard ▲

- *circa 1840*
English half-pint pewter tankard
with splayed lip and C scroll
handle on a pedestal foot.
- *11.5cm x 12cm*
- **£60** • **Jane Stewart**

Expert Tips

*When not in use, silver should
be kept away from contact
with the air, ideally in sealed,
airtight bags.*

French Pewter Dish ▶

- *circa 1900*
French pewter plate of Lada and
the swan, signed by Jules Desbois.
- *diameter 27.5cm*
- **£2,000** • **Victor Arwas**

Silver Goblets ▶
- **1970**

Set of four silver goblets with silver gilt interiors with rusticated stems on circular bases, by Christopher Lawrence.
- *height 15cm*
- **£1,000**   • Themes

French Measures ▼
- *circa 1850*

Set of French pewter jug measures from demi-litre to demi-decilitre.
- *17cm x 12cm*
- **£200**   • Jane Stewart

Pewter Coffee Pot ▼
- *circa 1860*

Coffee pot by James Dickson of Sheffield of baluster form with scroll handle and acorn leaf finial.
- *23cm x 23cm*
- **£70**   • Jane Stewart

Cigar Case ▲
- *circa 1920*

Silver cigar case with three compartments allowing for half caronas.
- *length 12cm*
- **£160**   • H. Gregory

English Quart Tankard ▼
- *circa 1860*

Pewter quart tankard with strap handle and banded decoration.
- *18cm x 13cm*
- **£100**   • Jane Stewart

Continental Pewter Plate ▲
- *circa 1780s*

Continental pewter plate with single reeded rim.
- *25cm*
- **£70**   • Jane Stewart

Georgian Silver Basket ◀
- *circa 1799*

Oval Georgian sweetmeat basket, with a swing handle, pierced foliate designs and apron support.
- *11cm x 38cm*
- **£4,000** • Barrett & Towning

Adam Style Teapot

- *circa 1860*

English Adam style pewter teapot with floral and swag decoration, surmounted by ivory finial.

- *16cm x 25cm*
- £65
- Jane Stewart

Silver Perfume Spray

- *circa 1910*

Silver perfume spray on a faceted glass circular bottle.

- *height 17cm*
- £175
- Barrett & Towning

Glass Sugar Shaker

- *circa 1906*

Glass sugar castor of baluster form, with a pierced silver cover, engraved floral designs and ball finial.

- *height 16.5cm*
- £225
- Barrett & Towning

English Pewter Ladle

- *circa 1820*

English pewter ladle with a wide circular bowl.

- *33cm*
- £50
- Jane Stewart

Pepper Caster

- *circa 1800*

English pewter pepper caster of baluster form with acorn finial.

- *12cm*
- £30
- Jane Stewart

Georgian Silver Candlesticks

- *1782*

A superb set of four Georgian silver candlesticks, fully hallmarked by John Parsons, Sheffield, England.

- *height 34cm*
- £10,750
- Percy's

Silver Cream Jug ▼
• *circa 1920*
Silver cream jug with scallop shell design and scrolled handle, supported on a raised circular foot.
• *height 11.5cm*
• **£317**   • **Barrett & Towning**

Tea and Coffee Service ▲
• *1842*
A solid silver four piece tea and coffee service of 'Melon' design. Fully hallmarked, by Charles Fox, London.
• *height of coffee pot 28cm*
• **£4,750**   • **Percy's**

Scent Bottle ▼
• *1890*
Late Victorian scent bottle, with a deeply cut glass body surmounted by a silver stopper with embossed floral and scallop designs.
• *height 15cm*
• **£250**   • **Evonne Antiques**

Claret Jug ▼
• *circa 1880*
Victorian claret jug with silver spout and collar with scrolled decoration, made in London.
• *height 21cm*
• **£1,350**   • **Tagor**

German Jardinières ◀
• *circa 1875*
A superb pair of jardinières with large double ring handles, the bodies finely chased and pierced.
• *width 40cm*
• **£7,500**   • **Percy's**

Regency Silver Coasters
- *1823*
A set of four coasters, finely chased with flowers and shells. Made in Sheffield by T & J Settle.
- *width 17.5cm*
- £5,750   • Percy's

Dutch Nautilus Cup
- *circa 1875*
A rare Dutch nautilus cup in the 17th century style. The shell is finely engraved with classical scenes.
- *height 25cm*
- £5,250   • Percy's

Teak Cigarette Box
- *1903*
Teak cigarette box within a silver frame with the letters 'Cigarettes' in silver on the lid.
- *width 13cm*
- £260   • H. Gregory

Cigarette Box
- *circa 1900*
Sheffield silver cigarette box with a diamond pattern lid and plain panel, the interior containing two compartments.
- *width 17cm*
- £180   • H. Gregory

'Neff' Model Ship
- *circa 1875*
A German solid silver model of a mythiczt.
- *28cm*
- £2,750   • Percy's

Silver Cruet Set ◄

- *circa 1930*

Silver Art Deco cruet set consisting of mustard, salt and pepper in the style of tankards.
- *height 5cm*
- £360   • H. Gregory

English Charger ▼

- *circa 1740*

Georgian English pewter charger, of plain design with a single reeded rim.
- *46cm*
- £350   • Jane Stewart

Silver Vesta Box ▲

- *circa 1880*

Ladies' silver vesta box with floral engraving and a plain shield panel, ring to the side.
- *length 5cm*
- £70   • H. Gregory

Silver Vesta Box ▲

- *circa 1880*

Small silver vesta box with floral engraving and a ring at the side.
- *length 3.5cm*
- £70   • H. Gregory

Vesta Box ▲

- *circa 1880*

Plain silver vesta box with hinged lid and striker on the base.
- *length 5.5cm*
- £72   • H. Gregory

Four Section Cigar Case ▲

- *circa 1930*

Four section silver plate cigar case.
- *length 13cm*
- £49   • H. Gregory

Georgian Silver Tureen ▶

- *circa 1825*

Georgian oval entrée dish of plain design with banded decoration, surmounted by a handle in the form of a coiled snake.
- *length 28cm*
- £895   • Barrett & Towning

Spoons and Fruit Scissors ▶

● *circa 1860*

Fruit scissors with a fleur de lys on the join and a pair of silver plated fruit spoons, with the initials J. E., complete with the original presentation box.

● *length 23cm*

● **£425** ● **Barrett & Towning**

Slim Cigarette Case ▲

● *circa 1920*

Slim silver cigarette case with a diamond pattern design within banded borders.

● *length 11cm*

● **£68** ● **H. Gregory**

Silver Sugar Spoon ▲

● *1816*

Silver sugar spoon, the bowl embossed with fruit, the letters J.R. on the handle and engraved lattice designs.

● *length 18cm*

● **£165** ● **Barrett & Towning**

Expert Tips

When deciding to purchase a silver box always check the hinges as they are are almost impossible to repair.

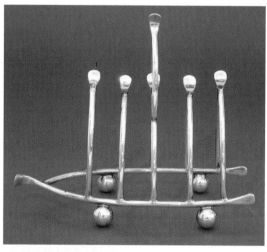

Wish Bone Toast Rack ▲

● *circa 1880*

Silver toast rack incorporating a wish bone design, standing on four ball feet.

● *height 13cm*

● **£155** ● **Barrett & Towning**

Silver Cigar Case ◀

● *circa 1920*

Silver bullet shaped cigar case with three compartments.

● *length 11cm*

● **£160** ● **H. Gregory**

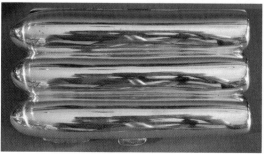

Georgian Silver Salt ▲

- *circa 1794*
Elegant silver Georgian salt with a fluted body, scrolled handles, standing on a square base.
- *height 8cm*
- **£210**   • **Barrett & Towning**

Set of Four Salts ▶

- **1883**
Set of four silver salts embossed with bird and floral designs, four silver spoons with gilt bowls, in original box finished in velvet and silk.
- *width of box 21cm*
- **£675**   • **Barrett & Towning**

Art Nouveau Creamer ▼

- *circa 1936*
Art Nouveau silver cream jug, with moulded lip, strap handle and raised on a square moulded base.
- *height 8.5cm*
- **£160**   • **Barrett & Towning**

Continental Pewter Dish ▼

- *circa 1790*
Continental dish with single reeded rim and the owner's initials I.F.B. on the front and rear.
- *diameter 35cm*
- **£200**   • **Jane Stewart**

Stamp and Cigarette Case ▼

- *circa 1910*
Silver stamp and cigarette case with blue enamel lid.
- *width 9cm*
- **£275**   • **Barrett & Towning**

Silver Cocktail Shaker ◀

- *circa 1910*
Art Deco silver cocktail shaker with plain sides and banded decoration.
- *height 22cm*
- **£575**   • **Barrett & Towning**

Silver Ash Tray ▶

• *1900*
Silver ashtray made in London
with five recesses within the
border.
• *width 8cm square*
• **£1,900**   • **H. Gregory**

Silver Art Nouveau Vase ▼

• *1850*
Silver Art Nouveau vase with
green glass lining and profuse
pierced decoration.
• *height 34cm*
• **£1,850**   • **Tagor**

Silver Soap Box ▲

• *circa 1888*
Victorian silver soap box of plain
design with curved corners.
• *width 8cm*
• **£225**   • **Barrett & Towning**

Four Silver Salts ▼

• *circa 1808*
Set of four urn-shaped silver salts
with gadrooned and fluted
decoration, made in London.
• *height 6cm*
• **£475**   • **Barrett & Towning**

Claret Jug ▲

• *circa 1880*
Victorian claret jug with silver
spout and collar with scrolled
decoration, made in London.
• *height 21cm*
• **£1,350**   • **Tagor**

Vignelli Carafe ▶

- **1970**
Christofle and Venini silver
carafe and six shots, designed by
Vignelli. Stamped Christofle,
Italy.
- *height of carafe 22.5cm*
- **£2,000**   • **Themes**

Silver Photograph Frame ▲

- **1935**
Silver photograph frame with a
concave design.
- *height 26cm*
- **£350**   • **Evonne Antiques**

Pair of Decanters ▶

- **1910**
Pair of glass decanters with silver
mounts and handle, made by
Walker and Hall.
- *height 23cm*
- **£3,900**   • **S. Kalms**

Twenties Toast Rack ▼

- *circa 1929*
Silver Art Deco toast rack with
six bays, canted corners and a
pieced apron.
- *height 6cm*
- **£190**   • **Barrett & Towning**

Archibald Knox Barrel ◀

- **1902**
Tudric pewter biscuit barrel
designed by Archibald Knox,
with blue and green enamelling.
- *15cm x 13cm*
- **£1,500**   • **Liberty**

Silver Tea Strainer ▶
- **1942**
Silver double-handled tea strainer
made in London with pierced and
chassed decoration.
- *length 16cm*
- **£250** • S. Kalms

French Liquor Set ▼
- **1880**
French liquor set of twelve silver
cups with foliate scrolling, and
matching tray, engraved with the
initials J. C.
- *height of cup 5cm*
- **£575** • Tagor

German Armorial Dish ▼
- **19th century**
German armorial pewter plate
decorated with the coat of arms,
within a lobed border and a wide
rim with floral sprays.
- *diameter 33cm*
- **£175** • Jane Stewart

Georgian Ink Well ▶
- **1767**
Georgian inkwell set in a pierced
tray standing on small ball and
claw feet, made in London.
- *8cm x 18cm*
- **£1,950** • S. Kalms

Silver Cigar Box ▲
- **circa 1912**
Fine silver cigar case with four
sections engraved with a floral
design centered with a vacant
panel.
- *length 13cm*
- **£425** • Barrett & Towning

Pilgrim Bottle ▶
- **1884**
Silver pilgrim bottle of pineapple
form, made in London, with lion
mask handles linked with a silver
chain.
- *height 32cm*
- **£4,740** • S. Kalms

Liberty & Co. Tea Set ◀
- **1903**

Pewter tudric tea set with turquoise enamel mounts, and tray designed by Archibald Knox for Liberty & Co.
- *length 42cm*
- **£4,500**   • Liberty

Silver Pierced Dish ▼
- **1950**

Silver dish with pierced border, supported on a pedestal base with banded decoration.
- *height 15cm*
- **£175**   • S. Kalms

Silver Gilt Heron Cigarette Box ▲
- *circa 1909*

Silver gilt heron standing on a silver box, the mechanism opens the cover for the heron to bend and pick out a cigarette. Made by W. H. Sparrow of Birmingham.
- *height 30cm*
- **£4,250**   • S. Kalms

Set of Salts ▶
- **1880**

Set of six silver gilt salts with individual spoons with original presentation box.
- *width 24cm*
- **£1,100**   • S. Kalms

Polar Bear Inkwell ◀
- *circa 1900*

Continental silver polar bear inkwell and tray, with a pair of silver candlesticks, together with silver letter opener.
- *18cm x 29cm*
- **£2,250**   • S. Kalms

Swan Centrepiece

- *circa 1880*

Victorian centrepiece by
Elkington of England, with
elaborate foliate chassed designs.
The stand supporting an opaque
glass dish, flanked by two silver
swans on a moulded base standing
on silver scrolled supports.
- *height 34cm x 51cm*
- £6,500   • S. Kalms

Silver Toast Rack

- *circa 1930*

Elegant silver toast rack with an
ecclesiastical theme and a cross
thumb piece.
- *width 8cm*
- £95   • Barrett & Towning

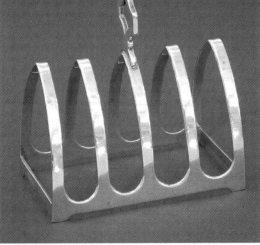

Silver Frame

- *1899*

William Commings heart shaped
silver frame with pierced
decoration, cherub, scrolling and
mask designs.
- *height 18cm*
- £450   • Evonne Antiques

Expert Tips

*Large and decorative silver
items which are difficult to
clean may be professionally
lacquered with a fine layer of
plastic, which is invisible to the
naked eye.*

Tudric Rose Bowl

- *circa 1903*

Liberty & Co tudric rose bowl
with stylised foliate designs
signed by Archibald Knox.
Previously attributed to Rex
Silver.
- *23cm x 19cm*
- £2,250   • Liberty

Horse Hooves Ink Well ▶

- *circa 1900*

Silver writing set made of two
horse hooves, set in silver with
two ink wells with silver covers,
standing on a silver base on ball
feet.
- *width 46cm*
- £900 • S. Kalms

Small Silver Teapot ▼

- *circa 1904*

Edwardian silver teapot of small
proportions with bone handle
and finial lid.
- *height 15cm*
- £240 • Evonne Antiques

William Commings Frame ▼

- *1899*

Silver William Commings
hourglass frame decorated with
cherubs and folia.
- *height 22cm*
- £450 • Evonne Antiques

Letter Rack ▲

- *1937*

Silver letter rack, with a double
circle design, mounted on a
mahogany base.
- *height 17cm*
- £350 • Evonne Antiques

Victorian Sauce Boat ◀

- *circa 1891*

Victorian silver sauce boat with
vacant panel within embossed
decoration raised on a splayed
foot.
- *height 9.5cm*
- £240 • Barrett & Towning

Pair of Match Strikers ◀
- **1897**
Pair of glass match strikers with
silver rims, made in Birmingham.
- *height 10.5cm*
- **£750**   • **Evonne Antiques**

Victorian Pewter Cup ▼
- *circa 1870*
Victorian engraved pewter cup
with floral engraving, scrolled
handle and banded decoration,
inscribed with the name Maude.
- *7.5cm x 10cm*
- **£50**   • **Jane Stewart**

Silver Tea Strainer ▼
- *circa 1920*
Silver tea strainer, made in
Sheffield, England, with pierced
and engraved decoration and
lattice handle.
- *length 13cm*
- **£160**   • **Barrett & Towning**

Sheffield Silver Dish ▼
- **1937**
Octagonal silver dish with double
handles of ivory, made in
Sheffield, England.
- *diameter*
- **£180**   • **Evonne Antiques**

Expert Tips

*Regular cleaning of antique
silver produces a patina quite
different from that of new silver,
and one which cannot be
accelerated or reproduced
artifically.*

Silver and Glass Bowl ▶
- **1920**
Ladies' melon shaped glass bowl
with a silver banded collar and
tortoiseshell insert.
- *diameter15cm*
- **£280**   • **Evonne Antiques**

Sporting Items

The love of sport is truly international, from major events such as the Olympics to a game of cricket on the village green.

Nostalgia plays an important part in purchasing sporting related items, which have an extensive and world-wide appeal. From the avid collector seeking out his favourite sporting hero's football, to the interior designer furnishing a speciality sports restaurant, all contribute to the ever increasing demand for sporting memorabilia. The relatively new interest in football (soccer) memorabilia and the huge sponsorship given to sport has also helped to expand the market for sporting related items. A football clubhouse may spend vast amounts of money adorning their walls with football memorabilia for example shirts, caps and trophies of famous sporting heroes. This trend has pushed up the prices world-wide, and this has been further exacerbated by the profileration of sport themed restaurants emerging, especially in the United States.

General

Child's Football Boots ▶
- **1930**
Child's leather football boots in original condition.
- *length 18cm*
- **£125**   • Sporting Times

Riding Crop ▲
- *circa 1930*
Bamboo riding crop with 13 crosses on the bone handle, above a silver collar, engraved with the letters H. S.
- *length 61cm*
- **£65**   • Sporting Times

Bowling Balls ▼
- *circa 1900*
Pair of lignum bowling balls with ivory central plaques, on a stand.
- *12cm*
- **£110**   • Henry Gregory

Trophy Cap ▲
- **1923-24**
Black velvet cap with gold braiding and tassel with the letters S. S. O. B. in gold.
- *medium*
- **£45**   • Sporting Times

Snow Shoes ▲

- *circa 1900*

Canadian snow shoes made from wood with leather mesh base and fasteners.

- *length 103cm*
- **£95**   • **Sporting Times**

Bamboo Shooting Stick ▶

- *circa 1920*

Bamboo shooting stick with a folding rattan seat, with metal spike and brass fittings.

- *length 75cm*
- **£195**   • **Sporting Times**

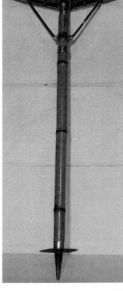

Leather Football Boots ▼

- *1930*

Leather football boots in excellent condition appointed by Stanley Matthews.

- *length 30cm*
- **£125**   • **Sporting Times**

Goggles ▲

- *1940*

Goggles with brass and metal rim on a leather backing with adjustable rubber straps.

- *width 18cm*
- **£28**   • **Sporting Times**

Thermos & Leather Case ▼

- *circa 1900*

Brass thermos with original leather case with the inscription 'B. R.' and a long leather carrying handle with leather buckle.

- *height 38cm*
- **£125**   • **Sporting Times**

Billiard Scorer ◀

- *circa 1910*

Wall-mounted mahogany billiard scorer, with brass numerals and sliding markers.

- *92cm x 35cm*
- **£280**   • **Henry Gregory**

Leather Riding Boots ▼
- **1930**

Pair of gentleman's brown leather polo boots with laces, three straps with brass buckles and wood shoe trees.
- *height 61cm*
- **£170**　　• Sporting Times

Leather Football ▼
- *circa 1940*

Novelty miniature leather football.
- *miniature*
- **£20**　　• Sporting Times

Child's Riding Seat ▶
- **1880**

A child's saddle made from wicker, with curved base and leather fasteners, to fit on a pony.
- *height 57cm*
- **£275**　　• Sporting Times

Expert Tips

Hesitate before buying an over-polished sporting item such as a saddle bag or football, as this can decrease the value of the item.

Leather Gators ▲
- *circa 1920*

Pair of leather gators with leather straps and metal buckles.
- *length 29cm*
- **£28**　　• Sporting Times

Saddle Bags ▲
- *circa 1930*

Brown leather saddle bags in fine condition with leather straps and brass buckles.
- *length 18cm*
- **£155**　　• Sporting Times

Football Trophy ▼
- **1956**

Football trophy presented to Mr. and Mrs. Clarke of Berkhampstead Football Club 1956.
- *height 17cm*
- **£45**　　• Sporting Times

Leather Gaming Bag ▼
- *circa 1900*

Leather gaming bag in original condition with brass clasp and leather carrying strap.
- *width 30cm*
- **£125**　　• Sporting Times

Travelling Primus Stove ▲
- *circa 1890*
Travelling primus in a circular leather case with leather strap.
- *diameter 13cm*
- £155   • Sporting Times

French Boules ▼
- *circa 1900*
Pair of French boules with original leather carrying strap.
- *diameter 20cm*
- £32   • Sporting Times

Riding Whip ▶
- *circa 1900*
Leather riding whip, with silver collar.
- *length 170cm*
- £140   • Henry Gregory

Travelling Sandwich Tin ▲
- *circa 1890*
Travelling leather case, the interior enclosing a sandwich tin and flask.
- *15cm x 15cm*
- £155   • Sporting Times

Child's Skis ▼
- *1920s*
Child's wooden skis with matching poles and bindings.
- *105cm x 8cm*
- £120   • Henry Gregory

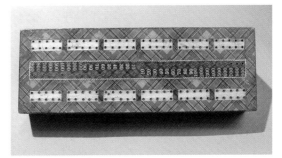

B. C. F. C. Cap ▼
- *1933*
B. C. F. C. velvet blue and maroon football cap with silver braiding and tassel on the inside 'English manufactured Christys, London, Horton Stephens, Ltd., The Shops Brighton College and Ward 1933–45.
- *diameter 20cm*
- £45   • Sporting Times

Cribbage Board ▼
- *circa 1900*
Marchline tartan ware cribbage board box.
- *26cm x 10cm*
- £310   • Henry Gregory

Wall Billiard Scorer ▲

- *circa 1910*
Mahogany and brass billiard scorer, with a slate panel in the centre.
- *60cm x 105cm*
- £700   • **Henry Gregory**

Silver Football Tropy ▼

- *1928*
Silver footballer trophy presented to the Alexanders Welfare Football League for the Annual Competition London.
- *45cm x 22cm*
- £680   • **Henry Gregory**

Brass Binoculars ▶

- *circa 1880*
Silver-plated brass binoculars engraved with hunting scenes.
- *5.5cm x 9cm*
- £120   • **Henry Gregory**

Swiss Army Ice Pick ▲

- *1940s*
Wooden ice pick with steel head and spike made for the Swiss Army.
- *90cm*
- £70   • **Henry Gregory**

Tennis Press ▼

- *circa 1920*
Mahogany tennis press in excellent condition with brass fittings.
- *diameter 27cm*
- £155   • **Sporting Times**

Rugby Ball ▼

- *1950s*
Brown leather rugby ball with original stitching.
- *33cm x 18cm*
- £85   • **Henry Gregory**

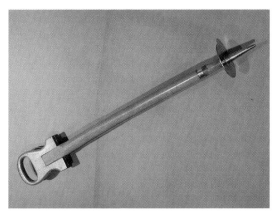

Oak Shooting Stick ▲

- *circa 1920*

Light oak shooting stick, with plain wooden seat and metal spike.
- *82cm*
- **£140**   • **Henry Gregory**

Tartan Shooting Stick ▲

- *1950s*

Chrome shooting stick with hinged seat and tartan liner.
- *83cm*
- **£48**   • **Henry Gregory**

Shooting Stick ▲

- *circa 1900*

Bamboo shooting stick, with hinged seat and brass fittings.
- *80cm*
- **£150**   • **Henry Gregory**

Propellor ▼

- *circa 1918*

Propellor belonging to an airplane made from mahogany with brass protective strips.
- *230cm*
- **£1,500**   • **Henry Gregory**

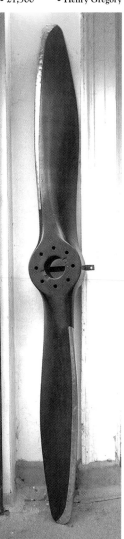

Bottle Opener ◄

- *circa 1940*

Metal bottle opener in the form of a jockey's riding cap, decorated with red and white enamel.
- *diameter 7cm*
- **£45**   • **Sporting Times**

Leather Fencing Mask ▼
- *circa 1890*
Leather Kendo fencing mask with metal mesh and leather padded interior.
- *diameter 18cm*
- £95   • Sporting Times

Leather Flying Helmet ▼
- *circa 1940*
Leather flying helmet with leather chin strap and headphone connectors.
- *medium*
- £110   • Sporting Times

Richie Benaud Bat ▼
- *1940*
Richie Benaud autographed cricket bat.
- *78cm*
- £68   • Henry Gregory

Stuart Surridge Bat ▶
- *1940s*
Stuart Surridge autograph Ken Barrington Cricket bat.
- *78cm*
- £72   • Henry Gregory

Croquet Mallet ▲
- *circa 1900*
Croquet mallet by Jacques, brass bound with original canvas case.
- *95cm*
- £95   • Henry Gregory

Football ▼
- *1950s*
Brown leather football in original condition.
- *25cm*
- £70   • Henry Gregory

York Rowing Cap ▼
- *1940s*
Rowing cap with the braid and cap badge of York City Rowing Club.
- *29cm x 18cm*
- £50   • Henry Gregory

Fishtail Tennis Racket ◀
- *circa 1900*
Fishtail tennis racket. Two colour string. Concave wedge.
- *68cm x 23cm*
- £180   • Henry Gregory

Fishing

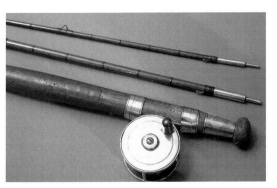

Wicker Creel ▼

- *circa 1940*
Wicker fishing creel with
adjustable leather carrying strap
with fasteners.
- *width 26cm*
- £55   • Sporting Times

Fishing Basket ▼

- *circa 1940*
Fine split reed fishing basket with
leather carrying strap and buckle
fasteners, on circular legs with a
canvas strap.
- *35cm x 42cm*
- £65   • Old School

Brass Telescopic Gaff ▶

- *circa 1920*
Brass telescopic gaff with turned
wooden handle.
- *length 61cm*
- £120   • Sporting Times

Brown Salatopia ▲

- *circa 1920*
Brown linen Salatopia hunting
hat with a leather lining and the
maker's inscription in gold
lettering 'by S. H. Batcha &
Sons, Moore Market, Madras'.
- *width 34cm*
- £60   • Sporting Times

Fly Rod ◀

- *circa 1880*
Green heart fly rod of three
sections with machine reels.
- *300cm*
- £150   • Henry Gregory

Japanned Fly Box ▲

- *circa 1910*
Tortoiseshell bakelite fly box with
ten ranks of fly hooks, containing
assorted flies.
- *21cm x 12cm*
- £95   • Henry Gregory

Landing Net ▲

- *circa 1900*
Landing net with tooled brass
fittings and a wood handle.
- *length 78cm*
- £120   • Sporting Times

Expert Tips

*Finely made early reels of brass,
ivorene and ebonite are highly
desirable. Names to look out for
include Hardy Bros, Charles
Farlow and S. Allcock.*

Fly Rod ◀
- *circa 1880*

Green heart trout rod of three sections, with brass reel and ivory handle.
- *280cm*
- £190 • Henry Gregory

Fly Box ▼
- *circa 1915*

Leather lined box with twelve glass and alloy containers for flies, with original tweezers and pocket.
- *13cm x 10cm*
- £90 • Henry Gregory

Small Fishing Reel ◀
- *circa 1920–40*

Small wood fishing reel with a brass plate and turned decoration.
- *diameter 7cm*
- £25 • Sporting Times

Fishing Reel ▼
- *circa 1920–40*

Wood fishing reel with brass handles and plate with turned decoration.
- *diameter 10cm*
- £45 • Sporting Times

Leather Fly Wallet ▼
- *circa 1920–40*

Leather fly wallet with eight compartments.
- *width 16cm*
- £28 • Sporting Times

Wood Fishing Reel ▼
- *circa 1920–40*

Wood fishing reel with banded decoration, brass fittings and ebonised double handles.
- *diameter 8cm*
- £35 • Sporting Times

Hardy Fly Box ◀
- *circa 1920*

Hardy alloy fly box, includes collection of trout flies.
- *13cm x 10cm*
- £110 • Henry Gregory

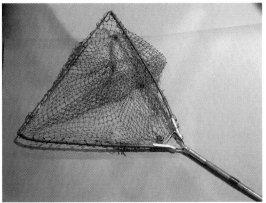

Hardy Landing Net ◀

- *circa 1890*

Hardy's triangular folding landing net with brass fittings.

- *115cm x 48cm*
- £230   • Henry Gregory

Starback Fishing Reel ▲

- *circa 1920–40*

Starback wood fishing reel with turned decoration and brass fittings.

- *diameter 12cm*
- £55   • Sporting Times

Hardy Fishing Reel ▲

- *circa 1930*

Hardy platewind fishing reel. Silex no 2.

- *10cm*
- £280   • Henry Gregory

Brass Reels ▲

- *circa 1910*

Three brass fly fishing reels.

- *7cm/left; 5.5cm/centre; 5cm/right*
- £35-50   • Henry Gregory

Wood Reels ▶

- *circa 1920*

Two wooden fly fishing reels with brass cross backs.

- *9cm/left; 9cm/right*
- £45-90   • Henry Gregory

Willow Creel ▼

- *circa 1900*

Small willow fishing creel with leather strap handle.

- *25cm x 19cm*
- £90   • Henry Gregory

Starbacks Reel ▲

- *circa 1920–40*

Starback wooden fishing reel with brass fittings and double handles.

- *diameter 9cm*
- £58   • Sporting Times

Allcocks Reel ◀

- *circa 1920–40*

Wood fishing reel by Allcocks with brass fittings and ebonised handles.

- *diameter 9cm*
- £50   • Sporting Times

Shooting

Leather Gun Case ▼
- *circa 1890*
Leather leg of mutton gun case
with leather shoulder strap and
carrying handle.
- *length 79cm*
- **£125** • **Sporting Times**

Cartridge Case ▶
- *circa 1890*
Gannochy loader canvas
cartridge case with holders for 30
rounds of ammunition.
- *26cm x 13cm*
- **£1,500** • **Holland**

Magazine Case ▲
- *circa 1920*
Ammunition case with brass
fittings and leather straps by
Penry Williams, Middlesbrough.
- *41cm x 16cm*
- **£950** • **Holland**

Magazine Box ▼
- *circa 1890*
Leather magazine box with strap,
buckle and a lock, by James
MacNaughton, Gun and Rifle
Maker, Edinburgh.
- *23cm x 24cm*
- **£650** • **Holland**

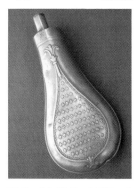

Brass Powder Flask ▲
- *circa 1875*
Brass black powder flask with
embossed decoration.
- *10cm x 19cm*
- **£48** • **Holland**

Holland & Holland Rifle ◀
- *2001*
Holland & Holland 375 H&H.
New bolt-action magazine rifle.
- *length 119cm*
- **£15,615** • **Holland**

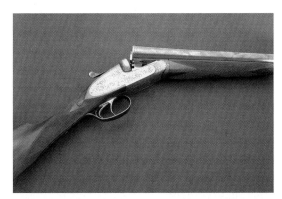

12-Bore Shotgun ◀

- **1939**

Holland & Holland Royal self opener. 12-bore shotgun, with double trigger.
- length 115cm
- £18,000 • Holland

Crocodile Rifle Case ▼

- *circa 1925*

Rifle case made from a fine crocodile skin, with leather straps and carrying handle, made by Manton and Co, Delhi & Calcutta, India.
- 76cm x 18cm
- £1,200 • Holland

Expert Tips

It is important to know the barrel wall thickness of an old, well used shotgun before shooting it. A rule of thumb states that the minimum barrel wall thickness should be .020" in a 12-bore gun.

Leg of Mutton Gun Case ▼

- *circa 1930*

Leg of mutton leather gun case with carrying handle and shoulder strap.
- length 89cm
- £550 • Holland

London Gun Department ▲

- *circa 1880*

Army and Navy C.S.L. London Gun Department ammunition case.
- 27cm x 13cm
- £975 • Holland

Holland & Holland Gun ▶

- **1929**

Holland and Holland leather gun and rifle case, with original inscription, brass fitting and well-fitted red felt interior.
- 74cm x 24cm
- £1,500 • Holland

Royal Rifle ◀

- **1945**

Holland & Holland Royal model 300 back-action double rifle, with sights.
- *length 114cm*
- **£32,000** • **Holland**

Cartridge Case ▲

- *circa 1890*

Gannochy loader leather cartridge case with canvas shoulder strap, made by McArthur and Prain.
- *25cm x 9cm*
- **£1,200** • **Holland**

4-Bore Shotgun ▲

- **1928**

Holland and Holland 4-bore shotgun with black powder only.
- *length 150cm*
- **£5,500** • **Holland**

Gun Case ▼

- *circa 1890*

Leather gun case with brass reinforced corners and leather carrying handle.
- *30cm x 82cm*
- **£380** • **Henry Gregory**

20-Bore Shotgun ▶

- **2001**

Holland & Holland sporting over and under 20-bore single-trigger shotgun.
- *length 115cm*
- **£25,000** • **Holland**

Bullet Mould ▼

- *circa 1895*

16-bore brass bullet mould. Paradox stock.
- *27cm x 8cm*
- **£550** • **Holland**

Pistol ▲

- *circa 1840*

Flintlock percussion double-barrel pistol with back-action locks, engraved lockplates and trigger guards.
- *25cm x 10cm*
- **£430** • **Holland**

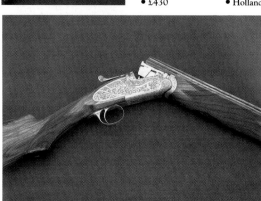

Expert Tips

When purchasing firearms it is important to ensure that they come with a proofing certifcate of fireworthiness.

Taxidermy

Photographers often use stuffed animals for advertisements because of their lifelike and naturalistic pose.

The art of taxidermy as a technique for keeping animals, birds, insects and fish in a preserved state is of great importance to both the scientist, academic researcher and sportsmen alike. Taxidermy has always been a popular and desirable way of preserving a trophy, especially at the turn of the century when big game was hunted in Africa and India. Nowadays however, it is more usual to find a smaller stuffed animal, such as your Aunt Betty's favourite dog, than to find a large stuffed lion in someone's house. These wilder and more exotic animals can now be found decorating a film set or photo shoot, where they are being used more and more, not only because they don't move, but also because it is a lot safer and cheaper than working with the real thing.

In the past, before the advent of photography and television, the majority of people would not have known what a polar bear, tiger or chameleon looked like, except from drawings or paintings.

Albino Cobra ▼

- *20th century*
Albino cobra shown in an aggressive pose.
- *60cm x 28cm*
- **£195**   • **Get Stuffed**

Mallard ▲

- *20th century*
Two male mallards, one shown standing and the other recumbent.
- *40cm x 64cm*
- **£295**   • **Get Stuffed**

Hooded Crow ▼

- *20th century*
Hooded crow shown perched on a branch and mounted on a plinth base.
- *57cm x 28cm*
- **£125**   • **Get Stuffed**

Bullfrog ◄

- *20th century*
Bullfrog skeleton in sections with documentation.
- *30cm x 40cm*
- **£140**   • **Get Stuffed**

479

Cock Pheasant ▲

● *20th century*
Cock pheasant in flight supported
by a branch and mounted on an
oval wooden base.
● *64cm x 70cm*
● **£175**   ● Get Stuffed

Magpie ▲

● *20th century*
Magpie perched on a wooden
branch and mounted on a
mahogany base.
● *52cm x 32cm*
● **£95**   ● Get Stuffed

Chameleon ▲

● *20th century*
Chameleon with a curious
expression shown with branch.
● *23cm x 38cm*
● **£175**   ● Get Stuffed

Bush Baby ▼

● *20th century*
Bush baby in good condition,
naturalistically posed within the
branches of a tree.
● *60cm x 54cm*
● **£195**   ● Get Stuffed

Teal ▼

● *20th century*
Teal with striking markings
mounted on a branch.
● *27cm x 25cm*
● **£95**   ● Get Stuffed

Victorian Dome ▼

● *circa 1880*
Victorian glass dome containing
tropical birds shown against a
painted background.
● *45cm x 42cm*
● **£450**   ● Get Stuffed

Amazon Parrots ▲

● *20th century*
Two Amazon parrots, theatrically
mounted on a branch.
● *55cm x 32cm*
● **£195**   ● Get Stuffed

Capucin Monkey ▲

● *20th century*
Capucin monkey mounted on a
branch on a large circular base.
● *60cm x 38cm*
● **£180**   ● Get Stuffed

Snipe ▲

● *20th century*
Snipe in good condition and
poised on a branch.
● *22cm x 25cm*
● **£75**   ● Get Stuffed

Tawny Owl ▼

● *20th century*
Tawny owl naturalistically posed and mounted on a circular base, with original glass dome.
● *55cm x 27cm*
● **£395**   ● **Get Stuffed**

Eagle Owl ▼

● *20th century*
Eagle owl in fine condition with a good expression mounted on a circular base.
● *65cm x 35cm*
● **£550**   ● **Get Stuffed**

Sparrowhawk ▼

● *20th century*
Sparrowhawk with wings pinned back.
● *27cm x 35cm*
● **£190**   ● **Get Stuffed**

Yorkshire Terrier ▲

● *20th century*
Yorkshire terrier seated with a curious expression and a red ribbon.
● *30cm x 20cm*
● **£245**   ● **Get Stuffed**

Tropical Birds ▲

● *circa 1880*
Victorian glass dome containing various tropical birds.
● *54cm x 36cm*
● **£650**   ● **Get Stuffed**

Roach ▼

● *1996*
Roach in a bow fronted case with natural grasses and weeds, with gilt lettering documenting the catch.
● *32cm x 50cm*
● **£385**   ● **Get Stuffed**

Barn Owl ▼

● *20th century*
Barn owl with wings outstretched at the point of take off, mounted on a branch.
● *70cm x 70cm*
● **£275**   ● **Get Stuffed**

Red Fox ▼

● *20th century*
Red fox vixen shown recumbent with head slightly raised.
● *35cm x 57cm*
● **£200**   ● **Get Stuffed**

Textiles & Fans

Most old textiles are too fragile to be put to their original use but they are enjoying a revival as wall hangings.

The interest in textiles has increased considerably in the past few years. They are not only popular because of their decorative appeal, they also give us an insight into history and the lives of the women who created them, from those who sewed for necessity, for example making clothes and bed covers, to those ladies of leisure who occupied their days at embroidery or needlepoint for cushion covers, fire screens and wall tapestries.

Samplers were originally used as a reference for stitch patterns, which could then be copied. Later they were used to record a child's name and age, houses, gardens, animals or plants, all common features on samplers.

The earliest English sampler known dates back to 1598, and is on display in the Victorian and Albert Museum in London, amongst a large selection of textiles and tapestries.

Patchwork quilts have a traditional quality, some come with geometric designs, while others have highly elaborate and decorative patterns.

Lobster-Tail Dress ▼
- *circa 1880*

Small Victorian cream cotton dress with lace trimming frill and lace 'lobster tail'.
- *small*
- **£595**   • Sheila Cook

Beaded Armorial Design ▲
- *1880*

Beaded armorial design on a turquoise background with a stylised fleur de lys surrounded by gold thistles, within a floral border.
- *75cm x 55cm*
- **£750**   • Sheila Cook

Silk Waistcoat ▼
- *circa 1770*

Gentleman's gold silk waistcoat with two pockets embroidered with trailing yellow and blue flowers, and maroon, pink and cream folia, surrounding two cartouches of embroidered silk, above insertions of lace and circular panels of painted silk.
- *medium*
- **£595**   • Sheila Cook

Victorian Lilac Quilt ◄
- *circa 1880*

Victorian lilac patterned quilt with small lilac flowers within plain borders.
- *160cm x 494cm*
- **£475**   • Sheila Cook

Welsh Patchwork Quilt ▲

- *circa 1880*
Welsh patchwork quilt with a white and lilac diamond design centered with lilac floral sprays.
- *80cm x 80cm*
- **£650**   • Sheila Cook

Smoking Hat ▲

- *circa 1880*
Black velvet smoking hat with white embroidered floral design, a central yellow silk button, pink gold and white tassel, with original box in good original condition.
- *size 7*
- **£165**   • Sheila Cook

Cut Pile Cushion Cover ▼

- *circa 1880*
Cut pile Victorian cushion cover with a red, green and pink geometric design.
- *42cm x 30cm*
- **£95**   • Sheila Cook

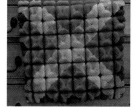

Ivory Fan ▼

- *circa 1904*
Cream silk fan with a trailing design of pink and yellow apple blossom mounted on carved ivory spines.
- *length 35cm*
- **£125**   • Sheila Cook

Slipper Pattern ▼

- *circa 1850*
Fine continental unused beaded slipper 'cut out' pattern, with a turquoise background, pink and yellow flowers and two deer by a river.
- *length 22cm*
- **£225**   • Sheila Cook

Purple Silk Kimono ▲

- *circa 1900*
Purple silk kimono with trailing pink apple blossom design.
- *medium*
- **£295**   • Sheila Cook

Gentleman's Smoking Hat ▲

- *circa 1880*
Black velvet gentleman's smoking hat with trailing foliate designs of pink and blue flowers, surmounted by a red satin-covered button on the top with a trailing green, white and red tassel.
- *size 6*
- **£110**   • Sheila Cook

Beaded Pelmet ◄

- *circa 1880*
Beaded cream pelmet with red tassel design below a gold and red diamond design.
- *length 320cm*
- **£495**   • Sheila Cook

Patchwork Quilt ▼

- *circa 1840–70*

Victorian patchwork quilt made up of predominantly pink and white hexagonal patches dating from the mid 19th century.

- *250cm sq*
- £895   • Sheila Cook

Patchwork Quilt ▼

- *circa 1950*

Patchwork quilt with a bold, multi-coloured and patterned, geometric design.

- *160cm x 156cm*
- £195   • Sheila Cook

Silk Smoking Hat ▲

- *circa 1870*

Brown silk smoking hat with trailing foliate embroidery of small white flowers.

- *size 6*
- £125   • Sheila Cook

Tartan Umbrella ▲

- *circa 1930*

Tartan umbrella with a handle in the shape of a swan with glass eyes.

- *length 67cm*
- £65   • Sheila Cook

Cream Child's Dress ▶

- *circa 1880*

Cream cotton child's dress with lace trim and navy blue ribboning on the hips and collar.

- *small*
- £265   • Sheila Cook

Victorian Cushion Cover ▼

- *circa 1880*

Cut pile cushion cover with a red and black diamond geometric design.

- *40cm x 45cm*
- £95   • Sheila Cook

Gentleman's Slipper Cut Out ▼

- *circa 1880*

Gentleman's unused embroidered slipper 'cut out' with a diamond design of cream, beige and variegated reds within black borders.

- *size 9*
- £95   • Sheila Cook

Mother of Pearl Fan ▲

- *circa 1910*

Cream silk lace fan covered with cream floral lace and a mother of pearl handle.
- *length 29cm*
- £275 • Sheila Cook

Red Lady's Hat ▲

- *circa 1920*

Red lady's soft silk mesh hat by Pauline Louy's, decorated with red felt flowers.
- *medium*
- £145 • Sheila Cook

Russian-Style Cape and Hat ▲

- *circa 1950*

Dramatic red Russian-style cape with black embroidery and white fur lining, with matching hat.
- *medium*
- £695 • Sheila Cook

Lace Fan ▼

- *circa 1905*

Cream lace fan with silk backing, and cream ivory handle with a cartouche of a raised lily.
- *length 32cm*
- £375 • Sheila Cook

Lady's Parasol ▲

- *circa 1920*

Lady's parasol with a black floral design and a handle with a black and beige geometric pattern.
- *length 53cm*
- £95 • Sheila Cook

Child's Shoes ◀

- *1870*

Child's leather shoes with black studs and metal fittings.
- *length 13cm*
- £65 • Sheila Cook

Italian Allegorical Panels ▼

- *1763*

Rare set of Italian silk-work allegorical panels signed Gaetano Pati, Rome. Part of a set of eight panels composed of fine silk threads, arranged and pressed into wax. The facial and body detailing is hand painted onto finely woven silk. The tonal detailing and intricacy is very fine.
- *34cm x 27cm*
- £32,000 • Anthony Outred

Toys, Games & Dolls

Until the 1940s the largest producers of toys were based in Germany, where they also created special versions of toys for export.

The international market for antique toys is extremely strong. Toy cars are very popular and include those manufactured by the early French C.I.J. Company in the late 1920s, commemorating the Grand Prix, along with British Dinky and Matchbox cars, and the German Orober vans, which have also risen steadily in value. German tinplate toys by Carette, Gunthermann and Lehmann, made between 1900 and 1930, are fetching premium prices. These companies also produced ships, aeroplanes and figures, all of which were pieces of remarkable engineering and are suitable for the serious collector. British manufacturers such as Wells, Brimtoy and Chad Valley began to compete with the Continental market in the 1930s and 40s, producing cars, aeroplanes and trains on a cheaper basis. At this time Tri-Ang began to produce small tinplate commercial vehicles with clockwork mechanisms known as Mimic Toys, which are now highly collectable.

Gold Cadillac ▲
- *circa 1950*
American gold cadillac with red interior and chromed fittings, made by Bandiai, Japan.
- *length 29cm*
- £150   • P. McAskie

Fred Flintstone ▼
- 1960
Tin plate 'Fred Flintstone' sitting astride his dinosaur 'Dino', made by Louis Marks in Japan.
- *length 2cm*
- £265   • P. McAskie

Smiley of the Seven Dwarfs ▲
- *circa 1930*
Padded soft toy of 'Smiley', one of the dwarfs from the children's story, 'Snow White and the Seven Dwarfs'.
- *height 27cm*
- £160   • Glenda

Huntley & Palmers Van ◄
- *circa 1920*
Brown toy van with a hinged lid to store biscuits and the gilt inscription, 'Huntley & Palmers Ltd, Reading Biscuits' and a Royal Crest above.
- *19cm x 25cm*
- £875   • P. McAskie

Mickey Mouse ▼
- *circa 1930*
Velvet padded Mickey Mouse
with a large smiling expression.
- *height 33cm*
- £110   • Glenda

Ferrari Pedal Car ▲
- 1970
Red Ferrari pedal car with the
number three on the side.
- *length 117cm*
- £250   • C.A.R.S.

Heubach Boy Doll ▼
- *circa 1890*
Heubach jointed porcelain boy
doll with a painted face, wearing
a matching beige and cream
outfit with hat.
- *height 25cm*
- £395   • Glenda

Steiff Owl ▲
- *circa 1950*
Steiff Owl with large glass eyes
and a menacing expression.
- *height 14cm*
- £49   • Glenda

Tri-ang Red Racing Car ▼
- 1950
Red Tri-ang Mimic racing car
with driver, the car bearing the
number three.
- *length 15cm*
- £45   • P. McAskie

Dream Baby ▲
- *circa 1920*
Porcelain jointed black 'Dream
Baby', in perfect condition.
- *height 28cm*
- £398   • Glenda

Expert Tips

*Any toys associated with
popular books or films today,
for example the Harry Potter
series, are worth investing in
now for the future.*

Bru Walker Doll ▲

- *circa 1880*

Bru 'Kiss throwing walker doll' with long auburn hair and brown glass eyes, wearing a cream cotton and lace dress, a bonnet with lilac bows and brown leather shoes.
- *height 62cm*
- £3,750   • Glenda

Wax Doll ▲

- *circa 1900*

Wax girl doll with blonde hair, blue eyes and a painted face, wearing a linen top and pantaloons with lace embroidery, and a lace cap.
- *height 48cm*
- £475   • Glenda

Tin Plate Racing Car ▼

- *circa 1930*

English tin plate cream racing car, with a red radiator grill and red line decoration, bonnet straps, and the number five on the side and on the tail back.
- *length 38cm*
- £265   • P. McAskie

Noddy ▼

- *1980*

Noddy wearing a red shirt, yellow spotted scarf and blue hat with a yellow pom-pom, in his yellow rubber car with red fenders.
- *19cm x 27cm*
- £30   • P. McAskie

Japanese Motor Launch ▼

- *circa 1950*

Japanese red, yellow, orange and blue motor launch with driver in a helmet, and hand crank.
- *length 21cm*
- £73   • P. McAskie

Drummer Boy ▲

- *1930*

Drummer boy with a tin plate body, legs and arms, and a celluloid head, with the makers name 'Fecuda', Japan.
- *24cm*
- £275   • P. McAskie

Red Double Decker Bus ▲

- *1960*

Red bus with 'Mobilgas' and 'Double Decker Bus' decals on the side, in fine condition.
- *height 22cm*
- £145   • P. McAskie

Spanish Racing Car ▼

- *circa 1920*

Blue and yellow racing car with driver and passenger, and the number 7 on the side. Manufactured by Paya in Spain.
- *length 27cm*
- £225   • P. McAskie

Simon & Halbig Doll ▼

- *circa 1880*

Jointed porcelain girl doll with
blue eyes, long dark hair and a
painted face, wearing a floral
dress and green leather shoes, by
Simon & Halbig.

- *height 52cm*
- £648 • Glenda

Snow White ▼

- *circa 1930*

French padded doll of Snow
White with composition face and
hands.

- *height 44cm*
- £368 • Glenda

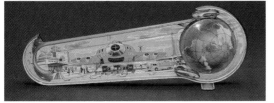

Norah Wellings Admiral ▲

- *circa 1880*

Soft toy of an admiral by Norah
Wellings, wearing a brown velvet
uniform with silver metal
buttons, and a blue hat with gold
trimmings.

- *height 28cm*
- £90 • Glenda

Steiff Pekinese ▲

- *circa 1940*

Velvet padded pekinese by Steiff,
with glass eyes.

- *height 10cm*
- £48 • Glenda

Red Fiat ▼

- *1960*

Red Fiat 600 made in Japan, in
excellent condition, with
working spring-back sunshine
roof.

- *length 22cm*
- £180 • P. McAskie

Black Seal ▼

- *circa 1950*

Black seal balancing a striped
ball, manufactured in Japan.

- *height 16cm*
- £90 • P. McAskie

Expert Tips

*Steiff teddy bears and other
animals, such as pekinese dogs,
deer and owls, are steadily
climbing upwards in value and
are worth looking out for.*

Round the World
Space Toy ◄

- *circa 1950*

Round the World space toy made
by Technofix, Germany.

- *length 60cm*
- £265 • P. McAskie

Petrol Tanker ▶

- *1930*
Red lead petrol tanker by Taylor
and Barrett.
- *length 10cm*
- £85　　　　• P. McAskie

Alfa Romeo ▼

- *circa 1960*
Red Alfa Romeo 1900 'Super
Sprint', made by Dinky, no. 85,
with original box.
- *length 10cm*
- £62　　　　• P. McAskie

Kestner Doll ▼

- *circa 1900*
Porcelain jointed doll by Kestner
with blue glass eyes and long
auburn hair, wearing linen and
lace dress and brown leather
shoes.
- *height 38cm*
- £595　　　　• Glenda

Oriental Baby Doll ▼

- *circa 1930*
Small Oriental porcelain jointed
baby doll with brown glass eyes
and a painted face.
- *height 18cm*
- £300　　　　• Glenda

Austin 7 ▲

- *circa 1940*
Cornflower-blue Austin 7, 35
series with pneumatic tyres.
- *height 3cm*
- £38　　　　• P. McAskie

Chad Valley Teddy ▼

- *1950*
Chad Valley padded teddy with
glass eyes and a pleasant
expression.
- *height 44cm*
- £250　　　　• Glenda

Horse and Milk Float ▲

- *1950*
Matchbox horse-drawn red milk
float with driver.
- *height 3cm*
- £18　　　　• P. McAskie

German Fire Engine ◀
- *1950*
Red German fire engine with fireman, manufactured by Gamma.
- *length 43cm*
- £110
- P. McAskie

Mummy Bear ▼
- *circa 1930*
Padded jointed bear with glass eyes and cloth paws.
- *height 39cm*
- £85
- Glenda

XK Yellow Jaguar ▲
- *circa 1950*
XK yellow Jaguar with a bottle green top, with a chromed bumper, made by Hoku.
- *length 25cm*
- £225
- P. McAskie

Ovaltine Van ▶
- *circa 1950*
Blue Dinky Bedford 10cwt Ovaltine van, inscribed 'Ovaltine' and 'Ovaltine Biscuits' on the side, with original box.
- *length 8cm*
- £65
- P. McAskie

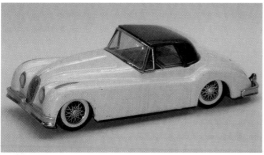

Mickey Mouse ▲
- *1950*
Mickey Mouse puppet carved from wood with yellow composition feet, by Pelham.
- *height 29cm*
- £75
- P. McAskie

Tri-ang Blue Van ▶
- *1950*
Tri-ang Mimic navy-blue London and North Eastern Railway van.
- *length 18cm*
- £225
- P. McAskie

Terrafish ◄

- **1960**

Green Terrafish with yellow spots and large white eyes, from the Gerry Anderson TV show, by Lakeside Toys, Japan.
- *length 23cm*
- **£275** • P. McAskie

Shoe-Shine Panda ▼

- *circa 1960*

Shoe-shine soft panda, battery-operated, sitting with a pipe in its mouth and a brush in each paw, wearing red dungarees.
- *height 25cm*
- **£80** • P. McAskie

American Racing Car ▲

- **1930**

Red and silver racing car and driver, made from an interesting combination of metals, die cast and cast iron, probably by Hubbly American. No. 22 on the side.
- *length 25cm*
- **£67** • P. McAskie

Bobby Bear ▶

- **1950**

Padded 'Bobby Bear' made by Pedigree, in good overall condition.
- *height 44cm*
- **£89** • Glenda

Yellow Milk Float ▼

- *circa 1960*

Rare yellow Dinky promotional milk float, with 'Jobs Dairy' inscribed on the front and rear, with red interior and hubs.
- *length 7cm*
- **£145** • P. McAskie

Orober Fire Engine ◄

- **1920**

Fire engine set of two vehicles with a driver on a pumper, and three figures on the fire engine carrier, complete with red garage, made by Orober in Germany.
- *19cm x 33cm*
- **£650** • P. McAskie

Telstar Kaleidoscope ▼
- **1960**

Telstar kaleidoscope with a rocket, stars and satellite and a blue background, made by Green Monk of England.
- **17cm**
- **£20** • P. McAskie

Nestlé's Austin Van ▲
- **circa 1950**

Red Austin van inscribed with 'Nestlé's' in gold letters on the side, made by Dinky, no. 471.
- **length 9cm**
- **£125** • P. McAskie

Baby Doll ▼
- **circa 1900**

Porcelain jointed baby doll with blue eyes, blonde hair and painted face, wearing a matching hat and outfit.
- **height 26cm**
- **£298** • Glenda

Daimler Ambulance ▲
- **circa 1950**

Primrose-yellow Dinky Daimler ambulance, no. 253, with a red cross on the side and red hub plates, and original box.
- **height 4cm**
- **£45** • P. McAskie

Matchbox Fire Engine ▲
- **1950**

Red Matchbox fire engine with driver.
- **height 3cm**
- **£22** • P. McAskie

Expert Tips

Look out for finely made jointed porcelain dolls by French makers such as G Vichy, or ballet dancers by Lambert, as these are very rare and highly collectable.

MG Midget TD ▼
- **1950**
Matchbox yellow MG Midget TD with red interior, driver, grey wheels and a wheel on the boot.
- *height 2cm*
- **£24**   • P. McAskie

Scalextric Green BRM ▼
- **1960**
Scalextric tin plate green BRM with racing driver. No. 3 on the side.
- *length 15cm*
- **£95**   • P. McAskie

Vespa and Driver ▲
- **1960**
Green Vespa with a driver wearing red, made in England by Benbros.
- *height 5cm*
- **£22**   • P. McAskie

Velam Bubble Car ◄
- **1960**
French cream Velam bubble car with grey roof, made by Quiralu, with original box.
- *height 4cm*
- **£78**   • P. McAskie

Pintel & Godchaux Doll ▲
- **circa 1900**
French porcelain jointed doll with blonde hair, blue eyes and painted face, wearing a lace dress, with a pink satin bow and lace socks, made by Pintel and Godchaux.
- *height 43cm*
- **£595**   • Glenda

Cottage Doll ▲
- **circa 1950**
Small padded 'Cottage Doll' made by Glenda O'Connor, with blonde plaits, blue eyes and a pleasant expression, wearing a pink gingham dress, green hat, top and shoes.
- *height 21cm*
- **£58**   • Glenda

Elephant See-Saw ▶

- *1950*

Two elephants on a toyland see-saw, with key winder playing drums, made by M. S. Toys, Japan.
- *18cm*
- £335   • P. McAskie

Shell Chemical Tanker ▼

- *circa 1950*

Dinky no. 591 red Shell chemical tanker, with yellow roof and hubs, and original box.
- *7cm x 16cm*
- £250   • P. McAskie

Tin Metal Boxers ▼

- *1920*

Tin metal boxers on wheeled base made by Einfeilt, Germany.
- *13cm x 19cm*
- £275   • P. McAskie

Konig & Wernig ▶

- *circa 1890*

Konig & Wernig character baby doll with blonde curly hair, brown glass eyes and jointed porcelain body, wearing a lilac dress with small red spots and a pink velvet hat with lace and satin bows.
- *height 24cm*
- £525   • Glenda

Transitional Green Car ◀

- *circa 1900*

Electric tin plate green car, 'Penny Toy', made in Germany.
- *height 6cm*
- £275   • P. McAskie

Motorbike with Rider ▶

- *1930*

Grey motorbike with rider made by Arnold Germany, Reg A643.
- *length 25cm*
- £230   • P. McAskie

Treen

The most mundane item was not beneath the notice of imaginative craftsmen, and the ordinary in their hands quickly became a work of art.

Treen applies to those items which are carved from wood, and encompasses a wide range of items, from the simple napkin ring to the highly decorative and heavily carved oak plaque. The word treen actually means 'made from trees' and therefore the beauty of collecting treen lies in the variety of artefacts that are available. Occasionally objects dating back to the seventeenth century arrive on the market, with the workaday items, such as cups and other vessels being fashioned from hardwoods such as sycamore and holly, while the more important were carved from lignum vitae, which had to be imported into England.

If you are about to embark on your first journey to collect treen it is worth noting that boxes and love tokens are amongst the most desirable types of treen. Look out for burr walnut or rosewood snuff boxes, which attract the collector with their sleek lines and simple design.

As a new collector treen is a good place to start as some of the items are still relatively inexpensive.

Rosewood Box ▼
- *circa 1825*
Small rosewood box with a silver plaque with the letters E. M.
- *4cm x 7cm*
- **£225** • Rupert Gentle

Pressed Wood Box ▼
- *circa 1840*
Pressed circular wood box with a carving of a boy and sword beside a dog jumping.
- *diameter 6cm*
- **£550** • Rupert Gentle

Fruitwood Box ▲
- *1830*
Small fruitwood box with gold foliate banding between bands of gold leaves on a black background.
- *2cm x 8cm*
- **£275** • Rupert Gentle

Tunbridge Ware Box ▲
- *circa 1850*
Tunbridge Ware box by Burrows. From Tunbridge Wells.
- *8cm square*
- **£140** • Jasmin Cameron

Carved Deer Heads ▼
- *circa 1860*
One of a pair of Continental carved reindeer with red paint and genuine horns.
- *height 64cm*
- **£1,800** • Anthony Sharpe

French Carved Flowers

- *1780*

One of a pair of French carved
stands, with scrolled foliate
designs and seven giltwood
flowers on a moulded serpentine
base.
- *height 93cm*
- **£1,450**
- Heytesbury

Four Egg Cups ▲

- *circa 1840*

A set of four turned mahogany
egg cups.
- *height 9cm*
- **£375**
- Rupert Gentle

Yew Wood Coaster ▲

- *circa 1840*

Yew wood coaster with a raised
diamond flower in the centre and
a linked border, with maker's
name, M. Scott.
- *diameter 17cm*
- **£650**
- Rupert Gentle

Austrian Stamp Box ▲

- *1860*

Small Austrian stamp box with
carved relief of oak leaves.
- *1.5cm x 5cm*
- **£35**
- Jasmin Cameron

Rosewood Snuff Box ▲

- *circa 1780*

Circular snuff box with the
inscription 'A. C. B. to J. G. B.
1821'.
- *diameter 9cm*
- **£380**
- Rupert Gentle

Burr-Walnut Snuff box ▲

- *circa 1770*

Burr-walnut snuff box with a
vacant silver plaque on the lid.
- *length 8.5cm*
- **£380**
- Rupert Gentle

Pipe Taper with
Royal Charter ▼

- *circa 1780*

Pipe taper with a 'Royal Charter'
label on the base.
- *length 7.5cm*
- **£350**
- Rupert Gentle

Tribal Art

Tribal art is not only highly decorative, it also gives us a unique insight into the culture and life of the artist.

As the world becomes smaller with the rise in travel, and the onset of mass globalisation begins to turn us into a global village, tribal art has become an important way for countries to preserve and promote their cultural heritage and present their unique identity to the world.

Obviously travel has also opened up the world and it is because of people's hunger to find new andisolated destinations that more tribal art is finding its way onto the market place, as even twenty years ago some of these countries would have been far too remote to reach. Tribal art was created to mark rites and watersheds in a person's life, from the birth of a child to going into battle, all were recorded with these works of art and sculpture.

Some of the tribal artefacts on the collector's market today, such as the wrought iron stick men figures used on the Cameroon borders in the late nineteenth century, were originally created as currency, but we now consider them to be works of art, collected to be displayed.

Zuni Fetish Frog ▼
- 1930
Large Zuni fetish circular silver pendant with a central turquoise styled frog flanked by silver leaves.
- *length 4.5cm*
- £59
- Wilde One's

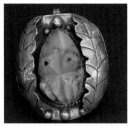

Kple Kple Mask ▲
- *circa 1920*
Kple Kple junior mask of the Golidance, one of the most abstracted masks of Africa, from a collection in France.
- *height 43cm*
- £5,500
- Gordon Reece

Nigerian Delta Region ◄
- *circa 1910*
Spirit mask from the Nigerian Delta region, the head crowned by four men and a boat, with classical red pigmentation. The figures, originally white, have been overpainted black.
- *height 53cm*
- £1,100
- Gordon Reece

Suku Fetish ▼
- *circa 1900*
Suku finely carved figure used as a fetish with additional fibre, beads and feathers, from Northern Zaire.
- *height 43cm*
- £950
- Gordon Reece

Buffalo Helmet Mask ◀

- *circa 1920*

Kanos buffalo carved wood mask from the Ivory coast of Africa.

- *height 38cm*
- £1,400
- Gordon Reece

M'Bun Currency ▼

- *unknown*

M'Bun status currency in throwing knife form.

- *48cm x 39cm*
- £720
- Gordon Reece

Pulley Goure Bete ▲

- *circa 1890*

Figure of a Pulley Goure Bete.

- *height 19cm*
- £490
- Gordon Reece

Guardian of the Spirits ▼

- *circa 1820*

West Nepalese bronze figure of a village guardian of the spirits.

- *height 22cm*
- £720
- Gordon Reece

Man Betu Gabon ▼

- *circa 1890*

A cephalomorphic ceramic from the Man Betu, Gabon, used only in court art.

- *height 42cm*
- £630
- Gordon Reece

Igbo Tribe Figures ▲

- *circa 1910*

One of a pair of figures from the Igbo tribe. A terracotta seated ancestorial couple, displaying typical central crested headdress and multiple anklets, bracelets and necklaces symbolising wealth.

- *height 54cm*
- £6,500
- Gordon Reece

Bhutan Nepal Mask ◀

- *circa 1700*

Early mask of dynamic primitive form relying on simplicity, from Bhutan on the Nepalese border. Very rare and in excellent condition.

- *height 33cm*
- £1,380
- Gordon Reece

Indian Gloves ▲

- *1950*

Pair of Indian gloves with a glass beadwork woodland design and fringing. Lined with pink silk and worn in Wild West Shows.
- *length 28cm*
- £299　　　• Wilde One's

Stylised Bird ▲

- *circa 1890*

Stylised Pulley Goure Bete.
- *height 16cm*
- £475　　　• Gordon Reece

Ivory Coast Mask ▼

- *circa 1910*

Heavily encrusted Dan mask from the Ivory Coast, Africa.
- *height 24cm*
- £680　　　• Gordon Reece

Heavily Patinated Mask ▼

- *circa 1910*

Heavily patinated tribal mask.
- *height 26cm*
- £740　　　• Gordon Reece

Naga Figure ◀

- *circa 1910*

Carved wood Naga figure depicting a standing male with hands clasped.
- *height 64cm*
- £950 the pair • Gordon Reece

Baule Tribe ▲

- *circa 1910*

Well formulated naturalistic human face with a delicate pouting mouth, finely shaped nose, almond eyes painted white, crossbanded hair and surmounted by a white crescent moon, in excellent condition, from the west coast of Africa.
- *height 48cm*
- £3,200　　　• Gordon Reece

Calabar Mask ▲

- *circa 1910*

Calabar mask from Benue River, Nigeria, with a strong Cameroon influence.
- *height 29cm*
- £720　　　• Gordon Reece

Figure used by Trance Diviners ▼

- *circa 1890*

Magnificent example of a seated male figure showing scarification and detailed coiffeur. Used by trance diviners and kept in their private shrines. From the Ivory Coast.
- *height 34cm*
- £15,000 • **Gordon Reece**

Wild Bronze Boar ▼

- *circa 1890*

Cast bronze wild boar of strong form with raised spine from the Khond tribe in middle India.
- *13cm x 19cm*
- £280 • **Gordon Reece**

Bronze Cobra ▶

- *circa 1840*

Cast bronze cobra from the Khond tribe of central India.
- *height 30cm*
- £339 • **Gordon Reece**

Apache Bag ▲

- *1950*

Apache suede pipe bag with a long strap and fringing and a central glass bead work of a red and black frog.
- *length 50cm*
- £169 • **Wilde One's**

Naga Tribal Pendant ▲

- *circa 1890*

Double-headed Naga tribal pendant with original blue beaded necklace.
- *width 9.5cm*
- £140 • **Gordon Reece**

Naga Figure ▲

- *circa 1910*

Carved wood Naga figure with hands held across her stomach, and head looking down.
- *height 64cm*
- £950 the pair • **Gordon Reece**

Bamilere Currency ▲

- *unknown*

Bamilere status currency in the shape of a mushroom.
- *54cm x 37cm*
- £385 • **Gordon Reece**

Dan-Karan Mask ▲

● *circa 1900*
Fine heavily patinated Dan-Karan mask, a powerful and abstracted mask from the Ivory Coast. From a collection in France.
● *height 25cm*
● £3,600   ● Gordon Reece

Himalayan Tribal Mask ▲

● *unknown*
Himalayan tribal mask with heavy patination on the inside, the exterior has been constantly painted with red, black and cream paint. Origin unknown.
● *height 28cm*
● £620   ● Gordon Reece

Apache Smoking Pouch ▼

● *1950*
Apache Indian smoking pouch with a red, white and black butterfly, and an orange background made from glass beads sewn on leather.
● *12cm x 7cm*
● £160   ● Wilde One's

Mask with Cowrie Shells ▼

● *circa 1910*
Mask with applied cowrie shells on the nose and cheeks, iron rings through the nose and ears, and erect hair.
● *height 36cm*
● £3,200   ● Gordon Reece

Yonba Maternity Figure ▲

● *circa 1910*
Yonba carved wood maternity figure of a seated woman with a child at her breast.
● *height 59cm*
● £1,700   ● Gordon Reece

Kul Status Currency ▲

● *unknown.*
Kul status currency in abstract human form, from Chad in West Africa.
● *height 51cm*
● £320   ● Gordon Reece

Tshokwe-Mbuna ◄

● *circa 1910*
Striking Tshokwe-Mbuna mask with natural patination and fibre additions.
● *height 37cm*
● £400   ● Gordon Reece

Twentieth-Century Design

The designers Charles Eames and Eero Saarinen were the first to experiment with moulded plywood, fibreglass and plastic.

From the 1900s the design of furniture and ceramics took on an exciting futuristic vibrancy, with designers experimenting with moulded plywood, fibreglass, plastic and leather. The famous Eames chair, successfully manufactured from the 1950s by the Herman Miller Company, with its moulded rosewood veneer and steel base, exemplifies this. These new materials completely changed the way furniture design was viewed, and the moulded organic shape became popular, with the innovators Eames and Saarinen winning prizes for their prototype chairs at the Organic Design in Home Furnishings Exhibition held at the Museum of Modern Art in New York in 1940. This exhibition was to have a profound effect on post war ceramic design.

Roy Midwinter designed two startling ranges of ceramics known as 'Stylecraft' and 'Fashion' in the new curving shapes, and commissioned innovative new ranges of patterns from the resident designers Jessie Tait and Terence Conran.

Ceramics

Italian Fishbone Vase ▲
- *1970*
Grey Italian flask-shaped vase with a raised grey fishbone design on a burnt orange ground.
- *height 33cm*
- £95 • **Goya Hartogs**

Owl by Goldsheider ▼
- *1890*
Owl by Goldsheider, with menacing glass eyes, standing on two books.
- *height 32cm*
- £700 • **Heytesbury**

Totem ▶
- *circa 2000*
'Giogold' by E. Sottsass, a vase of cylindrical form with dark blue and gold banding above a blue circular base.
- *height 38cm*
- £380 • **Francesca Martire**

Torso by Zaccagnini ▼
- *circa 1940*
Ceramic torso of a nude lady by
Zaccagnini.
- *height 61cm*
- £1,050   • Vincenzo

Tissue and Cotton Jars ▼
- *circa 1950*
Italian jars by Fornasetti for
cotton and tissues with mermaids,
scallop shells and gilt banding.
- *height 23cm*
- £250   • Vincenzo

Taurus ▶
- *1950*
Blue stylised bull 'Taurus'
standing on all fours with head
bowed and tail up by Gambone.
- *height 25cm*
- £2,000   • Themes

Retino ▲
- *circa 2000*
'Retino' by E. Sottsass, container
of conical form, with a design of
turquoise and gold banding above
a gilded circular base.
- *height 16cm*
- £250   • Francesca Martire

French Grey Vase ▲
- *1950*
Small French vase of conical form
with a textured finish and a black
geometric design with a large red
dot.
- *height 16cm*
- £55   • Goya Hartogs

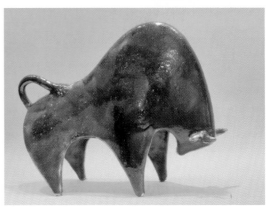

Plate by Capron Valaurido ▼
- *1970*
Plate by Roger Capron for
Valaurido with a red and orange
design within borders of matt
grey.
- *diameter 22cm*
- £85   • Goya Hartogs

Basket Pattern ▼
- *1956-57*
Basket pattern Poole pot designed
by Anne Read.
- *height 19cm*
- £220   • Richard Dennis

Butter Container ▼

- *circa 1940*

Cream ceramic butter dish with a lattice and apple blossom design in relief.
- *12cm x 18cm*
- £30   • Old School

William de Morgan ▼

- *circa 1900*

William de Morgan designed pottery, decorated with a yellow bird with a trailing cornflower design on a turquoise border, painted by Charles Passenger.
- *diameter 20cm*
- £200   • Richard Dennis

Ovoid Vase ▲

- *circa 1920*

Italian bottle-shaped vase with yellow, green and brown abstract design.
- *height 29cm*
- £250   • Iconastas

English Cup and Saucer ▲

- *circa 1920*

English cup, saucer and plate with a cartouche of a painted bird within gilt borders, surrounded by pink roses and cornflowers.
- *height 7.5cm*
- £38   • A. Piotrowski

Cigarette Holder ▼

- *1950*

Circular cigarette holder with push-action lid to extinguish the cigarettes.
- *height 21cm*
- £38   • Ventesimo

Janice Tchlenko Vase ▼

- *circa 1999*

Poole pottery vase of baluster form with a vibrant cany strip design by Janice Tchalenko.
- *height 37cm*
- £200   • Richard Dennis

Dutch Jar ◄

- *circa 1923*

Dutch jar with cover by Corona Gouda, designed by W. P. Harispring.
- *height 11cm*
- £280   • Pieter Oosthuizen

Shelley Tea Plate ▲
- **1927**
Shelley tea plate with orange border, black trees and green woodland border.
- *diameter 16cm*
- £20   • Susie Cooper

Vase Tulip Pattern ▲
- **1934**
Vase of baluster form, hand painted by Clarice Cliff with a 'tulip' pattern and green and red banding on a blue ground.
- *height 12cm*
- £650   • Susie Cooper

Butterfly Charger ▲
- **2001**
Charger with painted butterflies by Tania Pike for Dennis China Works.
- *diameter 37cm*
- £445   • Richard Dennis

Highland Stoneware Vase ▼
- *circa 2000*
Highland stoneware vase of baluster form with a narrow neck and splayed lip painted with trout underwater.
- *height 31cm*
- £145   • Richard Dennis

Alan Caiger Smith Goblet ▼
- *circa 1963*
Lustre glaze goblet by Alan Caiger Smith, the bowl with swirled designs above a knopped stem, raised on a circular base.
- *height 14cm*
- £100   • Richard Dennis

Ocelot Vase ▼
- **2000**
Catherine Mellor vase with a design of a leopard in blue on a leopard spot ground.
- *height 24cm*
- £411   • Richard Dennis

Rosenthal Pottery ▲
- *circa 1950*
Peynet design plate of ovoid form, depicting a hand-painted design of a couple in a boat with birds circling.
- *diameter 20cm*
- £100 • Richard Dennis

Clarice Cliff Cup and Saucer ▲
- *1934*
Clarice Cliff cup and saucer with a 'tulip' pattern and wedge-shaped handle, the saucer with pink and blue banding.
- *height 8cm*
- £350 • Susie Cooper

Susie Cooper Jug ▲
- *1929*
'Cubist' collection cream jug by Susie Cooper for Grays Pottery.
- *height 13cm*
- £350 • Susie Cooper

Fantasque by Clarice Cliff ▼
- *1936*
Plate by Clarice Cliff from the Fantasque collection centred with a hand-painted design of a country setting within black and orange borders.
- *diameter 18cm*
- £450 • Susie Cooper

Tea Cup and Saucer ▲
- *1936*
Clarice Cliff 'Spring' cup and saucer hand painted with crocuses with gilt banding and pale green borders.
- *height 7cm*
- £110 • Susie Cooper

Clarice Cliff Pallet Plate ▲
- *circa 1900*
Clarice Cliff palette plate by Wilkinson with a lady in the wind, her scarf blowing, and a ship in turbulent seas.
- *diameter 24cm*
- £400 • Victor Arwas

Troika ▼

- *circa 1965*
Troika pottery vase with cream
and turquoise geometric design
from St. Ives.
- *36cm x 17cm*
- £895 • The Country Seat

Cornish Moon Troika ▼

- *circa 1960*
Pottery blue vase of conical form
by Troika St. Ives with cream
circles on a textured brown and
green ground.
- *height 26cm*
- £285 • The Country Seat

Italian Ribbed Vase ▲

- *1950*
Italian elegant bottle-shaped vase
with long neck, ribbed body and a
matt black finish.
- *height 33cm*
- £65 • Ventesimo

Italian Ceramic Jug ▲

- *1950*
Matt brown Italian jug of ovoid
form with stylised black and
white enamel horses and strap
handle.
- *height 22cm*
- £75 • Ventesimo

Plate by Geramim ▼

- *1970*
Circular plate with a floral design
in red, black and yellow enamels
by Geramim S. Rocco, Torrita de
Sirvo.
- *diameter 38cm*
- £145 • Ventesimo

Royal Doulton Vase ▼

- *circa 1900*
Lambeth Ware vase by Royal
Doulton with a border of yellow
and green petals with a dark blue
centre, and a lilac body.
- *height 28cm*
- £350 • Victor Arwas

Expert Tips

*By the 1960s Scandinavian
'good taste' and high quality
production were being replaced
by witty, disposable, low cost
designs in psychedelic colours.*

Rosenthaul Butterfly ◄
- *circa 1930*
Rosenthaul butterfly with green,
black and blue enamels on a
circular base.
- *height 5.5cm*
- £400 • Victor Arwas

German Red Vase ▼
- *1950*
Red vase of inverted conical form
with a raised black and white
abstract design around the middle
of the vase.
- *height 22cm*
- £30 • Goya Hartogs

Nude by M. Guevara ▶
- *circa 1900*
Painted clay figure of a nude girl
wearing a hat by Monica
Geuvara.
- *height 28cm*
- £450 • Victor Arwas

Clarice Cliff Plate ▲
- *circa 1900*
Clarice Cliff palette shape 'Cruise
Ware', with a parasol and a pair
of lady's legs on the left side, and
a funnel of a ship above, made by
Wilkinson Ltd.
- *diameter 24cm*
- £400 • Victor Arwas

Whieldon Ware Vase ▼
- *circa 1930*
Whieldon Ware bulbous blue and
orange floral design vase with
gold leaves by F. Winkle & Co.
Ltd, England. Orient design.
- *height 11cm*
- £160 • Victor Arwas

Royal Dux Sculpture ▶
- *circa 1950*
Royal Dux abstract wall sculpture
by Cernoch.
- *height 41cm*
- £600 • Victor Arwas

Royal Worcester ▶

- *circa 1930*
Royal Worcester turquoise bulb
vase with dark blue butterflies
and birds.
- *height 27cm*
- £850 • **Victor Arwas**

Limoges Plate ▲

- *circa 20th century*
Limoges plate with hand-painted
sprays of flowers within gilt
borders arranged around a central
floral design.
- *diameter 28cm*
- £67 • **London Antique**

Denby Vase ▲

- *circa 1960s*
Bourne Denby vase of conical
form with white vertical stripes
within a border of variegated
dots.
- *height 30cm*
- £45 • **Francesca Martire**

Martin Brothers Pot ▲

- *circa 1960*
Medium size grey pot of bulbous
proportions with variegated sized
yellow spots, with separate raised
moulding, by Martin Brothers.
- *height 17cm*
- £1,906 • **Richard Dennis**

Vase by John Criswick ▼

- *1960*
John Criswick vase of inverted
conical form, dated and signed on
the base 10.11.1960.
- *height 44cm*
- £380 • **Francesca Martire**

Eagle Vase ▼

- *circa 2000*

Large vase of baluster form with a design of an eagle with wings folded and head turned to one side.

- *height 41cm*
- **£611**   • **Richard Dennis**

Ceramic Jar ▶

- *circa 1940s*

Pale green ceramic biscuit jar and cover, with a raised Chinoiserie cherry blossom design and basket-style handle.

- *13cm x 10cm*
- **£65**   • **Old School**

Cake Server ▲

- *circa 1930*

Cream ceramic cake stand with orange and yellow flowers and folia, and a geometric metal handle.

- *13cm x 23cm*
- **£30**   • **Old School**

Alfred Read ▼

- *circa 1953-4*

Poole pottery vase No. YHP, designed by Alfred Read.

- *height 25cm*
- **£175**   • **Richard Dennis**

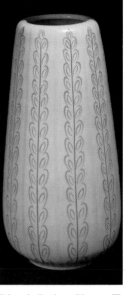

Eduardo Paolozzi Plate ▼

- *circa 1950*

Wedgwood bone china plate made in England by Eduardo Paolozzi with a red, black and gold geometric design.

- *diameter 27cm*
- **£150**   • **Richard Dennis**

Susie Cooper Jug ◀

- *circa 1930*

Crown Devon yellow, black, orange and aubergine geometric design jug by Fieldings of England.

- *height 14cm*
- **£240**   • **Victor Arwas**

Butter Container ▲
- *circa 1940*

Cream cheese dish and cover
with a floral design and moulded
rim.
- *14cm x 20cm*
- £30 • Old School

Poole Pottery Vase ▲
- *circa 1930*

Poole pottery bulbous vase with
stylised yellow lilac flowers and
green folia.
- *height 13cm*
- £75 • Richard Dennis

Lambeth Vase ▼
- 900

Lambeth vase with green foliate
design and pale blue flowers on a
dark grey background, by Francis
Pope.
- *height 30cm*
- £1,900 • Richard Dennis

Poole Vase ▼
- *circa 1930*

Poole vase of ovoid form with
yellow, blue and green design.
- *height 26cm*
- £400 • Richard Dennis

Rosenthal Pottery ◄
- *circa 1950*

Peynet vase of conical form
designed by Rosenthal Pottery
entitled 'The Marriage'.
- *height 29cm*
- £300 • Richard Dennis

Poole Pottery Vase ▲
- *circa 1930*

Poole pottery vase with stylised
yellow and purple flowers and a
purple, green and lilac design
around the rim.
- *height 20cm*
- £200 • Richard Dennis

Peynet Design Plate ▲
- *circa 1950*

Rosenthal Germany pottery
plate, showing spring with a
couple on a bridge.
- *height 30cm*
- £200 • Richard Dennis

Expert Tips

*An important influence in
Italian postwar design was
surrealism, which can be clearly
seen in the prolific designs of
Piero Fornaseti in the 1950s.*

Ribbed Italian Jug ▼

- *1950*

Brown Italian jug of conical form
with small neck and ear-shaped
handle with a ribbed incised
design.
- *height 19cm*
- £45   ● Ventesimo

Highland Pottery Vase ▼

- *circa 1974*

Highland Stoneware Pottery
baluster-shaped vase, hand
painted with a coastal scene.
- *height 25cm*
- £150   ● Richard Dennis

Sèvres Group ▶

- *1920*

'Les Pecheurs', a Sèvres group
showing two ladies and two
children. One of the ladies holds
a fishing net beside a basket of
fish, the whole on a rustic base.
- *height 27cm*
- £1,500   ● Stockspring

Alan Caiger Smith Jug ▲

- *circa 1978*

Large white pottery water jug
with green and blue design by
Alan Caiger Smith.
- *height 38cm*
- £400   ● Richard Dennis

Zebra Vase ▶

- *1999*

Dennis China Works vase with a
zebra design on a zebra pattern
background, designed by Sally
Tuffin and painted by Heidi Warr.
- *height 23cm*
- £298   ● Richard Dennis

Parrot Plate ▼

- *2000*

Parrot designed by Sally Tuffin
and painted by Tania Pike for
Dennis China Works.
- *diameter 16cm*
- £70   ● Richard Dennis

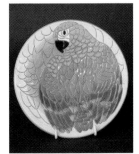

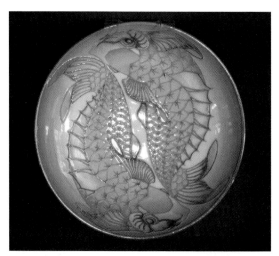

Carp Charger ▲
- *circa 2000*

Pottery charger with a design of two carp on a green background, by Dennis China Works.
- *diameter 36cm*
- £540   ● Richard Dennis

Ocelot Design Vase ▶
- *2000*

Dennis China Works pottery vase of a leopard on a leopard spot background, painted by Catherine Mellor.
- *height 24cm*
- £411   ● Richard Dennis

Shelley Bon-Bon Dish ▼
- *1927*

Bon-bon dish with a serpentine rim, orange centre and four black trees.
- *diameter 11cm*
- £65   ● Susie Cooper

Shelley Cake Plate ▼
- *1927*

Shelley cake plate with a scalloped border and bold black trees within an orange border.
- *diameter 24cm*
- £65   ● Susie Cooper

Bulb Vase ▼
- *1936*

Clarice Cliff bulb vase with metal rim from the 'Citrus Delicier' collection.
- *diameter 20cm*
- £350   ● Susie Cooper

Nuage by Clarice Cliff ◀
- *1935*

'Nuage' bowl by Clarice Cliff, with hand painted flowers and leaves with an orange centre on a green ground.
- *diameter 19cm*
- £950   ● Susie Cooper

Clarice Cliff Jam Pot ▲

- **1934**
Bon-jour shape pot by Clarice
Cliff with a 'tulip' pattern painted
on the lid, with stylised acorn
finial and a blue and green glazed
body.
- *height 9cm*
- **£750** • Susie Cooper

Clarice Cliff Mustard Pot ▲

- **1934**
Clarice Cliff mustard pot with a
'tulip' pattern.
- *height 5cm*
- **£160** • Susie Cooper

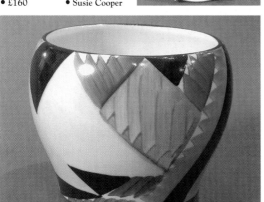

Bauhaus Jug ▼

- *circa 1930*
Bauhaus pink and orange
moulded jug by Leuchtenburg.
- *height 19cm*
- **£450** • Victor Arwas

Ross's of Belfast ▼

- **1929**
Small bowl by Susie Cooper
inscribed with the advertisement
for Ross's of Belfast and Lime
Juice Cordial.
- *diameter 14cm*
- **£250** • Susie Cooper

Enamel Vase ▼

- **1960**
Enamel vase of conical form with
a gilded neck and lip.
- *height 20cm*
- **£45** • Ventesimo

Susie Cooper Sugar Pot ◄

- **1929**
Sugar pot by Susie Cooper with a
black, orange, yellow, brown and
green geometric pattern.
- *height 9cm*
- **£275** • Susie Cooper

Susie Cooper Tea Set ◀

- **1929**

Seventeen piece Susie Cooper tea set consisting of five cups and saucers, a milk jug and a sugar bowl, with a black, yellow, orange and grey geometric design.
- *height of cup 9cm*
- £2,600   • Susie Cooper

Grays Pottery Jug ▼

- **1929**

Water jug with an abstract pattern and gilding designed by Susie Cooper for Gray's pottery.
- *height 35cm*
- £300   • Susie Cooper

Moon & Mountain ▲

- **1928**

'Moon and Mountain' plate with a hand-painted abstract design by Susie Cooper.
- *length 26cm*
- £325   • Susie Cooper

Spring Vase ▶

- **1936**

'Spring' vase of ovoid form with a hand-painted design of crocuses by Clarice Cliff.
- *height 15cm*
- £465   • Susie Cooper

Arts Stable Jug ▼

- *circa 1930*

Arts stable jug with geometric design by Poole Pottery.
- *height 17cm*
- £400   • Victor Arwas

Susie Cooper Tea Trio ◀

- **1929**

Susie Cooper tea trio cup and saucer and plate with a yellow, green, black and yellow 'lightning' pattern.
- *height 9cm*
- £450   • Susie Cooper

Poole Ware Jug ▼
- *1932*

Small Poole ware bulbous jug with a yellow, black and grey abstract design on a chalk white ground.
- *height 13cm*
- £350   • Victor Arwas

Cruise Ware Plate ▶
- *circa 1900*

'Cruise Ware' Clarice Cliff plate by Wilkinson, with a young lady leaping beside a net holding a ring, and a funnel above her.
- *diameter 24cm*
- £400   • Victor Arwas

Troika ▼
- *circa 1965*

Troika pottery vase of abstract design with a rusticated finish from St. Ives.
- *36cm x 17cm*
- £895   • The Country Seat

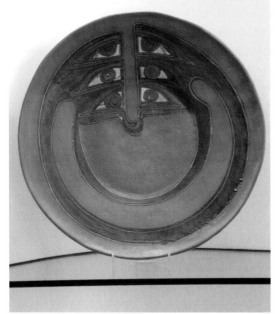

Teapot by Clarice Cliff ▼
- *1936*

'Blue Chintz' collection teapot with pink crocus by Clarice Cliff.
- *height 15cm*
- £450   • Susie Cooper

Ceramic Plate ◀
- *1973*

Large ceramic plate with six-eye design, on a grey base, by Salvatori Meli.
- *diameter 59cm*
- £3,000   • Themes

Furniture

Red Leather Chair ▲
• *circa 1960*
One of a pair of Italian chairs, one red and the other black leather, with teak legs and back rest.
• *height 98cm*
• £800   • **Vincenzo**

Wine Table ▲
• *1900–1915*
Edwardian wine table with a circular top, satinwood banding and a central flower, the whole standing on a turned column with a tripod base.
• *47cm x 26cm*
• £169   • **Amandini**

English Hall Cupboard ▼
• *circa 1900*
English hall cupboard in medium oak with marquetry panel of a Dutch genre scene. With copper strapwork, hinges and escutcheons.
• *83cm x 62cm*
• £1,500   • **Liberty**

Reclining Armchair ▼
• *circa 1900*
One of a pair of oak reclining armchairs of solid design with slated side panels, raised on square tapered legs.
• *90cm x 70cm*
• £900   • **Old Cinema**

Arts and Crafts Chair ▲
• *circa 1905*
One of three Arts and Crafts single chairs with moulded top rail and curved splat with fruitwood inlay standing on straight square legs.
• *88cm x 44cm*
• £2,250   • **Liberty**

Dieter Rams Armchairs ▼
• *1962*
Armchairs by Dieter Rams, for Vitsoe, made from green leather on a white fibreglass base.
• *69cm x 86cm*
• £2,900   • **Themes**

Modernist Table ▼
- *circa 1930*

Modernist table for use as a library table or cocktail cabinet, made from oak with crossbanded decoration raised on moulded bracket feet.
- 51cm x 60cm
- £185
- Old Cinema

Walnut Coffee Table ▼
- *circa 1920s*

Walnut reproduction coffee table with scalloped decoration and cabriole legs with acanthus leaf carving.
- 52cm x 100cm
- £275
- Old Cinema

'Medea' Chairs ▲
- *circa 1955*

One of a pair of moulded beechwood 'Medea' chairs by Vittoria Nobli, with an oblong hole in the seat and straight black metal legs.
- height 82cm
- £450
- Francesca Martire

Walnut Sofa ◄
- *circa 1920*

A fine walnut three-piece suite with canned back rest and side panels and turned decoration, raised on circular bun feet.
- 91cm x 182cm
- £3,900
- Old Cinema

Art Deco Table ▼
- *circa 1940s*

An oak two-tier art deco side table with square tapered supports.
- 70cm x 53cm
- £225
- Old Cinema

Revolving Bookcase ▼
- *circa 1905*

An Edwardian mahogany revolving bookcase with pierced side panels raised on four splayed legs.
- 80cm x 43cm
- £795
- Old Cinema

Writing Desk ▶

•*circa 1900s*
An Edwardian ladies writing
desk/dressing table with mirrored
writing surface above three
drawers and brass lattice panels,
all above straight tapered legs.
• *88cm x 121cm*
• £1,250   • John Riordan

Italian Red S Chair ▲

•*circa 1960*
One of a pair of Italian red
padded soft man-made fabric S-
bend chairs with tubular metal
base.
• *height 80cm x 46cm*
• £600   • Vincenzo

Oak Corner Cupboard ▲

•*circa 1900*
Substantial oak Arts and Crafts
corner cabinet/hall cupboard with
tracerie copper overlay in the Art
Nouveau manner. Made by
Shapland & Petter, England.
• *205cm x 115cm*
• £3,500   • Liberty

Franco Albini Chairs ▲

•*circa 1950*
One of a pair of Italian walnut
chairs with green upholstered
padded seats and back, by Franco
Albini.
• *height 78cm*
• £1,200   • Francesca Martire

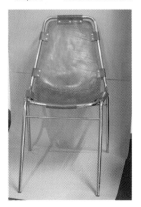

Arts and Crafts
Dining Chairs ▼

•*circa 1910*
One of a set of six light oak
English Arts and Crafts single
dining chairs and two carvers.
• *104cm x 38cm*
• £2,995   • Liberty

Charles Perriand Chairs ◀

•*circa 1973*
Set of four chairs with brown
leather upholstery, stitching and
metal studs looped to moulded
tubular chrome, designed by
Charles Perriand.
• *height 84cm*
• £950   • Francesca Martire

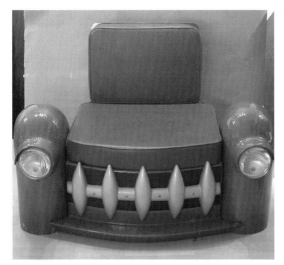

Car Radiator Chair ▲

- *circa 1970*
French-commissioned green
fibreglass chair with square vinyl
cushions, in the style of a car
radiator and wings with
headlights in working order.
- *82cm x 120cm x 75cm*
- £2,200 • Country Seat

Art Nouveau Chair ▶

- *circa 1910*
One of a set of six Art Nouveau
oak chairs consisting of two
carvers and four single chairs,
with slated back splat and curved
top rail above square tapered legs.
- *140cm x 53cm*
- £825 • Old Cinema

Bedside Cabinet ▼

- *circa 1920s*
Figured walnut bedside cabinet
with pull-out writing slope and
plain panelled door, raised on
carved feet.
- *74cm x 38cm*
- £325 • Old Cinema

Edwardian Occasional Table ▼

- *circa 1905*
A very good quality Edwardian
satinwood and inlaid octagonal
occasional table.
- *72cm x 54cm*
- £495 • Old Cinema

Hardwood Dining Table ◀

- *circa 1920*
Oak dining table from a West
Country cricket club, with pull-
out leaves above square
chamfered legs, raised on bun
feet.
- *76cm x 91cm*
- £975 • Old Cinema

Swedish Desk ▶
- *1920–1930*
Gustavian-style Swedish free-standing desk.
- *76cm x 144cm*
- £2,900 • Rupert Cavendish

Edwardian Three-Tier Stand ▲
- *circa 1905*
An unusual wrought iron and copper Edwardian three-tier stand with scrolled decoration.
- *95cm x 25cm*
- £135 • Old Cinema

Oak Hallstand ▲
- *circa 1880*
A very good quality Arts and Crafts hallstand and two matching hall chairs by 'Minton Hollins and Co. Patent Tile Works, Stoke-on-Trent'.
- *208cm x 128cm*
- £1,850 • Old Cinema

Arts and Crafts Table ▼
- *circa 1910*
Arts and Crafts oak table of solid construction with straight supports and circular stretcher.
- *52cm x 69cm*
- £280 • Old Cinema

Art Nouveau Bureau ▼
- *circa 1905*
Art Nouveau oak bureau with folding writing slope above a single drawer with organically designed copper metalwork.
- *120cm x 90cm*
- £565 • Old Cinema

Nursery Chest ▲
- *circa 1930*
Heal's oak nursery chest with double and single panelled doors, three short drawers and two long drawers.
- *150cm x 115cm*
- £1,850 • Old Cinema

Arts and Crafts Lamp Table ▲
- *circa 1905*
Arts and Crafts mahogany occasional table with three supports and carved and pierced decoration.
- *69cm x 43cm*
- £220 • Old Cinema

Chair by Carl Jacobs ▼
- *circa 1950*

One of a set of six red chairs by
Carl Jacobs for Kandya Ltd., with
teak legs.
- *72cm x 51cm*
- £485 • Country Seat

Walnut and Chrome Table ▼
- *circa 1980*

Small circular walnut table with
metal circular ashtray standing on
a teak pedestal and circular base
with metal turned legs.
- *height 58cm*
- £365 • Country Seat

Brass Brolly Stand ▲
- *circa 1910*

Art Nouveau brass brolly stand
with hand-beaten finish and
embossed tulip design.
- *height 63cm*
- £375 • Old Cinema

Edwardian Plant Stand ▼
- *circa 1910*

Oak plant stand with copper
banded decoration, raised on
three carved supports with tripod
stretcher.
- *88cm x 28cm*
- £145 • Old Cinema

Kasthole Armchair ▶
- *circa 1970*

One of a pair of leather and bent
rosewood armchairs with metal
and leather arms by Fabricius and
Kastholme.
- *82cm x 72cm*
- £1,950 • Country Seat

Pair of Eames Armchairs ▲
- *circa 1975*
A pair of Eames padded brown armchairs with aluminium arms and base.
- *height 101cm*
- £1,450   • Country Seat

Leather Rotating Chair ▲
- *1970*
Tan leather rotating and adjustable desk chair with padded seat and back, and metal legs on wheels.
- *height 74cm*
- £495   • Country Seat

Walnut Buffet ▶
- *1930*
Art Deco breakfront walnut buffet with solid supports and moulded decoration.
- 84cm x 106cm
- £650   • Old Cinema

Black Leather Armchair ▼
- *circa 1960*
Black leather armchair with padded seat and back, with metal and leather arms, standing on a rotating star-shaped metal base.
- *height 89cm*
- £750   • Country Seat

Edwardian Chest of Drawers ▼
- *circa 1905*
Edwardian chest of two small and two long drawers, with metal foliate handles standing on straight legs.
- 82cm x 108cm
- £240   • Old School

Butterfly Chair ▲
- *circa 1950*
One of a pair of plastic mock snakeskin butterfly chairs on a early tubular frame, manufactured by Knoll.
- *height 100cm*
- £550   • Country Seat

White Folding Bench ▲
- *circa 1920*
Continental pine folding bench, painted white, on metal legs and arms.
- 90cm x 125cm
- £220   • Old School

French Leather Chairs ▼
●*1977*
Pair of chairs by Michel Cadestin and George Laurent for the Library of the Centre Pompidou Beaubourg, made from wire with leather seat and back. Illus: Les Années 70, by Anne Bony.
●*74.5cm*
● £1,200　　　● **Themes**

Arts and Crafts Dining Chairs ▼
●*circa 1905*
One of a pair of oak Arts and Crafts carvers with scrolled arms and turned supports.
● *105cm x 58cm*
● £550　　　● **Liberty**

Japanese Chest ▲
●*circa 1920s*
Special Japanese Isho Dansu (storage chest) for fabrics. The wood has not been sealed or lacquered first.
● *102cm x 54cm*
● £2,650　　　● **Gordon Reece**

Chrome Dining Chairs ▲
●*1975*
Set of four dining chairs with grey leather and chrome, by Prebenfabricus & Dorgen Kastholm for Alfred Kill.
●*height 70cm*
● £2,200　　　● **Themes**

Mahogany Dining Chairs ▼
●*circa 1950s*
A set of six mahogany dining chairs with pierced backsplat, drop-in seat cushion and cabriole legs.
● *100cm x 48cm*
● £1,250　　　● **Old Cinema**

Stool by Verner Panton ▼
●*circa 1960*
Wire stool with original circular suede padded cover, by Verner Panton Danish.
●*height 43cm*
● £745　　　● **Country Seat**

Harlow Chairs ◄
●*1971*
Set of four 'Harlow' chairs with red wool-padded seats and backs, standing on aluminium bases and stands, by Ettore Sottsass for Poltronova.
●*height 82cm*
● £3,500　　　● **Themes**

French Chinese-Style Chair ▼

• *circa 1920*
One of a pair of French oak chairs with a strong Chinese influence and a distressed paint effect, standing on straight square legs.
• *height 74cm*
• **£1,250**   • **Anthony Sharpe**

Art Deco Cabinet ▼

• *circa 1930*
Art deco figured mahogany walnut cocktail cabinet of circular design with pull-out mixing surface.
• *161cm x 85cm*
• **£995**   • **Old Cinema**

Art Deco Three-Piece Suite ▶

• *circa 1930*
A very rare and unusual Art Deco upholstered leather three-piece suite.
• *86cm x 95cm*
• **£5,330**   • **Old Cinema**

Red Stereophonic Chair ▼

• *circa 1960s*
Red moulded fibreglass egg chair on a circular metal base, with grey and white wool-padded upholstery and leather-padded seat cover and back rest, with fitted stereo and matching ottoman, designed by the Lee Co. of California for a commission.
• *129cm x 86cm*
• **£4,200**   • **Country Seat**

Dressing table ◀

• *circa 1950*
Modernist oak dressing table with two columns of graduated drawers and single drawer above knee hole.
• *165cm x 122cm*
• **£225**   • **Old Cinema**

Liberty Oak Stand ▲

• *circa 1900*
Liberty's oak stand with three moulded shelves, slated side panels and shaped carrying handle.
• *80cm x 30cm*
• **£190**   • **Old Cinema**

Walnut Bureau ▲

• *circa 1940*
A very good early 20th century figured walnut bureau in the George II style.
• *104cm x 84cm*
• **£1,895**   • **John Riordan**

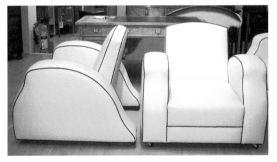

Arne Jacobsen Egg Chair ▲

- **1958**
Padded wool turquoise 'Egg
Chair' by Arne Jacobsen,
together with ottoman.
- *height 130cm*
- **£2,850**   • Country Seat

Oak Cabinet ▲

- *circa 1895*
Arts and Crafts cabinet in oak
with copper hinges and handle,
and moulded and crossbanded
door panel.
- *77cm x 49cm*
- **£420**   • Old Cinema

Edwardian Bookcase ▶

- *circa 1905*
A good quality Edwardian
bookcase with moulded
decoration above three-tiered
shelves.
- *118cm x 125cm*
- **£995**   • Old Cinema

Oak Hall Cupboard ▼

- *circa 1900*
Art Nouveau oak hall cupboard
with mirror panelled door and
carved decoration.
- *200cm x 103cm*
- **£495**   • Old Cinema

Walnut Side Table ▶

- *circa 1905*
Walnut Arts and Crafts table.
The design and quality of this
table suggests the work of C. R.
Ashbee and the Guild of
Handicraft.
- *52cm x 40cm*
- **£650**   • Liberty

Oak Sideboard by
Richter ▲

- *circa 1930*
Oak sideboard with central
stepped cupboard flanked by two
short and two long drawers with
bun handles, standing on square
straight legs. Made in Bath,
England and illustrated in
Modern British Furniture.
- *height 112cm*
- **£1,490**   • Country Seat

Teak Armchairs ▶

•*circa 1960*
Pair of teak and black leather
armchairs by Hans Wegner for
Carl Hanse.
•*height 70cm*
• £2,800 • Themes

White Fibreglass Lounger ▲

•*circa 1960*
Moulded fibreglass lounger with
oval headrest, square moulded
body and raised moulded leg rests,
by Olivia Morgue.
•*length 164cm*
• £500 • Country Seat

Harry Bertoia Wire Chair ◀

•*circa 1950*
Wire chair and stool by Harry
Bertoia, who was born in Italy
and later worked with Charles
and Ray Eames at Evans, and also
with his ground-breaking wire
chairs at Knoll International.
•*height 104cm*
• £1,800 • Country Seat

Mahogany Armchair ▼

•*circa 1950s*
Mahogany elbow chair with
pierced back splat, curved arm
rests and cabriole legs.
• *110cm x 62cm*
• £250 • Old Cinema

Eames Chair ◀

•*circa 1950*
Leather lounge chair designed in
1946 by Ray Eames and
manufactured by Herman Miller.
Sold as a set with a stool.
•*height 83cm*
• £3,950 • Country Seat

Table ◄
- *circa 1950s*

Oak circular coffee table with turned supports and circular moulded stretcher, raised on bun feet.
- 51cm x 100cm
- £495   • Old Cinema

Reclining Armchair ▼
- *1920s*

Oak reclining armchair with carved and turned decoration with slated side panels.
- 100cm x 65cm
- £395   • Old Cinema

Art Deco Chest ▲
- *circa 1930s*

A very good quality Art Deco chest in solid oak with wonderful early plastic handles.
- 83cm x 94cm
- £450   • Old Cinema

Butterfly Stool ▼
- *circa 1950*

Butterfly stool designed by Son Yanagi for Tendo Mokko.
- *height 46cm*
- £985   • Country Seat

Charles and Ray Eames Chair ▶
- *circa 1950*

Bent birchwood chair by Charles and Ray Eames, for Evans.
- *height 84cm*
- £1,150   • Country Seat

Danish Sideboard ▶

- **1960**

Danish sideboard Jacaranda, by Korod Larsenfor Faarup Mobel Fabarik.
- *78cm x 230cm x 50cm*
- **£3,500**   • **Themes**

Oak Book case ▲

- *circa 1910*

Glazed oak bookcase with arched pediment and double-glazed doors above two panel doors.
- *190cm x 80cm*
- **£890**   • **Old Cinema**

Finnish Armchair & Footstool ▼

- *circa 1970*

Armchair and footstool in brown padded leather and aluminium by Ilmari Lappalainen, Finland.
- *height 77cm*
- **£1,600**   • **Themes**

European Pine Cupboard ▲

- *circa 1940*

European pine cupboard of two long drawers and panelled cupboards below, standing on a moulded base.
- *85cm x 113cm*
- **£420**   • **Old School**

Universe Chair ▲

- *circa 1967*

'Universe' design black plastic stacking chair by Joe Columbo.
- *70cm x 43cm*
- **£220**   • **Country Seat**

Folding Chair ▼
•*circa 1930*
Eastern European painted green
metal folding chair.
• *90cm x 44cm*
• £35   • Old School

School Cupboard ▶
•*circa 1940*
European pine cupboard with
panelled cupboards below and
above, standing on a straight
square base.
• *227cm x 167cm*
• £1,100   • Old School

Green Chair for
Kandya Ltd ◀
•*circa 1950*
One of a set of six lime-green
chairs by Carl Jacobs for Kandya
Ltd., with teak legs.
• *72cm x 51cm*
• £485   • Country Seat

Oak Wardrobe ▼
•*circa 1890*
Aesthetic movement oak
wardrobe with mirror panelled
door flanked by two tongue-and-
groove panel doors with brass
hinges.
• *205cm x 183cm*
• £1,750   • Old Cinema

Teak Bedroom Suite ▼
•*circa 1930s*
Teak Art Deco bedroom suite.
• *175cm x 95cm*
• £1,650   • Old Cinema

Antelope Chairs ◀
•*circa 1950*
One of a set of six 'Antelope'
painted metal chairs, with Ernest
Rays, London, England on the
base of the seat. Made for the
Festival of Britain.
• *83cm x 55cm*
• £1,050   • Country Seat

Glass

Mazzega Murano Glass ▼
- *circa 1960*
Italian circular clear and dark blue glass object, designed by Mazzega, with the option of being wall-mounted.
- *diameter 40cm*
- £400   • Vincenzo

Spanish Abstract ▲
- *circa 1960s*
Spanish hand-blown abstract glass object, with yellow, black and blue design. Signed Vinas.
- *height 27cm*
- £850   • Francesca Martire

Barovier and Toso ▲
- *circa 1970*
Italian Murano vase of globular form by Barovier and Toso with black, green and red geometric design.
- *height 35cm x 19cm*
- £950   • Vincenzo

Nichetti Vase ▼
- *circa 1990*
Hand-blown orange vase with a gold and grey abstract geometric design and a moulded rim, by Nichetti for Murano.
- *height 28cm*
- £380   • Francesca Martire

Expert Tips

In the early post-war years designers created a fresh start with a feel good factor through a 'new look' based on curves and natural organic shapes.

Cenedese Ash Tray ▼
- *circa 1970*
Lime-green ash tray in the form of a halved lime, by S. Cenedes.
- *width 35cm*
- £185   • Vincenzo

Pale Pink Jug ▲
- *1960*
Pale pink Murano jug with slender neck, pinched lip and clear strap handle.
- *height 49cm*
- £85   • Francesca Martire

Mila Schon for Arte Vetro Murano ▶
- *circa 1970*
Large Murano purple glass plate with circular vortex design, by Mila Schon for Arte Vetro. It has the option of being wall-mounted.
- *width 63cm*
- £450   • Vincenzo

Toni Zuccheri for Venini ▲
- *circa 1970*
Fine glass and bronze stork by Toni Zuccheri for Venini.
- *height 33cm*
- £550   • Vincenzo

V. Ferro for Murano ▲
- *1998*
Yellow vase of bulbous proportions with black cobweb effect, raised on a splayed circular foot.
- *height 28cm*
- £1,500   • Francesca Martire

Scandinavian Green Glass Vase ▼
- *1950*
Scandinavian green glass vase of conical form with blue abstract inclusions.
- *height 29cm*
- £180   • Francesca Martire

Venini Bottle ▶
- *circa 1950*
Italian emerald-green bottle with large stopper by Venini.
- *height 36cm*
- £800   • Victor Arwas

Archimede Seguso Vases ▼
- *circa 1950*
Italian Murano green and orange dimple vases of globular form, with a gold leaf border and a crumpled moulded design.
- *height 30cm*
- £800   • Vincenzo

Spanish Abstract by Vinas ◀

• *circa 1990*
Spanish hand-blown lozenge-shaped glass with yellow, black and turquoise abstract circles and geometric design. Signed.
• *width 28cm*
• £780   • Francesca Martire

Mazzega Murano Glass ▼

• *circa 1960*
Italian glass object with a red and white glass dome within a circular clear glass halo, has the option of being wall-mounted, designed by Mazzega.
• *diameter 40cm*
• £400   • Vincenzo

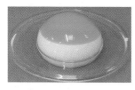

Orange Striped Vase by Venini ▼

• *1960*
Venini Murano glass vase with an orange and white striped design within the glass and a moulded, pinched rim.
• *height 34cm*
• £650   • Vincenzo

Murano Glass Duck ▶

• *1950*
Murano glass duck with silver and gold iridescence.
• *length 34cm*
• £590   • Castello Antiques

Antonio Da Ros ▼

• *circa 1960*
Clear Murano glass with dark blue teardrop and secondary droplet, by Antonio Da Ros, designed for Cenedese.
• *height 29cm*
• £600   • Vincenzo

Green Vase ▲

• *1960*
Green Murano bottle-shaped vase with long slender neck and black and white banding around the rim.
• *height 49cm*
• £65   • Francesca Martire

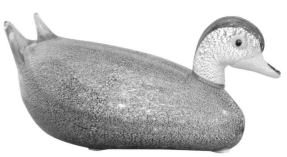

Abstract Glass Structure ▲

- *circa 1990*
Orange and black abstract glass
vase of cylindrical form with gold
flaked inclusions, by Nichetti for
Murano.
- *height 27cm*
- £380 • Francesca Martire

Mosaic Vase by Ferro ▲

- *1998*
Mosaic Murano glass vase by
Ferro, for the Venice Biennale
1998.
- *height 29cm*
- £1,200 • Francesca Martire

Tiffany's Centrepiece ▶

- *circa 1930*
L. Tiffany's gold iridescent
centrepiece with organic designs.
- *diameter 25cm*
- £4,000 • Victor Arwas

Glass Paperweight Abstract Sculpture ▼

- *circa 1960*
Italian orange, red, black and
white abstract glass sculpture.
- *height 16cm*
- £125 • Francesca Martire

Murano Paperweight ▼

- *circa 1960*
Murano paperweight of
compressed globular form with an
abstract pattern of blue, white,
lime green, pink and gold.
- *diameter 23cm*
- £325 • Francesca Martire

Blue Cactus Vase ▼

- *circa 1950*
Blue glass 'Cactus' vase by
Recardo Licata for Murano.
- *height 44cm*
- £1,200 • Francesca Martire

Venini Glass Bowl ▶

- *1962*
Glass bowl with bright red
trailing design signed Venini
Italia and designed by Ludovioc
di Santilliana.
- *diameter 25cm*
- £2,000 • **Themes**

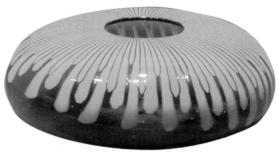

Whitefriars Drunken Bricklayer ▲

- *circa 1969*
Large tangerine 'Drunken
Bricklayer'object by Baxter.
- *height 33.5cm*
- £650 • **Country Seat**

Vase for Venini ▲

- *1965*
Blue vase for Venini designed by
T. Zucheri.
- *height 31cm*
- £1,200 • **Themes**

Bubble Vase by Baxter ▼

- *circa 1957*
Whitefriars strawberry bubble
glass vase by Baxter of organic
form with a blue recess.
- *19.5cm x 16cm*
- £115 • **Country Seat**

Whitefriars Red Lamps ▼

- *1964*
A pair of Whitefriars 'Studio
Range' red glass candle holders of
globular form by Harry Dyer.
- *height 24cm*
- £125 • **Country Seat**

Sunburst Mirror ▲

- *1950*
One of a pair of sunburst mirrors.
- *diameter 63cm*
- £285 • **Goya Hartogs**

Tangerine Oblong Vase ▲

- *1969*
Tangerine Whitefriars rectangular
vase with twelve globular
inclusions, resembling a mobile
phone, by Baxter.
- *height 16.5cm*
- £95 • **Country Seat**

Fern by Lalique ▲

- *1920*
Lalique vase of ovoid form with narrow circular neck and a raised 'Fern' pattern.
- *height 19cm*
- £1,400   • Susie Cooper

Cucumber Vase ▲

- *1967*
Whitefriars red 'Cucumber' vase, with a frosted textured finish, by Baxter.
- *height 30cm*
- £185   • Country Seat

Studio Range Vase ▼

- *circa 1969*
Whitefriars old gold and amber striped vase of conical form, 'Studio range' no S6.L13 by Peter Wheeler.
- *height 29cm*
- £130   • Country Seat

Muller Circular Box ▼

- *circa 1900*
Muller circular box and cover with overlay of red poppies and folia.
- *height 8cm*
- £1,300   • The French

Lalique Vase ▼

- *1920*
'Estoril' pattern Lalique glass vase of conical design with concentric leaf pattern in relief.
- *height 13cm*
- £1,000   • Susie Cooper

Lalique Bird ▼

- *1920*
Lalique naturalistically formed glass finch.
- *length 13cm*
- £280   • Susie Cooper

Mosaic Murrina Vase ▼
- **1998**
Mosaic vase of baluster form, with blue and yellow organic design by 'Murrina'.
- *height 29cm*
- **£1,500**   • Francesca Martire

Amber Bowl ▼
- *circa 1970*
Amber glass bowl on a clear stand by Cevedex.
- *height 23cm*
- **£500**   • Themes

Fish in Glass by Cenedese ▲
- **1950**
Glass object with a seascape design including a tropical fish with underwater plants, by Cenedese for Murano.
- *width 14cm*
- **£225**   • Francesca Martire

Green Vase with Cactus ▲
- *circa 1950s*
Green 'Cactus' vase by Recardo Licata for Murano.
- *height 44cm*
- **£1,200**   • Francesca Martire

Hutton Vase ▼
- *circa 1920*
Clear glass vase by Oroffords and etched by John Hetton.
- *height 33cm*
- **£1,000**   • Victor Arwas

Italian Glass Fish ▼
- **1960**
Italian glass object fashioned as a stylised coiled fish.
- *height 24cm*
- **£285**   • Ventesimo

Small Daum Jug ◄
- *circa 1900*
Small Daum variegated amber to pink jug with 'Bleeding Heart' floral overlay.
- *6cm x 12cm*
- **£2,200**   • The French

Cranberry Glass Vases ▲
- *circa 1900*

A pair of Bohemian cranberry glass vases with engraved decoration depicting castles and a forest setting with a leaping deer, on a faceted and moulded base.
- *height 44cm*
- £4,200
- Sinai

Vase by Baxter ▲
- *circa 1969*

Whitefriars kingfisher-blue vase by Baxter with an abstract design and textured finish.
- *height 29cm*
- £235
- Country Seat

Martini Jug by Baxter ▼
- *circa 1962*

Whitefriars kingfisher-blue Martini jug with a clear handle. A 'Whitefriars Studio' range by Peter Wheeler.
- *height 36cm*
- £95
- Country Seat

Silvio Vigliaturo Sculpture ▼
- *1999*

Glass 'Ikomos' series sculpture by Silvio Vigliaturo, signed and dated.
- *height 40cm*
- £1,200
- Francesca Martire

Tall Italian vase ▲
- *1982*

Italian tall glass vase with a moulded lip, ceruluan blue variegated to paler blue with moulded banding within the glass.
- *height 63cm*
- £1,000
- Themes

Red Bubble Ashtray ▲
- *1958*

Ruby red lobed bubble ashtray with an organic moulded design by Harry Dyer.
- *diameter 13cm*
- £25
- Country Seat

Overlay Gallé Vase ▲

• *circa 1900*
Gallé red overlay vase with red
foliate design over amber.
• *height 17cm*
• £1,700   • The French

Amber Glass ▲

• *circa 1940*
Amber glass jelly mould by
William Wilson of globular
design. No 9250.
• *17cm x 20cm*
• £140   • Country Seat

Modernist Lalique Vase ▲

• *1920*
Rare 'Modernist' Lalique vase
with raised geometric structural
design.
• *height 15cm*
• £1,400   • Susie Cooper

Raison by Lalique ▼

• *1920*
'Raison' design vase by Lalique,
with a raised floral design.
• *height 16cm*
• £1,200   • Susie Cooper

French Opaline Goblets ▼

• *circa 1900*
A pair of French opaline goblets
with gilt and floral enamel
decoration.
• *height 36cm*
• £2,300   • Sinai

Ruby Red Bubble Vase ▲

• *1965*
Ruby red bubble vase Whitefriars
Studio range, by Harry Dyer.
• *height 18cm*
• £130   • Country Seat

Expert Tips

*Glass was the ideal medium for
the expression of the new look
that emerged in the 1950s –
plastic and malleable, it could be
free or mould blown.*

Incalmo Glass Vase ▼

- **1990–91**

'Incalmo' glass vase with a vermilion red cane design neck, and a white glass globular shape base, by Laura Diaz de Santillana.
- *height 41cm*
- **£2,400**   • **Themes**

Vase with Poppy Design ▼

- **1920**

Glass vase by Lalique with raised poppy-head border and tapering stems with blue patina.
- *height 14cm*
- **£950**   • **Susie Cooper**

Tangerine Log Vase ▲

- **1969**

Tangerine Whitefriars 'Log Vase' of cylindrical form with a bark textured finish, by Baxter.
- *height 23cm*
- **£140**   • **Country Seat**

Tangerine Vase by Baxter ▼

- *circa 1969*

Large tangerine dimpled vase with an amorphic globular design by Baxter.
- *height 30cm*
- **£245**   • **Country Seat**

Scrolled Pattern Lalique ▼

- **1920**

Lalique glass vase with raised interlaced scrolled design.
- *height 14cm*
- **£1,400**   • **Susie Cooper**

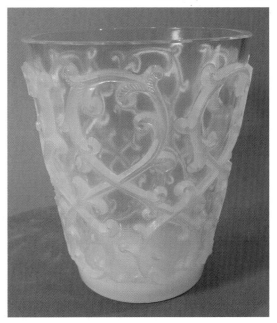

Whitefriars Vase ▶

- *circa 1969*
Rare Whitefriars ovoid brown
and orange vase. 'Studio range' by
Peter Wheeler.
- *height 22.5cm*
- £245   ● Country Seat

Glass Vase by Laura Diaz ▼

- **1990–91**
'Incalmo' ink-blue glass vase,
with a cane pattern neck and
white glass wheel carved bulbous
base by Laura Diaz, Ref: il vetro a
venezia by Marino Baronier.
- *height 30cm*
- £1,800   ● Themes

Swedish Translucent Vase ▼

- **1955–56**
Swedish translucent tall glass
vase with white trailing lines and
one red line made for Kosta.
- *height 38cm*
- £2,200   ● Themes

Tangerine Vase ▶

- **1969**
Tangerine vase with concentric
circular design and a textured
finish by Baxter.
- *height 18cm x 17cm*
- £140   ● Country Seat

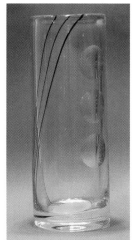

Glass Vase ▲

- **1973**
Glass vase with circular design by
Olle Alerius. Orrefors Co. 1973,
Expo A 248, signed and
illustrated by Lilane.
- *height 20cm*
- £2,200   ● Themes

Guitar Mirror ▼

- **1950**
Guitar shaped metal mirror.
- *length 83cm*
- £120   ● Goya Hartogs

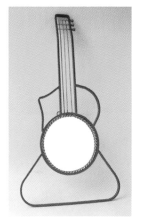

Lighting

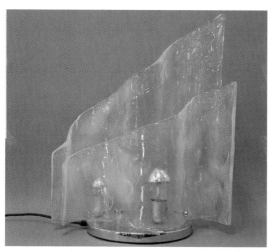

Mazzega Table Lamp ▲
- *circa 1960*
Italian Murano glass wave-effect
table lamp by Mazzega.
- *54cm x 43cm*
- £1,150 • Vincenzo

Pagani Mesh Lamp ▲
- *circa 1970*
Italian black metal mesh lamp
stylised as a flower by Luciano
Pagani.
- *width 76cm*
- £385 • Vincenzo

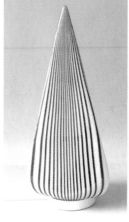

Italian Striped Lamp ▲
- *1950*
One of a pair of tear-shaped,
brown and white striped Italian
table lamps.
- *height 23cm*
- £250 • Ventesimo

Italian Hat Lamp ◄
- *circa 1960*
Large Italian table lamp in the
form of a large striped sunhat
with red flowers on one side and a
large black ribbon.
- *diameter 44cm*
- £290 • Castello

Vistosi Lamp ▼
- *1978*
Italian Murano white glass lamp
of ovoid form by Vistosi.
- *height 57cm*
- £1,200 • Themes

Gaku Light ▼
- *circa 1990*
Gaku light by Ingo Maurer made
from Japanese paper on an
aluminium stand.
- *height 95cm*
- £560 • Themes

Tubular Lamp ▲

- *1950*
Italian chrome graduated tubular
lamp with coiled decoration.
- *height 44cm*
- £250　　　　● **Ventesimo**

Italian Gold Mesh Lamp ▼

- *circa 1940*
Table lamp with mesh lampshade
supported on a black and white
marble base.
- *height 49cm*
- £900　　　　● **Vincenzo**

Expert Tips

*Italian designers were at the
forefront of early postwar
lighting producing stylish,
sophisticated lamps in organic
shapes.*

Art Deco Verdigris Lantern ▼

- *circa 1930*
Art Deco bronze lantern of
tapered form, each side centred
by a moulded oval motif below a
stepped fan cresting, fitted with
replaced glass, the sides at the
base of the lantern centred by
scrolls issuing palmettes, with s-
scroll brackets leading to a lower
suspended bracket.
- *94cm x 41.5cm sq*
- £6,500　　● **Anthony Outred**

Yellow Sunhat Lamp ▼

- *circa 1960*
Large yellow Italian sunhat lamp
with a green ribbon and assorted
floral design.
- *diameter 44cm*
- £290　　　　● **Castello**

Murano Glass Lamps ▲

- *circa 1960*
Murano Italian glass lamp with
yellow and orange ribbed body.
The metal covers are ashtrays.
- *height 32cm*
- £450　　　　● **Vincenzo**

Pan-Pipes Lamp ▲

- *circa 1970*
Italian pan-pipes table lamp with
chrome and perspex columns
surmounted by lights.
- *height 85cm*
- £1,000　　　　● **Themes**

Perspex Lamp ▼
- *1970*
Italian U shaped perspex lamp on
a metal base by Stilnovo.
- *38cm x 32cm*
- £1,200   • Themes

Brancusi Standing Light ▼
- *1990*
Brancusi standing light made
from Japanese paper with a metal
base, by Tom Dixon.
- *height 280cm*
- £1,600   • Themes

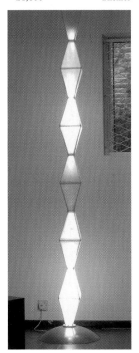

Art Deco Lamp ▲
- *circa 1930*
Art deco lamp with a twisted
metal stand and a white glass
lampshade with a grey geometric
pattern.
- *height 47cm*
- £75   • Old School

Italian Light ▲
- *circa 1950*
Italian light with a white conical
shade supported on a black
circular base.
- *height 40cm*
- £280   • Francesca Martire

Wall Lights by Vemini ▼
- *circa 1950*
One of a pair of abstract Italian
glass wall lights with a design of
assorted squares with amber,
tobacco and clear glass, by
Vemini.
- *31cm square*
- £1,280   • Francesca Martire

Cube Floor Light ▼
- *1970*
Free-standing floor light made
from three white and yellow glass
cubes, connected by metal bands
with a circular metal top and
handle.
- *height 115cm*
- £1,100   • Themes

Italian Globe Lamps ▼

- *circa 1960*

One of a pair of clear and ripple effect globe table lamps with a white band running through the body.
- *height 54cm*
- £300 • Vincenzo

Kodak Lampshade ▲

- 1970

Plastic lampshade with the lettering Kodak in red on a deep yellow background.
- *height 25cm*
- £149 • Jessops

Art Deco Lamp ◄

- 1930

French Art Deco chrome table lamp with a domed shade, curved stand and circular base.
- *height 32cm*
- £250 • Ventesimo

Italian Wall Light ▼

- *circa 1970*

Italian wall light by Marlotta, with a perspex background with metal tubes projecting from it in a variety of sizes, the whole on a square metal frame.
- *60cm x 60cm*
- £1,600 • Themes

Italian Table Lamp ▼

- 1950

Black Italian table lamp of baluster form with blue, yellow and red dots, within a white graffiti-patterned border.
- *height 15cm*
- £50 • Manic Attic

Baccarat-Style Chandeliers ◄

- **20th century**

One of a pair of Baccarat-style cranberry glass chandeliers with scrolled moulded decoration and numerous crystal glass droplets, with 36 arms.
- *height 208cm*
- £20,000 • Sinai

Metalware

Cigar Holder ▼
- *circa 1900*
Brass stand incorporating
openings to hold cigars.
- *height 30cm*
- £250   • H. Gregory

Stacking Ash Trays ▼
- *1970*
Set of ten brass stacking ash trays.
- *diameter 11cm*
- £130   • Ventesimo

Bronze Nude ▲
- *circa 1900*
English bronze figure of a nude
lady standing on a plinth by
March.
- *height 36cm*
- £1,500   • Victor Arwas

Arts and Crafts Bowl ▼
- *circa 1900*
Arts and Crafts pot pourri copper
bowl with two handles, standing
on four legs.
- *13cm x 26cm*
- £280   • Victor Arwas

Bronze by C Vorton ▼
- *circa 1900*
French bronze study of a cat in a
crouching position chewing a fish
by Charles Virion.
- *height 8cm*
- £1,600   • Victor Arwas

Pontiac Car Mascot ▼
- *circa 1920*
American chrome car mascot for
a Pontiac of a nude lady with
outstretched body and her chin
resting on her hands, by Petty.
- *length 30cm*
- £500   • Victor Arwas

A. Clergel Inkpot ◄
- *circa 1900*
Gilt bronze figure of a young girl
entwined by leaves and a large
poppy inkpot, signed by A.
Clerget.
- *width 24cm*
- £3,000   • Victor Arwas

Gilt Bronze Lady ▲
- *1900*
Gilt patinated bronze figure of a
lady by H. Varenne, signed and
dated 1905, with bronze founder's
mark of Susse Freres.
- *18.5cm*
- **£2,500** • Victor Arwas

French Telavia Television ▲
- *circa 1970*
French 'Telavia' television and
stand with radio on teak pedestal
legs.
- *height 127cm*
- **£1,120** • Country Seat

Bronze Cow ▶
- *circa 1925*
Bronze reclining calf, signed by
Richard Garve.
- *7cm x 14cm*
- **£2,500** • Victor Arwas

Bronze and Ivory Figure ▲
- *circa 1920*
A lovely bronze and ivory figure
of a young girl playing the
accordion with original gilding
and marble base.
- *height 25cm*
- **£4,900** • Gavin Douglas

Italian Bronze Boy ◀
- *1904*
A fine Italian bronze of a naked
young boy playing with kittens.
He holds one up while cuddling
the other. The bronze is signed
Marcuse, Roma. On a chamfered
marble base.
- *height 75cm*
- **£5,950** • Gavin Douglas

Bronze Vase ▼

- *circa 1900*

Two-colour patinated gilt bronze with cats' heads around the rim and field mice, wheat and poppies encircling the body, signed by Leopold Savine, L. Colin and Cie. With Paris founder's mark.
- *height 27cm*
- **£6,500**   • **Victor Arwas**

Italian Seal ▼

- *1950*

Italian silver torpedo-shaped seal stamp with base by Murini.
- *height 18cm*
- **£120**   • **Ventesimo**

Fugare Spelter Figure ▲

- *circa 1893*

Gilded spelter figure of winged Mercury engraved 'A. Recompense by Fugare' and exhibited in Paris in 1893.
- *height 34cm*
- **£430**   • **Hayman**

Bronze Lady ▲

- *1911*

Gilt bronze figure of a lady with a parasol by H. Varenne.
- *height 20cm*
- **£2,500**   • **Victor Arwas**

Letter Rack ▼

- *circa 1950*

Black wire cat letter rack, the body in the form of a spring with plastic eyes and rotating eye balls.
- *height 14cm*
- **£45**   • **Francesca Martire**

Italian Chrome Teapot ▼

- *circa 1950*

Round chrome teapot with cork stopper for the spout.
- *height 19cm*
- **£65**   • **Castello**

Chrome Coffee Pot ▼

- *circa 1950*

Italian circular chrome coffee pot.
- *height 24cm*
- **£50**   • **Castello**

La Musicienne ▼

- *1912*

French gilt bronze of a lady with a Sistrum, by Muller.

- *18.5cm*
- **£2,500**   ● **Victor Arwas**

Benson Tea Set ▶

- *circa 1900*

Copper and brass tea set designed and made by W.A.S Benson. Stamped 'Benson'.

- *42cm x 18cm*
- **£895**   ● **Liberty**

World War I Frame ▲

- *circa 1914*

Iron sculpture of a winged angel of Mercury and a soldier with a lion, fashioned as a picture frame.

- *height 47cm*
- **£285**   ● **Hayman**

French Bon-Bon Dish ◀

- *circa 1900*

French gilt bronze bon-bon dish with a young girl on the lid, by A. Charpentiers.

- *16cm x 29cm*
- **£3,500**   ● **Victor Arwas**

Circular Electric Fire ▲

- *circa 1960*

Salmon-pink circular metal electric fire standing on metal legs.

- *diameter 65cm*
- **£120**   ● **Country Seat**

Metal Door Handles ▲

- *1950*

Metal door handles with ceramic and enamel yellow and brown geometric design.

- *26cm x 10cm*
- **£155**   ● **Francesca Martire**

Lifesize Bronze Torso ▶

- *circa 1930*
Emotive life-size bronze torso by
Hubert Yenge from the foundry of
Alexis Rudier, Paris founder to
Rodin.
  - *71cm x 55cm*
  - £8,750   • Country Seat

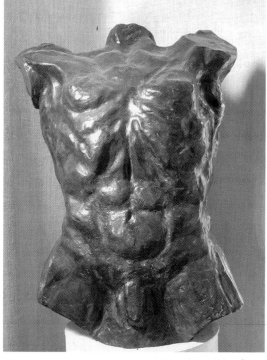

Figure by H. Varenne ▲

- *1912*
Figure of a lady with a large hat
by H. Varenne, founder's mark
Susse Freres.
  - *19cm*
  - £2,500   • Victor Arwas

Chrome Egg Cups ▶

- *circa 1950*
Pair of Italian chrome egg cups
with covers.
  - *height 11cm*
  - £50   • Castello

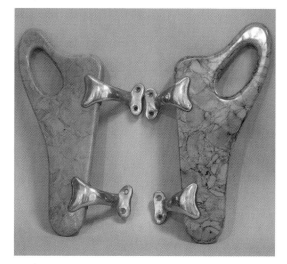

Turquoise Door Handles ◀

- *circa 1960*
Italian stylised pallette-shape
metal door handles with
turquoise marbleised enamel
overlay and large brass mounts.
  - *length 33cm*
  - £320   • Francesca Martire

Wine-Related Items

Wine related items are a great place to start your collection with as there is an abundant supply to choose from.

There is a tremendous interest in wine related items covering a wide range of styles and periods, from George III silver punch ladles to champagne taps, all have their place in the collector's market. The humble corkscrew has been elevated to a work of art and comes in a huge range of different styles, from the staghorn corkscrew made by McBindes in the 1900s, to rosewood corkscrews with grip shanks and brushes to remove the dust off bottles from the cellars. Decanters are also hugely popular. The first decanters, made in the seventeenth century, were of heavy blown moulded glass with indentations in the base. These early decanters were used to serve wine but not to store it. They often have imitation labels bearing the name in gilt lettering of the wine or spirit for which they were intended. Some were made in sets of three with labels for brandy, rum and gin.

Bottle trolleys and tantaluses are highly collectable and were especially popular in the Victorian period. Keep a look out for rare three bottle trolleys.

Champagne Corkscrew ▼

- *circa 1900*
Rare and unusual boxwood champagne corkscrew made by McBindes.
- *length 11cm*
- **£295** • Jasmin Cameron

Wine Funnel ▲

- *circa 1820*
Clear glass wine funnel.
- *diameter 10cm*
- **£75** • Jasmin Cameron

Brass Cocktail Shaker ▼

- *circa 1930*
Brass cocktail shaker with screw lid.
- *height 20cm*
- **£48** • H. Gregory

Cut-Glass Claret Jug ▲
- *1875*

Victorian cut-glass claret jug, the silver mount chased with Bacchus mask spout. By C.B., London.
- *height 35cm*
- **£3,750**   • **Percy's**

Punch Ladle ▲
- *circa 1765*

George III silver punch ladle with feathered stem and whalebone handle.
- *length 38cm*
- **£150**   • **Jasmin Cameron**

Rochefort Corkscrew ▼
- *circa 1880*

Large French corkscrew with Guinot, Nivernais and Rochefort stamped on the handle.
- *length 18cm*
- **£135**   • **Jasmin Cameron**

Spire Stopper Decanter
- *circa 1880*

Victorian spire stopper decanter.
- *height 33cm*
- **£78**   • **H. Gregory**

Silver Wine Coaster ▼
- *circa 1820*

One of a pair of silver wine coasters.
- *diameter 15cm*
- **£320**   • **Jasmin Cameron**

Staghorn Corkscrew ▲
- *circa 1841*

Staghorn crossbar corkscrew.
- *length 9cm*
- **£55**   • **Jasmin Cameron**

Ice Bucket ▲
- *circa 1930*

Silver-plate ice bucket with bun handles each side and two sets of ring patterns.
- *height 21cm*
- **£130**   • **H. Gregory**

Expert Tips

On many old decanters a white deposit caused by corrosion has been buffed out by using a mild abrasive. Such restoration does not spoil the decanter.

Victorian Claret Jug ▼
- *1888*

A rare claret jug, the body cut with an unusual design, by Barnards, London.
- *height 40cm*
- **£4,750**   • **Percy's**

Magnum Claret Jug ▼
- *1872*

An extremely rare Victorian magnum claret jug with beautiful engraving, the cast silver mount with dragon handle, by Stephen Smith, London.
- *height 40cm*
- **£8,750**   • **Percy's**

Queen Anne Shilling Ladle ▲
- *circa 1777*

18th century punch ladle with whalebone handle and a Queen Anne shilling incorporated in the base of the bowl.
- *length 33cm*
- **£150**   • **Jasmin Cameron**

Rosewood Corkscrew ▲
- *circa 1850–80*

Rosewood corkscrew with grip shank and brush.
- *length 13cm*
- **£120**   • **Jasmin Cameron**

Rosewood Corkscrew ▼
- *circa 1850*

Rosewood gripshank corkscrew.
- *length 12cm*
- **£180**   • **Jasmin Cameron**

Small Silver Coaster ▼
- *circa 1820*

Old Sheffield silver-plated wine coaster with lattice work decoration.
- *diameter 10cm*
- **£95**   • **Jasmin Cameron**

Staghorn Corkscrew ▼
- *circa 1890*

Staghorn corkscrew with brush.
- *length 15cm*
- **£120**   • **Jasmin Cameron**

Fluted Wine Funnel ▲
- *circa 1820*
Clear fluted glass wine funnel.
- *diameter 10cm*
- £85   • Jasmin Cameron

Silver Wine Taster ▲
- *1939*
Silver wine taster engraved
'Souvenir of Schroder and
Schyler & Co. Bordeaux
1739–1939'.
- *diameter 8cm*
- £145   • Jasmin Cameron

Claret Jug ▲
- *1880*
Victorian claret jug with diamond
faceted body and silver handle
and lid.
- *height 21cm*
- £270   • H. Gregory

Spirit Decanter ▼
- *1890*
Spirit decanter with moulded
body, fluted silver neck and four
spouts, known as a Kluk Kluk.
- *height 27cm*
- £420   • Jasmin Cameron

Bee Hive Spirit Decanter ▼
- *1880*
Bee hive spirit decanter with
spout.
- *height 24cm*
- £165   • Jasmin Cameron

Pair of Spirit Decanters ▲
- *1840*
One of a pair of fine oblong spirit
decanters with faceted shoulders
and lid.
- *height 28cm*
- £540   • Jasmin Cameron

Henley Corkscrew ▲
- *circa 1890*
Steel corkscrew made by Henley.
- *height 16cm*
- £180   • H. Gregory

Oak Handle Corkscrew ▼
- *circa 1880*
Oak handle corkscrew with a
metal screw and brush.
- *length 13cm*
- £96 • H. Gregory

Silver Plate Wine Strainer ▲
- *circa 1820*
Silver-plated wine strainer.
- *height 14cm*
- £220 • Jasmin Cameron

Rum Label ▼
- 1830
Silver rum label, made in
London.
- *length 5cm*
- £68 • H. Gregory

Victorian Port Decanter ▲
- *circa 1890*
Victorian circular port decanter
with faceted design on the body.
- *height 30cm*
- £55 • H. Gregory

Spirit Labels ▼
- 1910
Spirit labels on chains for port,
shrub and madeira.
- *length 5cm*
- £45 • H. Gregory

Ice Bucket ▲
- *circa 1930*
Silver-plate ice bucket with plain
moulded handles to the sides.
- *height 21cm*
- £185 • H. Gregory

Claret Jug ▲
- 1890
English claret jug with floral
engraving and a silver handle and
lid.
- *height 30cm*
- £620 • Jasmin Cameron

Silver Beer Mugs

- *circa 1940*
Silver beer mugs with glass
bottoms and bamboo decoration.
- *height 13cm*
- £130 the pair   • H. Gregory

Cocktail Shaker ▼

- **1920**
Silver-plate cocktail shaker.
- *height 20cm*
- £68   • H. Gregory

Claret Jug ▼

- *circa 1880*
Continental elegant claret jug
with fine engraving around the
body and a silver geometric band
around the neck, standing on a
plain silver circular base.
- *height 29cm*
- £335   • H. Gregory

Pair of Glass Decanters ▲

- *circa 1890*
Pair of glass decanters with
diamond pattern on the body and
stopper.
- *height 27cm*
- £150   • H. Gregory

Spirit Barrels ▼

- *circa 1880*
Three oak spirit barrels with
silver banding and taps, on an
oak stand with silver banding.
- *36cm x 37cm*
- £1,080   • H. Gregory

Oak Water Jug ▶

- *circa 1880*
Oak cordial jug with silver lid,
ball finial and spout with a shield
below, standing on three ball feet.
- *height 29cm*
- £330   • H. Gregory

Dutch Decanter ▼
- *1830*
Dutch oblong decanter with flash gilding flowers.
- *height 25cm*
- £175
- Jasmin Cameron

Pair of Silver Coaster ▶
- *circa 1920*
Pair of silver coasters with scrolled rim and teak base with a circular silver disc.
- *diameter 16cm*
- £180
- H. Gregory

Kluk Kluk ▲
- *1850*
Spirit decanter with a moulded body known as a Kluk Kluk.
- *height 27cm*
- £275
- Jasmin Cameron

Glass Flask ▼
- *circa 1720*
Glass flask in the fashion of Venice moulding.
- *height 15.5cm*
- £180
- Jasmin Cameron

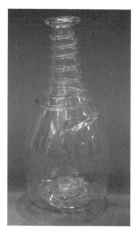

Ivory Handle Corkscrew ▼
- *circa 1880*
Ivory handle corkscrew with metal screw and brush.
- *length 14cm*
- £120
- H. Gregory

Regency Wine Cooler ◀
- *circa 1820*
English mahogany wine cooler of sarcophagus form, the rectangular ebony strung edged top with canted corners above a cavetto moulding and cross-banded frieze with an ebonised upper and lower strung edge. Each side of the body decorated with an ebonised string inlay, the sides fitted with finely cast lions' heads, the base finished with a triple-reeded moulding above finely cast brass hairy paw feet.
- *61cm x 71cm*
- £11,500
- Anthony Outred

Spirit Decanter ▲

- 1930

Spirit decanter with moulded body and lozenge shape stopper with foliate and bird engraving.
- *height 27cm*
- £320 • Jasmin Cameron

Horn Corkscrew ▲

- *circa 1910*

Corkscrew with a horn handle and metal screw.
- *length 12cm*
- £44 • H. Gregory

Silver Coaster ▶

- *circa 1920*

Silver-plated circular coaster, one of a pair with scrolled rim and a teak base.
- *diameter 17cm*
- £160 • H. Gregory

Claret Jug ▼

- 1850

Deeply faceted claret jug, electroplated lip and cover, twisted rope handle and an acorn finial.
- *height 20cm*
- £440 • Jasmin Cameron

Lion Handles Coaster ▼

- *circa 1900*

Silver circular coaster with scrolling to the rim and lion ring handles to the side.
- *height 16cm*
- £70 • H. Gregory

Bone Handle Corkscrew ▲

- *circa 1900*

Bone handle corkscrew with brass end and metal screw.
- *length 14cm*
- £70 • H. Gregory

Wine Coaster ▲

- *circa 1900*

Silver-plate wine coaster with scrolled handles and pierced floral and geometric design.
- *height 57cm*
- £72 • H. Gregory

Works of Art & Sculpture

The Japanese were more prolific than the Chinese in their carving, particularly in the second half of the nineteenth century.

Works of art and sculpture covers a broad spectrum of antiques and we have therefore focused in this book on the works of art of four areas which include Oriental, Islamic, Russian and European.

It is interesting to note how the market place is affected by the political climate of the time, for example, during the mid-1990s there was a sudden influx of Russian art due to the fall of the Communist regime. This in turn has led to the rise in popularity of Soviet works of art and sculpture, which now have great historical value as they depict a way of life that no longer exists.

There is currently a huge rise of interest in Islamic works of art reflecting the current political climate. It is therefore worth being up to date on world affairs when you go to seek out works of art. This is a huge area so make sure you do your research before you embark on your journey.

Asian/Oriental

Indian Door ▼
- *circa 1910*
An Indian door from Rajasthan with six hand-painted scenes of celebrations.
- *180cm x 87cm*
- £700   • Sharif

Jade Lion ▲
- *17th century*
Jade lion group shown with its jaws clamped around its captured prey. Ming Dynasty.
- *length 15cm*
- £650   • Ormonde

Head of Horse ▶
- *206 BC–220 AD*
A Chinese terracotta model of a horse's head naturalistically styled, with pigmentation from the Han Dynasty.
- *height 24cm*
- £550   • Ormonde

Malachite Axe Head ▼
- *1600–1000 BC*
Bronze axe head encrusted with malachite from the Shang Dynasty.
- *length 20cm*
- £750 • Ormonde

Incense Burner ▼
- *Han Dynasty 206 BC–220 AD*
Incense burner in the shape of a mountain (representing the Isles of the Blessed), the abode of the mortals. The incense burner rests on a tall tray with a solid foot hollowed out beneath the stem.
- *height 21cm*
- £300 • Ormonde

Witch Doctor ▼
- *Han Dynasty 206 BC–220 AD*
Chinese Han Dynasty witch doctor with large ears and a ferocious face holding a snake.
- *height 110cm*
- £2,800 • Ormonde

Machang-type Jar ▲
- *late 3rd or early 2nd millennium BC*
Machang-type jar of painted pottery, Gansu or Qinghai province, with an unusual circular design and geometric pattern.
- *height 32cm*
- £650 • Ormonde

Bronze Belt Hook ▲
- *3rd–4th century BC*
Bronze belt hook.
- *length 15cm*
- £150 • Ormonde

Han Dynasty Vase ▲
- *06 BC–220 AD*
Unusual garlic-headed bottle-shaped vase with original pigment of pink, white and crimson with a geometric design around the neck. Han Dynasty.
- *height 34cm*
- £750 • Ormonde

Stick Figure ▼
- *206 BC–220 AD*
Stick figure of a man standing, from the Han Dynasty.
- *height 60cm*
- £1,200 • Ormonde

Shaman Beads ▼
- *206 BC–220 AD*
Cream jade beads that once belonged to a Shaman, from the Han Dynasty.
- *length 2cm*
- £2,000 • Ormonde

Zodiac Animals ▼
- *7th–9th century AD*
Rare group of pottery Zodiac animals from the China Tang Dynasty.
- *height 28cm*
- £550 • Ormonde

Terracotta Horse ▲
- *206 BC–220 AD*
Horse and groom standing with
hand extended, from the Han
Dynasty.
- *height of horse 29cm, height of
groom 26cm*
- £1,200   • Ormonde

Lacquer Figure ▲
- *206 BC–220 AD*
Wooden figure of a lady with
arms folded, wearing a dress with
red and black lacquer details,
from the Han Dynasty.
- *height 51cm*
- £1,200   • Ormonde

Reclining Lion ▲
- *circa 17th century*
Grey selegon jade lion shown in a
reclining position. Ming Dynasty.
- *height 8cm*
- £850   • Ormonde

Burmese Table ▼
- *circa 1900*
Carved wood circular table top
with carved legs in the style of an
elephant's head and trunk.
- *70cm x 100cm*
- £1,200   • Sharif

Chinese Burial Object ▼
- *206 BC–220 AD*
Burial object of a well-modelled
horse's head, with strong traces of
pigment, highlighting a red
bridle, from the Han Dynasty.
- *height 15cm*
- £300   • Ormonde

Banshan Pottery Jug ▼
- *mid 3rd millennium BC*
Banshan-type painted pottery jug
from the Gansu or Qinghai
province of Majiayao culture.
- *height 35cm*
- £1,250   • Ormonde

Group of Soldiers ▲
- *206 BC–220 AD*
Group of five soldiers standing,
from the Han Dynasty.
- *height 47cm*
- £750   • Ormonde

Dinosaur Egg ▲
- *60–70 million years old*
Dinosaur egg from outer
Mongolia.
- *height 13cm,*
- £300   • Ormonde

Expert Tips

*Ivories from the Ming dynasty
are usually distinguishable by
extensive surface cracking
caused by oils within the ivory
evaporating over time.*

European

Esmeralda and her Goat ▲
- *1881*
Italian statuary marble figure of Esmeralda, the gypsy-girl heroine from Victor Hugo's *The Hunchback of Notre Dame*, and her goat. Signed Prof. P. Romanelli.
- *height 102cm*
- £21,000   • Crowther

Proserpine & Mercury ▲
- *mid-20th century*
Composition stone group of Proserpine and Mercury. Mercury with winged helmet, standing contraposto with drapery drawn across his torso and playing a pipe. The figure of Proserpine kneels at his side.
- *height 196cm*
- £28,000   • Crowther

Young Bacchus ▼
- *circa 1860*
Marble figure of the young Bacchus clad in a crumpled tunic and carrying a bunch of grapes in his left hand whilst clutching another bunch in the crook of his elbow.
- *height 102cm*
- £15,750   • Crowther

Marble Bust ▼
- *circa 1790*
Fine marble bust of an unknown gentleman shown l'antica with a toga about his shoulders.
- *height 56cm*
- £7,500   • Crowther

Walter Scott ▲
- *circa 19th century*
Marble bust of Sir Walter Scott on original socle, signed by the sculptor James Fillans, born in Paisley, Scotland.
- *height 81cm*
- £5,750   • Crowther

Figure by Pocchini ▲
- *circa 1890*
Italian white marble figure of a young woman by V. Pocchini, the girl in rustic costume and clasping a flower. Signed V. Pocchini.
- *height 94cm*
- £14,500   • Crowther

Milo of Croton ▼

- *circa 19th century*
Bronze figure of Milo of Croton,
the legendary athlete renowned
for his strength who lived at
Croton, a Greek settlement in
the 6th century BC.
- *height 84cm*
- £14,500   ● Crowther

Fisher Boy ▼

- *1849*
German white marble figure of a
fisher boy by Carl Johann
Steinhauser. Signed C.
Steinhauser. F. Rom. 1849.
- *height 99cm*
- £22,500   ● Crowther

Expert Tips

*Be aware of chips and cracks
when purchasing a sculpture
as this can seriously devalue
the item.*

Bust of Niobe ▲

- *circa 18th century*
Larger than life size statuary
marble classical bust of Niobe,
attributed to the 18th-century
sculptor, F. Harwood.
- *height 96cm*
- £15,000   ● Crowther

Putto Astride a Dolphin ▲

- *circa 1890*
A contemporary bronze replica of
a late nineteenth century
Doulton Stoneware fountain
figure of a putto astride a dolphin.
- *height 70cm*
- £4,950   ● Crowther

John Locke ▶

- *circa 1650*
Marble bust of John Locke, who
was once secretary to the Earl of
Shaftesbury.
- *height 71cm*
- £5,500   ● Crowther

Marble Figure of Ceres ▼

- *circa 17th century*
Rare 17th-century marble figure
of Ceres, the goddess of summer
carved with flying drapery in the
Baroque manner. She stands
contraposto, clasping a sheaf of
corn to her side.
- *height 95cm*
- £5,500   ● Crowther

Corneille van Cleeve ▼

- *circa 1880*
Fine French Rococo marble bust of the 17th-century sculptor Corneille van Cleeve, looking dexter, after the original by Jean Jacques Caffieri. The original is to be found in the Musée de Louvre, Paris.
- *height 71cm*
- £9,800 • Crowther

Faustina ▲

- *late 18th–early 19th century*
An Italian plaster bust of Faustina, attributed to Bartolomeo Caveceppi.
- *60cm x 38cm*
- £2,200 • Crowther

Young Bacchus ▲

- *circa 1860*
Marble figure of the young Bacchus clad in only a crumpled tunic and carrying a bunch of grapes in his left hand, whilst clutching another bunch in the crook of his elbow.
- *height 102cm*
- £15,700 • Crowther

Lead Cockerel ▲

- *18th century*
A rare eighteenth century lead cockerel. Provenance: ex Drakelow Hall, Burton on Trent.
- *72cm x 48cm*
- £10,500 • Crowther

The Sleeping Shepherd Boy ▶

- *circa 1817–18*
Italian marble figure of 'The Sleeping Shepherd Boy', by John Gibson, made for the Lord George Cavendish, the nephew of the 6th Duke of Devonshire.
- *height 105cm*
- £100,000 • Crowther

Islamic

Cylindrical Flask ▶

- *7th century BC*
Islamic cylindrical flask with brown, cream and blue marbling.
- *height 13cm*
- £1,200 • Pars

Syrian Table ▲

- *circa 1920*
Hexagonal mother-of-pearl and bone inlay table with pierced masharabi panels on turned legs.
- *49cm x 35cm*
- £200 • Sharif

Syrian Tea Table ▲

- *circa 1910*
A tea table from Damascus with a brass circular top.
- *47cm x 59cm*
- £150 • Sharif

Vase Bowl and Saucer ▲

- *circa 1910*
Matching blue and turquoise floral pattern vase bowl and saucer.
- *height 37cm*
- £300 • Sharif

Persian Copper Vase ▼

- *circa 1950*
A Persian copper and brass vase.
- *height 75cm*
- £250 • Sharif

Islamic Chess Pieces ▼

- *9th century BC*
Islamic wooden chess pieces.
- *height 5cm*
- £3,000 • Pars

Turkish Table ▲
● *circa 1920*
Turkish table with mother-of-pearl and bone inlay on architecturally carved legs.
● *64cm x 44cm*
● £400   ● Sharif

Damascus Table ▲
● *circa 1920*
Side table from Damascus with mother-of-pearl and bone inlay, single small drawer with brass handle, standing on cabriole legs.
● *43cm x 36cm*
● £150   ● Sharif

Persian Charger ▲
● *circa 1940*
Persian oval brass charger or tray.
● *75cm*
● £200   ● Sharif

Mirror and Stand ▲
● *circa 1900*
Elaborate mother-of-pearl and ivory oblong inlay mirror with scrolled carving, and chest with one long drawer and two smaller, with carved moulded top, and feet, from Damascus.
● *height 210cm*
● £6,000   ● Sharif

Architectural Table ▶
● *circa 1910*
Mother-of-pearl hexagonal table with geometric patterns and architectural legs.
● *55cm x 43cm*
● £200   ● Sharif

Persian Vases ▼

- *circa 1930*

A pair of fluted Persian blue and
turquoise floral pattern vases with
two handles on circular bases.
- *height 56cm*
- £200   • Sharif

Algerian Brass Jug ▼

- *circa 1930*

Brass inlay teapot on a tall brass
stand with circular base.
- *length 172cm*
- £650   • Sharif

Mother-of-Pearl Chair ▲

- *circa 1930*

Mother-of-pearl and bone inlay
chair, with carved top rail and
scrolled arms.
- *93cm x 64cm*
- £500   • Sharif

Mother-of-Pearl Table ▲

- *circa 1920*

Mother–of-pearl and bone inlay
in geometric patterns with
architecturally carved legs.
- *64cm x 44cm*
- £400   • Sharif

Crystal Chess Piece ◄

- *8th–7th century BC*

Clear lozenge-shape crystal chess
piece.
- *height 4cm*
- £1,000   • Pars

Russian

Russian Gilt Enamel Spoon ▶
- *circa 1900*
Silver gilt spoon with pink, blue, red and yellow foliate design.
- *length 18cm*
- £1,000 • Iconastas

Fabergé Hand Mirror ▲
- *1910*
Silver hand mirror by Fabergé, with raised engraved crest.
- *length 21cm*
- £1,400 • Iconastas

Moscow Yacht Tankard ▼
- *circa 1871*
Miniature silver tankard with arms of the Moscow Yacht Club.
- *height 6cm*
- £750 • Iconastas

Fabergé Kovsh ▲
- *1910*
Fabergé ceramic and silver kovsh with set cut amethysts.
Provenance: Princess of Baden, from the Baden collection.
- *height 15cm*
- £5,000 • Iconastas

Miniature Tankard ▲
- *circa 1787*
Miniature 'Charka', or silver tankard, engraved with two eagles above two flowers connected by a ribbon.
- *height 4cm*
- £625 • Iconastas

Soviet Pen Tray ▼
- *circa 1930*
Soviet pottery pen tray with a reclining Uzbek reading Pravda after Natalia Danko.
- *width 19cm*
- £650 • Iconastas

Enamel Blotter ▼
- *circa 1900*
Enamel blue and pink floral design blotter with gold borders by Semonova.
- *length 14cm*
- £900 • Iconastas

Enamelled Spoon ◀
- *circa 1900*
Silver spoon enamelled with a dark blue, green and pink foliate design on a cream background.
- *length 15cm*
- £1,300 • Iconastas

Silver Gilt and Gold Enamel ▼

- *circa 1900*
Silver gilt spoon with turquoise, white, green and dark blue, foliate design with an emerald-green border.
- *length 11cm*
- £400 • Iconastas

Russian Frame ▶

- *circa 1920*
Russian rosewood picture frame with brass borders and crest of two eagles with Tsar Nicholas II of Russia.
- *28cm x 21cm*
- £1,300 • Iconastas

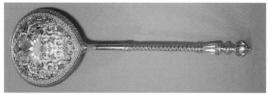

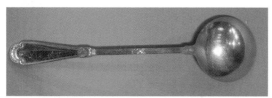

Silver Gilt and Enamel Beaker ▼

- *circa 1885*
Silver gilt beaker with blue scrolling and white flowers.
- *height 11.5cm*
- £1,850 • Iconastas

Small Fabergé Mirror ▲

- *1910*
Small Fabergé silver mirror with raised engraved crest.
- *length 17.5cm*
- £1,400 • Iconastas

Fabergé Spoon ▼

- *circa 1900*
Silver spoon with gilt bowl, by Fabergé.
- *length 16cm*
- £425 • Iconastas

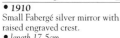

Musicians by Yakovlevich ◀

- *circa 1910*
Pair of terracotta musicians by Golovin Alexander Yakovlevich.
- *height 28cm*
- £5,500 the pair • Iconastas

Russian Kovsh ▶

- *circa 1900*

Russian enamel kovs, highly decorated with blue turquoise foliate design by Lubwin.

- *length 19cm*
- £1,200 • Iconastas

Soviet Tea Holder ▼

- *1967*

Soviet silver propaganda tea glass holder with a scene showing a man in the foreground with a harvest and a rocket flying into space and the sun in the background.

- *height 10cm*
- £80 • Iconastas

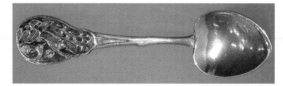

Arts and Crafts Spoon ▲

- *circa 1900*

Arts and crafts silver spoon by Knox, with a handle fashioned as a peacock and the bowl as a leaf.

- *length 16cm*
- £800 • Iconastas

Silver Gilt Spoon ▼

- *circa 1900*

Silver gilt spoon with blue flowers on a cream background with a green and orange foliate design.

- *length 17cm*
- £750 • Iconastas

Enamel Russian Spoon ▲

- *circa 1900*

Russian silver spoon enamelled with blue and pink floral design on gold with a turquoise circular border design.

- *length 20cm*
- £600 • Iconastas

Silver Gilt Tea Set ▼

- *circa 1875*

Silver gilt tea pot, water jug and milk jug, with foliate scrolling and a central cartouche of a palace, by Ovchinnikov.

- *height 15cm*
- £2,500 • Iconastas

Silver Gilt Engraved Goblet ▲

- *1839*

Silver fluted gilt goblet from Moscow with foliate design.

- *height 20cm*
- £1,200 • Iconastas

Baboushka ▲

- *circa 1930*
Soviet white glazed porcelain
figure of a baboushka with
impressed hammer and sickle
mark and initials of Boris
Kustodiev (1878–1927) from the
Lomonosov factory.
- *height 27cm*
- **£1,250** • Iconastas

Lenin Ink Well ▼

- *circa 1924*
The Lenin inkwell, with facsimile
signatures and inscription
'Proletariat of the World unite'
and anniversary inscription on
the cover. By Natalia Danko
(1892–1942) from the
Lomonosov factory.
- *height 17cm*
- **£1,250** • Iconastas

Set of Salts ▼

- *circa 1877*
Set of six circular silver salts on
three ball feet with silver spoons
by Gachen in original oak box.
- *diameter 18cm*
- **£750** • Iconastas

Stalin ▼

- *circa 1920*
Soviet white glazed porcelain
figure of Stalin shown in his
youthful revolutionary 'Hero'
style. Signed.
- *height 36cm*
- **£2,450** • Iconastas

Soviet Inkwell ▶

- *circa 1929*
Soviet pottery inkwell,
surmounted by a young lady with
a red headscarf reading a book,
the lid modelled as books and
pamphlets. After Danko.
- *height 16cm*
- **£1,250** • Iconastas

Opalin Glass Sweet Jars ▲

- *circa 1905*
Opalin glass sweet jars modelled
as busts of the Tsar and Tsarina
Nicholas and Alexandra, made
for the Imperial visit to France.
- *height 35cm*
- **£500 the pair** • Iconastas

Puss in Boots ▲

- *circa 1930*
A brightly coloured Soviet figure
of Puss in Boots, unmarked,
probably by Boris Kustodiev.
- *height 23cm*
- **£450** • Iconastas

Lenin ▼

- *circa 1920*
Rare plaster figure of Lenin by
Mauetta.
- *height 34cm*
- £2,450 • Iconastas

Grey Horses with Riders ▲

- *circa 1930*
Pair of grey horses with riders,
one pointing, on a foliate square
base.
- *26cm x 18cm*
- £2,650 • Iconastas

Soviet Porcelain Plate ▲

- *circa 1920*
Russian, Soviet porcelain plate
with floral design and stylised
'CCCP' by Natalya Girshfeld.
- *diameter 23cm*
- £1,650 • Iconastas

Constructivist Plate ▲

- *1928*
Constructivist plate painted with
female skiers in linear form with
strong colours. Signed and dated
1928.
- *diameter 24cm*
- £1,650 • Iconastas

Accordion Player ▼

- *circa 1930*
Soviet white glazed figure of an
accordion player by Boris
Kustodiev.
- *height 23cm*
- £490 • Iconastas

Soviet Bowl ▼

- *circa 1921*
Soviet bowl painted with strong
brush-strokes in vibrant colours
by Rudolf Vilde (1868–1942).
- *diameter 26cm*
- £2,200 • Iconastas

Arctic Rescue Tea Set ◄

- *circa 1925*
Tea set commemorating an
Arctic rescue of the Swedish
Arctic Expedition, led by Nobel,
by the Soviet icebreaker 'Krasin'.
- *diameter of plate 24cm*
- £2,500 • Iconastas

Tea Caddy Spoon ▶

- *circa 1900*
Silver gilt tea caddy spoon
showing an Imperial Russian
scene and a foliate design.
- *length 8cm*
- £180   • Iconastas

Commemorative Tea Holder ▼

- *1970*
Soviet silver tea holder with a
central cartouche showing
Lenin's head, an industrial scene
and the dates 1920–1970,
surrounded by a foliate design.
- *height 10cm*
- £80   • Iconastas

Fabergé Picture Frame ◀

- *circa 1890*
Fabergé satinwood picture frame
with silver beading, the gold
initial 'A', and four silver roses at
each corner. The photo shows
Tsarina Alexandra.
- *14cm x 11cm*
- £4,500   • Iconastas

Expert Tips

*Ex Soviet works of art are
becoming increasingly popular
and are gaining in value,
especially figures depicting
Lenin in uniform.*

Silver Tankard ▲

- *circa 1900*
A Russian silver tankard made for
political propaganda, with
engraved cartouches showing a
bountiful harvest.
- *height 8cm*
- £1,900   • Iconastas

Reclining Man Reading Newspaper ◀

- *circa 1930*
Reclining figure of a man reading
a newspaper dressed in white with
a black and white hat.
- *length 21cm*
- £580   • Iconastas

Russian Enamel Spoon ▲

- *circa 1900*
Silver Russian spoon with gilt
bowl, and pink, blue and green
enamelling.
- *length 18cm*
- £850 • **Iconastas**

Silver Enamel Spoon ▼

- *circa 1900*
Silver gilt small spoon with
enamel blue foliate and gold
design.
- *length 11cm*
- £180 • **Iconastas**

Fabergé Belt Buckle ▼

- *circa 1880*
Fabergé silver belt buckle with a
fine leaf design with five large
rubies.
- *8cm x 5cm*
- £2,000 • **Iconastas**

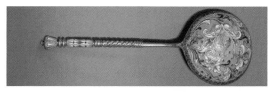

Six Russian Spoons ▼

- *circa 1900*
Six small Russian silver gilt
teaspoons, with pink flowers with
a turquoise and blue background.
- *length 10cm*
- £650 • **Iconastas**

Plate by Freze ▼

- *circa 1921*
Soviet plate decorated with a
vase and flowers by Varvara Freze
(1883–1970).
- *diameter 22.5cm*
- £1,200 • **Iconastas**

Russian Revolutionary Plate ▲

- *circa 1920*
Soviet Russian large porcelain
revolutionary plate decorated
with a fantasy architectural scene
of Rome by Vladimir Mosyagin,
painted by Vasilii Timorev
(1870–1942).
- *diameter 31cm*
- £2,750 • **Iconastas**

Fan with Imperial Cypher ▼

- *circa 1900*
Fine amber fan with diamond
scrolled initials 'A. M.', belonging
to the Grand Duchesse
Alexandra Mickolevich with the
Imperial cipher.
- *length 36cm*
- £1,500 • **Iconastas**

Tea Spoons ◀

- *circa 1900*
Set of six silver gilt spoons with
enamel blue and cream foliate
design with scrolled handle.
- *length 10cm*
- £650 • **Iconastas**

Writing Equipment

The art deco period produced some beautifully designed ink pots and pens which are now highly sought after.

The vast range of collectable writing equipment is overwhelmingly Victorian. The Victorians were fervent writers, and as a result an abundance of writing related items were created in this period. Victorian ink trays were often inlaid with mother of pearl and are highly decorative. Some were made of enamel and decorated in a chinoiserie style, which was a very fashionable decorative effect at the time.

If you are a first-time collector, the field of writing equipment is a great place to start with as there is huge scope for the collector and the items can be very affordable, and are also usuable. They can make a bold and striking statement on any desk or in a study as they are not only decorative, but are also a great talking point.

Pens are always collectable with the leading brands such as Parker, Mont Blanc and Waterman continuing to attract the highest prices because of their timeless workmanship and superior quality.

Quill Box ▶
- 1920
Quill box made from ebonised wood and quills.
- 5cm x 16cm
- £45 • Sporting Times

Salter Letter Balance ▼
- 1930
Small metal letter balance with a brass dial, with the manufacturer's mark Salter and made in England on the dial.
- *height 22cm*
- £48 • Rookery Farm

French Inkwell ◀
- *circa 1900*
French art nouveau ink well of a lady reclining on large flowers with a lid concealed on the top of her long hair.
- *height 16cm*
- £1,200 • Victor Arwas

Rosewood Paper Knife ▶

- *circa 1810*
Rosewood paper knife with brass filigree decoration.
- *ength 29cm*
- £78 • Hayman

Stone Inkwell ▼

- *circa 1950*
Inkwell in the shape of a curling stone with a brass lid and handle.
- *diameter 6cm*
- £45 • Sporting Times

Austrian Inkwell ◀

- *circa 1890*
Austrian green and purple glass ink pot with a stylised leaf design and a hinged brass lid.
- *diameter 15cm*
- £460 • Jasmin Cameron

'Lucky Cup' Pen ▼

- *circa 1928*
Canadian duofold junior, mandarin yellow Parker pen.
- *length 14cm*
- £640 • Jasmin Cameron

Silver Basket Ink Pot ▼

- *circa 1896*
Silver basket on fluted legs, with a faceted square glass ink pot with a silver lid and a silver base.
- *height 8cm*
- £325 • Barrett Towning

Silver Ink Pot ◀

- *circa 1937*
Silver ink pot with hinged lid within a glass moulded base, and pen holder. Made in Birmingham.
- *length 14.5cm*
- £295 • Barrett Towning

Faceted Glass Inkpot ▼

- *circa 1830*
Faceted glass inkpot with brass hinge.
- *height 9cm*
- £85 • Jasmin Cameron

Beehive Ink Pot ▼

- *circa 1905*
Silver inkwell with hinged lid. Made in London by Mappin & Webb.
- *height 6.5cm*
- £350 • Barrett Towning

Waterman Fountain Pen ▲

- *circa 1920*
Waterman 0552 gold plated basket weave fountain pen with half G. P.
- *length 14cm*
- £900 • Jasmin Cameron

Dip Pen and Pencil ▲

- *circa 1890*
Rare pair of dip pens and pencils, with pugs' heads with ringed brass collars.
- *length 20cm*
- £160 • Jasmin Cameron

Silver Tray with Inkwell ▼

- *circa 1901*
Silver moulded tray on raised feet, with a pen holder and faceted glass inkpot with scrolled silver lid.
- *height 11cm*
- £375 • Barrett Towning

Large Bacarrat Inkwell ▼

- 1880
Large bulbous glass inkpot with a textured wave relief and an American moulded silver lid, by Bacarrat. Fully marked.
- *height 15cm*
- £740 • Jasmin Cameron

'Lovers' by Bernard ◀

- *circa 1900*
French sculpture of two lovers embracing on a moulded base, by Bernard.
- *width 17cm*
- £3,000 • Victor Arwas

Brass Blotter ◀

- *circa 1912*
Arts and crafts brass boat blotter period. Marked GESCi 9121.
- *length 15cm*
- £260 • Jasmin Cameron

Silver Capstan Inkpot ▼

- *1913*
Capstan silver inkwell with hinged lid and large splayed base. Made in Birmingham by H. Greaves Ltd.
- *diameter 14cm*
- £640 • Jasmin Cameron

Travelling Ink Set ▼

- *circa 1850*
Travelling ink set in original burgundy leather box fashioned as a trunk, with brass interior, two bottles with brass lids and a bone quill.
- *4cm x 9cm*
- £185 • Jasmin Cameron

Amber and Clear Glass Dip Pens ▼

- *1850*
Very rare amber and clear glass dip pens, in excellent condition.
- *length 20cm*
- £130 • Jasmin Cameron

Oak Desk Stand ▼

- *circa 1890*
Oak desk stand with single drawer and two inkwells with brass lids and handles, standing on bun feet.
- *11cm x 38cm*
- £85 • Sporting Times

Art Nouveau Inkwell ▶

- *circa 1900*
French art nouveau pewter ink well of a lady with long hair.
- *width 12cm*
- £1,200 • Victor Arwas

Double Glass Inkwell ▶

- *circa 1910*
Double glass inkwell with silver rims around the lids, in a square oblong container.
- *width 11cm*
- £96　　　　● H. Gregory

Parker Propelling Pencil ▲

- *circa 1930–35*
Mottled green Parker propelling pencil.
- *length 13cm*
- £220　　　● Jasmin Cameron

Swirl Glass Ink Pot ▼

- *1890*
Swirl glass ink pot with silver-plated hinged lid with floral design.
- *height 16cm*
- £640　　　● Jasmin Cameron

Ebony Ink Tray ▼

- *circa 1820*
Ebony ink tray with two square inkwells with brass lids, and central stamp compartment.
- *width 34cm*
- £195　　　　● Hayman

Ball Inkwell ▼

- *1914*
Brass inkwell consisting of four brass balls resting on each other, one of which contains the ink, with a metal and wood base.
- *diameter 17cm*
- £78　　　　● Hayman

Circular Glass Inkwell ◀

- *circa 1890*
Circular inkwell with a brass hinged lid.
- *height 9cm*
- £270　　　● H. Gregory

Glass Inkwell ▶

- *circa 1901*

Glass inkwell with faceted base and silver hinged lid.
- *height 9cm*
- £290　　　　● **H.Gregory**

Green Malachite Blotter ▼

- *circa 1860*

Green malachite blotter with knob handle.
- *length 19cm*
- £160　　　　● **Hayman**

Victorian Writing Tray ◀

- *circa 1870*

Victorian double-handled brass writing tray with two inkwells and a central sander, decorated with c-scrolling and raised on four paw feet.
- *width 27cm*
- £175　　　　● **Hayman**

Glass Square Ink Pot ▲

- *circa 1860*

Square glass ink pot with faceted stopper and moulded shoulders.
- *height 9cm*
- £85　　　● **Jasmin Cameron**

Paper Weight Ink Pot ▼

- *1890*

Victorian circular paperweight inkwell with brass lid.
- *diameter 11cm*
- £48　　　　● **Hayman**

Butterfly Letter Rack ◀

- *circa 189*

Brass butterfly letter rack standing on a rustic base.
- *height 10cm*
- £238　　　　● **Hayman**

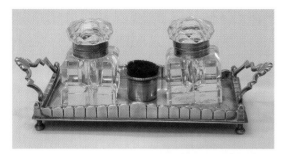

Cut-Glass Inkwell ▼
- *circa 1900*
Cut-glass inkwell with a hinged
silver cover.
- *height 10cm*
- £260   • H. Gregory

Non-Spill Ink Pot ▲
- *circa 1900*
Non-spill vaseline glass ink pot of
ovoid form with a central tear
drop reservoir.
- *height 6cm*
- £24   • Hayman

Wood Blotter ▲
- *circa 1860*
Wood ink blotter with brass inlay.
- *length 19cm*
- £160   • Hayman

Old Sheffield Ink Stand ▶
- *circa 1840*
Old Sheffield silver ink stand
with serpentine border decorated
with floral and leaf design, two
faceted glass inkwells and a
central silver sander.
- *width 27cm*
- £300   • Jasmin Cameron

Brass Ink Stand ◀
- *1830*
Double-handled brass ink stand
with scalloped design, holding
two glass inkpots with faceted lids
and brass rims, and a brush in a
brass container.
- *length 21cm*
- £340   • Jasmin Cameron

Silver Inkwell ▲
- *1930*
Small silver circular inkwell with
hinged lid.
- *diameter 9cm*
- £60   • H. Gregory

Satin Glass Ink Pot ▲
- *circa 1870*
Satin glass turquoise ink pot with
a white flower and hinged lid.
- *height 11cm*
- £220   • Hayman

Ivory Boat Blotter

- *circa 1890*
Ivory boat blotter with knob handle.
- *length 11cm*
- £175 • Jasmin Cameron

Victorian Ink Pot

- *circa 1830*
Victorian ink pot of ovoid form with ball stopper.
- *height 7cm*
- £85 • Jasmin Cameron

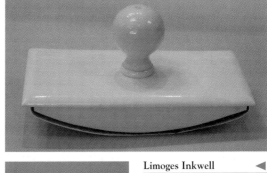

Limoges Inkwell

- *1930*
Limoges enamel inkwell with red flowers on a white ground and brass banding.
- *height 5.5cm*
- £115 • Hayman

Glass Ink Pot

- *circa 1830*
Faceted clear glass ink pot with star-cut stopper.
- *height 9cm*
- £85 • Jasmin Cameron

Gutherpercha Writing Set

- *circa 1860*
Ink tray made from gutherpercha with two inkwells set on a scrolled base.
- *width 27cm*
- £125 • Hayman

Slide Action Dip Pens

- *1890*
Edward pod slide action travelling dip pen in 'Gothic design' with rolled gold nib.
- *length 14cm*
- £125 • Jasmin Cameron

Owl Pen Holder ▶

- *circa 1890*
Owl inkwell standing on a
circular base with a scrolled
handles for holding pens.
- *height 21cm*
- £280   • H. Gregory

Parker Pencil ▼

- *1934–5*
Mottled green Parker pencil.
- *length 11cm*
- £175   • Jasmin Cameron

Papier Mâché Pentray ▼

- *1880*
Black and gold papier mâché pen
tray decorated with a gilt
chinoiserie scene.
- *length 25cm*
- £55   • Jasmin Cameron

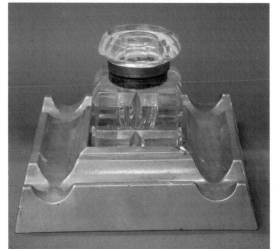

Square Ink Pot ▲

- *1880*
Victorian heavy square faceted
ink pot standing on a brass tray
with indentations for pens.
- *18cm square*
- £125   • Hayman

Quill Knife

- *1820*

Mother of pearl quill knife.
- *length 10cm*
- **£125** • **Jasmin Cameron**

Circular Inkwell ▲

- *circa 1930*

Large silver circular inkwell with a hinged lid.
- *diameter 11.5cm*
- **£190** • **H. Gregory**

Art Deco Ink Pot ▶

- *circa 1920*

Moulded brass art deco inkwell with cover and porcelain bowl.
- *width 13cm*
- **£68** • **Hayman**

Conway Stewart Dinkie Pen ▲

- *circa 1935*

Conway Stewart dinkie pen with a blue and amber marbling effect.
- *length 12cm*
- **£220** • **Jasmin Cameron**

Silver Ink Stand ◀

- *February 1852*

Electroplated silver ink stand with pierced frieze of cherubs and vines, by Elkington Mason & Co.
- *width 14cm*
- **£520** • **Jasmin Cameron**

Enamel Pen Tray ▶

- *circa 1860*

Enamel chinoiserie pen tray with a nightingale in flight and pink and yellow flowers, with brass dragon handles, scrolled feet and a brass rim.
- *length 33cm*
- **£168** • **Hayman**

Main Chinese Periods

SHANG DYNASTY	C. 1523 – 1027 BC
CHOW DYNASTY	1027 – 221 BC
WARRING STATES PERIOD	481 – 221 BC
CH'IN DYNASTY	221 – 206 BC
HAN DYNASTY	206 BC – 220 AD
THREE KINGDOMS	220 – 280
SIX DYNASTIES	280 – 589
NORTHERN WEI	385 – 535
EASTERN WEI	535 – 550
WESTERN WEI	535 – 557
NORTHERN CH'I	550 – 577
NORTHERN CHOW	557 – 581
LIU SUNG (SOUTH)	420 – 478
SOUTHERN CH'I	479 – 501
LIANG	502 – 557
CH'EN	557 – 588
SUI DYNASTY	589 – 618
T'ANG	618 – 906
FIVE DYNASTIES	907 – 959
SUNG DYNASTIES	960 – 1280
YUAN DYNASTIES	1280 – 1368
MING DYNASTIES	1368 – 1643
CH'ING DYNASTIES	1644 – 1912

Ming Period

HUNG WY	1368 – 1398
CHIEN WIEN	1399 – 1402
YUNG LO	1403 – 1424
HUNG HSI	1425 – 1425
HSUAN TE	1426 – 1435
CHENG T'UNG	1436 – 1449
CHING T'AI	1450 – 1457
T'IEN SHUN	1457 – 1464
CH'ENG HUA	1465 – 1487
HUNG-CHIH	1488 – 1505
CHENG TE	1506 – 1521
CHIA CHING	1522 – 1566
LUNG CH'ING	1567 – 1572
WAN LI	1573 – 1619

Ch'ing Period

SHUNG CHIH	1644 – 1661
K'ANG HSI	1662 – 1722
YUNG CHENG	1723 – 1735
CH'IENG LUNG	1736 – 1795
CHIA CH'ING	1796 – 1820
TAO KUANG	1821 – 1850
HSIEN FENG	1851 – 1861
T'UNG CHIH	1862 – 1873
KUANG HSU	1874 – 1908
HSUAN T'UNG	1909 – 1912

Korean Periods

LO LANG	106 BC – 313 AD
PAEKCHE	18 BC – 663 AD
KOGURYO	37 BC – 668 AD
SILLA	57 BC – 668 AD
GREAT SILLA	668 – 936
KORYO	918 – 1392
YI	1392 – 1910

Japanese Periods

JOMON PERIOD	1000 BC – 200 BC
YAYOI PERIOD	200 BC – 500 AD
TUMULUS PERIOD	300 – 700
ASUKA PERIOD	552 – 645
EARLY NARA PERIOD	645 – 710
NARA PERIOD	710 – 794
EARLY HEIAN PERIOD	794 – 897
HEIAN OR FUJIWARA PERIOD	897 – 1185
KAMAKURA PERIOD	1185 – 1392
ASHIKAGA PERIOD	1392 – 1573
MOMOYAMA PERIOD	1573 – 1615
TOKUGAWA PERIOD	1615 – 1868

French General Periods

FRANÇOIS–PREMIER	**1515 – 1547**	**Reign of Francis I**
HENRI–DEUX	**1547 – 1559**	**Reign of Henri II**
	1559 – 1560	**Reign of Francis II**
	1560 – 1574	**Reign of Charles IX**
	1574 – 1589	**Reign of Henri III**
HENRI–QUATRE	**1589 – 1610**	**Reign of Henri IV**
LOUIS–TREIZE	**1610 – 1643**	**Reign of Louis XIII**
LOUIS–QUATORZE	**1643 – 1715**	**Reign of Louis XIV**
LOUIS–QUINZE	**1715 – 1774**	**Reign of Louis XV**
LOUIS–SEIZE	**1774 – 1793**	**Reign of Louis XVI**
EMPIRE	**1799 – 1814**	**Reign of Napoleon**

English General Periods

TUDOR	**1485 – 1558**	**Reigns of Henry VII**
		Henry VIII
		Edward VI
		Mary
ELIZABETHAN	**1558 – 1603**	**Reign of Elizabeth I**
JACOBEAN	**1603 – 1649**	**Reigns of James I**
		Charles I
COMMONWEALTH	**1649 – 1660**	**Protectorship of Cromwell**
CAROLEAN / LATE STUART	**1660 – 1689**	**Reigns of Charles II**
		James II
WILLIAM AND MARY	**1689 – 1702**	**Reign of William and Mary**
QUEEN ANNE	**1702 – 1727**	**Reigns of Anne**
		George I
GEORGIAN	**1727 – 1820**	**Reigns of George II**
		George III
REGENCY	**1800 – 1830**	**Reigns of George III**
		George IV
WILLIAM IV	**1830 – 1837**	**Reign of William IV**
VICTORIAN	**1837 – 1901**	**Reign of Victoria**
EDWARDIAN	**1901 – 1910**	**Reign of Edward VII**

English Monarchs since 1066

WILLIAM I	1066 – 1087
WILLIAM II	1087 – 1100
HENRY I	1100 – 1135
STEPHEN	1135 – 1154
HENRY II	1154 – 1189
RICHARD I	1189 – 1199
JOHN	1199 – 1216
HENRY III	1216 – 1272
EDWARD I	1272 – 1307
EDWARD II	1307 – 1327
EDWARD III	1327 – 1377
RICHARD II	1377 – 1399
HENRY IV	1399 – 1413
HENRY V	1413 – 1422
HENRY VI	1422 – 1461
EDWARD IV	1461 – 1470
HENRY VI	1470 – 1471
EDWARD IV	1471 – 1483
EDWARD V	1483 – 1483
RICHARD III	1484 – 1485
HENRY VII	1485 – 1509
HENRY VIII	1509 – 1547
EDWARD VI	1547 – 1553
MARY	1553 – 1558
ELIZABETH	1558 – 1603
JAMES I	1603 – 1625
CHARLES I	1625 – 1649
COMMONWEALTH	1649 – 1660
CHARLES II	1660 – 1685
JAMES II	1685 – 1688
WILLIAM AND MARY	1688 – 1694
WILLIAM III	1694 – 1702
ANNE	1702 – 1714
GEORGE I	1714 – 1727
GEORGE II	1727 – 1760
GEORGE III	1760 – 1820
GEORGE IV	1820 – 1830
WILLIAM IV	1830 – 1837
VICTORIA	1837 – 1901
EDWARD VII	1901 – 1910
GEORGE V	1910 – 1936
EDWARD VIII	1936 – 1936
GEORGE VI	1936 – 1952
ELIZABETH II	1952 –

Not all of the terms that follow appear in this volume, but they may all prove useful in the future.

abadeh Highly-coloured Persian rug.

acacia Dull yellow hardwood with darker markings used for inlay and bandings towards the end of the eighteenth century.

acanthus A leaf motif used in carved and inlaid decoration.

Act of Parliament clock Eighteenth-century English clock, wall mounted and driven by weights, with a large, unglazed dial and a trunk for weights. These clocks often hung in taverns and public places and were relied on by the populace after the Act of Parliament of 1797, which introduced taxation on timepieces.

air-beaded Glass with air bubbles resembling beads.

air-twist Spiral pattern enclosed in a glass stem with air bubbles.

albarello Waisted ceramic drug jar.

alder Wood used for country-style furniture in the eighteenth century.

ale glass Eighteenth-century glass drinking vessel with long stem and tall, thin bowl.

amboyna West Indian wood used for veneers, marquetry and inlays. Light brown with speckled grain.

anchor escapement Late seventeenth-century English invented clock movement, named after the anchor shape of the linkage which moves the escape wheel.

angle barometer Also known as signpost barometers. Barometers where the movement of mercury is shown almost on the horizontal.

andiron Iron support for burning logs.

annulated Ringed (of glass).

apostle spoon Spoon with the figure of an apostle as the finial.

applied Attached or added, rather than modelled or carved as part of the body.

apron The decorative panel of wood between the front legs of a chair or cabinet.

arbor The axle on which the wheel of a clock's mechanism is mounted.

arch (clockmaking) The arch above the dial of a post-1700 longcase clock.

argyle Double-skinned metal pouring jugs and tea and coffee pots.

armoire French wardrobe, linen press or large cupboard.

ash Hardwood used for making country furniture and for its white veneer.

astragal Small semi-circular moulding, particularly used as glazing bar in furniture.

automaton clock A clock where the strike is performed by mechanically operated figures.

backboard The unseen back of wall furniture.

backplate The rear plate supporting the movement of a clock, often the repository of engraved information relating to its manufacture.

baff Knot in rug-making.

balance Device counteracting the force of the mainspring in a clock's movement.

balloon-back chair Popular, rounded-backed Victorian dining or salon chair.

baluster (adj.) Having a dominant convex swell at the base, culminating in a smaller, concave one at the neck. (noun) One of a set of upright posts supporting a balustrade.

banjo barometer Wheel barometer dating from circa 1775-1900, with shape resembling a banjo.

barley-sugar twist Spiral-turned legs and rails popular in the seventeenth century. Colloquial.

bat printed Transfer printed (of ceramics).

beech Hardwood used in the manufacture of country furniture and, when stained, as a substitute for mahogany.

bellarmine Stoneware flagon made in Germany from the sixteenth century.

bergère French for an armchair, used in English to describe a chair with caned back and sides.

bevel Decorative, shaved edge of glass, particularly mirror.

bezel The metal rim of a glass cover or jewel.

bird-cage Support mechanism at the top of the pedestal of some eighteenth-century tilt-top tables.

birch Hardwood used principally for carcassing; occasionally for low-quality veneer.

bird's eye maple Wood of the sugar maple with distinctive figure caused by aborted buds. Used in veneering.

biscuit (bisque) Ceramics fired but unglazed, originating in France in the eighteenth century.

blind fretwork Fretwork carving on a solid background.

block front Front shaped from thick boards allowing for a recessed centre section.

blue-dash Blue dabs around the rim of a delftware plate.

bob The weight at the bottom of a pendulum.

bobbin Turned furniture element, resembling a row of connected spheres.

bocage Foliage, bushes and shrubs supporting, surrounding or standing behind porcelain or pottery figures.

bombé Having an outswelling front.

bone china Clay with bone ash in the formula, almost entirely porcellanous. First produced at the end of the eighteenth century.

bonheur du jour Small, lady's writing desk with a cabinet and drawers above. Originally French, from the mid eighteenth century.

bottle glass Low quality coloured glass for bottles, jars etc.

boulle An eighteenth-century marquetry style employing brass and tortoiseshell.

boxlock Flintlock gun with the mechanism enclosed in the breach.

boxwood Pale yellow, close-grained hardwood used for carving and turning and for inlay and pattern veneers.

bow front Convex curve on the front of chests of drawers.

bracket clock Domestic clock so called because of the necessity of standing it on a bracket to allow its weights to hang down, the term later applied to domestic clocks of the eighteenth and nineteenth centuries regardless of their motive force.

bracket foot Plain foot carved into the rail or stretcher to form an ornamental bracket.

brandy saucepan Miniature, bulbous or baluster shaped saucepan with long handle at right angles to the spout.

breakfront Describing a piece of furniture with a central section which projects forward.

breech Rear end of the barrel of a gun.

breech-loading Gun loaded through an opening in the breech.

bright cut Late eighteenth-century silver engraving technique, making the design brilliant in relief.

Bristol glass Eighteenth century coloured (often blue) glass produced in Bristol.

Britannia metal Form of refined pewter used as a silver substitute in the early nineteenth century.

British plate Silver substitute from the nineteenth century, immediately preceding the introduction of EPNS.

broken arch Arch above the dial of a long-case clock which is less than a semi-circle, indicating an early Georgian date.

broken pediment Pediment with a symmetrical break in the centre, often accommodating an urn or some such motif.

bun foot Flattened spherical foot often found on later seventeenth-century furniture.

bureau Desk with a fall front enclosing a fitted interior, with drawers below.

bureau bookcase Bureau with glazed bookcase above.

burr Veneer used in furniture making, with a decorative pattern caused by some abnormality of growth or knotting in the tree. Usually taken from the base of the tree.

cabriole leg Leg of a piece of furniture that curves out at the foot and in at the top.

Introduced in the seventeenth century.

caddy Tea caddy.

caddy spoon Short-handled, large bowled spoon for extracting tea from the caddy.

calendar / date aperture Window in the dial of a clock displaying day, month or date.

canted corner Decoratively angled corner.

canterbury An eighteenth-century container for sheet music.

carcase/carcass The inner frame of a piece of furniture, usually made of inferior wood for veneering.

card case Case for visiting cards, usually silver, nineteenth century.

carriage clock Portable timepiece, invented in nineteenth-century France, with handle above.

cartel clock Eighteenth-century French wall clock with profusely decorated case.

case furniture Furniture intended as a receptical, e.g. chest of drawers.

caster / castor 1. Sprinkling vessel for e.g. sugar. 2. Pivoted wheel attached to foot.

Castleford ware Shiny white stoneware made in Castleford and elsewhere from circa 1790.

caudle cup Covered cup, often in silver.

cellaret A wine cooler or container, usually eighteenth century.

centrepiece Ornament designed to sit in the centre of a dining table. Often in silver.

chafing dish Serving dish, often in silver, with stand incorporating a spirit lamp to retain heat.

chain fusée The fusée of a clock from which a chain unwinds on to the barrel of the mainspring.

chamfer A flattened angle; a corner that has been bevelled or planed.

chapter ring The ring on a clock dial on which the numbers of the hours are inscribed.

Chesterfield Deep-buttoned, upholstered settee from the nineteenth century.

chest on chest Tallboy having two chests fitting together, the lower with bracket feet, the upper with pediment. From the seventeenth and eighteenth centuries.

chest on stand Known as a tallboy or highboy, a chest of drawers on a stand.

cheval mirror Tall mirror supported by two uprights on swivels.

chiffonnier Side cupboard, originally, in the eighteenth century, with solid doors, but latterly with latticed or glazed doors.

chinoiserie Oriental-style decoration on lacquered furniture or artefacts.

chronometer Precision timepiece, often for navigation.

circular movement Clock movement of circular plates.

cistern Chamber containing mercury at the base of the tube of a barometer.

claw-and-ball foot Foot modelled as a ball clutched in a claw, frequently used to terminate a cabriole leg.

clock garniture Mantelpiece ornamentation with a clock as centrepiece.

close helmet Helmet covering the whole head and neck.

coaster Small, circular tray, often in silver, for holding a bottle.

cockbeading Bead moulding applied to the edges of drawers.

cock bracket Bracket supporting a watch mainspring.

coin glass Early eighteenth-century English drinking glass with a coin moulded into the knop of the stem.

commode High quality, highly decorated chest of drawers or cabinet, with applied mounts.

compensated pendulum Pendulum with mercury reservoir, the mercury rising and falling to compensate for the effects on the pendulum of changes of temperature.

composition Putty-like substance for moulding and applying to e.g. mirror frames, for gilding.

console table Often semi-circular table intended to stand against a wall on the pier between two windows (hence also pier table). Usually with matching mirror above.

cordial glass Glass originating in the seventeenth century, with a small bowl for strong drinks.

corner chair Chair with back splats on two sides and a bowed top rail, designed to fit into a corner.

cornice Horizontal top part of a piece of furniture; a decorative band of metal or wood used to conceal curtain fixtures

coromandel Wood from India's Coromandel coast, used for banding and inlay.

counter-well The small oval wooden dishes inset into early Georgian card tables for holding chips or cash, hence also guinea-well.

country furniture Functional furniture made outside the principal cities. Also provincial furniture.

countwheel strike Clock mechanism determining the number of strikes per hour.

cow creamer Silver or china cream jug modelled as a cow.

crazing Fine cracks in glaze.

creamware Earthenware glazed in a cream colour giving a porcelain effect, in a widely used technique originally devised by Wedgwood in the 1760s.

credence table Late seventeenth-century oak or walnut table with folding top.

credenza Long Victorian side cabinet with glazed or solid doors.

crenellated Crinkly, wavy.

crested china Ware decorated with heraldic crests; originally by Goss, but subsequently by many Staffordshire and German potteries.

crinoline stretcher Crescent-shaped stretcher supporting the legs of some Windsor chairs.

cross-banding Decorative edging with cross-grained veneer.

cruet Frame for holding condiment containers.

crutch The arm connecting a clock's pendulum to the pallet arbor.

cuirass Breastplate (of armour).

cup and cover Round turning with a distinctly separate top, common on legs until circa 1650.

damascene Inlay of precious metal onto a body of other metal for decorative purposes.

davenport Small English desk, reputedly originally produced by Gillow for a Captain Davenport in 1834. A day-bed or sofa in the USA.

deadbeat escapement Version of the anchor escapement that eliminates recoil and improves accuracy.

deal Sawn pine wood.

delftware Seventeenth- and eighteenth-century tin-glazed earthenware, often decorated in the style of Chinese blue and white porcelain or after Dutch seventeenth-century painting, after the style pioneered by the Delft pottery.

Delft ware Items of delftware which actually emanate from Delft.

dentil Small, block-shaped moulding found under a furniture cornice.

dialplate Frontplate of a clock.

diamond cut (of glass) Cut in diamond shape.

dinanderie Fifteenth-century brass artefact from the factories of Dinant, Belgium.

dished table top Hollowed-out, solid top, particularly of a pie-crust, tripod table.

distressed Artificially aged.

dovetails Interlocking joints used in drawers.

double-action A gun which may be cocked or self-cocking.

douter Scissor-like implement for extinguishing a candle.

dowel Peg holding together wooden joint.

dram glass Small, short-stemmed glass with rounded bowl.

drop-in seat Framed, upholstered seat which sits in the framework of a chair.

drop handle Pear-shaped brass furniture handle of the late seventeenth and early eighteenth centuries.

drop-leaf table Table with a fixed central section and hinged flaps.

drum table Circular writing table on a central pedestal with frieze drawers.

dry-edge With unglazed edges.

dummy drawer False drawer with handle.

Dutch strike Clock chime which strikes the next hour on the half hour.

ebonize To stain a wood to the dark colour of ebony.

ebony Much imitated exotic black hardwood, used as veneer in Europe from the seventeenth century, generally for very high quality pieces.

écuelle Two-handled French soup bowl with cover and stand, often Sèvres.

electroplate The technique of covering one metal with the thin layer of another.

elm Hardwood used in the manufacture of chair seats, country furniture and coffins.

embossing Relief decoration.

enamel Second, coloured glaze fired over first glaze.

endstone In a clock mechanism, jewel on which an arbor pivots.

English dial Nineteenth-century English wall clock with large painted dial, previously a fixture in railway stations.

Engshalskrüge Large German tin-glaze jug with cylindrical neck.

épergne Centrepiece of one central bowl surrounded by smaller ones.

escritoire Cabinet with a fall-front which forms a writing surface. With a fitted interior.

escutcheon Brass plate surrounding the edges of a keyhole.

étuis Small, metal oddments box.

everted Outward turned, flaring (e.g. of a lip).

facet-cut (of glass) Cut criss-cross into straight-edged planes.

faience Tin-glazed earthenware.

fairings Porcelain figures, especially German, made in the nineteenth and twentieth centuries in the mould. Usually comical and carrying descriptive captions.

fall front Flap of a bureau or secretaire that pulls out to provide a writing surface.

famille rose Predominantly pink-coloured Oriental porcelain.

famille verte Predominantly green-coloured Oriental porcelain.

fauteuil Open-sided, upholstered armchair with padded elbows.

feather banding Two bands of veneer laid at opposite diagonals.

field Area of a carpet within its decorated borders.

fielded panel Raised panel with chamfered edge fitting into a framework.

figure Natural pattern created by the grain through the wood.

finial Decorative, turned knob.

flamed veneer Veneer cut at an angle to enhance the figuring.

flatware Plates, knives and forks.

flintlock Gun mechanism whereby the priming in the pan is ignited by a spark created by a flint.

flute glass Glass with tall, slender bowl.

fluting Decorative parallel grooving.

foliate carving Carved flower and leaf motifs.

foliot Primitive form of balance for clock mechanisms.

fretwork Fine pierced decoration.

frieze Long ornamental strip.

frit The flux from which glass is made. An ingredient of soft-paste porcelain.

frizzen The metal which a flint strikes to create a spark in a flintlock mechanism.

fruitwood Generally the wood of apple, cherry and pear trees, used for ebonising and gilding, commonly in picture frames.

fusee The conical, grooved spool from which a line or chain unwinds as it is pulled by the mainspring of a clock movement.

gadroon Carved edge or moulded decoration consisting of a series of grooves, ending in a curved lip, with ridges between them.

Gainsborough chair Deep, upholstered armchair with padded, open arms and carved decoration.

galleried Having a wood or metal border around the top edge.

garniture Set of ornamental pieces of porcelain.

gateleg Leg that pivots to support a drop leaf.

gesso Plaster-like substance applied to carved furniture before gilding or moulded and applied as a substitute for carving.

gilt-tooled decoration Gold leaf impressed into the edges of leather on desk-tops.

gimbal Mounting which keeps a ship's barometer level at all times.

girandole Wall-mounted candle holder with a mirrored back.

gorget Item of armour for protecting the throat.

Goss china Range of porcelain, particularly heraldic, produced in Stoke-on-Trent from 1858.

greave Armour protecting lower leg.

Greek key Ancient key-shaped decoration often repeated in fretwork on furniture.

gridiron pendulum Clock pendulum consisting of rods of a mix of metals positioned in such a way that the dynamics of their behaviour when subjected to heat or cold keep the pendulum swing uniform.

halberd Double-headed axe weapon with projecting spike.

half hunter Watch with an opening front cover with glass to the centre and a chapter ring, giving protection to the glass over the dial.

hallmark The mark by which silver can be identified by standard, place of assay and date.

hard-paste porcelain Porcelain made with kaolin and petuntse in the Chinese fashion, pioneered in Europe at Meissen in the early eighteenth century.

hunter Watch with a hinged, opening front cover in solid metal.

husk Formalised leaf motif.

ice glass Glass with uneven, rippling surface.

Imari Japanese porcelain made in and around Arita from the early eighteenth century and shipped to Europe from the port of Imari. Blue, red and gold coloured.

improved A pejorative term implying that a piece has been altered in order dishonestly to enhance its value.

inlay The decorative setting of one material into a contrasting one.

intaglio Incised design.

ironstone Stoneware patented by Mason in 1813, in which slag from iron furnaces was mixed with the clay to toughen the ware.

istoriato Of some Italian majolica, meaning 'with a story on it'.

japanned Painted and varnished in imitation of Oriental style lacquer work.

jardinière An ornamental pot or vase for plants.

jasper ware Variety of coloured stoneware developed by the Wedgwood factory.

joined Manufactured with the use of mortice and tenon joints and dowels, but without glue.

kabuto Japanese Samurai helmet.

kingwood Exotic, purplish hardwood used in veneer.

kneehole desk Desk with a recessed cupboard beneath the frieze drawer.

knop Rounded projection or bulge in the stem of a glass.

lacquer Resinous substance which, when coloured, provides a ground for chinoiserie and gilding.

ladder-back Chair with a series of horizontal back rails.

lantern clock Clocks made in England from the sixteenth century, driven entirely by weights and marking only the hours. Similar in appearance to a lantern.

lappit Carved flap at the top of a leg with a pad foot.

latten Archaic term for brass.

lead crystal Particularly clear, brilliant glass including lead in the process.

lead-glazed the earliest glaze for Western pottery, derived from glass making.

lever escapement Modification of the anchor escapement for carriage clocks and, particularly, watches.

lion's paw foot Foot carved as a lion's paw. Commonly eighteenth century and Regency.

lock Firing mechanism of a gun.

lockplate Base holding firing mechanism on a gun barrel.

loo table Large Victorian card or games table.

longcase clock The 'grandfather' clock, housed in a tall wooden case containing the weights and pendulum.

loper Pull-out arm that supports the hinged fall of a bureau.

lowboy Small side table with cabriole legs, from the seventeenth century.

lustre ware Ceramic ware decorated with a metallic coating which changes colour when fired.

mahogany The hardwood most used in the production of furniture in England in the eighteenth and nineteenth centuries. Used as a solid wood until the nineteenth century, when its rarity led to its being used for veneer.

majolica Originally tin-glazed earthenware produced in Renaissance Italy, subsequently all nineteenth century wares using the same technique.

mantel clock Clock with feet designed to stand on a mantelpiece.

maple North American hardwood used for its variety of veneers.

marine chronometer Precision clock for use in navigation at sea.

marquetry The use of wooden and other inlays to form decorative patterns.

married Pejorative term applied to a piece of furniture which is made up of more than one piece of the same period.

matchlock Firing mechanism of a gun achieved by lowering a slow match into the priming pan.

mazarine Metal strainer fitting over a dish.

mercury twist Air-twist in glass of a silver colour.

millefiori Multi-coloured or mosaic glass.

moonwork Clock mechanism which computes and displays the phases of the moon.

moquette Heavy imitation velvet used for upholstery.

morion Helmet with upturned front peak.

mortice Slot element of a mortice and tenon joint.

moulding decorative, shaped band around an object or a panel.

mount Invariably metal mounting fitted to a piece of furniture.

mule chest Coffer with a single row of drawers to the base.

musical clock Clock with a cylinder which strikes bells to play a tune.

Nailsea Late eighteenth-century, boldly coloured, opaque glass from Nailsea, near Bristol.

nest of tables Set of three or four occasional tables which slot into each other when not in use.

oak Hardwood which darkens with age, predominant in English furniture manufacture until the middle of the seventeenth century.

obverse The front side of a coin or medal.

ogee An S-shaped curve.

ogee arch Two S-shaped curves coming together to form an arch.

oignon Onion-shaped French watch of the eighteenth century.

ormolu From French *dorure d'or moulu*: 'gilding with gold paste', gold-coloured alloy of copper, zinc, and sometimes tin, in various proportions but usually containing at least 50% copper. Ormolu is used in mounts (ornaments on borders, edges, and as angle guards) for furniture, especially eighteenth-century furniture.

orrery Astronomical clock which shows the position of heavenly bodies. Named after Charles Boyle, fourth Earl of Orrery.

overglaze See **enamel**.

overmantel mirror Mirror designed to hang over a mantelpiece.

ovolo A rounded, convex moulding, making an outward curve across a right angle.

oyster veneer Veneer resembling an open oyster shell, an effect achieved by slanting the cut across the grain of a branch.

pad foot Rounded foot on a circular base, used as termination for cabriole legs.

pair-case A double case for a watch, the inner for protection of the movement, the outer for decoration.

pallet Lever that engages in a clock's escapement wheel in orderb to arrest it.

papier mâché Moulded and lacquered pulped paper used to make small items of furniture and other artefacts.

parian Typically uncoloured, biscuit-style porcelain developed in the nineteenth century by Copeland and named after Parian white marble.

parquetry Veneered pattern using small pieces of veneer, often from different woods, in a geometrical design.

patera Circular ornament made of wood, metal or composition.

patina The layers of polish, dirt, grease and general handling marks that build up on a wooden piece of furniture over the years and give it its individual signs of age, varying from wood to wood.

pearlware White, shiny earthenware, often print decorated.

pedestal desk A flat desk with a leathered top standing on two banks of drawers.

pediment Architectural, triangular gable crowning a piece of furniture or a classical building.

pegged furniture Early furniture constructed with the use of mortice and tenon joints and pegged together with dowels.

pembroke table Small, two-flapped table standing on four legs or a pedestal.

pepperette Vessel, often in silver, for sprinkling pepper.

petuntse Chinese name for the feldspathic rock, an essential element of porcelain, which produces a glaze.

pewter Alloy of tin, lead and often various other metals.

pie-crust Expression used to describe the decorative edge of a dished-top tripod table.

pier glass Tall mirror for hanging on a pier between windows.

pietra dura Composition of semi-precious stones applied to panels of – usually Italian – furniture.

pillar (watchmaking) A rod connecting the dial-plate and backplate of a movement.

pillar rug Chinese rug made to be arranged around a pillar.

pine Softwood used for carcassing furniture.

platform base Flat base supporting a central pedestal and table-top above and standing on three or four scrolled or paw feet.

plinth base Solid base not raised on feet.

pole screen Adjustable fire screen.

pommel Knob at the end of the handle of a dagger.

pontil mark Mark made by the pontil, or blowpipe, on the base of hand-blown glass.

porcellanous Having most of the ingredients or characteristics of porcelain.

porringer Large, two-handled cup with cover.

potboard Bottom shelf of a dresser, often just above the floor.

pounce box A sprinkler for pounce, a powder for drying ink.

Prattware Staffordshire earthenware of the late eighteenth and early nineteenth centuries, decorated in distinctive colours on a buff ground.

print decoration Mass-produced decoration. Not hand painting.

provincial furniture See **country furniture**.

punch bowl Large bowl for the retention and dispensation of punch.

quartered top Flat surface covered with four pieces of matching veneer.

quartetto tables Nest of four occasional tables.

quillon Cross-piece of a sword.

rail A horizontal member running between the outer uprights of a piece of furniture.

rating nut Nut under the bob of a clock's pendulum by which the rate of swing may be adjusted.

redware Primitive eighteenth-century American ware made from a clay which turns red when fired.

reeding Parallel strips of convex fluting.

re-entrant corner Shaped indentation at each corner of a table.

register plate Plate on a barometer with inscriptions to be read against the level of mercury.

regulator Precision timepiece of the eighteenth century.

relief Proud of the surface.

repeating work Mechanism by which the pull of a cord or the press of a button operates the striking mechanism of a clock or watch to the last hour.

repoussé An embossed design which has been refined by chasing.

rosewood Named after its smell when newly cut, rather than its flower or colour, a dark-brown hardwood with an attractive stripe or ripple, used for veneering.

rule joint Hinge on furniture which fits so well that, when open, no join can be detected between two hinged parts.

runners Strips of wood, fitted to furniture, on which drawers slide.

sabre leg Chair leg in the shape of a sabre, typical of the Regency period.

saltglaze Stoneware in which salt is added to the recipe creating a porcellanous, glassy surface. Dates back to the early eighteenth century.

salver A large metal dish or tray for transporting smaller dishes.

satinwood A light golden-coloured, close-grained hardwood used for veneer, panelling and turning from the mid-eighteenth century onwards.

scagiola Composite material resembling marble.

scalloped Having a series of circular edges in the shape of a scallop shell.

scalloped leaf Serpentine flap on some pembroke tables.

sconce 1. Cup-shaped candle holder. 2. Metal plate fixed to the wall, supporting candle holder or light.

scratch blue Eighteenth-century saltglaze decoration where the body is incised and the incisions painted blue.

scroll, scrolling Carving or moulding of a curled design.

seat rail Horizontal framework below the chair seat uniting the legs.

secretaire Writing desk with false drawer front which lets down to reveal a writing surface and fitted interior.

secretaire bookcase Secretaire with bookcase fitted above.

serpent The arm holding the match or flint by which the priming of a gun was ignited.

serpentine Of undulating shape.

settee Upholstered settle.

settle Hard bench seat with back. The earliest form of seating for two or more people.

Sheffield plate Rolled sheet silver placed either side of a layer of copper and fused. Recognised by the Sheffield assay office in 1784, but made elsewhere, notably Birmingham, as well.

shoe piece Projection on the back rail of a chair into which the splat fits.

side chair Chair without arms designed to stand against the wall.

side table Any table designed to stand against the wall.

skeleton clock Clock with the workings exposed.

slipware Earthenware to which mixed clay and water has been added as decoration.

sofa Well-upholstered chair providing seating for two or more people.

sofa table Rectangular table with hinged flaps designed to stand behind a sofa.

soft-paste porcelain Porcelain using frit or soapstone instead of the petuntse of hard-paste porcelain. English, from the eighteenth century.

spade foot Square, tapered foot.

spandrel Pierced, decorative corner bracket found at the tops of legs.

sparrow-beak jug Jug with a triangular spout.

spill vase Container for lighting-tapers.

spindle Thoroughly turned piece of wood. The upright bars of a spindle-back chair.

splat The central upright of a chair back.

sprig Applied or relief ornamentation of any kind on a ceramic artefact.

squab Detachable cushion or upholstered seat of a chair or bench.

standish Inkstand, often in silver.

stick barometer Barometer with a straight, vertical register plate running alongside the mercury tube.

stiles Archaic term for the vertical parts of the framework of a piece of furniture.

stoneware Earthenware that is not porous after firing.

stretcher Rail joining the legs of a table or chair.

strike / silent ring Dial to disengage or re-engage the striking of a clock.

stringing Fine inlaid lines around a piece of furniture.

stirrup cup Cup used for alcoholic refreshment prior to hunting, usually shaped in the head of a fox or, less usually, a hound.

stuff-over seat Chair that is upholstered over the seat rail.

subsidiary dial Small dial, usually showing seconds, within the main dial of a clock or watch. Hence **subsidiary seconds**.

swagged With applied strips formed in a mould (of metal).

swan-neck pediment Pediment with two broken curves.

swan-neck handle Curved handle typical of the eighteenth century.

sycamore Hardwood of the maple family, light yellow in colour, used for veneering.

tang The end of the blade of a sword, covered by the hilt.

tankard Large beer-mug with a hinged lid and thumb-piece.

tazza Italian plate, cup, basin or wide-bowled glass.

teapoy Small piece of furniture designed for holding tea leaves. Usually Anglo-Indian.

tenons The tongues in mortice and tenon joints.

thumb moulding Decorative concave moulding.

thumb-piece Projection attached to a hinged lid which will open the lid when pressure is applied by the thumb.

tine Prong of a fork.

tin-glazed Lead-glazed earthenware to which tin is added, e.g. majolica.

toilet mirror Small dressing mirror with a box base and drawers.

touch mark Individual mark of the maker of a piece of early English pewter.

transfer Ceramic print decoration using colours held in oil.

trefid spoon A seventeenth-century spoon with the handle terminating in the shape of a bud, usually cleft or grooved into two lobes.

trefoil Having three lobes.

trembleuse Cup-stand with feet.

tripod table Small, round-topped table on three-legged base.

tulipwood Pinkish, naturally patterned hardwood used in veneer.

turnery Any wood turned on a lathe.

tureen Large bowl in porcelain or metal, usually with a lid and two handles.

turret clock Clock of any size driven by a weight suspended by a rope wrapped round a drum.

underglaze Colour or design painted below the glaze of a ceramic artefact.

uniface Medal or coin with modelling on one side only.

urn table Eighteenth-century table designed to hold an urn.

veneer A thin sheet of wood laid across a cheaper carcase or used as inlay decoration.

verge escapement Mechanism for regulating a clock movement before the anchor escapement.

Vesta case Match box for Vesta matches, often in silver, from circa 1850.

vinaigrette Small, eighteenth-century box, often silver, to hold a sponge soaked in vinegar to ward off germs and the unpleasant odours of the day.

wainscot chair Joined chair with open arms and a panelled back.

walnut The hardwood used in England for the manufacture of furniture from the Restoration, originally in solid form but mostly as veneer, particularly burr walnut, after the beginning of the eighteenth century.

well Interior of a plate or bowl.

Wemyss ware Late nineteenth-century lead-glazed earthenware originally from Fife, Scotland.

whatnot Mobile stand with open shelves.

wheel-back chair Originally late eighteenth-century chair with circular back with radiating spokes.

windsor chair Wooden chair with spindle back.

yew Tough, close-grained hardwood used for turning, particularly in chair legs, and in veneer.

There follows a list of antique dealers, many of whom have
provided items in the main body of the book and all of whom will be happy
to assist within their areas of expertise.

Aaron Gallery
(ref: Aaron)
34 Bruton Street,
London W1X 7DD
Tel: 020 7499 9434
Fax: 020 7499 0072
www.AaronGallery.com
*Islamic and ancient art; New
Eastern, Greek, Roman and
Egyptian antiquities.*

Abacus Antiques
(ref: Abacus)
Grays Antiques Market,
58 Davies Street,
London W1Y 2LP
Tel: 020 7629 9681
Antiques.

Abbey Green Antiques
(ref: Abbey Green)
Mariaplatts 45,
Utrecht 3511 LL
The Netherlands
Tel: 030 232 8065

Emmy Abe
Stand 33, Bond Street
Antiques Centre,
124 New Bond Street,
London W1X 9AE
Tel: 020 7629 1826
Fax: 020 7491 9400
*Exclusively selected antique and
modern jewellery.*

Aberg Antiques
(ref: Aberg)
42 The Little Boltons,
London SW10 9LN
Tel: 020 7370 7253
Fax: 020 7370 7253
Furniture.

A. D. Antiques
The Swan at Tetsworth,
High Street,
Tetsworth, Thame,
Oxfordshire, OX9 7AB
Tel: 07939 508171
www.adantiques.com
Decorative arts.

Norman Adams Ltd
8–10 Hans Road,
London SW3 1RX
Tel: 020 7589 5266
Fax: 020 7589 1968
www.normanadams.com
*Eighteenth-century fine English
furniture, works of art, mirrors,
paintings and chandeliers.*

After Noah
121 Upper Street,
London N1 8ED
Tel: 020 7359 4281
Fax: 020 7359 4281
www.afternoah.com
*Antique furniture, linen and
postcards.*

After Noah (Kings Road)
(ref: After Noah (KR))
261 Kings Road,
London SW3 5EL
Tel: 020 7351 2610
Fax: 020 7351 2610
www.afternoah.com
*Antique furniture, linen and
postcards.*

Albany Antiques
(ref: Albany)
8–10 London Road, Hindhead,
Surrey GU26 6AF
Tel: 01428 605 528
Fax: 01428 605 528
*Georgian furniture, eighteenth-
century brass, Victorian antiques,
porcelain and statuary.*

AM-PM
V35 Antiquarias Antiques
Market,
135 Kings Road,
London SW3
Tel: 020 7351 5654
Antique and modern watches.

Fred Anderson Antiques
(ref: Fred Anderson)
5/6 Hight Street
Welshpool
Powys SY2 1JF
Tel: 01938 553340
Mob: 07773 795931
Fine antique furniture.

Paul Andrews Antiques
The Furniture Court,
553 Kings Road,
London SW10 0TZ
Tel: 020 7352 4584
Fax: 020 7351 7815
www.paulandrewsantiques.co.
uk
*Eclectic furniture, sculpture,
tapestries, paintings and works
of art.*

Angel Antiques
Church Street, Petworth,
West Sussex GU28 0AD
Tel: 01798 343 306
Fax: 01798 342 665
Oak, country furniture.

**The Antique and Interiors
Group Ltd.
(ref: A.I.G)**
The Old Cinema
160 Chiswick High Road
London W4 1PR
Tel: 020 8742 8080
Fax: 020 8878 0184
Antiques in general.

Antique Warehouse
9–14 Dentford Broadway,
London SE8 4PA
Tel: 020 8691 3062
Fax: 020 8691 3062
www.antiquewarehouse.co.uk
Decorative antiques.

Antiques Pavilion
175 Bermondsey Street,
London SE1 3LW
Tel: 020 7394 7856
*Furniture from the Georgian
period to the 1930s; also
restorations.*

Arca
R & E Innocenti
Stand 351
Grays Antique Centre
Davies Street
London W1 2LP
Tel: 020 7692 729
e-mail:Innocenti@
arcaantiques.freeserve co.uk
Sewing and smoking items.

**Armoury of St James, The
(ref: The Armoury)**
17 Piccadilly Arcade,
London SW1Y 6NH
Tel: 020 7493 5083
Fax: 020 7499 4422
www.armoury.co.uk/home
*Royal memorabilia and model
soldiers.*

**Sean Arnold Sporting
Antiques
(ref: Sean Arnold)**
1 Pembridge Villas,
London W2 4XE
Tel: 020 7221 2267
Fax: 020 7221 5464
Sporting antiques.

**Victor Arwas Gallery
(ref: Arwas)**
3 Clifford Street,
London W1X 1RA
Tel: 020 7734 3944
Fax: 020 7437 1859
www.victorarwas.com
*Art Nouveau and Art Deco,
glass, ceramics, bronzes,
sculpture, furniture, jewellery,
silver, pewter, books and posters,
from 1880–1940. Paintings,
watercolours and drawings,
1880 to date. Original graphics,
lithographs, etchings and
woodcuts from 1890 to date.*

**Ash Rare Books
(ref: Ash Books)**
153 Fenchurch Street,
London EC3M 6BB
Tel: 020 7626 2665
Fax: 020 7626 2665
www.ashrare.com
Books, maps and prints.

**Ashcombe House
(ref: Ashcombe)**
Ashcombe Coach House,
Brighton Road, Lewes,
East Sussex BN7 3JR
Tel: 01273 474794
Fax: 01273 705959
*Eighteenth and nineteenth-
century furniture and
decorative objects.*

Garry Atkins
107 Kensington Church Street,
London W8 7LN
Tel: 020 7727 8737
Fax: 020 7792 9010
www.englishpottery.com
*English and continental pottery
from the eighteenth century and
earlier.*

Aurum
Grays Antiques Market,
58 Davies Street,
London W1K 5LP
Tel: 020 7409 0215
www.aurum.uk.com
*Antique and period jewellery,
and Shelly china.*

**Axia Art Consultants Ltd
(ref: Axia)**
21 Ledbury Road,
London W11 2AQ
Tel: 020 7727 9724
Fax: 020 7229 1272
*Islamic and Byzantine works
of art, textiles, metalwork,
woodwork, ceramics and icons.*

B. and T. Antiques
79–81 Ledbury Road,
London W11 2AG
Tel: 020 7229 7001
Fax: 020 7229 2033
*Eighteenth-century Art Deco
English and continental furniture,
and objets d'art.*

Dr Colin B. Baddiel
B24 Grays Antiques Market,
Davies Mews,
London W1
Tel: 020 7408 1239
Fax: 020 74939344
Die-cast and tin toys.

David Baker
Grays Mews Antique Market,
1–7 Davies Mews,
London W1Y 2LP
Tel: 020 8346 1387
Fax: 020 8346 1387
Oriental art.

Gregg Baker Oriental Art
(ref: Gregg Baker)
132 Kensington Church Street,
London W8 4BH
Tel: 020 7221 3533
Fax: 020 7221 4410
www.greggbaker.com
*Japanese and Chinese works
of art.*

Barham Antiques
(ref: Barham)
83 Portobello Road,
London W11 2QB
Tel: 020 7727 3845
Fax: 020 7727 3845
*Victorian walnut and inlaid
continental furniture, writing
boxes, tea caddies, inkwells and
inkstands, glass épergnes, silver
plate, clocks and paintings.*

R. A. Barnes Antiques
(ref: R. A. Barnes)
26 Lower Richmond Road,
London SW15 1JP
Tel: 020 8789 3371
Fax: 020 8780 3195
*Continental glass, English and
continental porcelain, Art
Nouveau, small furniture,
paintings, English metalware,
eighteenth and nineteenth-century
brass, Belleed and Wedgwood.*

Les Barrett & Ian Towning
(ref: Barrett Towning)
Bourbon-Hanby Antiques
Centre
151 Sydney Street
London SW3 6NT
Tel: 020 7352 2106
Fax: 020 7565 0003
www.antiques-u.co.uk/bourbon-hanby
*English ceramics, silver, writing
equipment and antique jewellery.*

Don Bayney
Grays Mews Antiques Market,
1–7 Davies Mews,
London W1Y 2LP
Tel: 020 7629 3644
Fax: 020 8578 4701
Japanese works of art.

Bazaart 51 Antiques
(ref: Bazaart)
51 Ledbury Road,
London W11 2AA
Tel: 020 7615 3472
Fax: 020 7615 472
*Italian ceramics and Venetian
glass from 1500–1900.*

Beauty and the Beasts
(ref: Beauty)
Antiquarius Antique Centre
Q9-10
141 King's Road
London SW3 4PW
Tel: 020 7351 5149
Antique handbags.

Frederick Beck Ltd.
(ref: F. Beck)
22–26 Camden Passage,
Islington, London N1 8ED
Tel: 020 7226 3403
Fax: 020 7288 1305
General antiques.

Linda Bee
Grays in the Mews Antiques
Market,
1–7 Davies Mews,
London W1Y 1AR
Tel: 020 7629 5921
Fax: 020 7629 5921
*Vintage costume jewellery and
fashion accessories.*

Bellum Antiques
Bourbon-Hanby Antiques
Centre
151 Sydney Street
London SW3 6NT
Tel: 020 7352 2106
Fax: 020 7565 0003
www.antiques-uk.co.uk/
bourbon-hanby
English ceramics.

Julia Bennet (Antiques)
Flemings Hill Farm,
Great Easton, Dunmow,
Essex CM6 2ER
Tel: 01279 850279
*Eighteenth and early nineteenth-
century furniture.*

Bentleys
204 Walton Street
London SW3 2JL
Tel: 020 7584 7770
Fax: 020 7584 8182
e-mail: lf@bentleyslondon.com
www.bentleyslondon.com
*Antique luggage and gentlemen's
accessories.*

Yasha Beresiner
Gallery at 114 Islington
High Street
(Inside the Camden Passage)
London N1 8EG
020 7354 2599
Fax: 020 8346 9539
Mob: 07468 292 066
www.intercol.co.uk
Scripophily and paper money.

Beverley
30 Church Street,
Marylebone,
London NW8 8EP
Tel: 020 7262 1576
Fax: 020 7262 1576
*English ceramics, glass, metal,
wood, pottery, collectables and
decorative items from
1850–1950.*

Andrew Bewick Antiques
287 Lillie Road,
London SW6 7LL
Tel: 020 7385 9025
Fax: 020 7385 9025
Decorative antiques.

**Big Baby & Little Baby
Antiques
(ref: Big Baby Little Baby)**
Grays Antiques Market,
Davies Mews,
London W1
Tel: 020 8367 2441
Fax: 020 8366 5811
*Dolls, teddies, prams and related
collectables.*

Bike Park
63 New Kings Road,
London SW3
Tel: 020 7565 0777
*Bikes, rentals, repairs and
clothing.*

Bizarre
24 Church Street,
London NW8 8EP
Tel: 020 7724 1305
Fax: 020 7724 1316
www.antiques-uk/bazarre
*Art Deco, continental furniture,
wrought iron, glass, and
ceramics.*

**David Black Oriental Carpets
(ref: David Black)**
96 Portland Road
London W11 4LN
Tel: 020 7727 2566
Fax: 020 7229 4599
Antique carpets and rugs.

**Oonagh Black Antiques
(ref: Oonagh Black)**
Lower Farm House,
Coln Rogers,
Gloucestershire GL54 3LA
Tel: 01285 720717
Fax: 01285 720910
*French and English country
furniture, decorative accessories,
and French science and textiles.*

**N. Bloom & Son Ltd.
(ref: N.Bloom)**
Antique Jewellery
124 Bond Street Antique
Centre
124 New Bond Street
London W18 IDX
Tel: 020 7629 5060
Fax: 020 7493 2528
e-mail: nbloom@nbloom.com
www.nbloom.com
Antique jewellery.

John Bly
27 Bury Street,
London SW1Y 6AL
Tel: 020 7930 1292
Fax: 020 7839 4775
www.johnbly.com
*Eighteenth and nineteenth-
century English furniture, works
of art, objets d'art, paintings,
silver, glass, porcelain and
tapestries.*

Paolo Bonino
Stand S001, Alfie's Antique
Market,
13–25 Church Street,
London NW8 8DT
Tel: 020 7723 6066
*European twentieth-century glass
and ceramics.*

**Book and Comic Exchange
(ref: Book & Comic)**
14 Pembridge Road,
London W11 3HL
Tel: 020 7229 8420
www.buy-sell-trade.co.uk
*Modern first editions, cult books
and comics.*

**Malcolm Bord Gold Coin
Exchange
(ref: Malcolm Bord)**
16 Charing Cross Road,
London WC2 0HR
Tel: 020 7836 0631/
020 7240 0479/020 7240 1920
*Dealing in all types of coin, medal
and bank note.*

Julia Boston
2 Michael Road,
London SW6 2AD
Tel: 020 7610 6783
Fax: 020 7610 6784
www.juliaboston.co.uk
*Tapestry cartoons, engravings and
eighteenth and nineteenth-century
decorative antiques.*

M. J. Bowdery
12 London Road, Hindhead,
Surrey, GU26 6AF
Tel: 01428 606376
*Eighteenth and nineteenth-
century furniture.*

Patrick Boyd-Carpenter
(ref: P. Boyd-Carpenter)
Unit 331–332
Grays Antiques Market,
58 Davies Street,
London W1Y 2LP
Tel: 020 7491 7623
Fax: 020 7491 7623
Wide range of antiques, sixteenth
and eighteenth-century sculpture,
paintings and prints.

Elizabeth Bradwin
75 Portobello Road,
London W11 2QB
Tel: 020 7221 1121
Fax: 020 8947 2629
www.elizabethbradwin.com
Animal subjects.

Lesley Bragge
Fairfield House, High Street,
Petworth, West Sussex
Tel: 01798 342324
Wine-related items.

Augustus Brandt
Middle Street
Petworth
West Sussex GU28 OBE
Tel: 01798 344722
Fax: 01798 344772
e-mail: brandt@easynet.co.uk
www.augustus-brandt-
antiques.co.uk
Scandinavian, French, Italian
and English 18th century
furniture, mirrors and lighting
and unusual decorative furnishing
and objects d'art.

Brandt Oriental Art
(ref: Brandt)
First Floor, 29
New Bond Street,
London W1Y 9HD
Tel: 020 7499 8835
Fax: 020 7409 1882
Chinese and Japanese works
of art.

Bridge Bikes
137 Putney Bridge,
London SW15 2PA
Tel: 020 8870 3934
Bikes.

F. E. A. Briggs Ltd
5 Plaza Parade,
Winchester Road,
Romsey, Hampshire SO51 8JA
Tel: 01794 510061
Victorian and Edwardian
furniture and textiles.

Lynda Brine Antiques
The Assembly Antiques
Centre
Saville Row
Bath BAI 2QP
Tel: 01225 448488
Fax: 01225 429661
e-mail: lyndabrine@yahoo.
co.uk
www.scentbottlesandsmalls.
co.uk
Scent bottles and bags.

Aubrey Brocklehurst
124 Cromwell Road,
London SW7 4ET
Tel: 020 7373 0319
Fax: 020 73737612
English clocks and barometers.

Gerald Brodie
Great Grooms Antique Centre
Hungerford
Berks RG 17 OEP
Fine furniture from the 18th
century.

David Brower Antiques
(ref: David Brower)
113 Kensington Church Street,
London W8 7LN
Tel: 020 7221 4155
Fax: 020 7721 6211
www.davidbrower-antique.com
Porcelain, European bronzes,
and Japanese works of art.

Brown
First Floor, 533 Kings Road,
London SW10 0TZ
Tel: 020 7352 2046
Furniture.

I. and J. L. Brown Ltd
(ref: I. & J. L. Brown)
632–636 Kings Road,
London SW6 2DU
Tel: 020 7736 4141
Fax: 020 7736 9164
www.brownantiques.com
English country and French
provincial antique and
reproduction furniture.

Brown's Antique Furniture
(ref: Browns)
First Floor, The Furniture
Cave,
533 Kings Road,
London SW10 0TZ
Tel: 020 7352 2046
Fax: 020 7352 6354
www.thecave.co.uk
Library and dining, and
decorative objects from the
early eighteenth century.

S. Brunswick
Alfie's Antiques Market,
13–25 Church Street,
London NW8 8DT
Tel: 020 7724 9097
Fax: 020 8902 5656
Functional and decorative
furnishings for house, garden
and conservatory.

**Peter Bunting Antiques
(ref: Peter Bunting)**
Harthill Hall, Alport,
Bakewell,
Derbyshire DE45 1LH
Tel: 01629 636203
Fax: 01629 636190
*Early oak and country furniture,
portraits and tapestries.*

**Butchoff Antiques
(ref: Butchoff)**
220 Westbourne Grove,
London W11 2RH
Tel: 020 7221 8174
Fax: 020 7792 8923
*English and continental furniture,
decorative items, porcelain and
mirrors.*

Butchoff Interiors
229 Westbourne Grove,
London W11 2SE
Tel: 020 7221 8163
Fax: 020 7792 8923
*One-off items, textiles,
collectables, dining tables, chairs,
consoles and accessories.*

Vincenzo Caffarella
Alfie's Antique Market,
13–25 Church Street,
London NW8 8DT
Tel: 020 7723 1513
Fax: 020 8731 8615
www.vinca.co.uk
*Twentieth-century decorative arts
and antiques.*

Cameo Gallery
151 Sydney Street,
London SW3 6NT
Tel: 020 7352 0909
Fax: 020 735 20066
Art Nouveau to Art Deco.

Jasmin Cameron
Antiquarias Antiques Market,
135 Kings Road,
London SW3 4PW
Tel: 020 7351 4154
Fax: 020 7351 4154
*Drinking glasses and decanters
1750–1910, vintage fountain
pens and writing materials.*

**Canonbury Antiques Ltd
(ref: Canonbury)**
174 Westbourne Grove,
London W11 2RW
Tel: 020 7229 2786
Fax: 020 7229 5840
www.canonbury-antiques.co.uk
*Eighteenth and nineteenth-
century furniture, reproduction
furniture and accessories.*

Vivienne Carroll
Stand N1, Antiquarius
135–141 Kings Road,
London SW3 4PW
Tel: 020 7352 8882
Fax: 020 7352 8734
*Silver, jewellery, porcelain and
ivory.*

**C. A. R. S. of Brighton
(ref: C. A. R. S.)**
4–4a Chapel Terrace Mews,
Kemp Town, Brighton BN2
1HU
Tel: 01273 622 722
Fax: 01273 601 960
www.carsofbrighton.co.uk
*Classic automobilia and regalia
specialists, and children's pedal
cars.*

**Cartoon Gallery, The
(ref: Cartoon Gallery)**
39 Great Russell Street,
London WC1 3PH
Tel: 020 7636 1011
Fax: 020 7436 5053
Comics.

**Mia Cartwright Antiques
(ref: Mia Cartwright)**
20th C. Theatre Arcade,
291 Westbourne Grove (Sats),
London W11
Tel: 01273 579700

**Rupert Cavendish Antiques
(ref: R. Cavendish)**
610 Kings Road,
London SW6 2DX
Tel: 020 7731 7041
Fax: 020 7731 8302
www.rupertcavendish.co.uk
*European twentieth-century
paintings.*

Cekay
Stand 172, Grays Antique
Market,
58 Davies Street,
London W1Y 2LP
Tel: 020 7629 5130
Fax: 020 7730 3014
Antiques.

**Ronald G. Chambers Fine
Antiques
(ref: Ronald G. Chambers)**
Market Square, Petworth,
West Sussex GU28 0AH
Tel: 01798 342305
Fax: 01798 342724
www.ronaldchambers.com
*Eighteenth and nineteenth-
century furniture, paintings,
objets d'art, clocks and jewellery.*

Bill Chapman
Shop No. 11, Bourbon/
Hanby Antique Centre,
151 Sydney Street,
London SW3 6NT
Tel: 020 7351 5387
Collectables.

Chelsea Gallery and Il Libro
(ref: Chelsea Gallery)
The Plaza, 535 Kings Road,
London SW10 0SZ
Tel: 020 7823 3248
Fax: 020 7352 1579
Antique illustrated books,
literature, prints, maps,
specialising in natural history,
travel, architecture and history.

Chelsea Military Antiques
(ref: Chelsea (OMRS))
Stands N13–14, Antiquarius,
131–141 Kings Road,
London SW3 4PW
Tel: 020 7352 0308
Fax: 020 7352 0308
www.chelseamilitaria.co.uk
Pre-1945 militaria, edge
weapons, medals including British
and foreign campaign/gallantry
medals.

Cine Art Gallery
(ref: Cine Art)
759 Fulham Road
London SW6 5UU
Tel: 020 7384 0728
Fax: 020 7384 0727
www.cineartgallery.com
Vintage film posters.

Circa
L43, Grays Mews Antique
Market,
1–7 Davies Mews,
London W1Y 2LP
Tel: 01279 466260
Fax: 01279 466 260
Decorative and collectable glass.

Clarke and Denny Antiques
Ref: Clarke & Denny
Great Grooms Antiques
Centre
Billingshurst
West Sussex RH14 9EU
Antique furniture.

Classic Fabrics with Robin
Haydock
(Ref: Classic Fabrics)
Unit 18
Bourbon Hanby Antiques
Centre
151 Sydney Street
London SW3 6NY
Tel: 020 7349 9100
Mob: 07770 931240
Antique textiles and fabrics.

John Clay Antiques
(ref: John Clay)
263 New Kings Road,
London SW6 4RB
Tel: 020 7731 5677
Furniture, objets d'art, silver and
clocks from the eighteenth and
nineteenth century.

Clock Clinic Ltd, The
(ref: Clock Clinic)
85 Lower Richmond Road,
Putney,
London SW15 1EW
Tel: 020 8788 1407
Fax: 020 8780 2838
www.clockclinic.co.uk
Antique clocks and barometers,
all overhauled and guaranteed.

Clock Workshop, The
17 Prospect Street, Caversham,
Reading, Berkshire RG4 8JB
Tel: 0118 947 0741
www.lapada.co.uk
English clocks and French
carriage clocks.

Cobwebs
73 Avery Hill Road,
New Eltham,
London SE9 2BJ
Tel: 020 8850 5611
Furniture, general antiques and
collectables.

Cohen & Cohen
101b Kensington Church
Street,
London W8 7LN
Tel: 020 7727 7677
Fax: 020 7229 9653
www.artnet.com
Chinese export porcelain works
of art.

Garrick D. Coleman
(ref: G. D. Coleman)
75 Portobello Road,
London W11 2QB
Tel: 020 7937 5524
Fax: 020 7937 5530
www.antiquechess.co.uk
Antiques, fine chess sets and
glass paperweights.

J. Collins & Son
28 High Street, Bideford,
Devon EX39 2AN
Tel: 01237 473103
Fax: 01237 475658
Georgian and Regency furniture,
Victorian oil paintings and
watercolours.

Rosemary Conquest
(ref: R. Conquest)
4 Charlton Place,
London N1 8AJ
Tel: 020 7359 0616
Continental and Dutch lighting,
copper, brass and decorative
items.

Hilary Conqy
Antiquarias Antiques Market,
135 Kings Road,
London SW3 4PW
Tel: 020 7352 2099
Jewellery.

**Marc Constantini Antiques
(ref: M. Constantini)**
313 Lillie Road,
London SW6 7LL

Sheila Cook Textiles
184 Westbourne Grove,
London W11 2RH
Tel: 020 7792 8001
Fax: 020 7229 3855
www.sheilacook.co.uk
*European costume, textiles
from the mid eighteenth century
to the 1970s.*

**Susie Cooper Ceramics
Gallery 1930
(ref: Susie Cooper)**
18 Church Street
Marylebone
London NW8 8EP
20th century ceramics.

**Barry Cotton Antiques
(ref: Barry Cotton)**
By appointment only
Tel: 020 8563 9899
Mob: 07831 354324
e-mail: barrycottonantiques@
tinyonline.co.uk
www.barrycottonantiques.fsnet.
co.uk
*Fine quality 18th and 19th
century period furniture.*

The Country Seat
Huntercome Manor Barn
nr. Henley on Thames
Oxon RG9 5RY
Tel: 01491 6431349
Fax: 01491 641533
e-mail: fery&clegg@
thecountryseat.com
www.thecountryseat.com
www.whitefriarsflass.com
*20th century furniture, ceramics
and glass.*

Sandra Cronan Ltd
18 Burlington Arcade,
London W1V 9AB
Tel: 020 7491 4851
Fax: 020 7493 2758
Art Deco jewellery.

Crowthers of Syon Lodge
Architectural Antiques
for Interior and Exteriors
77/79 Pimlico Road
London SW1 W8PH
Tel: 020 7730 8668
*Architectural antiques and
sculpture.*

**Curios Gardens & Interiors
(ref: Curios)**
130c Junction Road,
Tufnell Park,
London N19 5LB
Tel: 020 7272 5603
Fax: 020 7272 5603
*Garden furniture, statuary,
reclaimed pine furniture and
antique furniture.*

Ronan Daly Antiques
Alfie's Antiques Market,
13–25 Church Street,
London NW8 8DT
Tel: 020 7723 0429

Andrew Dando
4 Wood Street
Queen Square
Bath BA1 1JQ
Tel: 01225 422702
Fax: 012255 31017
e-mail:
andrew@andrewdando.uk
www.andrewdando/co.uk
English ceramics.

Michael Davidson
54 Ledbury Road,
London W11 2AJ
Tel: 020 7229 6088
Fax: 020 7792 0450
*Eighteenth-century furniture,
regency furniture, objects and
objets d'art.*

**Jesse Davis Antiques
(ref: Jesse Davis)**
Stands A9–11 Antiquarius,
131–141 Kings Road,
London SW3 4PW
Tel: 020 7352 4314
*Nineteenth-century pottery,
majolica, Staffordshire and other
collectable factories, and
decorative objects.*

Decodence
21 The Mall,
359 Upper Street,
London N1 0PD
Tel: 020 7354 4473
Fax: 020 7689 0680
*Classic plastics such as bakelite,
celluloid and catalin; vintage
radios, lighting, telephones and
toys.*

Deep, The
The Plaza, 535 Kings Road,
London SW10 0SZ
Tel: 020 7351 4881
Fax: 020 7352 0763
Recovered shipwrecked items.

Richard Dennis Gallery
(ref: Richard Dennis)
144 Kensington Church Street,
London W8 4BH
Tel: 020 7727 2061
Fax: 020 7221 1283
*Antique and modern studio
ceramics.*

Dial Post House
Dial Post, Near Horsham,
West Sussex RH13 8NQ
Tel: 01403 713388
Fax: 01403 713388
Furniture.

Dodo
Stand Fo73,
Alfie's Antiques Market,
13–25 Church Street,
London NW8 8DT
Tel: 020 7706 1545
Fax: 020 7724 0999
*Posters, tins and advertising signs,
1890–1940.*

Dolly Land
864 Green Lanes,
Winchmore Hill,
London N21 2RS
Tel: 020 8360 1053
Fax: 020 8364 1370
www.dollyland.com
Dolls.

Dolly Land (Steiff Club)
864 Green Lanes,
Winchmore Hill,
London N21 2RS
Tel: 020 8360 1053
Fax: 020 8364 1370
www.dollyland.com
*Dolls, Steiff bears, Scalextric,
trains and die-cast toys.*

Gavin Douglas
75 Portobello Road,
London W11 2QB
Tel: 020 7221 1121
www.antique-clocks.co.uk
*Clocks, bronzes, sculpture
and porcelain.*

**Drummonds Architectural
Antiques Ltd
(ref: Drummonds)**
The Kirkpatrick Buildings,
25 London Road, Hindhead,
Surrey GU26 6AB
Tel: 01428 609444
Fax: 01428 609445
www.drummonds-arch.co.uk
*Restored original and new
bathrooms, reclaimed wood and
stone flooring, fireplaces, statues,
garden features, lighting, gates
and railings, doors and door
furniture, radiators, antique
furniture, windows and large
architectural features.*

H. Duffield
Unit So54
Alfie's Market
13/25 Church Street
London NW8 8DT
Tel: 020 7723 2548
Early 20th century telephones.

S. Duggan
First Floor, 533 Kings Road,
London SW10 0TZ
Tel: 020 7352 2046
Antiques.

Eastern Interiors
Bourbon Hanby Antiques
Centre
151 Sydney Street
London SW3 6NT
Tel: 020 7795 2658
Fax: 020 7565 0003
Mob: 07803 701 778
www.eastern-interiors.co.uk
Oriental boxes and furniture.

**Emanouel Corporation
U.K. Ltd.
(ref: Emanouel)**
64 South Audley Street,
London W1Y 5FD
Tel: 020 7493 4350
Fax: 020 7499 0996
*Important antiques and fine
works of art from the eighteenth
and nineteenth century, and
Islamic works of art.*

Emerson
Bourbon & Hanby Antiques
Centre,
Shop No. 2, 151 Sydney Street,
London SW3 6NT
Tel: 020 7351 1807
Fax: 020 7351 1807
Corkscrews and collectables.

Penny Fawcett at Tilings
High Street, Brasted,
Kent TN16 1JA
Tel: 01959 564735
Fax: 01959 565795

**Finchley Fine Art Galleries
(ref: Finchley)**
983 High Road, North
Finchley,
London N12 8QR
Tel: 020 8446 4848
*Watercolours, paintings, fine
eighteenth and nineteenth-century
furniture, pottery and porcelain.*

J. First Antiques
Stand 310, 58 Davies Street,
London W1Y 1LB
Tel: 020 7409 2722
Fax: 020 7409 2722
www.firstsilver18@hotmail.com
*Antique English silver
collectables.*

Flower Antiques
Great Grooms Antique Centre
Hungerford
Berkshire RG17 0EP
Antique furniture.

David Ford
2 Queenstown Road, Battersea,
London SW8
Tel: 020 7622 7547

A. & E. Foster
Little Heysham, Forge Road,
Naphill, Buckinghamshire
HP14 4SU
Tel: 01494 562024
Fax: 01494 562024
*Antique treen works of art
and early treen.*

**Judy Fox Antiques
(ref: J. Fox)**
81 Portobello Road/
176 Westbourne Grove,
London W11
Tel: 020 7229 8130/8488
Fax: 020 7229 6998
Furniture.

Lynda Franklin
25 Charnham Street,
Hungerford,
Berkshire, RG17 0EJ
Tel: 01488 682404
Fax: 01488 626089
*Antiques and interior design,
french furniture from the
seventeenth and eighteenth
centuries.*

**Vincent Freeman Antiques
(ref: Vincent Freeman)**
1 Camden Passage
Stand G 57
Islington
London N1 8EA
Tel: 020 7226 6178
Fax 020 7226 7231
Mob: 07889 966 880
*19th century musical boxes,
furniture and ceramics.*

**French Country Living
(ref: French Country)**
Rue des Remparts,
Mougins, France
Tel: 00 33 4 93 75 53 03
Fax: 00 33 4 93 75 63 03
Antiquities and decoration.

**French Glasshouse, The
(ref: French Glasshouse)**
P14–P16 Antiquarias
Antiques Market,
135 Kings Road,
London SW3 4PW
Tel: 020 7376 5394
Fax: 020 7376 5394
*Gallé and Daum glassware, and
Japanese works of art.*

French Room, The
5 High Street, Petworth,
West Sussex GU28 0AU
Tel: 01798 344454
Fax: 01403 269880
*French period furniture and
decorative wares.*

Freshfords
High Street, Freshford,
Bath BA3 6EF
Tel: 01225 722111
Fax: 01225 722991
www.freshfords.com
*Fine antique furniture and works
of art, specialising in dining and
library furniture.*

**Charles Frodsham & Co. Ltd
(ref: C. Frodsham)**
32 Bury Street,
London SW1Y 6AU
Tel: 020 7839 1234
Fax: 020 7839 2000
*Clocks, watches, marines
chronometers and other
horological items.*

**Fulham Antiques
(ref: Fulham)**
320 Munster Road,
London SW6 6BH
Tel: 020 7610 3644
Fax: 020 7610 3644
*Antique and decorative furniture,
lighting and mirrors.*

**Furniture Vault, The
(ref: Furniture Vault)**
50 Camden Passage,
London N1 8AE
Tel: 020 7354 1047
Fax: 020 7354 1047
*Eighteenth and nineteenth-
century furniture.*

G Whizz
17 Jerdan Place,
London SW6 1BE
Tel: 020 7386 5020
Fax: 020 8741 0062
www.metrocycle.co.uk
Bikes.

Marilyn Garrow
The Farmhouse, Letheringham,
Woodbridge,
Suffolk IP13 7RA
Tel: 01728 746215
Fine and rare textiles.

Rupert Gentle Antiques
(ref: Rupert Gentle)
The Manor House,
Milton Lilbourne
nr Pewsey
Wiltshire SN9 5LQ
Tel: 01672 563344
Fax: 01672 563563
Decorative antiques and works
of art.

Geri
Unit S 057
Alfie's Antique Market
13-15 Church Street
Marylebone
London N W8 8DT
Tel: 020 7723 254
www.alfies.com
Antique telephones.

Michael German Antiques
(ref: Michael German)
38b Kensington Church Street,
London W8 4BX
Tel: 020 7937 2771
Fax: 020 7937 8566
www.antiquecanes.com
www.antiqueweapons.com
Antique walking canes, antique
arms and armour.

Get Stuffed
105 Essex Road,
London N1 2SL
Tel: 020 7226 1364
Fax: 020 7359 8253
www.thegetstuffed.co.uk
Taxidermy and natural history
artefacts.

Ghaznavid
A30 Grays Antiques Market,
1–7 Davies Mews,
London W1Y 2LP
Tel: 020 7629 2813
Fax: 020 8896 2114
Roman.

Gabrielle de Giles
The Barn at Bilsington,
Swanton Lane, Bilsington,
Ashford, Kent TN25 7JR
Tel: 01233 720917
Fax: 01233 720156
Antique and country furniture,
home interiors, designer for
curtains and screens.

Glenda Antique Dolls and
Collectables
(ref: Glenda Dolls)
Gray's Antique Market
Davies Street
London WI
Tel: 020 8367 2441
Dolls and collectables.

Gooday Gallery, The
(ref: Gooday Gallery)
14 Richmond Hill, Richmond,
Surrey TW10 6QX
Tel: 020 8940 8652
Arts and Crafts, Art Nouveau,
Art Deco, post modernism, tribal
art, and African and Oceanic
masks.

John Goodison/Chris
Paraskeva Antiques
(Ref: Goodison Paraskeva)
30 Camden Passage
London N1 8EA
Mob: 07711 839177
e-mail:goodison.paraskeva
@tinyworld.co.uk
Antique lighting and boxes
and decorative items.

Gordon's Medals
Stand 14–15 Grays Antiques
Market,
Davies Mews,
London W1Y 1AR
Tel: 020 7495 0900
Fax: 020 7495 0115
www.gordonsmedals.co.uk
Militaria, uniforms, headgear,
badges, medals and documents.

Gosh
39 Great Russell Street,
London WC1B 3PH
Tel: 020 7436 5053
Fax: 020 7436 5053

Goya
Stand S002, Alfie's Market,
13–25 Church Street,
London NW8 8DT
Tel: 020 7723 6066
Twentieth-century glass.

Denzil Grant Antiques
(ref: Denzil Grant)
Drinkston House
Drinkston
Bury St. Edmunds
Suffolk IP30 9TT
Tel: 01449 736576
Fax: 01449 737679
mobile 07836 2233112
e-mail:denzil@denzilgrant.com
www.denzilgrant.com

Anita & Solveig Gray
58 Davies Street,
London W1Y 2LP
Tel: 020 7408 1638
Fax: 020 7495 0707
www.chinese-porcelain.com
Oriental and European porcelain
works of art from the sixteenth
to the eighteenth century.

Great Grooms Antique
Centre
(ref: Great Grooms)
Great Grooms, Parbrook,
Billinghurst, West Sussex
RH14 9EU
Tel: 01403 786202
Fax: 01403 786224
www.great-grooms.co.uk
Furniture, porcelain, jewellery,
silver, glass and pictures.

Anthony Green Antiques
(ref: Anthony Green)
Unit 39, Bond Street
Antiques Centre,
124 New Bond Street,
London W1S 1DX
Tel: 020 7409 2854
Fax: 020 7409 2854
www.anthonygreen.com
Vintage wristwatches and antique
pocket watches.

Henry Gregory
82 Portobello Road,
London W11 2QD
Tel: 020 7792 9221
Fax: 020 7792 9221
Silver-plate, silver, sporting goods
and decorative antiques.

W. John Griffiths
Great Grooms Antique Centre
Hungerford
Berkshire RG17 OEP
Antique furniture.

Guest & Gray
Grays Mews Antique Market,
1–7 Davies Mews,
London W1Y 2LP
Tel: 020 7408 1252
Fax: 020 7499 1445
www.guest-gray.demon.co.uk
Oriental and European
ceramics and works of art,
and reference books.

Guinevere Antiques Limited
(ref: Guinevere)
574–580 Kings Road,
London SW6 2DY
Tel: 020 7736 2917
Fax: 020 7736 8267
Mirrors, cabinets, lights and
chandeliers.

Gurr and Sprake Antiques
(ref: Gurr & Sprake)
283 Lillie Road,
London SW6 7LL
Tel: 020 7381 3209
Fax: 020 7381 9502
Eighteenth and nineteenth-
century English and French
furniture, lighting and unusual
architectural pieces.

Gutlin Clocks and Antiques
(ref: Gutlin)
616 Kings Road,
London SW6
Tel: 020 7384 2439
Fax: 020 7384 2439
www.gutlin.com
Longcase clocks, mantle clocks,
furniture and lighting, all
eighteenth and nineteenth
century.

J. de Haan & Son
(ref: J. de Haan)
PO Box 95, Newmarket,
Suffolk CB8 8ZG
Tel: 01440 821388
Fax: 01440 820410
Old English furniture,
barometers, gilt mirrors and fine
tea caddies.

Hadji Baba Ancient Art
(ref: Hadji Baba)
34a Davies Street,
London W1Y 1LG
Tel: 020 7499 9363
Fax: 020 7493 5504
Near and Middle East antiquities.

Robert Hales Antiques
(ref: Robert Hales)
131 Kensington Church Street,
London W8 7LP
Tel: 020 7229 3887
Fax: 020 7229 3887
Oriental and Islamic arms,
armour, from medieval
to nineteenth century.

Ross Hamilton Antiques Ltd
95 Pimlico Road,
London SW1W 8PH
Tel: 020 7730 3015
Fax: 020 7730 3015
www.lapada.uk/rosshamilton/
Seventeenth to nineteenth-century
fine English and continental
furniture, sixteenth to
twentieth-century paintings,
oriental porcelain, objets d'art
and bronzes.

Jim Hanson &
Argyll Etkin Ltd
18 Claremont Field,
Ottery St Mary,
Devon EX11 1NP
Tel: 01404 815010
Fax: 01404 815224
Philatelist and postal historian.

Keith Harding's World of
Mechanical Music
(ref: Keith Harding)
The Oak House,
High Street, Northleach,
Gloucestershire GL54 3ET
Tel: 01451 860181
Fax: 01451 861133
www.mechanicalmusic.co.uk
Harpur Deardren
First Floor, 533 Kings Road,
London SW10 0TZ
Tel: 020 7352 2046
Furniture.

Adrian Harrington
Antiquarian Bookseller
(ref: Adrian Harrington)
64a Kensington Church Street,
London W8 4DB
Tel: 020 7937 1465
Fax: 020 7368 0912
www.harringtonbooks.co.uk
Antiquarian, rare and
secondhand books on literature,
children's illustrated and travel.

Peter Harrington
Antiquarian Bookseller
100 Fulham Road
London SW3 6HS
Tel: 020 7591 02220
Fax:020 7225 7054
www.peter-harrington-
book.com
Antique books and maps.

Kenneth Harvey Antiques
(ref: Kenneth Harvey)
Furniture Cave,
533 Kings Road,
London SW10 0TZ
Tel: 020 7352 8645
Fax: 020 7352 3759
www.kennethharvey.com
English and French furniture,
chandeliers and mirrors from the
late seventeenth to twentieth
century, and leather armchairs.

Victoria Harvey at Deuxieme
(ref: Victoria Harvey)
44 Church Street,
London NW8 8EP
Tel: 020 7724 0738
Fax: 020 7724 0738
General decorative antiques.

W. R. Harvey & Co. Ltd
86 Corn Street, Witney,
Oxfordshire OX8 7BU
Tel: 01993 706501
Fax: 01993 706601
www.wrharvey.co.uk
Important stock of English
furniture, clocks, pictures,
mirrors and works of art from
1680–1830.

Hatchwell Antiques
(ref: Hatchwell)
533 Kings Road
London SW10 0TZ
Tel: 020 7351 2344
Fax: 020 7351 3520
e-mail:hatchwell@callnetuk.
com
Period furniture, fine furniture
and bronzes.

Gerard Hawthorn Ltd
(ref: Gerard Hawthorn)
104 Mount Street,
London W1Y 5HE
Tel: 020 7409 2888
Fax: 020 7409 2777
Chinese, Japanese and Korean
ceramics and works of art.

Henry Hay
Unit 5054, 2nd floor,
Alfie's Market,
13–25 Church Street,
London NW8
Tel: 020 7723 2548
Art Deco and twentieth-century
chrome and brass lamps and
bakelite telephones.

Hayman and Hayman
Stand K3 Antiquarius
135 Kings Road
London SW3 4PW
Tel: 020 7351 6568
Fax: 020 8741 0959
e-mail:hayman@wahlgren.
demon.co.uk
Art deco and brass photograph
frames, scent bottles and writing
equipment.

Heytesbury Antiques
(ref: Heytesbury)
PO Box 222, Farnham,
Surrey GU10 5HN
Tel: 01252 850893
Antiques.

Hill Farm Antiques
(ref: Hill Farm)
at The Old Cinema
160 Chiswick High Road
London W4 1PR
Tel: 020 8994 2998 and 01488
638 541/361
e-mail:beesley@
hillfarmantiques.demon.co.uk
Antique furniture.

Holland & Holland
31–33 Bruton Street,
London W1X 8JS
Tel: 020 7499 4411
Fax: 020 7409 3283
Guns.

Hope & Glory
131a Kensington Church
Street
(entrance in Peel Street),
London W8 7LP
Tel: 020 7727 8424
Commemorative ceramics
including royal and political
subjects.

Paul Hopwell Antiques
(ref: Paul Hopwell)
30 High Street
Westhaddon
Northamptonshire NN6 7AP
Tel: 01788 510636
Fax: 01788 510044
e-mail:
paulhopwell@antiqueoak.co.uk
www.antiqueoak.co.uk
Seventeenth and eighteenth-
century English oak furniture.

Jonathan Horne
66c Kensington Church Street,
London W8 4BY
Tel: 020 7221 5658
Fax: 020 7792 3090
www.jonathanhorne.co.uk
Early English pottery, medieval
to 1820.

Howard & Hamilton
(ref: H. & H.)
151 Sydney Street,
London SW3 6NT
Tel: 020 7352 0909
Fax: 020 7352 0066
Scientific instruments.

Hulton Getty Picture Gallery
(ref: Hulton Getty)
3 Jubilee Place
London SW3 3TD
Tel: 020 7376 4525
Fax: 0207 376 4524
www.getty-images.com
*Photographs from late
19th–20th century.*

Huxtable's Old Advertising
(ref: Huxtable's)
Alfie's Market,
13–25 Church Street,
London NW8 8DT
Tel: 020 7724 2200
*Advertising, collectables, tins,
signs, bottles, commemoratives
and old packaging from late
Victorian.*

Iconastas
5 Piccadilly Arcade,
London SW1
Tel: 020 7629 1433
Fax: 020 7408 2015
Russian fine art.

In Vogue Antiques
Martin Lister
The Swan Antiques Centre
High Street
Tetsworth, Thame
Oxfordshire OX9 7AB
Tel: 01844 281777
Fax: 01844 281770
mobile 0773 786 103
e-mail:invogueantiques@aol.
com
www.theswan.co.uk
Antique furniture.

J. A. N. Fine Art
134 Kensington Church Street,
London W8 4BH
Tel: 020 7792 0736
Fax: 020 7221 1380
*Japanese, Chinese and Korean
ceramics, bronzes and works
of art.*

P. L. James
590 Fulham Road,
London SW6 5NT
Tel: 020 7736 0183
*Gilded mirrors, English and
oriental lacquer,
period objects and furniture.*

Japanese Gallery Ltd
(ref: Japanese Gallery)
66d Kensington Church Street,
London W8 4BY
Tel: 020 7729 2934
Fax: 020 7229 2934
*Japanese woodcut prints,
Japanese ceramics, swords,
armour and Japanese dolls.*

Jessop Classic Photographica
(ref: Jessop Classic)
67 Great Russell Street,
London WC1
Tel: 020 7831 3640
Fax: 020 7831 3956
*Classic photographic equipment,
cameras and optical toys.*

Juke Box Services
15 Lion Road,
Twickenham TW1 4JH
Tel: 020 8288 1700
www.jbs-ltd.co.uk
Juke boxes.

Stephen Kalms Antiques
(ref: Stephen Kalms)
The London Silver Vaults,
Chancery Lane,
London WC2A 1QS
Tel: 020 7430 1254
Fax: 020 7405 6206
*Victorian and Edwardian silver,
silver plate and decorative items.*

Kieron
K6 Antiquarias Antiques
Market,
135 Kings Rd,
London SW3 4PW
Tel: 020 7352 2099
Decorative arts.

Kitchen Bygones
13–15 Church Street,
Marylebone,
London NW8 8DT
Tel: 020 7258 3405
Fax: 020 7724 0999
Kitchenalia.

Shirly Knight
Antiques and Decorative
Furnishing
Great Grooms Antique Centre
Hungerford
Berkshire RG17 0RP
Tel: 01488 6823114
Fax: 01487 8233130
Antique furniture.

L. & E. Kreckovic
559 Kings Road,
London SW6 2EB
Tel: 020 7736 0753
Fax: 020 7731 5904
*Early eighteenth to nineteenth-
century furniture.*

La Boheme
c21 Grays Mews,
1–7 Davies Mews,
London W1Y 2LP
Tel: 020 7493 0675
Glass.

Lacquer Chest, The
(ref: Lacquer Chest)
75 Kensington Church Street,
London W8 4BG
Tel: 020 7937 1306
Fax: 020 7376 0223
Military chests, china, clocks,
samplers and lamps.

Lamberty
The Furniture Cave,
533 Kings Road,
London SW10 0TZ
Tel: 020 7352 3775
Fax: 020 7352 3759
www.lamberty.co.uk

Langfords
Vault 8–10,
London Silver Vaults,
Chancery Lane,
London WC2A 1QS
Tel: 020 7242 5506
Fax: 020 7405 0431
www.langfords.com
Antique and modern silver
and silver plate.

Langfords Marine Antiques
(ref: Langfords Marine)
The Plaza, 535 Kings Road,
London SW10 0SZ
Tel: 020 7351 4881
Fax: 020 7352 0763
www.langfords.co.uk
Nautical artefacts.

Judith Lassalle
7 Pierrepont Arcade,
Camden Passage,
London N1 8EF
Tel: 020 7607 7121
Optical toys, books and games.

Michael Laws
Bartlett Street Antiques
Centre
Bath BA1 2QZ
Tel: 01225 446322
Fax: 01249 658366
Antique fishing tackle and curios.

Lennox Gallery Ltd
(ref: Lennox Gallery)
4 Davies Mews,
London W1Y 1LP
Tel: 020 7491 0091
Fax: 020 7491 0657
Antiquities and numismatics.

Liberty plc
210–220 Regent Street,
London W1R 6AH
Tel: 020 7734 1234
Fax: 020 7578 9876
www.liberty.co.uk
Twentieth-century furniture,
jewellery, ceramics, clothes
and kitchenware.

Libra Antiques
131D Kensington Church
Street
London W8 7PT
Tel: 020 7727 2990
English ceramics.

Libra Designs
34 Church Street,
London NW8 8EP
Tel: 020 7723 0542
Fax: 020 7286 8518
www.libradeco.com

Linden & Co. (Antiques) Ltd
(ref: Linden & Co.)
Vault 7, London Silver Vaults,
Chancery Lane,
London WC2A 1QS
Tel: 020 7242 4863
Fax: 020 7405 9946
Silver plate and works of art.

P. Lipitch
120 and 124 Fulham Road,
London SW3 6HU
Tel: 020 7373 3328
Fax: 020 7373 8888
General antiques.

Little River Oriental Antiques
(ref: Little River)
135 Kings Road,
London SW3 4PW
Tel: 020 7349 9080
Chinese antiquities and domestic
ceramics.

London Antique Gallery
(ref: London Antique)
66e Kensington Church Street,
London W8 4BY
Tel: 020 7229 2934
Fax: 020 7229 2934
Meissen, Dresden, Worcester,
Minton, Shelley, Sèvrea, Lalique
and bisque dolls.

Stephen Long
348 Fulham Road,
London SW10 9UH
Tel: 020 7352 8226
Painted furniture, small
decorative items and English
pottery, from 1780–1850.

Lotus House
Great Grooms
Hungerford
Berkshire RG17 OEP
Tel: 01488 6823114
Oriental antiques.

**M. Luther Antiques
(ref: M. Luther)**
590 Kings Road, Chelsea,
London SW6 2DX
Tel: 020 7371 8492
Fax: 020 7371 8492
*Eighteenth and nineteenth-
century English and continental
furniture, tables, chairs, mirrors
and lighting.*

**Mac Humble Antiques
(ref: Mac Humble)**
7–9 Woolley Street, Bradford
on Avon,
Wiltshire BA15 1AD
Tel: 01225 866329
Fax: 01225 866329
www.machumbleantiques.co.uk
*Eighteenth and nineteenth-
century furniture, needlework,
samplers, metalware and
decorative items.*

**Mac's Cameras
(ref: Mac's)**
262 King Street,
Hammersmith,
London W6 0SJ
Tel: 020 8846 9853
Antique camera equipment.

**Joyce Macnaughton-Smith
(ref: Macnaughton-Smith)**
The Swan Antique Centre
Tetsworth
Thame
Oxfordshire
Berkshire OX9 7AB
Tel: 01884 281777
Antique furniture.

Magpies
152 Wandsworth Bridge Road,
London SW6 2UH
Tel: 020 7736 3738
*Small furniture, kitchenware,
door furniture, cutlery, lighting,
silver and silver-plate.*

C. H. Major
154 Kensington Church Street,
London W8 4BH
Tel: 020 7229 1162
Fax: 020 7221 9676
*Eighteenth and nineteenth-
century English furniture.*

E. & H. Manners
66a Kensington Church Street,
London W8 4BY
Tel: 020 7229 5516
Fax: 020 7229 5516
www.europeanporcelain.com
*Eighteenth-century European
porcelain and pottery.*

Map House, The
54 Beauchamp Place,
London SW3 1NY
Tel: 020 7584 8559
Fax: 020 7589 1041
www.themaphouse.com
*Antique maps from fifteenth to
nineteenth century, decorative
engravings from sixteenth to
nineteenth century.*

Marks Antiques
49 Curzon Street,
London W1Y 7RE
Tel: 020 7499 1788
Fax: 020 7409 3183
www.marksantiques.com
Antique silver.

**David Martin-Taylor Antiques
(ref: D. Martin-Taylor)**
558 Kings Road,
London SW6 2DZ
Tel: 020 7731 4135
Fax: 020 7371 0029
www.davidmartintaylor.com
*Eighteenth and nineteenth-
century continental and English
furniture, objets d'art, decorative
art, from the eccentric to the
unusual.*

**Megan Mathers Antiques
(ref: M. Mathers)**
571 Kings Road,
London SW6 2EB
Tel: 020 7371 7837
Fax: 020 7371 7895
*Nineteenth-century continental
and English furniture, porcelain,
lighting and objets d'art.*

A. P. Mathews
283 Westbourne Grove,
London W11
Tel: 01622 812590
Antique luggage.

Gerald Mathias
Stands 3–6, Antiquarius,
131–141 Kings Road,
London SW3 4PW
Tel: 020 7351 1484
Fax: 020 7351 0484
www.geraldmathias.com
*Antique wooden boxes, tea
caddies and stationery cabinets.*

Francesca Matire
Alfie's Antique Market
13-25 Church Street
London NW8 8DT
Tel: 020 7723 6066
www.@alfies.com
Open Tues-Sat 10-6.
*20th century lighting, glass,
furniture and jewellery.*

**Sue Mautner Costume
Jewellery
(ref: Sue Mautner)**
Stand P13, Antiquarius,
131–141 Kings Road,
London SW3 4PW
Tel: 020 7376 4419
*Costume jewellery from the
1940s and 1950s, including
Christian Dior, Miriam Haskell,
Schiaparelli, Coppolo Toppo,
Har and Schreiner.*

Pete McAskie Toys
Stand A12–13, Basement,
1–7 Davies Mews,
London W1Y 2LP
Tel: 020 7629 2813
Fax: 020 7493 9344
Tin toys from 1895–1980, die-cast toys, robots, battery operated toys and lead figures.

Nicholas E. McAuliffe
(ref: N. E. McAuliffe)
First Floor, 533 Kings Road,
London SW10 0TZ
Tel: 020 7352 2046
Furniture.

Fiona McDonald
57 Galveston Road,
London SW15 2RZ
Tel: 020 2270 5559
Mirrors, decorative furniture and lighting.

Metro Retro
1 White Conduit Street,
London N1 9EL
Tel: 020 7278 4884/
01245 442047
www.metroretro.co.uk
Industrial-style and stripped steel furniture, lighting and home accessories.

Midwinter Antiques
(ref: Midwinter)
31 Bridge Street,
Newcastle under Lyme,
Staffordshire ST5 2RY
Tel: 01782 712483
Fax: 01630 672289
Seventeenth and eighteenth-century town and country furniture, clocks and textiles.

Arthur Millner
180 New Bond Street,
London W1S 4RL
Tel: 020 7499 4484

www.arthurmillner.com
Indian and Islamic art and related European material.

Nicholas Mitchell
The Swan Antique Centre
Tetsworth
Thame
Oxfordshire
OX9 7AB
Tel: 01844 281777
Fax: 01844 281770
www/theswan.co.uk
English and continental furniture.

Mora & Upham Antiques
(ref: Mora Upham)
584 Kingís Road
London SW6 2DX
Tel: 020 7331 444
Fax: 020 7736 0440
e-mail: mora.upham@talk21.com
Fine English and continental furniture, mirrors and lighting.

More Than Music
Collectables
(ref: More Than Music)
C24–25 Grays Mews Antiques Market,
1–7 Davies Mews,
London W1Y 2LP
Tel: 020 7629 7703
Fax: 01519 565510
www.mtmglobal.com
Rock and popular music memorabilia, specialising in The Beatles.

Clive Morley Harps Ltd
(ref: Clive Morley)
Unit 121,
Grays Antiques Market,
58 Davies Street,
London W1 5LP
Tel: 020 7495 4495
Fax: 01367 860 659
www.morleyharps.com
Harps.

Robert Morley and Company
Limited
(ref: Robert Morley)
34 Engate Street, Lewisham,
London SE13 7HA
Tel: 020 8318 5838
Fax: 020 8297 0720
Pianoforte and harpsichord workshop.

Terence Morse & Son
(ref: T. Morse & Son)
237 Westbourne Gove,
London W11 2SE
Tel: 020 7229 4059
Fax: 020 7792 3284
Eighteenth and nineteenth-century fine English and continental furniture, linen presses and library furniture.

Motor Books
33 St Martin's Court,
London WC2N 4AN
Tel: 020 7836 3800
Fax: 020 7497 2539
Motoring books.

Mousa Antiques
(ref: Mousa)
B20 Grays Mews Antiques
Market,
1–7 Davies Mews,
London W1Y 1AR
Tel: 020 7499 8273
Fax: 020 7629 2526
Bohemian glass specialists.

Murray Cards (International)
Ltd
(ref: Murray Cards)
51 Watford Way,
London NW4 3JH
Tel: 020 8202 5688
Fax: 020 8203 7878
www.murraycards.com
Cigarette and trade cards.

**Music & Video Exchange
(ref: Music & Video)**
38 Notting Hill Gate,
London W11 3HX
Tel: 020 7243 8574
www.mveshops.co.uk
*CDs, memorabilia, vinyl –
deletions and rarities.*

**Myriad Antiques
(ref: Myriad)**
131 Portland Road,
London W11 4LW
Tel: 020 7229 1709
Fax: 020 7221 3882
*French painted furniture, garden
furniture, bamboo, Victorian and
Edwardian upholstered chairs,
mirrors and objets d'art.*

Stephen Naegel
Grays Antiques Market,
1–7 Davies Mews,
London W1Y 2LP
Tel: 020 7491 3066
Fax: 01737 845147
www.btinternet.com/~naegel
Toys.

**Colin Narbeth and Son
(ref: C. Narbeth)**
20 Cecil Court,
London WC2N 4HE
Tel: 020 7379 6975
Fax: 0172 811244
www.colin-narbeth.com
*Banknotes, bonds and shares
of all countries and periods.*

New Century
69 Kensington Church Street,
London W8 8BG
Tel: 020 7937 2410
Fax: 020 7937 2410
Design from 1860–1910.

**New Kings Road Vintage
Guitar Emporium
(ref: Vintage Guitar)**
65a New Kings Road,
London SW6 4SG
Tel: 020 7371 0100
Fax: 020 7371 0460
www.newkingsroadguitars.co.uk
Vintage guitars.

**Chris Newland Antiques
(ref: C. Newland)**
30–31 Islington Green,
Lower Level, Georgian Village,
London N1 8DU
Tel: 020 7359 9805
Fax: 020 7359 9805
Furniture.

John Nicholas Antiques
First Floor, 533 Kings Road,
London SW10 0TZ
Tel: 020 7352 2046
www.thecave.co.uk
*Eighteenth to twentieth-century
furniture, accessories,
chandeliers, lighting and
tapestries.*

**North West Eight
(ref: North West 8)**
36 Church Street,
London NW8 8EP
Tel: 020 7723 9337
Decorative antiques.

**Oasis Ancient and
Islamic Arts
(ref: Oasis)**
Stand E14, Grays Mews
Antiques Market,
1–7 Davies Mews,
London W1Y 1AR
Tel: 020 7493 1202
Fax: 020 8551 4487
*Ancient and Islamic art from
2000BC to eighteenth century.*

Ocean Leisure
11–14 Northumberland
Avenue,
London WC2N 5AQ
Tel: 020 7930 5050
Fax: 020 7930 3032
www.oceanleisure.co.uk

Old Advertising
Keith Gretton
26 Honeywell Road
London SW11 6EG
Tel: 020 7228 0741
Advertising items.

The Old Cinema
160 Chiswick High Road
London W4 1PR
Tel: 020 8995 8801
Mob: 0777 5945482
*Antique furniture from the 18th
and 19th century.*

**Old Cinema Antiques
Warehouse, The
(ref: Old Cinema)**
157 Tower Bridge Road,
London SE1 3LW
Tel: 020 7407 5371
Fax: 020 7403 0359
www.antiques-uk.co.uk
*Victorian, Edwardian,
reproduction furniture, babies'
chairs, telephone boxes, and
reproduction leather Chesterfields.*

**Old Father Time Clock
Centre**
101 Portobello Road,
London W11 2QB
Tel: 020 8546 6299
Fax: 020 8546 6299
www.oldfathertime.net
Unusual and quirky clocks.

Old School
130c Junction Road,
Tufnell Park,
London N19
Tel: 020 7272 5603
Gardens and interiors.

Old Telephone Company, The
(ref: Old Telephone Co.)
The Battlesbridge Antiques
Centre,
The Old Granary,
Battlesbridge,
Essex SS11 7RE
Tel: 01245 400 601
www.theoldtelephone.co.uk
*Antique and collectable
telephones.*

Old Tool Chest, The
(ref: Old Tool Chest)
41 Cross Street,
London N1 0PG
Tel: 020 7359 9313
*Ancient and modern tools of all
trades, woodworking, dentistry,
veterinary, mason's, and books.*

Old World Trading Co
565 Kings Road,
London SW6 2EB
Tel: 020 7731 4708
Fax: 020 7731 1291
*Eighteenth and nineteenth-
century English and French
chimney places, fire dogs and
grates.*

Oola Boola Antiques London
(ref: Oola Boola)
166 Tower Bridge Road,
London SE1 3LS
Tel: 020 7403 0794
Fax: 020 7403 8405
*Victorian, Edwardian, Art
Nouveau, Art Deco, and Arts
and Crafts furniture.*

Jacqueline Oosthuizen
Antiques
23 Cale Street, Chelsea,
London SW3 3QR
Tel: 020 7352 6071
Fax: 020 7376 3852
*Staffordshire pottery and
jewellery.*

Pieter Oosthuizen
(ref: P. Oosthuizen)
Unit 4, Bourbon Hanby
Antiques Centre,
151 Sydney Street,
London SW3
Tel: 020 7460 3078
Fax: 020 7376 3852
*Dutch and European Art
Nouveau pottery and
Boer War memorabilia.*

Oriental Rug Gallery Ltd
Eton Group Office
115-116 High Street
Eton
Berkshire SL4 6AN
Tel: 01753 623000
e-mail: rug@orientalruggallery.
com
*Antique carpets, rugs and
cushions.*

Ormonde Gallery
156 Portobello Road
London W11 2EB
020 7229 9800
e-mail:frankormondegallery.
com
*Oriental ceramics, furniture,
sculpture and works of art.*

Paul Orssich
2 St Stephens Terrace,
London SW8 1DH
Tel: 020 7787 0030
Fax: 020 7735 9612
www.orssich.com
*Maps and 20,000 rare
secondhand books.*

Fay Orton Antiques
(ref: Fay Orton)
First Floor, 533 Kings Road,
London SW10 0TZ
Tel: 020 7352 2046
Furniture.

Anthony Outred Antiques
Ltd
(ref: Anthony Outred)
46 Pimlico Road
London SW1 8LP
Tel: 020 7730 4782
Fax: 020 7730 5643 fax
e-mail:antiques@outred.co.uk
www.outred.co.uk
English and continental antiques.

John Owen
(ref: John Owen)
Great Grooms Antiques
Centre
Hungerford
Berkshire RG17 OEP
Furniture from the 18th century.

Pacifica
Block 7, 479 Park West Place,
Edgware Road, London W2
Tel: 020 7402 6717
Tribal art.

Pars Antiques
(ref: Pars)
35 St George Street,
London W1R 9FA
Tel: 020 7491 9889
Fax: 020 7493 9344
Antiquities.

Pendulum of Mayfair
King House, 51 Maddox Street,
London W1R 9LA
Tel: 020 7629 6606
Fax: 020 7629 6616
*Clocks: including longcase,
bracket and wall,
and Georgian period furniture.*

Percy's Ltd
16 The London Silver Vaults,
Chancery Lane,
London WC2A 1QS
Tel: 020 7242 3618
Fax: 020 7831 6541
Eighteenth and nineteenth-
century decorative silver and
plate.

Period Pieces
Solihull
West Midlands
Tel: 0121 709 1205
Mob: 07778 452539
e-mail:susanshaw50@hotmail.
com
Antique boxes.

Trevor Philip & Son Ltd
75a Jermyn Street,
London SW1Y 6NP
Tel: 020 7930 2954
Fax: 020 7321 0212
www.trevorphilip.demon.co.uk
Early scientific instruments, and
seventeenth to nineteenth-century
globes.

Photographer's Gallery, The
(ref: Photo. Gallery)
5 Great Newport Street,
London WC2H 7HY
Tel: 020 7831 1772
Fax: 020 7836 9704
www.photonet.org.uk

David Pickup Antiques
(ref: David Pickup)
115 High Street, Burford,
Oxfordshire OX18 4RG
Tel: 01993 822555
Fine English furniture, emphasis
on the Cotswold Arts and Crafts
movement and early twentieth
century.

Pillows of Bond Street
(ref: Pillows)
Bond Street,
London W11
Tel: 0468 947265
Pillows.

Pimlico Antiques
(ref: Pimlico)
Moreton Street,
London SW1
Tel: 020 7821 8448
Furniture, works of art and
paintings.

A. Piotrowski
Bourbon-Hanby Antiques
Centre
151 Sydney Street
London SW3 6NT
Tel: 020 7352 2106
Fax: 020 7565 0003
www.antiques-uk.co.uk/
bourbon-hanby
English ceramics.

Nicholas S. Pitcher Oriental
Art
(ref: Nicholas S. Pitcher)
1st Floor, 29 New Bond Street,
London W1Y 9HD
Tel: 020 7499 6621
Fax: 020 7499 6621
Early Chinese ceramics and
works of art.

Planet Bazaar
151 Drummond Street,
London NW1 2PB
Tel: 020 7387 8326
Fax: 020 7387 8326
www.planetbazaar.co.uk
Designer furniture, art, glass,
lighting, ceramics, books and
eccentricities from the 1950s to
1980s.

Poppets Antiques
(ref: Poppets)
Bourbon Hanby Antiques
Centre
151 Sydney Street
London SW3 6NT
Tel: 020 7352 2108
19th century furniture.

Christopher Preston Ltd
(ref: C. Preston)
The Furniture Cave,
533 Kings Road,
London SW10 0TZ
Tel: 020 7352 4229
Antique furniture and decorative
objects.

Annette Puttnam
Norton House,
Nr. Lewes, Iford,
Sussex BN7 3EJ
Tel: 01273 483366
Fax: 01273 483366

R. & S. Antiques
Bourbon Hanby Antiques
Centre
151 SydneyStreet
Chelsea
London SW3 6NT
Tel: 020 73522106
Fax: 020 7565 0003

Radio Days
87 Lower Marsh,
London SE1 7AB
Tel: 020 7928 0800
Fax: 020 7928 0800
Lighting, telephones, radios,
clothing, magazines and cocktail
bars from the 1930s–1970s.

Raffety Walwyn
79 Kensington Church Street,
London W8 4BG
Tel: 020 7938 1100
Fax: 020 7938 2519
www.raffetyantiqueclocks.com
Fine antique clocks.

Rainbow Antiques
(ref: Rainbow)
329 Lillie Road,
London SW6 7NR
Tel: 020 7385 1323
Fax: 0870 052 1693
*Italian and French period lighting
from 1880–1940, chandeliers,
lamps and lanterns.*

Ranby Hall Antiques
(ref: Ranby Hall)
Barnby Moor, Retford,
Nottingham DN22 8JQ
Tel: 01777 860696
Fax: 01777 701317
www.ranbyhall.antiques-
gb.com
*Antiques, decorative items and
contemporary objects.*

Mark Ransom Ltd
(ref: Mark Ransom)
62 and 105 Pimlico Road,
London SW1W 8LS
Tel: 020 7259 0220
Fax: 020 7259 0323
*Decorative Empire and French
furniture.*

Rasoul Gallery
South Asian Antiques
K34/35 Grays Antiques
1-7 Davies Mews
London W1Y 2LP
Tel: 020 7495 7422
Mob: 07956 809760
e-mail:rasoulgallerya@hotmail.
com
Islamic ceramics and antiquities.

RBR Group at Grays
(ref: RBR Group)
Stand 175, Grays Antiques
Market,
58 Davies Street,
London W1Y 2LP
Tel: 020 7629 4769
Jewellery and objects.

Red Lion Antiques
(ref: Red Lion)
New Street, Petworth,
West Sussex GU28 0AS
Tel: 01798 344485
Fax: 01798 342367
www.redlion-antiques.com
*Seventeenth to nineteenth-century
furniture.*

Gordon Reece Gallery
(ref: Gordon Reece)
16 Clifford Street,
London W1X 1RG
Tel: 020 7439 0007
Fax: 020 7437 5715
www.gordonreecegalleries.com
*Flat woven rugs and nomadic
carpets, tribal sculpture,
jewellery, furniture, decorative
and non-European folk art
especially ethnic and oriental
ceramics.*

Reel Poster Gallery
(ref: Reel Poster)
72 Westbourne Grove,
London W2 5SH
Tel: 020 7727 4488
Fax: 020 7727 4499
www.reelposter.com
Original vintage film posters.

Reel Thing, The
(ref: Reel Thing)
17 Royal Opera Arcade,
Pall Mall,
London SW1Y 4UY
Tel: 020 7976 1830
Fax: 020 7976 1850
www.reelthing.co.uk
*Purveyors of vintage sporting
memorabilia.*

Retro Exchange
20 Pembridge Road,
London W11
Tel: 020 7221 2055
Fax: 020 7727 4185
www.l/fel.trade.co.uk
*Space age-style furniture and
1950's kitsch.*

Retro Home
20 Pembridge Road,
London W11
Tel: 020 7221 2055
Fax: 020 7727 4185
www.l/fel.trade.co.uk
*Bric-a-brac, antique furniture
and objects of desire.*

A. Rezai Persian Carpets
123 Portobello Road,
London W11 2DY
Tel: 020 7221 5012
Fax: 020 7229 6690
*Antique oriental carpets, kilims,
tribal rugs and silk embroideries.*

John Riordan
Great Grooms Antique Centre
Charnham Street
Hungerford
Berkshire RG17 OEP
Tel: 01235 527698
Mob: 0780 8741823
e-mail: mrjohnriordan@
hotmail.com
www.bronzegriffin.com
Bronzes and antique furniture.

**Riverbank Gallery Ltd
(ref: Riverbank)**
High Street, Petworth,
West Sussex GU28 0AU
Tel: 01798 344401
Fax: 01798 343135
*Large English eighteenth and
nineteenth-century furniture,
decorative items, garden furniture
and decorative paintings.*

**Rookery Farm Antiques and
Sara Lemkow
(ref: Rookery Farm)**
12 Camden Passage
London N1 8ED
Tel: 020 7359 0190
Fax: 020 7704 2095
Mob: 07798 920060
e-mail: Rachel.lemko@
btinternet.com
www.antique-kitchenalia.co.uk
Kitchenalia and pine furniture.

Michele Rowan
V38 Antiquarias Antiques
Market,
135 Kings Road,
London SW3 4PW
Tel: 020 7352 8744
Fax: 020 7352 8744
Antique jewellery.

Malcolm Rushton
Studio 3, 13 Belsize Grove,
London NW3 4UX
Tel: 020 7722 1989
Early oriental art.

Russell Rare Books
81 Grosvenor Street,
London W1X 9DE
Tel: 020 7629 0532
Fax: 020 7499 2983
www.folios.co.uk
Rare books.

Salem Antiques
Great Grooms Antiques
Centre
Hungerford
Berkshire RG17 OEP
Tel: 01488 682314
Furniture from the 18th century.

Samiramis
M14–16 Grays Mews Antiques
Market,
1–7 Davies Mews,
London W1Y 1FJ
Tel: 020 7629 1161
Fax: 020 7493 5106
*Islamic pottery, silver, Eastern
items and calligraphy.*

Christopher F. Seidler
G13 Grays Mews Antiques
Market,
1–7 Davies Mews,
London W1Y 2LP
Tel: 020 7629 2851
Medals, arms and militaria.

Serendipity
Rosemary Ford
The Tythings
Preston Court
nr Ledbury
Herefordshire HR8 2LL
Tel: 01531 660245
Mob: 07836 7222411
*Traditional antiques, fine English
and continental furniture from the
18th and 19th century.*

**Shahdad Antiques
(ref: Shahdad)**
A16–17 Grays-in-Mews,
1–7 Davies Mews,
London W1Y 2LP
Tel: 020 7499 0572
Fax: 020 7629 2176
Islamic and ancient works of art.

**Bernard J. Shapero Rare
Books
(ref: Bernard Shapero)**
32 George Street,
London W1R 0EA
Tel: 020 7493 0876
Fax: 020 7229 7860
www.shapero.com
*Guide books from the sixteenth to
the twentieth century, antiquarian
and rare books, English and
continental literature, specialising
in travel, natural history and
colour plate.*

Sharif
27 Chepstow Corner,
London W2 4XE
Tel: 020 7792 1861
Fax: 020 7792 1861
*Oriental rugs, kilims, textiles and
furniture.*

Anthony Sharpe
16 Craven Hill Mews
London W2 3DY
Tel: 020 7706 2118
e-mail:s@anthonysharpe.com
*19th century lighting, bronzes,
screens and toile lighting. By
appt. only*

**Nicholas Shaw Antiques
(ref: N. Shaw)**
Great Grooms Antique Centre,
Parbrook, Billinghurst,
West Sussex RH14 9EU
Tel: 01403 786 656
Fax: 01403 786 656
www.nicholas-shaw.com
*Scottish and Irish fine silver, small
silver and collector's items.*

Shiraz Antiques
(ref: Shiraz)
1 Davies Mews,
London W1Y 1AR
Tel: 020 7495 0635
Fax: 020 7495 0635
Asian art, antiquities, glass,
marble and pottery.

Sieff
49 Long Street, Tetbury,
Gloucestershire, GL8 8AA
Tel: 01666 504477
Fax: 01666 504478
Eighteenth and nineteenth-
century French provincial
fruitwood, and some twentieth-
century furniture.

Sign of the Hygra
(ref: Hygra)
2 Middleton Road,
London E8 4BL
Tel: 020 7254 7074
Fax: 0870 125669
www.hygra.com
Boxes.

Sign of the Times
St Oswalds Mews,
London N6 2UT
Tel: 020 7584 3842
www.antiquesline.com
Furniture, decorative metalware
and glass.

B. Silverman
26 London Silver Vaults,
Chancery Lane,
London WC2A 1QS
Tel: 020 7242 3269
Fax: 020 7430 7949
www.silverman-london.com
Seventeenth to nineteenth-century
fine English silverware and silver
flatware.

Jack Simons Antiques Ltd
(ref: Jack Simons)
37 The London Silver Vaults,
Chancery Lane,
London WC2A 1QS
Tel: 020 7242 3221
Fax: 020 7831 6541
Fine antique English and
continental silver and objets d'art.

Sinai Antiques
219–221 Kensington Church
Street,
London W8 7LX
Tel: 020 7229 6190
Antiques and works of art.

Gloria Sinclair
Stand F023
Alfie's Antique Market
25 Church Street
London NW8 8DT
Tel: 020 7724 7118
European ceramics.

Sleeping Beauty
579–581 Kings Road,
London SW6 2DY
Tel: 020 7471 4711
Fax: 020 7471 4795
www.antiquebeds.com
Antique beds.

Julian Smith Antiques
(ref: Julian Smith)
Bartlett Street Antique Centre
Bath.
Also
The Lodge
Wheelwrights Close
Sixpenny Handley
Dorset SP5 5SA
Tel: 01725 552 820
Mob: 07879 624734
Luggage and gentlemen's
accessories.

Ruth Macklin Smith
(ref: R. Macklin Smith)
Great Grooms Antiques
Centre
Hungerford
Berkshire RG17 OEP
Antique furniture.

Solamani Gallery
Gray's Antiques Centre
Stand A20
1-7 Davies Mews
London W1Y 2LP
Tel: 020 7491 2562
Mob: 07956 546468
Islamic ceramics.

Solaris Antiques
(ref: Solaris)
170 Westbourne Grove,
London W11 2RW
Tel: 020 7229 8100
Fax: 020 7229 8300
Decorative antiques from France
and Sweden, from all periods up
to 1970s

Somervale Antiques
6 Radstock Road
Midsomer Norton
Bath BA3 2AJ
Tel: 01761 4122686
e-mail: ronthomas@
somervaleantiquesglass.co.uk
www.somervaleantiquesglass.
co.uk
Specialist in 18th and early 19th
century English, Bristol and
Nailsea glass. Shop open by appt.
only, 24-hour telephone service.

Something Different
254 Holloway Road,
London N7 6NE
Tel: 020 7697 8538
Fax: 020 7697 8538
Individually made African wood
and stone sculptures

Somlo Antiques Ltd
7 Piccadilly Arcade,
London SW1Y 6NH
Tel: 020 7499 6526
Fax: 020 7499 0603
www.somloantiques.com
Vintage wristwatches and antique pocket watches.

Ian Spencer
17 Godfrey Street,
London SW3 3TA
Large desks, sets of chairs and dining tables.

Sporting Times
Unit C 2A
Fitzaarland Road
Arundel
West Sussex
BN18 9JS
Tel: 01903 885656
Mob: 07976 9422059
e-mail: MartinQ.Sportingtimes.
isnet.co.uk
www.sportingtimes.co.uk
Antique sporting items.

Star Signings
Unit A18–A19 Grays Mews
Antiques Market,
1–7 Davies Mews
London W1Y 2LP
Tel: 020 7491 1010
Fax: 020 7491 1070
Sporting autographs and memorabilia.

Steinway & Sons
44 Marylebone Lane,
London W1M 6EN
Tel: 020 7487 3391
Fax: 020 7935 0466
New and refurbished pianos.

Jane Stewart
C 26–27, Grays Mews
Antiques Market,
1–7 Davies Mews,
London W1Y 2LP
Early seventeenth to nineteenth-century pewter, oak and writing slopes.

Constance Stobo
31 Holland Street,
London W8 4HA
Tel: 020 7937 6282
Eighteenth and nineteenth-century pottery, English lustre ware, and Staffordshire animals.

Stockspring Antiques
114 Kensington Church Street
London W8 4BH
Tel: 020 7727 7995
e-mail:stockspringand
porcelain.co.uk
www.antique-porcelain.co.uk
Antique English and continental porcelain.

June & Tony Stone
(ref: J. & T. Stone)
75 Portobello Road,
London W11 2QB
Tel: 020 7221 1121
Fine antique boxes.

Succession
18 Richmond Hill, Richmond,
Surrey TW10 6QX
Tel: 020 8940 6774
Art Nouveau, Art Deco, furniture, bronzes, glass and pictures.

Sugar Antiques
(ref: Sugar)
8–9 Pierrepont Arcade,
Camden Passage,
London N1 8EF
Tel: 020 7354 9896
Fax: 020 8931 5642
www.sugarantiques.com
Wristwatches, pocketwatches, costume jewellery, lighters, fountain pens and small collectables.

Mark Sullivan
14 Cecil Court,
London WC2N 4EZ
Tel: 020 7836 7056
Fax: 020 8287 8492
Antiques and decorative items.

Sultani Antiques Ltd
(ref: Sultani)
Unit K29, Gray's Antique
Centre
1-7 Davies Mews
London W1Y 1AR
Tel: 020 7491 3842
Mob: 07956 814 541
Islamic ceramics and antiquities.

Swan at Tetsworth, The
(ref: The Swan)
High Street, Tetsworth,
Thame,
Oxfordshire OX9 7AB
Tel: 01844 281777
Fax: 01844 281770
www.theswan.co.uk
Seventy dealers in historic Elizabethan coaching inn.

Talbot
65 Portobello Road,
London W11 2QB
Tel: 020 8969 7011
Fine scientific instruments.

Talking Machine, The
30 Watford Way,
London NW4 3AL
Tel: 020 8202 3473
www.gramophones.endirect.co.
uk
Mechanical antiques typewriters,
radios, music boxes, photographs,
sewing machines, juke boxes,
calculators and televisions.

Telephone Lines Ltd
(ref: Telephone Lines)
304 High Street, Cheltenham,
Gloucestershire GL50 3JF
Tel: 01242 583699
Fax: 01242 690033
Telephones.

Templar Antiques
(ref: Templar)
28 The Hall Antiques Centre,
359 Upper Street,
London N1 0PD
Tel: 020 7704 9448
Fax: 01621 819737
www.templar-antiques.co.uk
Eighteenth and nineteenth-
century glass, English, Irish
and Bohemian.

Temple Gallery
6 Clarendon Cross,
Holland Park,
London W11 4AP
Tel: 020 7727 3809
Fax: 020 7727 1546
www.templegallery.com
Russian and Greek icons, from
twelfth to sixteenth century.

Themes & Variations
231 Westbourne Grove,
London W11 2SE
Tel: 020 7727 5531
Post-War design.

Thimble Society, The
(ref: Thimble Society)
Geoffrey van Arcade, 107
Portobello Road, London W11
2QB
Tel: 020 7419 9562
Thimbles, sewing items, snuff
boxes and lady's accessories.

30th Century Comics
17 Lower Richmond Road
London SW15 1JP
Tel: 020 8788 2052
e-mail:rob@thirtiethcentury.
free-online.co.uk
www.thirtiethcentury.free-
online.co.uk

Sue & Alan Thompson
(ref: S. & A. Thompson)
Highland Cottage, Broomne
Hall Road,
Cold Harbout RH5 6HH
Tel: 01306 711970
Fax: 01306 711970
Objects of vertu, antique
tortoiseshell items, period
furniture and unusual
collector's items.

Through the Looking Glass
(ref: Looking Glass)
563 Kings Road,
London SW6 2EB
Tel: 020 7736 7799
Fax: 020 7602 3678
Nineteenth-century mirrors.

Through the Looking Glass
(ref: Looking Glass)
137 Kensington Church Street,
London W8 7LP
Tel: 020 7221 4026
Fax: 020 7602 3678
Nineteenth-century mirrors.

Tin Tin Collectables
(ref: Tin Tin)
Ground Units 38–42, Antiques
Market,
13–25 Church Street,
London NW8 8DT
Tel: 020 7258 1305
www.tintincollectables.com
Handbags, from Victorian to
present day, decorative
evening bags and luggage.

Tool Shop Auctions
78 High Street,
Needham Market,
Suffolk IP6 8AW
Tel: 01449 722992
www.uktoolshop.com
Auctioneers and dealers of
antique woodworking tools and
new Japanese, French and
American tools.

Tool Shop, The
(ref: Tool Shop)
High Street, Needham Market,
Suffolk IP6 8AW
Tel: 01449 722992
Fax: 01449 722683
www.toolshop.demon.co.uk
Antique and usable carpenter's
and joiner's tools.

Tower Bridge Antiques
(ref: Tower Bridge)
159–161 Tower Bridge Road,
London SE1 3LW
Tel: 020 7403 3660
Fax: 020 7403 6058

Town & Country Antiques
(ref: Town & Country)
88 Fulham Road,
London SW3 1HR
Tel: 020 7589 0660
Fax: 020 7823 7618
www.anthony-james.com
English furniture.

Travers Antiques
71 Bell Street,
London NW1 6SX
Tel: 020 7723 4376
*Furniture and decorative items
from 1820–1920.*

Tredantiques
77 Hill Barton Road, Whipton,
Exeter EX1 3PW
Tel: 01392 447082
Fax: 01392 462200
Furniture.

**Trio/Teresa Clayton
(ref: TRIO)**
L24 Grays Mews Antiques
Market,
1–7 Davies Mews,
London W1Y 2LP
Tel: 020 7493 2736
Fax: 020 7493 9344
*Perfume bottles and Bohemian
glass.*

Turn on Lighting
116–118 Islington High Street,
Camden Passage,
London N1 8EG
Tel: 020 7359 7616
Fax: 020 7359 7616
Antique lighting specialists.

Vale Antiques
Great Grooms Antiques
Centre
Hungerford
Berkshire RG 17 OEP
Tel: 01488 682314
Antique furniture.

James Vanstone
Unit 66 Admiral Vernan
Arcade
147 Portobello Road
London W11 2QB
Tel: 020 8541 4707
Mob: 07050 153018
Specialist in coins and medals.

Ventesimo
Unit S001
Alfie's Antique Market
13-25 Church Street
London NW8 8DT
Mob: 07767 498766
*20th century ceramics, glass
and lighting.*

Vintage and Rare Guitars
68 Kenway Road
London SW5 ORA
Tel: 020 7370 7834/6828
Fax: 020 7240 7500
Vintage and rare guitars.

**Vintage Wireless Shop
(ref: Vintage Wireless)**
The Hewarths Sandiacre,
Nottingham NG10 5NQ
Tel: 0115 939 3139
Radios.

**Michael Wakelin & Helen
Linfield
(ref: M.W. & H.L.)**
PO Box 48, Billingshurst,
West Sussex RH14 0YZ
Tel: 01403 700004
Fax: 01403 700004
*Metalware, pottery, treen,
lighting, textiles and mirrors.*

Graham Walpole
The Coach House,
189 Westbourne Grove,
London W11 2SB
Tel: 020 7229 0267
Fax: 020 7727 7584
*Small furniture, eighteenth and
nineteenth-century dolls' houses,
equestrian items, bronzes,
pictures and decorative items.*

Westland & Company
(ref: Westland & Co.)
St. Michael's Church,
The Clergy House,
Mark Street,
London EC2A 4ER
Tel: 020 7739 8094
Fax: 020 7729 3620
www.westland.co.uk
*Period fireplaces, architectural
elements and panelling.*

**Westminster Group Antique
Jewellery
(ref: Westminster)**
Stand 150, Grays Antiques
Market,
58 Davies Street,
London W1Y 2LP
Tel: 020 7493 8672
Fax: 020 7493 8672
*Victorian and Edwardian
secondhand jewellery and
watches.*

Wheels of Steel
B10–11 Grays Mews Antiques
Market,
1–7 Davies Mews,
London W1Y 2LP
Tel: 020 8505 0450
Fax: 020 7629 2813
Trains and toys.

Whitford Fine Art
(ref: Whitford)
6 Duke Street, St. James',
London SW1Y 6BN
Tel: 020 7930 9332
Fax: 020 7930 5577
Oil paintings and sculpture, from
late nineteenth century to
twentieth century; post-War
abstract and pop art.

Wilde Ones
283 Kings Road, Chelsea,
London SW3 5EW
Tel: 020 7352 9531
Fax: 020 7349 0828
Jewellery.

Jeff Williams
Grays Antiques Market,
58 Davies Street,
London W1K 5LP
Tel: 020 7629 7034
Toy trains.

Peter Wills
Room 4
The Swan Antique Centre
High Street
Tetsworth
Thame
Oxfordshire OX9 7AB
Tel: 01844 281 777
Fax: 01844 281 770
Antique furniture.

O. F. Wilson Ltd
(ref: O. F. Wilson)
Queen's Elm Parade, Old
Church Street,
London SW3 6EJ
Tel: 020 7352 9554
Fax: 020 7351 0765
Continental furniture, French
chimney pieces, English painted
decorative furniture and mirrors.

Rod Wilson
Red Lion, New Street,
Petworth,
West Sussex, GU28 0AS
Tel: 01798 344485
Fax: 01798 342367
Furniture.

Wimpole Antiques
Lynn Lindsay
Stand 349 Grays Antique
Market
5-8 Davies Street
London W1K 5LP
Tel: 020 7499 2889
e-mail: 1430@compuserve.com
Antique jewellery.

Yacobs
Grays Mews Antiques Market,
1–7 Davies Mews,
London W1Y 2LP
Tel: 020 7629 7034
Fax: 020 7493 9344
Islamic art.

Yazdani Mayfair Gallery
(ref: Yazdani)
128 Mount Street, Mayfair,
London W1Y 5HA
Tel: 020 7491 2789
Fax: 020 7491 3437
Ancient and Islamic art, Islamic
ceramics, sculpture and
antiquities.

Younger Antiques
Bourbon Hanby Antiques
Centre
151 Sydney Street
SW3 6NT
Tel: 020 7352 2106
Antique furniture.

Youll's Antiques
27–28 Charnham Street,
Hungerford,
Berkshire RG17 0EJ
Tel: 01488 682046
Fax: 01488 684335
www.youll.com
English/French furniture from
seventeenth to twentieth
century, porcelain, silver and
decorative items.

Zakheim
52 Ledbury Road,
London W11
Tel: 020 7221 4977
Russian art from icons to
Soviet, architectural, and
decorator's items.

Zoom
Arch 65, Cambridge Grove,
Hammersmith,
London W6 OLD
Tel: 0958 372 975
Tel: 07000 966620
Fax: 020 8846 9779
www.retrozoom.com
Twentieth-century furniture,
lighting, telephones and works
of art.

There follows our selection of the best antiques centres and markets in the country. These present the best of both worlds, with several dealers showing their particular specialities at the fair prices we expect from the reputable retailer.

BEDFORDSHIRE, BUCKINGHAMSHIRE, HERTFORDSHIRE
Antiques at Wendover Antiques Centre
The Old Post Office, 25 High Street,
Wendover HP22 6DU
Tel: 01296 625335
Dealers: 30

Barkham Antiques Centre
Barkham Street, Barkham RG40 4PJ
Tel: 0118 9761 355   Fax: 0118 9764 355

Buck House Antiques Centre
47 Wycombe End, Old Town,
Beaconsfield HP9 1LZ
Tel: 01494 670714

Luton Antiques Centre
Auction House, Crescent Road,
Luton LU1 2NA
Tel: 01582 405281   Fax: 01582 454080

Woburn Abbey Antiques Centre
Woburn Abbey, Bedfordshire MK17 9WA
Tel: 01525 290350   Fax: 01525 290271
Dealers: 50

BRISTOL, BATH, SOMERSET
Bartlett Street Antiques Centre
5-10 Bartlett Street, Bath BA1 2QZ
Tel: 01225 466689   Fax: 01225 444146
Dealers: 50+

Bath Saturday Antiques Market
Walcot Street, Bath BA1 5BD
Tel: 01225 448263   Fax: 01225.317154
Mobile: 083653 4893
Dealers: 70+

CAMBRIDGESHIRE
Fitzwilliam Antique Centre
Fitzwilliam Street, Peterborough PE1 2RX
Tel: 01733 565415

Hive Antiques Market, The
Unit 3, Dales Brewery, Gwydir St,
Cambridge CB1 2LG
Tel: 01223 300269

Gwydir Street Antiques Centre
Untis 1&2 Dales Brewery, Gwydir St,
Cambridge CB1 2LJ
Tel: 01223 356391

Old Bishop's, The Palace Antique Centre
Tower Road, Little Downham, Nr Ely
Cambridgeshire CB6 2TD
Tel: 01353 699177

CHESHIRE AND STRAFFORDSHIRE
Antique Furniture Warehouse
Unit 3-4 , Royal Oak Buildings, Cooper Street,
Stockport, Cheshire SK1 3QJ
Tel: 0161 429 8590   Fax: 0161 480 5375

Knutsford Antiques Centre
113 King Street, Knutsford, WA16 6EH
Tel: 01565 654092

CORNWALL
Chapel Street Antiques Market
61/62 Chapel Street, Penzance TR18 4AE
Tel: 01736 363267
Dealers: 30-40

Waterfront Antiques Complex
4 Quay Street, Falmouth, Cornwall TR11 3HH
Tel: 01326 311491
Dealers: 20-25

THE COTSWOLDS
The Antique and Interior Centre
51A Long Street GL8 8AA
Tel: 01666 505083
Dealers: 10

CUMBRIA AND LANCASHIRE
Carlisle Antiques Centre
Cecil Hall, 46A Cecil Street,
Carlisle CA1 1NT
Tel: 0122 8536 910   Fax: 0122 8536 910
carlsle-antiques.co.uk

Cockermouth Antiques Market
Courthouse, Main Street,
Cockermouth CA15 5XM
Tel: 01900 826746

DERBYSHIRE AND NOTTINGHAMSHIRE
Alfreton Antiques Centre
11 King Street, Alfreton DE55 7AF
Tel: 01773 520781
alfretonantiques@supanet.com

Castle Gate Antiques Centre
55 Castle Gate, Newark NG24 1BE
Tel: 01636 700076   Fax: 01636 700144
Dealers: 10

Chappells and the Antiques Centre Bakewell
King Street DE45 1DZ
Tel: 01629 812 496   Fax: 01629 814 531
bacc@chappells-antiques.co.uk
Dealers: 30

Memory Lane Antiques Centre
Nottingham Road, Ripley DE5 3AS
Tel: 01773 570184
Dealers: 40-50

Portland Street Antiques Centre
Portland Street, Newark NG24 4XF
Tel: 01636 674397   Fax: 01636 674397

Top Hat Antiques Centre
70-72 Derby Road, Nottingham NG1 5DF
Tel: 0115 9419 143
sylvia@artdeco-fairs.co.uk

DEVONSHIRE
Abingdon House
136 High Street, Honiton EX14 8JP
Tel: 01404 42108
Dealers: 20

Antique Centre on the Quay, The
The Quay, Exeter EX2 4AP
Tel: 01392 493501
home free.emailamail.co.uk

Barbican Antiques Centre
82-84 Vauxhall Street, Barbican PL4 0EX
Tel: 01752 201752
Dealers: 40+

Honiton Antique Centre McBains Antiques
Exeter Airport, Industrial Est., Exeter EX5 2BA
Tel: 01392 366261   Fax: 01392 365572
mcbains@netcomuk.co.uk
Dealers: 10

Newton Abbot Antiques Centre
55 East Street, Newton Abbot TQ12 2JP
Tel: 01626 354074
Dealers: 40

Sidmouth Antiques and Collectors Centre
All Saints Road, Sidmouth EX10 8ES
Tel: 01395 512 588

DORSET
Bridport Antique Centre
5 West Allington, Bridport DT6 5BJ
Tel: 01308 425885

Colliton Antique Centre
Colliton Street, Dorchester DT1 1XH
Tel: 01305 269398 / 01305 260115

Emporium Antiques Centre
908 Christchurch Road, Boscombe,
Bournemouth, Dorset BH7 6DL
Tel: 01202 422380   Fax: 01202 433348
Dealers: 8

Mattar Antique Centre
Mattar Arcade, 17 Newlands DT9 3JG
Tel: 01935 813464   Fax: 01935 813464

ESSEX
Baddow Antique Centre
The Bringey, Church Street, Great Baddow,
Chelmsford, Essex CM2 7JW
Tel: 01245 476159

Finchingfield Antiques Centre
The Green, Finchingfield, Braintree,
Essex CM7 4JX
Tel: 01371 810258   Fax: 01371 810258
Dealers: 45

Harwich Antique Centre
19 King's Quay Street, Harwich, Essex
Tel: 01255 554719   Fax: 01255 554719
Dealers: 50
harwich@worldwideantiques.co.uk

Saffron Walden Antiques Centre
1 Market Row, Saffron Walden,
Essex CB10 1HA
Tel: 01799 524534   Fax: 01799 524703

HAMPSHIRE AND ISLE OF WIGHT
Dolphin Quay Antique Centre
Queen Street, Emsworth,
Hampshire PO10 7BU
Tel: 01243 379994   Fax: 01243 379251
enquiriesnancy@netscapeonline.co.uk

Eversley Antique Centre Ltd
Church Lane, Eversley, Hook,
Hampshire RG27 0PX
Tel: 0118 932 8518
Dealers: 11

Lyndhurst Antique Centre
19-21 High Street, Lyndhurst,
Hampshire SO43 7BB
Tel: 0238 0284 000
Dealers: 50

The Antique Centre
Britannia Road, Southampton,
Hampshire SO14 0QL
Tel: 0238 0221 022
Dealers: 46

The Antique Quarter
'Old' Northam Road, Southampton,
Hampshire SO14 0QL
Tel: 0238 0233 393
Dealers: 15

GLOUCESTERSHIRE
Struwwelpeter
The Old School House,
175 London Road, Charlton Kings,
Cheltenham Gloucester GL52 6HN
Tel: 01242 230088
Dealers: 7

HEREFORD AND WORCESTERSHIRE

Antique Centre, The
5-8 Lion Street, Kidderminster,
Worcestershire DY10 1PT
Tel: 01562 740389   Fax: 01562 740389
Dealers: 12

Hereford Antique Centre
128 Widemarsh Street, Hereford HR4 9HN
Tel: 01432 266242
Dealers: 35

Leominster Antique Centre
34 Broad Street, Leominster HR6 8BS
Tel: 01568 615505
Dealers: 22

Leominster Antique Market
14 Broad Street, Leominster HR6 8BS
Tel: 01568 612 189
Dealers: 15+

Linden House Antiques
3 Silver Street, Stansted CM24 8HA
Tel: 01279 812 373

Malvern Link Antique Centre
154 Worcester Road, Malvern Link,
Worcestershire WR14 1AA
Tel: 01684 575750
Dealers: 10

Ross on Wye Antique Gallery
Gloucester Road, Ross on Wye,
Herefordshire HR9 5BU
Tel: 01989 762290   Fax: 01989 762291
Dealers: 91

Worcester Antiques Centre
15 Reindeer Court, Mealcheapen Street,
Worcester WR1 4DF
Tel: 01905 610680/1   Fax: 01905 610681
Dealers: 45

KENT

Antiques Centre, The
120 London Road, Tubs Hill TN13 1BA
Tel: 01732 452104

Coach House Antique Centre
2a Duck Lane, Northgate, Canterbury,
Kent CT1 2AE
Tel: 01227 463117
Dealers: 7

Copperfield Antique & Craft Centre
Unit 4, Copperfield's Walkway, Spital Street,
Dartford, Kent DA1 2DE
Tel: 01322 281445
Dealer: 35

Corn Exchange Antiques Centre
64 The Pantiles, Tunbridge Wells, Kent TN2 5TN
Tel: 01892 539652   Fax: 01892 538454
Dealers: 11

Tenterden Antiques Centre
66 High Street TN30 6AU
Tel: 01580 765885   Fax: 01580 765655
Dealers: 20+

Tunbridge Wells Antique Centre
12 Union Square, The Pantiles,
Tunbridge Wells TN4 8HE
Tel: 01892 533708
twantique@aol.com

Village Antique Centre
4 High Street, Brasted, Kent TN16 1RF
Tel: 01959 564545
Dealers: 15

LEICESTERSHIRE, RUTLAND AND NORTHAMPTONESHIRE

Finedon Antique (Centre)
11-25 Bell Hill, Finedon NN9 5NB
Tel: 01933 681260   Fax: 01933 681779
sales@finedonantiques.com

The Village Antique Market
62 High Street, Weedon NN7 4QD
Tel: 01327 342 015
Dealers: 40

LINCOLSHIRE

Astra House Antique Centre
Old RAF Helswell, Nr Caenby Corner,
Gainsborough, Lincolnshire DN21 5TL
Tel: 01427 668312
Dealers: 50

Guardroom Antiques
RAF Station Henswell,
Gainsborough DN21 5TL
Tel: 01427 667113
Dealers: 50

Henswell Antiques Centre
Caenby Corner Estate, Henswell Cliff
Gainsborough DN21 5TL
Tel: 01427 668 389   Fax: 01427 668 935
info@Hemswell-antiques.com
Dealers:270

St. Martin's Antique Centre
23a High Street, St Martin's, Stamford PE9 2LF
Tel: 01780 481158   Fax: 01780 766598

Stamford Antiques Centre
The Exchange Hall, Broad Street,
Stamford PE1 9PX
Tel: 01780 762 605   Fax: 01733 244 717
anoc1900@compuserve.com
Dealers: 40

LONDON

Alfie's Antique Market
13-25 Church Street NW8 8DT
Tel: 020 7723 6066   Fax: 020 7724 0999
alfies@clara.net

Antiquarius
131-41 King's Road SW3 4PW
Tel: 020 7351 5353   Fax: 020 7351 5350
antique@dial.pipex.com

Bermondsey
corner of Long Lane & Bermondsey Street
SE1 3UN
Tel: 020 7351 5353

Camden Passage
Upper Street, Islington N1
Tel: 020 7359 9969
www.camdenpassage.com

Grays Mews Antique Markets
58 Davis Street, and 1-7 Davis Mews WIY 2LP
Tel: 020 7629 7034
Dearlers: 300

Hampstead Antique and Craft Market
12 Heath Street, London NW3 6TE
Tel: 020 7431 0240   Fax: 020 7794 4620
Dealers: 20

Jubilee Market Hall
1 Tavistock Court, The Piazza
Covent Garden WC2 E8BD
Tel: 020 7836 2139

Lillie Road
237 Lillie Road, SW6
Tel: 020 7381 2500   Fax: 020 7381 8320

Portobello Road
In Notting Hill Gate W10 and W11
Tel: 020 7727 7684   Fax: 020 7727 7684
Dealers: 280

Spitalfields,
65 Brushfield Street E1 6AA
Tel: 020 8983 3779   Fax: 020 7377 1783

NORFOLK
Fakenham Antique Centre,
The Old Congregational Church, 14 Norwich
Road, Fakenham, Norfolk NR21 8AZ
Tel: 01328 862941
Dealers: 20

NORTHUMBERLAND AND DURHAM
The Village Antique Market
62 High Street, Weedon NN7 4QD
Tel: 01327 342015
Dealers: 40

OXFORDSHIRE
Antique on High Ltd
85 High Street, Oxford OX1 4BG
Tel: 01865 251075   Fax: 0129 665 5580
Dealers: 38

Country Markets Antiques and Collectables
Country Garden Centre, Newbury Road,
Chilton, nr. Didcot OX11 0QN
Tel: 01235 835125   Fax: 01235 833068
countrymarketsantiquesandcollectables
@breathnet.com
Dealers: 35

Old George Inn Antique Galleries
104 High Street, Burford, Oxfordshire OX18 4QJ
Tel: 01993 823319
Dealers: 22

Station Mill Antique Centre
Station Yard Industrial Estate, Chipping Norton,
Oxfordshire OX7 5HX
Tel: 01608 644563   Fax: 01608 644563
Dealers: 73

Swan at Tetsworth
High Street, Tetsworth, Oxfordshire OX9 7AB,
Tel: 01844 281777   Fax: 01844 281770
antiques@theswan.co.uk
Dealers: 80

SHROPSHIRE
Bridgnorth Antique Centre
Whitburn Street, Bridgnorth,
Shropshire WV16 4QP
Tel: 01746 768055
Dealers: 19

K. W. Swift
56 Mill Street, Ludlow SY8 1BB
Tel: 01584 878571   Fax: 01746 714407
Dealers: 20, book market.

Old Mill Antique Centre
Mill Street, Shropshire WV15 5AG
Tel: 01746 768778   Fax: 01746 768944
Dealers: 90

Princess Antique Centre
14a The Square, Shrewsbury SY1 1LH
Tel: 01743 343701
Dealers: 100 stallholders

Shrewsbury Antique Centre
15 Princess House, The Square,
Shrewsbury SY1 1UT
Tel: 01743 247 704

Shrewsbury Antique Market
Frankwell Quay Warehouse,
Shrewsbury SY3 8LG
Tel: 01743 350619
Dealers: 30

Stretton Antiques Market
36 Sandford Avenue, Stretton SY6 6BH
Tel: 01694 723718   Fax: 01694 723718
Dealers: 60

STAFFORDSHIRE

Lion Antique Centre
8 Market Place, Uttoxeter, Staffordshire ST14 8HP
Tel: 01889 567717
Dealers: 28

SUFFOLK

Church Street Centre
6e Church Street, Woodbridge, Suffolk IP12 1DH
Tel: 01394 388887
Dealers: 10

Long Melford Antiques Centre
Chapel Maltings, CO10 9HX
Tel: 01787 379287   Fax: 01787 379287
Dealers: 40

Woodbridge Gallery
23 Market Hill, Woodbridge, Suffolk IP12 4OX
Tel: 01394 386500   Fax: 01394 386500
Dealers: 35

SURREY

The Antiques Centre
22 Haydon Place, Corner of Martyr Road,
Guildford GU1 4LL
Tel: 01483 567817
Dealers: 6

The Antiques Warehouse
Badshot Farm, St George's Road,
Runfold GU9 9HY
Tel: 01252 317590   Fax: 01252 879751
Dealers: 40

Enterprise Collectors Market
Station Parade, Eastbourne, East Sussex BN21 1BD
Tel: 01323 732690
Dealers: 15

The Hampton Court Emporium
52-54 Bridge Road, East Molesey,
Surrey KT8 9HA
Tel: 020 8941 8876
Dealers: 16

The Kingston Antiques Market
29-31 London Road, Kingston-upon-Thames,
Surrey KT2 6ND
Tel: 020 8549 2004   Fax: 020 8549 3839
webmaster@antiquesmarket.co.uk
Dealers: 90

Packhouse Antique Centre
Hewetts Kilns, Tongham Road, Runfold,
Farnham, Surrey GU10 1PQ
Tel: 01252 781010   Fax: 01252 783876
hewett@cix.co.uk
Dealers: 80

Victoria and Edward Antique Centre
61 West Street, Dorking, Surrey RH4 1BS
Tel: 01306 889645
Dealers: 26

SUSSEX

Almshouses Arcade
19 The Hornet PO19 4JL
Tel: 01243 771994

Brighton Flea Market
31A Upper Street, James's Street BN2 1JN
Tel: 01273 624006   Fax: 01273 328665
arwilkinson@aol.com

Eastbourne Antiques Market
80 Seaside, Eastbourne BN22 7QP
Tel: 01323 642233
Dealers: 25

Lewes Antique Centre
20 Cliff High Street, Lewes BN7 2AH
Tel: 01273 476 148 / 01273 472 173
Dealers: 60

The Old Town Antiques Centre
52 Ocklynge Road, Eastbourne, East Sussex
BN21 1PR
Tel: 01323 416016
Dealers: 16

Olinda House Antiques
South Street, Rotherfield, Crowborough,
East Sussex TN6 3LL,
Tel: 01892 852609

Petworth Antiques Market
East Street, Petworth, GU28 0AB
Tel: 01798 342073   Fax: 01798 344566

WARWICKSHIRE

Barn Antique Centre
Long Marston Ground, Station Road, Long
Marsdon, Stratford-upon-Avon CV37 8RB
Tel: 01789 721399   Fax: 01789 721390
barnantiques@aol.com
Dealers: 50

Bridford Antique Centre
Warwick House, 94-96 High Street, Bidford on
Avon, Alcester, Warwickshire B50 4AF
Tel: 01789 773680
Dealers: 7

Dunchurch Antique Centre
16a Daventry Road, Dunchurch, Rugby,
CV22 6NS
Tel: 01788 522450
Dealers: 10

Malthouse Antique Centre
4 Market Place, Alcester, Warwickshire B49 5AE
Tel: 01789 764032
Dealers: 20

Stables Antique Centre, The
Hatton Country World, Dark Lane CV35 8XA
Tel: 01926 842405
Dealers: 25

Stratford Antiques and Interiors Centre Ltd
Dodwell Trading Estate, Evesham Road
CV37 9SY
Tel: 01789 297729   Fax: 01789 297710
info@stratfordantiques.co.uk
Dealers: 20

Vintage Antiques Centre
36 Market Place, Warwick CV34 4SH
Tel: 01926 491527
vintage@globalnet.co.uk
Dealers: 20

Warwick Antiques Centre
22 High Street, Warwick CV34 4AP
Tel: 01926 491382 / 01926 495704
Dealers: 32

WILTSHIRE
Brocante Antiques Centre
6 London Road, Marlborough SN8 1PH
Tel: 01672 516512   Fax: 01672 516512
brocante@brocanteantiquescentre.co.uk
Dealers: 20

Marlborough Parade Antique Centre, The
The Parade, Marlborough SN8 1NE
Tel: 01672 515331
Dealers: 70

YORKSHIRE
Arcadia Antiques Centre
12-14 The Arcade, Goole,
East Yorkshire DN14 5PY
Tel: 01405 720549
Dealers: 20

Banners Collectables
Banners Business Centre, Attercliffe Road,
Sheffield, South Yorkshire S9 3QS
Tel: 0114 244 0742
Dealers: 50

Barmouth Road Antique Centre
Barmouth Court
off Abbeydale, Sheffield, South Yorkshire S7 2DH
Tel: 0114 255 2711   Fax: 0114 258 2672
Dealers: 60

Cavendish Antique & Collectors Centre
44 Stonegate, York YO1 8AS
Tel: 01904 621666   Fax: 01904 644400
Dealers: 60

The Harrogate Antiques Centre
The Ginnel, off Parliament Street HG1 2RB
Tel: 01423 508857   Fax: 01423 508857
Dealers: 50

Halifax Antique Centre
Queens Road, Halifax,
West Yorkshire HX1 4OR
Tel: 01422 366 657   Fax: 01422 369 293
antiques@halifaxac.u-net.com
Dealers: 30

Malton Antique Market
2 Old Maltongate, Malton YO17 0EG
Tel: 01653 692 732

Pickering Antique Centre
Southgate, Pickering,
North Yorkshire YO18 8BN
Tel: 01751 477210   Fax: 01751 477210
Dealers: 35

Stonegate Antique Centre
41 Stonegate, York, North Yorkshire YO1 8AW
Tel: 01904 613888   Fax: 01904 644400
Dealers: 120

York Antiques Centre
2a Lendal, York YO1 8AA
Tel: 01904 641445 / 641582
Dealers: 16+

SCOTLAND
Clola Antiques Centre
Shannas School House,
Clola by Mintlaw AB42 8AE
Tel: 01771 624584   Fax: 01771 624584
Dealers: 10

Scottish Antique & Arts Centre
Abernyte PH14 9SJ
Tel: 01828 686401   Fax: 01828 686199

WALES
Antique Market
6 Market Street, Hay-on-Wye HR3 5AD
Tel: 01497 820175

Cardiff Antiques Centre
10-12 Royal Arcade CF10 2AE
Tel: 01222 398891
Dealers: 13

Chapel Antiques
Methodist Chapel, Holyhead Road, Froncysyllte,
Denbighshire, Llangollen LL20 7RA
Tel: 01691 777624   Fax: 01691 777624
Dealers: 20

Jacobs Antique Centre
West Canal Wharf, Cardiff C51 5DB
Tel: 01222 390939
Dealers: 50

advertising 158–169
Aeneid, The 65
Ainsley 184–190
Alfa Romeo 490
Alhambra 52
Ali, Muhammed 233
Allcock, Samuel 85
Allcocks 475
Alone 62
Alvez, Goncalo 310
Americas, map of 66
Ami Continental 226
amphoriskos 13
Andersen, Hans Christian
    Hans Andersen's Fairy Tales
    61
    La Reine des Neiges (The
    Snow Queen) 67
Anderson, Gerry 492
Annamese ware 123–130
antiquities 11–18
Arabian Nights, The 56
architectural furniture 19–32
archway, Gothic 26
armchairs 320–339,
    518–531
armour 33–42
arms 33–42
Armstrong, Louis 234
Army & Navy 204, 222, 477
art deco 503–551
    coffee pot 220
    fireplace 28
    perfume bottle 170–178
    storage box 217
art nouveau 503–551
    bag 207
    door 359
art tribal 498–502
Arts & Crafts 503–551
    chair 322
ash trays 167, 261–263, 532,
    539, 547
Asian/Oriental art 560–562
Atlas of Hollywood 212
atlases 51–67
Augustus Caesar 274
Austen, Jane
    Sense and Sensibility 56
Austin 493, 490
autometers 226–228
automobilia 43–50
aviator's chronograph 146

axe
    gothic 39
    Indian 40

B. P. antifrost 160
badges, car 43–50
Bacall, Lauren 231
Baccarat 229–230
Bacchus 86, 563, 565
Bactrian ware 22–18
bags 206–212, 501
    Bakelite 206, 207, 212
    leather gaming 468
    perspex 210
    saddle 468
    Turkaman 72
Bakelite
    bags 206, 207, 212
    brooch 421
    tape 259
    telephone 264–266
Baker, Ian 203
Balainot 419
Balda 179–183
balsamarium 11
Bambi 67
Bamiyan 115–122
Banshan ware 562
*Barbados, The Natural History
    of* 61
Bardot, Brigitte 242, 243
Barnel 275
barometer, brass 432
baths 32
bats, cricket 472
Batman 194, 195
Bauhaus 515
Baxter 532–542
beadwork
    armorial design 482
    bags 206–212
    pelmet 483
    screen 376
Beano, The 197, 199
bear
    ink well 112, 462
    panda 492
    pin cushion 260
    Rupert Bear 191–203
    Russian 106
    teapot 88
    teddy 486–495
    Winnie the Pooh 56, 63

Beatles, The 233, 244, 247,
    250
    see also John Lennon, The
    Travelling Wilburys, Wings
beds 291–294
    day beds 340
Beefheart, Captain 249, 252
Bell, Steve 200
Benaud, Richie 472
benches 19–32, 377
    folding 524
Benson 141–147
Bentley 43
bergères 320–339
Bible 60
    box 299
Biedermeier 308, 518–531
billiard scorer 467, 470
binoculars 470
bird cage 374
Bisto 158
Black & White 164
Blackstone, Sir William
    Blackstone's Commentaries
    63
black ware 76–104
Blade Runner 240
blotter 569, 576–585
Boer War 155
Bogart, Humphrey 231
Bohemian glass 400–413
Bolex 179–183
Bond, James 239, 240, 242
bone beaker 431
bone model boat 434
bonheur du jour 295
bookcases 296–298, 530
    revolving 519
books 51–67
    bookmark 167
    radio and TV diary 1957
    246
Boothby, Guy 51
Bothwell staircase 29
bottles 170–178
    bottle opener 471
    perfume 13
    Venini 533
    Wedgwood 178
Boucheron 422
Bourne, Charles 95
Bow ware 76–104
bowling balls 466

boxes 299–307
  bronze 60
  collecting 162
  cosmetic 122
  fly 473, 474
  hat 222–225, 299, 300
  snuff 261–263
  stocking 169
  tapestry 299
  wig 300
  wooden 496–497
boules 469
Boy Scouts, founder 83
bracket clock 131–140
Brancusi 545
Brasso 159
Brave New World 64
Brighton Rock 62, 67
British Isles, map of 57, 66
Broderip & Wilkinson 438
buckle 37, 575
buffet 524
Buffy the Vampire Slayer 202
Bulaggi 212
bullet mould 478
Bulletman 202, 203
Bullova 141–147
bureaux 308–309, 522, 526
Burnett, Francis Hodgson
  Little Lord Fauntleroy 55
bus, double decker 488
busby, Royal Engineers 34
Buster 201
busts 273–276
Butor, Michel 60
Byrd, Richard E.
  Alone 62
Byzantine 11–18

cabinet, bedside 521
cabinets 310–318
Cadillac 486
cake stand 363, 364
cameras 179–183
canapé 377
candelabras 277–285, 286–290
candleholder, pottery 17
candlestick telephone 266
candlesticks 79, 277–285,
  286–290, 442, 449, 453
canes, glass 405, 411
Canterburys 319
caps
  football 469

rowing 472
  trophy 466
Capucine 231
cars 43–50
  Alfa Romeo 490
  Austin 493, 490
  Bentley 43
  bubble 494
  Cadillac 486
  Ferrari 487
  Fiat 489
  Jaguar 43, 44, 491
  mascots 43, 547
  R.A.C. badge 43
  radiator chair 521
  Rolls–Royce 44
carpets 68–75
carriage clocks 131–140
cartoons 191–203
cassolettes 286
Castle Ballroom 158
Cat in the Hat, The 55
cathedral clocks 131–140
Caughley plates 78
cavalry officer, Staffordshire
  83
Caviar Volga 165
Central Park 234
ceramic
  bottles 170–178
  trap 32
ceramics 569–575
  beer coaster 167
  English 76–104
  European 105–114
  Islamic 115–122
  Oriental 123–130
  twentieth century 503–517
Chad Valley 490
chairs 320–339, 518–531
  elbow chair 321
chaises longues 340
Chamberlain, Neville 190
chandelier, nautical 433
chandeliers 277–285, 546
Chandler, Raymond
  The Long Goodbye 64
Charles II 61
chatelaine, gold 258
Chelsea Football Club 237
Chelseaware 95
chess pieces 566, 568
chest on chests 310–318
chests of drawers 341–351

Chichester, map of 66
chiffoniers 310–318
Chillexine 160
chimney sweep, ceramic 80
Chinese bottles 170–178
Chinese ware 123–130
Chippendale 320–339
Chiurazzi 290
choba dansu 344
chocolate pot, Chinese 130
Chown 184–190
Christie & Barrie 131
Christie, Agatha
  Hound of Death and Other
    Stories, The 55
chronographs 141–147
chronometers 429–434
Chrysler Building 233
cigars 261–263
  case 452
  holder 547
cigarettes 261–263
  case 445, 450
  holder 505
  Senior Service 167
Clarendon 53
Cleeve, Corneille van 565
Cliff, Clarice, 503–517
clocks 131–140
  Staffordshire 88
  travel 204
Coalport 76–104
coasters 440–465, 552–559
cocktail shaker 552
coconut
  cup 431
  powder flask 35
coffer, oak 351
coins 152–157
Coleman's mustard 161
collectors items 158–272
comics 191–203
commemorative ware
  184–190, 569–575
commodes 310–318, 341–351,
  391, 397–399
Common Prayer, The Book of
  59, 65
compasses see also scientific
  instruments
  mariner 148
  prismatic 33
Complete English Traveller, The
  53

Connery, Sean 239, 240, 242, 244
Constantin, Vacheron 141–147
Contax 179–183
Conway Stewart 585
Cooke's View of the Thames 62
Cooper, Gary 231
Cooper, Susie 503–517
Copeland 184–190
corkscrews 552–559
Coronet 179–183
Count de Grammont 54
Courage 191
Cox, Samuel S. 61
credenzas 310–318
Crete, The Sea Kings of 62
cribbage board 469
cricket 224, 466–472
Crimean War 152–157
croquet mallet 472
Crown Derby 76–104
Crown Devon 184–190
cup, coconut 431
Cure, The 247
currency 152–157, 499, 501, 502

Dahl, Roald
    Matilda 64
Daimler 493
Dali, Salvador 231
    brooch 414
Dandy, The 198, 203
Dansette 245–246
Davenport 76–104
davenports 352
day beds 340
decanters 400–413, 552–559
decorative arts 273–290
deer head 496
Delftware 76–104
Delon, Alain 241
Dennis Chinaworks 503–517
Dennis the Menace see also The Beano 200
Derby 77
desks 353–354, 522
Desk set, Quianlong 127
Diana the Huntress 105
dining tables 355–356
Dinky 492

dinosaur egg 562
Dior, Christian 237
Disney, Walt
    Mickey Mouse 180, 192, 487, 491
    Snow White 487, 489
Doctor Who 194
dolls 486–495
    Michael Jackson 247, 249, 251
doors 26, 357–360, 560
    glazed 26
    handles 550, 551
Doyle, Arthur Conan
    Hound of the Baskervilles, The 64
Dr Zhivago 56
Dresdenware 76–104, 105–114
dressers 361–362
dressing stands 310–318
Druce & Co. 309
Dubois, Paul 274
Dukes see also commemorative ware
    Wellington 83
    Windsor 185
    York 87
dumb waiters 363–365
Durer, Albrecht 276
durrie 69, 75
Dylan, Bob 251

E. A. R. 245–246
Eagle, The 196
Eames, Ray 518–531
earthenware 76–104
Eastwood, Clint 243
Ecologues, The 65
Edward VII 186
    florin 156
Edward VIII 185
egg cups 497, 551
elbow chair 321
electric fire 550
Ellington, Duke 236
Ensign 179–183
epergnés, glass 411
ephemera 191–203
Epiphone 435–439
Ericsson 264–266
Essex, map of 57
etagère 365
etui, ebonised 258
European art 563–565

Fabergé 569–575
Fairies
    Crimson Fairy Book 66
    Orange Fairy Book 54
    Tales of The Brothers Grimm 52
    Hans Andersen's Fairy Tales 61
fans 482–485, 575
    ivory fan 483
Fantastic Four, The 193
Farewell Nikola 51
fauteuils 320–339
Fellini, Federico 231
fencing mask 472
Fender 435–439
Ferrari 487
Fiat 489
finials 19–32
fire, electric 550
fireplaces 19–32
    Louis Philippe 19
firescreens 19–32
first empire clock 135
fishing 473–475
Fitzgerald, F. Scott 59
Flintstones, The 486
flower brick 90
fly box 473, 474
flying helmet 472
fob watches 141–147
Fonda, Henry 234
football 466–472
footstool 381
Fortunes of War, The 53
fountains 19–32
Franke & Heidecke 179–183
furniture 291–399
    architectural 19–32
    garden 19–32
    miscellaneous 373–374
    twentieth-century 518–531

Gable, Clark 231
gaff, telescopic 473
Gaku 543
Gallé 540
gallery seats 380
games 486–496
    chess pieces 566, 568
    cribbage board 469
    compendium 301
    Mah Jong set 302
    sporting items 466–478

Gannochy 476–478
garden furniture 19–32
gators, leather 468
Gaullin 140
gentleman's accessories 204–205
George II crown 155
George IV shilling 157
George V 186
Georgics, The 65
Ghaznavi Heart ware 115–122
Gibbon, Edward
  Roman Empire, Decline and Fall of the 63
Gibson 435–439
Girl 191
Gladstone, William 189
glass 11–18, 400–413, 433
  bottles 170–178
  jug 162
  paperweights 229–230
  twentieth-century 532–542
glasses, sand 151
globes 148–151, 429
gloves 500
Godfather, The 241, 242
Godfrey, Bob 200
Golden Leaf 167
Goldscheider 503
Goldsmith, Oliver
  The Vicar of Wakefield 65
Gone with the Wind 63
gong, iron 25
Gordon Beck Trio 249
Goss 184–190
Gothic
  archway 26
  axe 39
GPO 264–266
Graduate, The 239
Grahame, Kenneth
  Wind in the Willows, The 52, 61
Grand Central Station 236
Grant, Cary 235
Greene, Graham
  Brighton Rock 62, 67
Gretsch 435–439
Grima, Andrew 423
Grimm Brothers
  Tales of The Brothers Grimm 52
  Grimm's Household Tales 54

Guazin ware 115–122
Guevara, Monica 509
Guggenheim Museum 234
Guinness 161, 164
guitars 435–439
Gustavian bench 382
H. M. V. 245–246
Hacker 245–246
hall bench 379
hall stand 522
Han dynasty 560–562
handbags 206–212
Happy Prince and Other Tales, The 65
Harat ware 115–122
Hardy 473–475
Hardy, Bert 233
Harra Pan 12, 16
hats 482–485 *see also* helmets
  bowler 205
  busby 34
  football cap 469
  hat boxes 222–225, 299, 300
  hat–shaped lamp 543, 544
  hatstand, Chinese 130
  helmets 38, 39, 472
  officer's cap 39
  pith helmet 36
  rowing cap 472
  Salatopia hunting hat 473
  smoking 482, 484
  top hat 204, 205, 222
  top hat pins 423
  trophy cap 466
Heaton, Wallace 179–183
Heflin, Van 231
Hefna, Hugh 232
helmets
  flying 39, 472
  khula-khad 36, 42
  paratrooper 38
  pith 36
  Tibetan 39
Hendrix, Jimi 236
Henley 555
Hepburn, Audrey 238, 239, 243
Hepplewhite 320–339
Heubach 487
High Society 242
Himalayan kist 346
Hindenburg, General Field Marshall 188

Hitchcock, Alfred 232, 239, 240, 241, 243
Hoffman, Dustman 239, 244
Holland & Holland 476–478
Holliday, Billie 236
horn beakers 204
Hotspur, The 195
Hound of Death and Other Stories, The 55
Hound of the Baskervilles, The 64
House at Pooh Corner, The 56
How the Grinch Stole Christmas 56
Hughes, Ted
  Wodwo 65
Hulton Press 191–203
Huntingdonshire, map of 58
Huntley & Palmers 486
Hutton, Kurt 233, 234
Huxley, Aldous
  Brave New World 64

ice pick 470
Ideal Home cleanser 164
igbo art 498–502
ink pot 547
ink wells 15, 461, 462, 464, 572, 576–585
  bear 112
  Staffordshire 82
  Sung dynasty 129
instruments, musical 435–439
Iranian ware 115–122
Iron Man & Captain America 193
Islamic art 11–18, 566–568
Islamic ware 115–122
Italian Job, The 244
ivory
  fan 483
  sewing case 259
  tau cane 269

Jackson, Michael 247, 249, 251
Jacobs, Carl 522
Jaeger le Coultre 141–147
Jaguar 491
  mascot 43
jardinières 387, 454
Jarre, Jean Michel 250
Jeeves and the Feudal Spirit 64
jewellery 11–18, 414–428, 501
  case 225

Johnnie Walker 164
Joyce, James *Ulysses* 52
juke boxes 226–228

Kaiser Wilhelm II 185
Kashan ware 115–122
Kauffman, Angelica 111
Kennedy, Jacqueline 232
Kestner 490
Kew Gardens 67
Khayyam, Omar
    Rubaiyat of Omar Khayyam,
    The 56
khula-khad helmet 36, 42
kilim 70
kimono, silk 483
King George V 185
King George VI 189
King William IV 22
King of Prussia teapot 101
kitchenalia 213–221
Kitchener 187
kluk kluk 558
knife cleaner 373
Knox, Archibald 442, 447,
    460, 462
Kodak 546
Kodak Eastman 179–183
Konig & Wernig 495
Kriegsmarine colani jacket 33
Kufic ware 115–122
kusuri dansu 343

Lace, History of Hand-made 62
Lady Chatterley's Lover 55
Ladykillers, The 239
Lalique 532–542
lamps 277–285, 543–546
landing nets 473–475
Lane, Ken 209
Lang, Andrew
    Crimson Fairy Book 66
    Orange Fairy Book 54
lanterns 277–285
Laurel and Hardy 240
Lauren, Sophia 238
Lawrence of Arabia 241
Lawrence, D.H.
    Lady Chatterley's Lover 55
Lawson, William 164
Lee, Brenda 252
Leedware 76–104
lemonade jug 125
Lenin 572, 573

Lennon, John 233, 249, 251
    see also The Beatles
    signature watch 252
letter balance 576
letter rack 549
Levasseur, Henry 273
Lewis, C. S.
    The Lion, The Witch and The
    Wardrobe 62
Liberty 440–465
library steps 373
Lifebuoy soap 165
lighters 261–263
lighting 277–285
    oil lamp 148
    twentieth-century
    543–546
lightometer 183
Limoges 105–114, 510, 583
linen press 397–399
Lion, The Witch and The
    Wardrobe, The 62
Little Lord Fauntleroy 55
Little Red Riding Hood 86
Liverpool creamware 76–104
Liverpool fly 87
Locke, John 564
London
    Hyde Park 238
    Maitland's History of London
    53
    Map of London 66
    maps of 58, 62
    River Thames 62
    The Greater London 62
Long Goodbye, The 64
longcase clocks 131–140
Longines 141–147
Longton Hall plate 103
Look and Learn 191
Lord Byron 87
Lothian, map of 58
Louis Philippe fireplace 19
Louis, John F. 52
lounger 528
lowboy 384
Luftschutz dagger 41
Luftwaffe 152–157
    belt 36
    helmet 39
luggage 222–225
    rack 374
Lugrunge & Paris 140
Luisentasse 105–114

lustreware 76–104
Lyons 159, 161
lyre clock 131–140
Lysell & Bloomberg 265

Mah Jong set 302
Maitland's History of London 53
Malay Sketches 54
Mamiya 179–183
Mandarin ware 123–130
Manhattan 234
mantle clock 131–140
Map of London 66
maps 51–67
Marie Antoinette 273
marine items 429–434
    mariner compass 148
marriage
    Marriage Act, the 87, 88
    marriage plate, Chinese
    127
    marriage rug 71
Martin 435–439
Martin Brothers 510
Marvel comics 191–203
Marx, Groucho 231
masks 498–502
    fencing 472
    sumarian 12
Masons 184–190
match holder, nautical 434
match strikers 465
Matchbox 493, 494
Matthews, Jessie 237
Maxfield, Parish 56
Maynard, John 53
Maynooth College 237
mechanical music 226–228
medals 152–157
Meek, Joe, 251
meerschaum 261–263
Meiping ware 123–130
Mercator, Gerard 63
Merian, Mathaus the Elder
    57
metalware 286–290
    twentieth-century 547–551
Mexico, Conquest of 51
Mickey Mouse 487, 491
    camera 180
    Mickey Mouse Weekly 192
microscopes 148–151
Midas of Miami 210
military uniforms 33–42

Milne, A.A.
    When We Were Very Young
        56
    Winnie the Pooh 56, 63
    Now We Are Six 56
    The House at Pooh Corner
        56
Ming ware 123–130
Ming dynasty 560–562
Minoae ware 115–122
Minton 76–104
mirrors 366–372, 441, 567,
    569, 570
    art nouveau 448
    guitar 542
Mitchell, J. & W. 139
Mitchell, Margaret
    Gone with the Wind 63
money bonds 253–256
money, paper 253–256
Monkees, The 250
Monroe, Marilyn 238, 239,
    241
Morgan, William de 505
Movado 141–147
Mughal art 19–32
    panels 29
Murano, glass 532–542, 543,
    544
Murray, John 65
music stand 373, 374
music, mechanical 226–228
    musical boxes 226–228
    musical sewing box 260
musical equipment
    gramophone needle tins 161
    record players 245–246
musical instruments 435–439
Mysonware 105–114

Nailsea glass 400–413
Nanking ware 123–130
Napoleon 274
National 439
Navajo jewellery 414–428
needlepoint panel 72
Nelson 432
Neptune 105
Nestlé 168, 493
New York
    Central Park 234
    Chrysler Building 233
    Grand Central Station 236
    Guggenheim Museum 234

Manhattan 234
Paramount Building 232
Newhalls Walberton teapot
    100
Newman & Guardia 179–183
Night and Day 64
Nishapur 115–122
Noh plays 53
Norfolk, map of 57
Northumberland, map of 58
Now We Are Six 56
Nudenmiller 105–114

obliques 277–285
Odd Couple, The 241
officer's wristwatch 143
Omega 141–147
organ, mahogany cased 438
oriental ceramics 433, 434
Orkney, map of 58
Ovaltine 190
Oxo 161, 162

Pacino, Al 241
packaging 158–169
Pagani, Luciano 543
Palmer & Co. 285
Palmolive soap 168
panels, silk 485
Panton, Verner 525
paper money 253–156
paperweights 229–230, 535,
    581
Paramount Building 232
parchment box 299
Parker 576–585
Pasternak, Boris 56
Pati, Gaetano 485
Paute & Fils, Le 131–140
Payne & Co. 132
Pearce Duff 158
Pearlware 76–104
Pedigree 492
pelmet 483
pens
    pen tray 569
    Parker 576–585
    Waterman 576–585
pendant 501
Perdio 245–246
perfume bottles 13, 170–178,
    454
Perriand, Charles 520
Persian ware 115–122

Persil 160
perspex
    bag 210
    lamp 545
Peter Rabbit, The Tale of 55
Peugeot Frères 217
pewter 440–465
photographs 231–238
pianos 435–439
pickettes 277–285
picnic cases 222–225
picture frames 570, 574
Picture Post 231–238
pillars, teak 28
Pillone, Odorico 59
Pinxton 104
pipes 261–263
    pipe taper 497
plants *see also* garden furniture
    holder 374
    Natural History of Barbados,
        The 61
    stand 365, 373, 523
plate rack 361
Playboy Club 232
Players 167
Poetical Works of Percy Bysshe
    Shelley, The 67
Police, The 248
Pontiac 547
Poole pottery 503–517
pop 247–252
postal weighing scale 447
posters 239–244
pot stand 373
Potter, Beatrix
    Peter Rabbit, The Tale of 55
Potter, Harry 55
powder
    flask 35
    horn 188
Powell, Baden 83
Prattware 76–104
Prehistoric Man 54
pre-Ottoman 115–122
Prescott, William Hickling 51
Presley, Elvis 248
Prince Charles 200, 229
Prince Phillip 230
Princess Diana 190
Princess Margaret 190
projectors 179–183
propellor 471
    blade clock 135

Puss in Boots 572
puzzle jug 89
Pye 245–246

quadrant, boxwood 151
quaiche 449
Queen Elizabeth II 190, 230
Queen Victoria 184, 186, 187, 189
  children of 86
Quianlong ware 123–130
quilts 482-485

R.A.F. (Royal Air Force)
  brooches 156
  chronograph 144
R.A.C. badge 43
radiator cover 28
radios 245–246
rafraichissoir 393
Rajar 179–183
Raleigh, Sir Walter 21
Ralph Wood 85
record players 245–246
Red-ware 76–104
Reine des Neiges, La (The Snow Queen) 67
Renaissance binding 59
Revere 179–183
Richard, Cliff 247, 252
Ridgway 76–104
Rinso 165
River Ottawa 237
River Thames 62
Robert the Bruce 290
Robert, David 52
Roberts 245–246
Robin starch 165
Robinson, W. Heath 52
rock music 247–252
Rock–ola 226–228
Rococo chimney piece 27
Rolex 141–147
Rolleicord 179–183
Rolleiflex 179–183
rolling pins, glass 400–413
Rolling Stones 232, 248, 249, 251
Rolls–Royce mascot 44
Romaine, Paul 276
Roman Empire, Decline and Fall of the 63
Roman art 11–18
Romer 141–147

Rosalind and Helen 60
Rosenthal 503–517
Rosenthal, Leonard
  Kingdom of the Pearl, The 67
Rossellini, Roberto 231
Rossetti, Christina 56
rowing cap 472
Rowling, J.K.
  The Philosopher's Stone 56
  The Chamber of Secrets 56
  The Prisoner of Azkaban 56
  The Goblet of Fire 56
Royal Doulton 76–104, 184–190, 508
Royal Vienna ware 105–114
Royal Wintonia 184–190
Royal Worcester 510
rugby ball 470
rugs 68–75
  Luri Gabbah 70
  marriage 71
Rupert Bear 191–203
Russian
  art 569–575
  bear 106
  cape and hat 485
  Sputnik camera 180
  walking stick 267
ryo baki 348
Rysbrach, Michael 274

saddle bag 468
Safaviv ware 115–122
Saint Mark 86
Salatopia hunting hat 473
Saljuk ware 115–122
Salmon, Nathanael 54
Salten, Felix
  Bambi 66
Samakan ware 115–122
sandwich tin 469
Satsuma ware 123–130
Saur, Abraham
  Map of London 66
Sawankalok ware 123–130
Scalextric 494
scent bottle 454
school cupboard 531
scientific instruments 148–151
sconces 277–285
Scotland, map of 57
Scott, Walter 563

screens 375–376
  firescreens 19–32
scripophily 253–256
seal 549
Seeburg 226–228
Senior Service 167
Sense and Sensibility 56
settees 377–379
Seuss, Dr
  Cat in the Hat, The 55
  How the Grinch Stole Christmas 56
Seutter, Mattheus 57
Sèvres 105–114, 513
sewing 257–260
  table 387
sextants 429–434
Shakespeare, William
  The Tempest 60, 67
  The Tragedies, Comedies and Histories of Shakespeare 54
  Shakespeare's house 305
Shang dynasty 560–562
Shanks
  canopy bath 32
  cistern 25
share certificates 253–256
Shell 495
Shelley ware 503–517
Shelley, Percy Bysshe
  Rosalind and Helen 60
  The Poetical Works of Percy Bysshe Shelley 67
shepherd's crook, glass 410
Shepherd, E. H. 56, 63
Sheraton bonheur 295
Sherlock Holmes 64, 240
Shetland Isles, map of 58
shilling label 554
shooting 476–478
shooting stick 467
Sica, Vittorio de 231
sideboards 310–318, 361
silver 440–465
  filigree case 260
  football trophy 470
  ink stand 585
  needle case 259
  pin cushion 258
  scissors 258
  silver-mounted walking stick 267
  snuff box 262
  wool-winder 258

Simon & Halbig 489
singing bird autometers 220–222
skeleton clock 134
skis 469
Slazenger 164
smoking equipment 261–263
  match holder, nautical 434
  ash tray 157, 161, 532, 539, 547
  cigar holder 547
  cigarette boxes 440–465
  cigarette holder 505
  Golden Leaf tobacco tin 167
  match holder 413
  match strikers 465
  Player's ashtray 167
  Redbreast tobacco tin 166
  Sam's Own Tobacco 168
  Senior Service tobacco 167
  smoking pouch 502
  snuff bottles 170–178
Snow Queen, The (La Reine des Neiges) 67
snow shoes 467
Snow White 487, 489
snuff
  boxes 261–263, 445. 497
  bottles 170–178
soap
  Camay 168
  Jester 165
  Lifebuoy 165
  Palmolive 168
  Wright's coal tar soap 167
sofas 377–379
Solar 212
Soligor 179–183
Somerset, map of 57
Sottsass, E. 503, 504
sound equipment 245–246
smoking hat 483
sphere, French armillary 151
Spiderman, The Amazing 191
Spirit of the East, The 61
spittoon 97
splint holders 288
Spode 76–104
Spriguns 250
sporting items 466–478
  Chelsea Football Club 237
  cricket case 224
  Slazenger 164
  Strange Sport Stories 192

Staffordshire 76–104, 184–190
staircase, Bothwell 29
Stalin 572
Standard cameras 179–183
Status Quo 250
Steiff 486–495
Steinway 438
Stewart, James 231
sticks
  shooting 466–472
  walking 267–272
Stiven, Charles 306
stools 73, 380–383, 525
  anotonian 74
  butterfly 529
  footstool 381
  kilim 71
  piano 374
storage chests 341–351
stove, travelling 469
Stowe, Harriet Beecher
  Uncle Tom's Cabin 63
Suffragette movement 417
suku art 498–502
sumarian art 11–18
sundials 19–32
Sung dynasty 123–130
Superman 193, 199
Surrey, Antiquities of 54
Surridge, Stuart 472
Susse Frères 289, 551
Swansea 76–104
Swato ware 123–130
symphonian 228

tables 384–396, 518–531, 566–568
  dining 355–356
  wine 518
tabourets 383
tallboys 341–351
Tang dynasty 560–562
tapestry box 299
taxidermy 479–481
Taylor of Bristol 132
Taylor, Elizabeth 233
tea caddies 299–307
tea tin 301
teapot 549
  holder 301
teddy bears 486–495 see also bears
Telavia 548

telephones 264–266
telescope, six draw 151
television 548
televisions 245–246
Telstar 493
Tempest, The 60, 67
Tennents lager can camera 181
tennis press 470
Tennyson, Lord Alfred
  Tennyson's Works 67
tent trappings 74, 75
Tessina 179–183
textiles 482–485
  stocking box 169
thermometer, travelling 150
Third Reich 152–157
  aiguilettes 34
Three Guineas 55
Tide 160
Tiffany & Co. 422, 535
  watch 142
Timori ware 115–122
Titanic 235
tobacco tins see also snuff
  boxes & smoking equipment
  Golden Leaf tobacco tin 167
  Redbreast 166
  Sam's Own 168
  Senior Service 167
Tôleware 286–290, 373
top hat 204, 205 see also hats
  boxes 222–225
  pins 423
torchère stand 374
towel rail 373
toys 486–495
Tragedies, Comedies and Histories of Shakespeare, The 54
Travelling Wilburys 252
tray 374
Treatise on Money, A 53
treen 496–497
Tri-ang 487, 491
tribal art 498–502
trivet 374
Troika 503–517
trophy
  cap 466
  football 468
Troughton & Simms 429
trunk, merchant's 303

Tunbridge ware 496
twentieth-century design
   503–551
Typhoo tea 159, 160

Ulysses 52
umbrellas 484
   stand 523
Uncle Tom's Cabin 63
uniforms 33–42
urns 19–32
Urquhart, David
   Spirit of the East, The 61

vases 76–130, 400–413,
   503–517, 532–542, 547–551
Velvet Underground, The 248
Venetian ware 17
Venini 532–542
Victoria Bridge 232
Vile Bodies 51
violinist, ceramic 80
Virgil
   The Ecologues 65
   The Georgics 65
   The Aeneid 65
vitrines 310–318
Volkstand 105–114
voting box 304
Vuitton, Louis 224, 225

walking sticks 267–272
   shooting stick 466–472
wardrobes 397–399
Warhol, Andy 248, 251
wash stand 363, 365, 387
watches 141–147
   John Lennon signature
      watch 252
Waterman 576–585
Waugh, Evelyn
   Vile Bodies 51
wedding basket 299
Wedgwood 76–104, 184–190,
   229–230
   bottle 178
   figure 78
Wellings, Norah 489
Wellington, Duke of 83
Westerwald 105–114
whatnots 363–365
When We Were Very Young 56
Whieldon ware 509
Whitbread 430

Whitefriars 229–230, 532–542
wig box 300
Wilde, Oscar
   *The Happy Prince and Other
      Tales* 65
Wileman and Co 78
Wilston, Sir Daniel
   Prehistoric Man 54
Wind in the Willows, The 52, 61
Windsor, Duke of 185
wine-related items 440–465,
   552–559
   barmaid's measure 440
   beer stein 189
   Black & White Scotch
      whisky 164
   bottle opener 471
   ceramic coaster 167
   decanters 400–413
   Grimbles brandy 167
   hip flask 441
   Johnnie Walker Scotch
      whisky 164
   spirit flasks 205
   Tennents lager can camera
      181
   William Lawson 164
   wine table 518
   wine strainer 12
Wings 252 *see also* The
   Beatles
Winnie the Pooh 56, 63
Winston Churchill 187, 190
Wit, Frederick de 66
Withnail and I 242
Wollstonecraft, Mary 63
Woman's Own 190
Wonder Woman 191
Wondergram 245–246
Woodhouse, P. G.
   Jeeves and the Feudal Spirit
      64
Woolf, Virginia
   Kew Gardens 67
   Night and Day 64
   Three Guineas 55
Worcester ware 76–104
   cake tin 219
World War I
   medals 152–157
   picture frame 550
World War II
   medals 152–157
   raid 237

World, map of 66
Wrayflex 179–183
Wright's coal tar soap 167
writing equipment 576–585
   blotter 569
   ink pot 547
   ink well 11, 15, 461, 462,
      464
   pen tray 569
   propelling pencil 146
   seal 549
   writing table 384

X–Men 191–203

Yachts 235
Yakovlevich, Golovin
   Alexander 570
yarlai lions 30
Yates 95
York, Duke of 87

Zaccagnini 504
Zeiss, Carl 179–183
Zenit 179–183
Zodiac 226–228
zodiac clock 131–140
Zuni art 498–502
Zuni jewellery 414–428

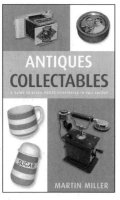